Diana Stainforth was secr——— Rebecca West before embarking on her own writ——— where she is currently wor———

DIANA STAINFORTH

Bird of Paradise

GRAFTON BOOKS

A Division of the Collins Publishing Group

LONDON GLASGOW
TORONTO SYDNEY AUCKLAND

Grafton Books
A Division of the Collins Publishing Group
8 Grafton Street, London W1X 3LA

Published by Grafton Books 1986

First published in Great Britain by
Century Publishing Co. Ltd. 1985

Copyright © Diana Stainforth 1985

ISBN 0-586-06755-8

Printed and bound in Great Britain by
Collins, Glasgow

Set in Times

My thanks to Chris Mann for his invaluable advice on vintage motor-racing.

Chapter 1

Koblenz, 1919

Spring came slowly that year and who could blame it. And when it did come there was nothing for it to do, except melt the snow and turn the frozen ground into a sea of mud. It looked for life to nurture – and found death and destruction. No mother animals waited to produce their young, they had all been slaughtered. No seedlings had been planted, the fields were pitted with shells, the men to plant were dead. No housewives planned their spring cleaning around the first sunny day, they were too busy scavenging for food and anyway the curtains they would have washed had long ago been cut up to make clothes.

But most poignant of all for Mara as she trudged through the streets of Koblenz, past ruined buildings gaunt against the sky, was the absence of flowers. How often before the war she had gone shopping with her mother, and they had stopped in some well-kept square to admire the nodding yellow daffodils or the fat and shiny tulips. She could almost hear her mother's English voice saying, 'You should see the flowers in England, Mara. I remember when I was in the orphanage . . .' and her mother would talk of her childhood, at an orphanage near Tunbridge Wells, then of her life as an English governess to the daughter of the wealthy Vogel family in Koblenz, where she had met and married Franz Vogel, the only son, Mara's father. Listening to her mother,

7

Mara, cocooned by a loving family – a mother, a father, an elder brother – would screw up her face, closing her eyes tightly, and try to imagine she too was penniless and alone.

No need to imagine it now, she thought ruefully, wrapping her coat tightly around herself as she left the shelter of the narrow streets and came out beside the Mosel just below the Balduin Bridge. There she turned right and followed the river down to the Deutsches Eck, the corner of Germany, where the lesser waters of the Mosel rushed headlong into the greater waters of the Rhine which had started their journey in Switzerland and would go on, through Germany, to Holland and the sea. People used to say I was spoiled, she mused, but they should see me now. They should just see me now.

She stopped when she reached the point, and looked down into the turbulent water, a tall thin girl shivering in the cold wind. To protect herself from the drizzle she wore a shawl around her head and shoulders which, being grey like her coat, added to her drabness, making her one with the rivers and the sky. But Mara wanted it that way. It was better to be inconspicuous. Dressed as she was, she could move about unnoticed, just another human bundle fighting for survival: but only until she lifted her head. And even then she wasn't pretty, she was compelling.

Her hair was long and thick and tawny with shades of fair and red and brown. Her face: a wide forehead and high cheekbones, made gaunt through lack of food, from which her cheeks seemed to sweep down in a soft curve to her generous mouth. Her skin: translucent like her mother's, though hunger had given it a feverish transparency accentuating the freckles on the bridge of her nose. Her eyes: big and grey and thoughtful with just a hint of sensuality in their luminous depths. It was a face to look at, and look again. A face which showed aggression, a product of the insecurity of war, and which at the same time or sometimes alternately allowed her underlying vulnerability to show through.

And that vulnerability showed through now as she stood on this spot. As a child the Deutsches Eck had reminded her of the prow of a ship, and she had always claimed to feel it moving forward with the water which rushed past on either side. Now it seemed to her that the ship was anchored fast and against its will, that it like her longed to break loose.

That brought Mara back to her father. How often he must have watched a cloud float across the prison compound and wished he could hook himself on to it and escape. It was nearly five years since he'd been arrested, since she'd seen him, and four months since the war had ended, and every week she went to the office where the Americans dealt with what they called 'Civil Affairs' – they spoke of it in the same way as they spoke of 'civil disturbances' – and every week the big red-haired official said, 'No news. Sorry.'

At first Mara thought that because her father had been imprisoned as a pacifist, and had not fought, the Americans would do all they could to trace him, but gradually she had come to realize that although a pacifist, to them he was just another German. They, the Americans, were the conquerors. They, the Americans, occupied Koblenz. All Germans were the defeated and the occupied. Her father was just another name, one more of the many missing people. And always a German.

But perhaps today would be different. The red-haired American would look up as she approached his desk, and say, 'Ah, Miss Vogel, I've good news for you. We've traced your father. He's in . . .' or better still, 'Your father's here,' and he would show her through into a small back room where her father would be waiting. He would be thinner and greyer, she must not expect his brown hair to be as thick and luxuriant as it had been, and his eyes would be sunken: everyone who had returned from the war had had sunken eyes. That he had not been to war would make no difference: he'd suffered imprisonment and hard labour, his eyes must be sunken. But they would still burn with life, she was sure they would, because he was a man who did not merely exist: he lived.

By the time Mara reached the office there were already twenty people waiting ahead of her. She joined the end of the queue, on the wooden bench which ran down one wall. No one spoke to her, they pretended not to see her, but the woman next to her moved closer to her other neighbour, and whispered, 'Franz Vogel's daughter . . . you know, Vogel the one who wouldn't fight . . . always thought his newspaper was tainted with treachery . . . bad blood in that family . . . surprised she's got the nerve to come here when . . .'

Mara ignored them. She was used to it.

At the far end of the room, behind a desk piled high with files, sat the big red-haired American. Near him, perched on the edge of an upright chair, sat a small grey-haired man in a worn black suit. He was the interpreter: a German civil servant who spoke English, and he kept looking awkwardly at the waiting people as if to say, 'It's not my fault I'm working for them.'

Mara pushed her shawl back from her head and ran her fingers through her hair, trying to tidy its long straggling ends. Then she sat back and gazed at the far wall which was painted the indeterminate cream of all

10

bureaucratic buildings, and like all buildings in Koblenz at that time it was in need of repainting. Other people came into the room, saw the queue, and sat down, but Mara didn't notice them, nor was she aware of the American shouting, 'Next!' every five minutes: automatically she moved up the bench. It was always the same when she came here and had to wait. She would start thinking of the past, although she tried to stop herself, because there was nothing else to think about, nothing to distract her thoughts.

She had been twelve when war broke out. She remembered as if it were yesterday, that hot August afternoon when she had found her mother crying in the rose garden. Within a week her father had been arrested and shortly afterwards her brother Hans had been drafted into the army: he'd died four months later, on Christmas Day. It had been the war which had broken up Mara's family but she hadn't seen it in terms of two opposing nations, she'd seen it as being between her German father and her English mother. Although her parents had been happy and had seldom argued, she'd seen it as if they had: her father's beliefs had taken him away from them as surely as if he had been obsessed by another woman instead of by an ideal. Mara's resentment had manifested itself in a rejection of her father, for if he had really loved them why had he subjected them to deprivation and the hostility of their neighbours? Why couldn't he be like other fathers and put on a uniform and go off to fight?

Before the war the Vogels had spoken German at home, although Mara's mother had insisted that both children learn English. But after her father's arrest Mara spoke only English, she read only her English books: she rejected the German side, the side which had deserted her.

11

Sitting on the hard bench Mara wondered if she were now paying for that resentment and rejection. The weekly pilgrimage through the cold streets, this cheerless room, the detached questions the red-haired official always asked her, and would ask her again today. The humiliation of it all. But surely she'd already paid for her resentment, and paid far over the top? That was something else she didn't want to think about. But it came back to her then, as it did every day, and to a certain extent it assuaged the guilt of having resented her father: it was a penance handed down to her by whoever it was who handed out these things, but because of its nature it had exceeded a penance and become a sacrifice, and had allowed her to see herself as a martyr: that was what had saved her from its brutality. That was why she could think of it, why she was able to face it.

She thought of her mother with a mixture of admiration and frustration. Frau Vogel had never once complained. Every three months she had visited her husband in prison, returning with a brave smile, until the previous spring when she had come home feverish and distraught; she'd been unable to see him, he'd been transferred to Cologne to work on the railway.

The fever had developed into pneumonia and within a week Frau Vogel was dead.

Mara had been frightened but not really surprised by her mother's death. It was all part and parcel of her mother's attitude to the war: she'd had a hard childhood and the war had brought a return of that hardship. It was the dust to dust syndrome, and she had accepted it as inevitable. She didn't believe life would improve for her, because she was convinced she had no right to expect it to do so. Happiness in the form of her marriage had come her way by chance, it was not written in her book.

12

The only thing which had kept her going was the thought of her husband. Her last words to Mara were, 'Try to understand your father.'

For her mother's sake Mara had finally forced herself to go to the police station to ask about her father. 'What! Franz Vogel!' the policemen at the desk had laughed in her face. That was, until their chief, the notoriously brutal Herr Steiger, had walked past.

'Next! Next! Come on, miss!'

Mara suddenly realized that the big red-haired American was shouting at her. Somehow, without being aware of moving, she had come to the head of the queue. She hurried over to the desk, her mind on that other desk where she had stood and been mocked by the policemen.

The American asked, 'Speak English?'

She nodded.

'Good. Name?'

'Vogel.'

'Spelling?'

'V O G E L.'

He wrote it down. 'Name of person sought?'

'Franz Vogel. My father.'

He shuffled through his pile of files until he came to one near the bottom. 'Vogel, Franz.' He looked up at her for confirmation. Mara nodded. He studied the file. 'Father imprisoned 20 August 1914. Held at Koblenz until March 1918.'

Mara sighed. She mustn't show irritation. 'I know that. It was I who told you.'

He closed the file. 'Then no news. Sorry.'

'But surely,' she clutched the edge of the desk, 'there must be some other records? My mother was told he'd been moved to a prison near Cologne. They sent him

13

to work on the railway there. Surely they must have records?'

The American sighed, and in his sigh Mara saw that he was fed up with her and with all the people like her. To him, they were like a lot of people who had left their unbrellas on a train and each week came pestering at the Left Luggage Office, as if it were his fault that they were careless with their possessions. And she saw too that he was fed up with his job and that, as a conqueror, he had expected something more than this. He was not an unkind man, just a disillusioned one; intelligent enough to see that if he found one missing person there would be hundreds more he would never find, because most were dead and buried in unmarked graves, and those who were not dead presumably did not want to come back. And who could blame them? He said, 'I'm sorry, Miss Vogel, but we're doing our best. You're not the only one.' He looked at the dozen or so waiting people and in his eyes they became the hundreds more he saw each week.

Mara nodded. 'I realize that. But isn't there anything . . .' She swallowed hard. 'I've been coming every week. Couldn't you try to find out . . . please.'

The American studied her for a moment. He had been on the point of telling her to go away but he stopped. Most of those who came to him were middle-aged men and women looking for their sons, or wives looking for their husbands, and they passed before him as faceless people. The fact that they seldom spoke English and therefore needed the interpreter added to their ignominy: all he heard was their guttural mumblings; he himself spoke directly to the interpreter. But this girl was different. Although she spoke English with a German accent, she spoke it very well. He opened her file and was

14

reminded that her mother had been English. He looked up at her face. It was grey and gaunt but she had wonderful clear grey eyes. And the more he looked at her, the more she stepped out of the crowd of faceless people and became an individual to him. Suddenly he wanted very much to help her. 'Look,' he said, 'I'll do my best. As you know, we Americans are only in Koblenz. The British are in Cologne. But I'll try. Come back next Wednesday. I'm on duty then and perhaps I'll have some news for you.'

Mara smiled and thanked him.

The American watched her as she walked the length of the room, pulled open the heavy doors and disappeared out into the cold street. He wished he could have gone with her, but he turned to the queue and shouted, 'Next!'

As Mara made her way along the street a truck full of soldiers lumbered towards her. This is all I need, she thought, wrapping the shawl around her head and hunching her back like an old lady.

But the wind lifted the shawl from her face, and the truck slowed down as it reached her. 'Hi, Fräulein,' the soldiers called, 'don't hide your face. It ain't that bad. Come on, give us a smile.'

Mara ignored them. She was used to the soldiers. All the women were. Harassment was the price women paid for the defeat of their men.

The truck began to reverse. It squelched backwards through the mud as it kept pace with her. 'Eh! You there! Come back, baby!'

Some twenty yards ahead of Mara, two old ladies were walking slowly along the pavement in the same direction as herself. She was about to ask if she could join them when she recognized one as her neighbour, Frau Muhlhauser.

15

The soldiers egged each other on. 'Fräulein! Fräulein! We love you.'

Mara walked faster, the truck keeping pace beside her.

Frau Muhlhauser and her companion turned round. They looked at Mara, nudged each other, then turned back and carried on walking. Only now they raised their voices. 'No wonder we lost the war with people like that in our midst. A pacifist for a father. An Englishwoman for a mother.'

'Pacifist! I say coward. He should have been shot. Prison was too good for him.' Their German voices mingled with the shouts of the soldiers.

'And to think how high the Vogels once stood in this town.'

Silently Mara cursed them. Once she would have risen to the bait but past experiences had taught her that was just what Frau Muhlhauser wanted.

'I'm a nice boy. I'll take you home to meet mother,' a soldier called to her.

'And I'll give you a jar of cranberry jelly if you'll give me a . . .' The remainder of the sentence was drowned in laughter.

Frau Muhlhauser spoke even louder. 'Spies! All of them. Father, mother, son. Spies and cowards.'

Her companion sniggered. 'She encourages them., Listen!'

'Come back! Come on! Come here!' The soldiers still shouted. The truck still lumbered in reverse.

Frau Muhlhauser squeaked with moral indignation, 'To think she was only sixteen when . . .' The truck revved out the remainder of the sentence.

'The chief of police. Disgraceful!'

'A good thing when he shot himself. The man was a brute and a murderer.'

'But he was our chief of police and a man in his position should have known better than to . . .'

'That's why she did it with him. They say she seduced him to save that rotten father of hers. Who else but Steiger would have had that sort of power?'

'I can't think why Franz Vogel married an English governess when there were so many decent German . . .'

Mara barged forward, knocking Frau Muhlhauser into the outstretched arms of the soldiers and her companion against the wall. Above the screams and the jeers, she shouted, 'Perhaps it was the example of you, Frau Muhlhauser, that made him prefer an Englishwoman,' and she hurried on, laughing when she looked back and saw the soldiers release the woman to the muddy gutter. But her satisfaction did not last. She needed much more than one petty victory.

The memory of Herr Steiger came back to her once more. His red, bulldog face and the way in which the folds of his thick neck rolled over his collar, as if it were a hangman's noose, when he turned to look at her where she stood beside the desk in the police station. The way in which the skin of his cheeks and jowls had reminded her of an orange, wide-pored and glistening, his piggy little eyes titillated by her face and body. 'Come with me, Fräulein,' he had said, taking her arm and leading her into his office. He'd sat her down in a chair on one side of his desk and gone round to the other side, to a huge leather button-backed chair.

'So you're Franz Vogel's daughter?'

'Yes.'

'And you want to know how your father is?'

'Yes. Before my mother died she told me he had been moved to Cologne.'

'Oh, she did, did she?' He looked momentarily surprised, but then went on, 'Yes, he's in Cologne and for the moment he's alive, but . . . you see, Fräulein, the war has been long and costly and we are running out of food. Our boys at the front are hungry. Why should we feed our prisoners? In fact, many aren't fed. It's a terrible sight when a man dies of hunger. First his tongue swells. Then his skin cracks. Then . . .'

'Please stop. What can I do? I'd pay if I could but I don't have any money. We've sold everything we could. We have furniture, but no one wants it.' She'd stood up and gone to the desk and looked down at him. 'Are you saying my father is starving to death?'

'He will starve unless . . .' He had stretched out his arm and seized one of her slender hands in his massive one. As she snatched it away, he had laughed, and said, 'Unless . . .'

At first Mara had not fully understood, then she had pretended not to understand, and then she had said, 'Never! Never!' and marched out of the room, slamming the door behind her.

But that could not be the end of it. From the moment she left the police station she thought of her father. He was with her in the street and in the house when she returned home. He was with her during the day. At night, she couldn't sleep: she pictured him, his tongue swollen and his skin cracked, and she was racked with guilt for how she had rejected him, although part of her still blamed him. But he was her father. She had loved him.

On the third night after Herr Steiger had made his offer, Mara had woken up to hear the front door being smashed open, followed by the crash of boots on the stairs, and before she had time to hide two policemen burst into the room. 'You're under arrest, Fräulein.'

'But why? What have I done?'

'Herr Steiger's orders.'

They had driven her to the police station and led her down into the basement, to the cells. There she had found Herr Steiger waiting. With false bravado, Mara had demanded, 'Why am I under arrest? What have I done?'

He'd laughed, his big face screwing up so that it almost devoured his piggy eyes. 'Oh, you're not under arrest, Fräulein. I just wanted to show you something. Come here.' He pulled her towards an open cell door. She peered inside. Lying on the stone floor was a crumpled heap of rags. It took her some moments to realize it was a man.

'My father! Oh, no!'

Herr Steiger pulled her close to him. 'No, not your father. Just another dead prisoner. I thought you might be interested to see what a dead man looks like, one who's died of starvation. If you go closer,' he made as if to push her nearer the body, 'you can see his cracked skin.'

Mara had stood and looked down at the dead man, who was really no man at all because there was nothing of him: no shape, no form, nothing human, nothing that could possibly ever have been alive. 'Very well,' she had said. 'I will do what you wish if you will save my father.'

The drizzle had turned to heavy rain though Mara hardly noticed it. I must get away from Koblenz, she decided, I must go somewhere where nobody knows me and where I know nobody so there's nothing to remind me of the past. But where? She listed all the cities she could think of, muttering their names under her breath, 'Berlin, Hamburg, Munich, Frankfurt.' But what was she going to do when she got there? Get a job? What job? She couldn't do anything. Her governess had left hot on the heels of her father's arrest, and although her mother had insisted Mara continue with her lessons, they had been about history and art and Charles Dickens. What use was *Little Dorrit* in a battle for survival? *A Tale of Two Cities* was no good for survival either: that had been her book of sacrifice. The first time she had gone to bed with Herr Steiger had been that night she had stood by the cell door and looked down at the man who was no longer a man. They had gone back to her house and as she walked up the stairs, with Herr Steiger lumbering after her, she had said to herself, just as Sydney Carton had said to himself, 'It is a far, far better thing that I do, than I have ever done.' Only poor Sydney Carton had of course been mounting a far more finite set of stairs.

'I must stop thinking about all that,' she told herself firmly. 'I must think about the future. But what future?'

As she walked on, her shoes squelching in the mud, she distracted herself from her wet feet with one of her favourite daydreams. A theatrical manager would drive past. He would recognize in her all the qualities with which Isadora Duncan had enchanted the civilized world: this, although Mara had never danced. The theatrical manager would stop his car, call to her and say, 'Fräulein, you are exactly what I am looking for.' And he would whisk her away to America where she would become the greatest star of all time, adored by her public, swathed in furs, fêted wherever she went. In a few years she would return to Germany at the personal invitation of the Kaiser who would have somehow rescinded his abdication: an invitation from a Kaiser, whatever his failings, sounded much more attractive than one from a mere Chancellor. And then – this was one of the best bits – she would publicly snub Frau Muhlhauser.

But it was only a daydream. Reality was here in Koblenz.

The road widened as it broke away from the town and began to curl slowly up the side of the hill. Before the war it had been lined with trees but they had all been cut down and used as firewood. On either side behind the tell-tale stumps were moderate-sized detached houses, each with its own moderate-sized garden, and as the road progressed up the hill so the houses and their gardens increased in size and grandeur, until each was sitting on its own little plateau looking down over the city. It had once been an area much sought after by the respectably well to do, with those living at the bottom of the road aspiring to move up it. The bottom for a young lawyer. The middle when he became a partner. The top if he became a judge. Step by step up the road of success. But now the houses and the gardens had fallen into disrepair, the men to pay for them and tend them were gone, dead or injured, the women to cherish them huddled with their children behind broken windows stuffed with newspapers to keep out the cold.

Among the last houses, before the road went on up into the forest behind, Mara turned into an overgrown drive which led to a large gabled house built of wooden beams and white plaster and topped with the inevitably grey slate roof of the region. Like those nearby, it sat on its own little plateau. The original idea had been for a spacious family home with sweeping lawns falling away on three sides, to a tennis court, to a rose garden, to the edge of the hill with its commanding view: at the back was a vegetable garden. Now the plaster was crumbling, the windows broken and the lawns unmown. An air of decay and abandon prevailed, and yet it retained a certain elegance, like an aged and aristocratic beauty fallen on hard times.

Mara unlocked the front door, wondering as she did each week why she bothered to lock it. Anyone could get in through the windows. Habit, that was what it was. Just habit. Like her habit of walking down to the Deutsches Eck. Perhaps I need habits, she thought as she crossed the big cold hall which rose right up to the roof as a well from which rooms and corridors branched off. They're little routines which one clings to. If next week I wasn't allowed to stop at the Deutsches Eck and look down on the rivers then I'd feel that things were even worse than they are today. She opened the kitchen door – why she bothered to shut it she didn't know. Another habit. To think how yesterday she'd cleaned the house in preparation for her father's arrival, how she'd washed the black and white tiled kitchen floor and scrubbed the long pine table and polished the copper pans which hung on the wall, the biggest one near the window, which looked out on the vegetable garden, the smallest one near the door. And all for nothing.

She sat down at the table with her elbows resting on its rough wooden surface and her chin pressed into her cupped hands. Surely something had to happen soon.

It didn't take long for the cold to drive Mara up to her room. Apart from the kitchen where she stored her food the only room Mara used, where she lived and slept, was her mother's old bedroom on the first floor. Before her mother had died they had used several rooms, but afterwards Mara had closed off the rest of the house, taking from each room her favourite objects to make this one room into a den, an oasis of treasures: of pictures,

22

ornaments, cushions, her mother's dainty inlaid desk, but nothing of her father's except for the few letters he had been allowed to write to her mother, letters which carried the smell of prison, and a dozen or so letters from her brother to her mother, letters which still bore the grime of the front. The last one was dated Christmas Day, 1914. She had found them all in an iron box in her mother's desk, and she had kept them there.

Breaking up the legs of an old chair to make a fire, Mara sat down in front of it, huddling up to its meagre warmth. She took off her shoes and balanced them on the grate to dry. Sometimes she wondered if she would ever be warm again, if the sun would ever shine again. Outside the rain pattered on the drive but that was the only sound she could hear. Silent room. Silent house. She sat there thinking. Not daydreaming, but with all the anger and frustration welling up inside her to colour her thoughts. Weeks of nothing, passing. Her life an existence, passing. War. Peace. What difference did it make to her?

I'm seventeen, she thought. In August I shall be eighteen. The following August I shall be nineteen. I've never been anywhere, never done anything, never met anyone. Concerts. Theatres. Operas. Balls. Nothing. Absolutely nothing. She closed her eyes and pictured herself going to a ball. Her dress would be white . . . no . . . ivory, and much more beautiful than any other girl's. She laid out the ballroom, shaped like a horseshoe with the orchestra at the far end. And she would be halfway up one side, standing . . . no . . . sitting; not alone of course but surrounded by admirers. Then HE would appear. She tried to imagine the face of her ideal man but it was impossible; she had met so few men. So she pictured a tall and dashing form without a face, or rather, with a nebulous face. But he would be dark. She liked dark hair. And they would dance. Miraculously, despite only having had a few dancing lessons, Mara would dance well. Of course she would. They would gaze into each other's eyes and float with the music, one of those Strauss waltzes her mother had loved, perhaps 'The Blue Danube'. Then he would lead her out into the moonlit garden and he would kiss her beside a fountain. And then . . .

Mara opened her eyes. Little shivers were running up and down her arms and legs, like a warm breeze beneath her skin. Don't be silly, she told herself, that's not going to happen. But surely that was what did happen, what was supposed to happen. Even if I met a man he wouldn't look at me twice, she thought despairingly. I'm haggard and bony. My clothes are hideous. I haven't had a new dress since . . . since I was twelve, and mother's look like tents on me. Anyhow, what would I talk to him about? I never talk to anyone. I don't even know how to. How could I? I never speak to anyone except for the red-haired American.

With vicious decision she picked up a pair of scissors from the desk and went over to the mirror. Her reflection through the dimness of the dull afternoon was worse than ever. And it was not only her face which depressed her, but also her hair. It hung almost to her waist and the ends were split and wispy while the streaks of red and fair, which had glowed when she was a child, were dulled into varieties of brown. Seizing the back of her hair she lifted it above her head and chopped it off some fifteen inches up so that when it fell it landed just below her shoulders. It looked worse. The back was short. The sides were long. But the grating of the scissors on the hair had given Mara a certain masochistic pleasure, so

24

she kept on chopping at it, all the way round, not even sure why she had begun to cut it except that it meant change.

She was trying to tidy up the back when there was a loud knock on the front door just below her room. The noise boomed through the empty house and echoed up the stairs. She stopped cutting and listened, the scissors frozen in one hand, her hair in the other. She waited. Silence. Had she imagined it? She began to wonder. Perhaps she'd gone round the bend: people did. Then there was another knock and a man's voice shouted something unintelligible. Mara held her breath. The hairs on her arms stood rigid with fright. No one ever came to the house, not any more. She crept over to the window and peered down. An English army officer was standing outside. She watched as he took two steps backwards, his boots crunching into the gravel. He was looking from side to side as though undecided if he should knock again, or go round to the back and try another door, or go away.

He moved towards the door. 'Is there anyone at home?' he shouted, hammering on the door.

Deciding that if she didn't answer he might break it down and if he did so she would have no way of mending it, Mara cautiously opened the window. The soldier heard the noise and looked up, smiling politely when he saw her. He certainly didn't look dangerous, he looked exactly as Mara had always thought an English gentleman should look: tall with broad shoulders, a smooth and pleasant face, rosy cheeks, a nose on the long side, a mouth on the small side, light brown hair cut very short and brushed back, with a centre parting, light brown eyes full of good behaviour. In fact he reminded her of a brown labrador she had once known: well-mannered, well-bred and perfectly safe with children.

'I'm sorry to disturb you,' he said, 'but I was looking for Hans Vogel.'

'My . . . brother?'

'Oh good, you speak English.' A pause. 'But of course you do. Your brother told me his mother was English. Is he here?'

'No.' What did he want with Hans? Mara was wary. One couldn't be too careful.

'I see. Will he be back soon?'

Watching his reaction Mara said, 'He's dead.'

'I'm so sorry.' He looked worried and she wondered why. Hadn't the English just spent the past five years trying to kill Germans like her brother?

Mara had the feeling he wanted to ask her another question. He didn't have the look of someone who called unexpectedly on strangers, particularly if they were his former enemies, without a definite reason. But he said nothing, and eventually she asked, 'How do you . . . did you know Hans?'

'We met at Ypres. The Christmas truce. His platoon was opposite mine.' He seemed embarrassed to mention the war.

'Christmas?'

'Fourteen.'

'Oh.' Mara frowned.

The soldier looked away, back down the drive as if wondering how to take his leave. Still Mara sensed he had more to ask her, that words were formulating in his mind, coming to the fore only to be pushed back. She watched him and waited, curious yet wanting him to go. She didn't want to be reminded of Hans. She had loved him, and she wanted to think of him as she had last seen him, glowing with all the nervous excitement of a boy setting off for the ultimate adventure. She and her mother had watched him walk down the drive. Just before he'd disappeared into the road he'd turned and waved. They had waved back. Then Mara had rushed up to her room, from where she could see the road below and Hans' fair head shining in the sun as he made his way down it, and she had thought, why couldn't Papa have gone like that?

All through those first few months of war and even after they heard that Hans was dead Mara had retained that memory of him. Her brother had done the right thing and if he had died, it was the right death. Now, if this Englishman were to talk of Hans then she would again be forced to recognize that he had existed beyond that glorious departure: that the departure might have been glorious but the arrival had been anything but. The shock when she had read Hans' letters after her mother died would be brought back to her, the questions those letters posed would go round and round in her head. The most puzzling: why had her mother spared her from the truth?

The Englishman was looking embarrassed, he was patting his thigh with the flat of his hand and shuffling his feet. At last he said, 'I've brought you some things. Coffee. Sugar. Powdered milk. Salt. Flour. I thought you might be short. They're on the doorstep. Shall I leave them there?'

Coffee! To Mara the word alone conjured up its delicious aroma. But would he grab her the moment she opened the door? She studied him carefully. 'No, I'll come down.'

When Mara opened the door the soldier smiled. Then his eyes dropped and his smile froze. Puzzled, Mara also looked down. The scissors were still clutched in her hand.

'Oh,' she laughed nervously, 'I was cutting my hair.' She put her spare hand up to its uneven ends. 'Did you think I was going to . . .'

But the soldier didn't laugh. He straightened his shoulders and assured her, 'You're perfectly safe with me, Miss Vogel, but I quite understand if you would prefer me to leave immediately.'

'Oh, no, please.' Mara hadn't intended to ask him in, but now she was embarrassed not to. She led the way through to the kitchen and pointed to a chair, saying, 'Sit down, sit down,' though she herself did not sit, being too unaccustomed to having a stranger in the house. Instead, she backed away and leaned against the sink, and watched him.

'I haven't introduced myself.' He stood up and held out his hand. 'Captain . . . I mean . . . Alexander Rushton. I'm delighted to meet you, Miss Vogel.'

Mara looked at his hand but did not take it. She merely nodded, not because she wanted to be rude, just that she preferred to keep her distance.

Pretending not to notice the snub, the soldier withdrew his hand and fished out some packets of food from his coat pocket. 'There we are. Now, how about a nice hot cup of coffee? You look as though you need one, if you don't mind my saying so.'

'I haven't tasted coffee for months,' said Mara abruptly, and she turned away, biting her lower lip. Cruelty she could cope with, kindness made her vulnerable. It broke through her brittle wall of self-defence, stripping her of its protection and exposing her for what she really was: a lonely and bewildered girl.

Alexander Rushton was unused to emotion, so he began to talk hurriedly over it. 'I must say it's pretty miserable weather you have here. People complain about the English climate . . . it's not nearly as cold . . . perhaps a little wetter . . . but I expect the summers here are . . . of course I haven't been here in summer yet. Have you ever been to England, Miss Vogel?'

Mara shook her head.

'Oh, you should go.' He might have been recommending a holiday resort, not a country with which her own had just been through a bloody war. 'Yes, you most certainly should. Oh, good. Water boiling. Whoever said men are hopeless in the kitchen? Now, where's the coffee? Ah, here it is.'

Mara smiled faintly. He did not seem to expect an answer, he talked because he was afraid of silence. Encircling her cup with her cold hands, she lifted it until the steam touched her face and the deliciousness filled her nostrils. 'Thank you.' She smiled at him, sorry now that she'd been unfriendly.

Alexander watched her. What a strange girl! he thought. Quite different from . . . He pictured the girls with whom he had danced at hunt balls or played tennis when on leave. Very different. But even in those ghastly clothes she's . . . well . . .

To Mara it seemed that the subject of Hans stood between herself and the soldier, that he was waiting for her to ask about her brother and by not doing so she was in some way rejecting Hans. She sat down, tucked her uneven hair behind her ears, and said, 'How was my brother when you saw him?'

'Very well. We only met the once. You must have heard about the Christmas truce. Quite unofficial, of course – the truce.' He said 'unofficial' in the same way an unadventurous little boy confesses to his mother, with a certain pride, that he and all the other little boys have done something 'naughty'. But not, of course, something very naughty. This was Alexander. He was the good little boy. He obeyed orders and he transmitted them, but he was no more capable of enlarging on them than the needle of a gramophone is capable of adding another few bars of Mozart to the record spinning round on its turntable. Even as he sat with Mara he was uneasy because he had used the staff car to come there and personal use of cars was strictly against orders. It made him feel exactly as he had felt when talking to Hans Vogel, a German.

'Tell me about the truce,' said Mara. 'I heard a little, but no details.'

'Well, we all climbed out of our trenches and met up with the enemy, I mean the Germans, in no-man's-land. That's how I met your brother. We had quite a chat really, considering the circumstances. But he spoke English and most of the . . . er . . . Germans didn't.'

'I see.' He had painted a picture of Hans exactly as she would have imagined had she not read the letters. There was nothing of her brother's despair at the senseless carnage, of his rebellion.

Alexander chatted on. 'We exchanged addresses and as I was here I decided to look him up. I thought I might have a problem finding the house but I found it easily. I don't know Koblenz that well, but it's funny how quickly one learns to find one's way around when one has to.'

Mara said, 'I thought only the Americans were in Koblenz.'

'You're right. But we have to liaise over various matters and my job brings me down here once or twice a week.'

'Where have you come from?'

'Cologne.'

Mara thought of her father and was about to ask the Englishman to help her but before she had formulated the words he had carried on talking. 'I have a staff car. I left it in the road. Your drive's a bit overgrown if you don't mind my saying so, but I suppose it's not easy to find people to help you.' He hesitated and fiddled with his cup. 'I'm sorry about your brother, Miss Vogel.'

Mara shrugged her shoulders helplessly.

'Of course it was extraordinary.'

'What was?'

'That we'd been fighting each other and then, there we all were, talking and laughing just as though the war didn't exist. Men playing football with those who, the previous day, had shot at them, running up and down on the ground where the next day they would be shot at again. And shot at by those with whom they were playing.'

Mara watched him as he talked. She could see that the truce had meant a great deal to him and he had wanted to talk about it for a long time, but had been unable to do so because afterwards the authorities had tried to hush up the whole thing. This was true of Germany; she suspected it was true of England. And as she watched him she thought how nice and normal he is, just like people were before the war.

He said, 'But there was a lot of trouble when it was over. You see, some of the men swopped their rations for German beer. We had tins of vegetables in gravy called Maconochie's and, although it really wasn't too bad, the men got sick of it. Not surprising as they had it nearly every day. Anyhow, a number of them swopped their Maconochie's for beer and got drunk. That wasn't the only trouble. The French heard about it and were pretty rude to some of our boys, and of course it all got back to High Command.'

'And they weren't pleased either.'

31

'No. But it was too late by that time, except that they made sure it never happened again.' He glanced round the kitchen. 'Is your mother here?'

'She's dead. She died last year.'

'Oh, I am sorry.' He gulped his coffee to cover his confusion. 'Where did she come from in England?'

'Kent.'

'Do you still have family there?'

'No, she was an only child and an orphan.'

He looked appalled. 'What about your father?'

Mara was about to answer, 'He's in Cologne,' but something stopped her and she said, 'He's dead too,' although she hated having to say it because she felt she might be tempting fate. But that was silly. In fact, she was silly not to have told him the truth; he was in Cologne, he would have access to the prison records. But it was too late now.

Alexander said, 'How awful for you. You have had a hard time of it. Did . . . he die in the war?'

'No.' She looked down at the pine table and picked at its ridged grain. 'My father didn't go to war. He didn't believe in it.'

'Didn't believe . . .' Alexander looked appalled, but only for a moment. Then he forced himself to say, with an understanding smile, 'Oh, I see, he was a pacifist.'

'Yes, a pacifist.' She knew now why some instinct had stopped her from telling him that her father was in Cologne. That she might have resented her father for his beliefs was one thing, that a stranger might disapprove of him was another. Her father was hers to criticize and she had the right to do so, just as the members of a family will criticize each other and the nationals of a country will voice their grumbles about it, but the criticism of an outsider is unacceptable to be saved by a critic is even worse. The sense of obligation is as galling as that of a family of prostitutes forced to borrow money from a vicar.

Still trying to look understanding, Alexander asked, 'What did he do during the war? Was he . . . imprisoned? We had pacifists in England too. I think some of them went to prison.'

Mara nodded. 'Yes, he did go to prison. They thought because he was a pacifist he must be a traitor, but he wasn't.'

'No, of course not.'

Alexander didn't ask her where or when her father had died, he didn't want to talk about him, and Mara decided that if the Englishman returned and found her father there she could easily say she'd been misinformed about his death. In any case the Englishman probably wouldn't come back.

'So who lives with you now?' Alexander inquired, looking at the door as if he half expected some elderly female relative to appear.

'I live alone.'

'Alone! Alone! With all this . . .' He waved his hand towards the window to indicate the turbulent world outside. 'Miss Vogel, may I ask how old you are?'

Mara shrugged her shoulders defiantly. 'I'm seventeen. Nearly eighteen. And I'm perfectly all right on my own.'

'Don't you have any friends or relatives?'

'No.'

'What did your . . . er . . . father do before the war?'

'His family owned the local newspaper. The Vogels are an old Koblenz family. But when he was arrested they turned against us.'

'His family?'

'Oh no, my father's parents were dead and he only had

a younger sister. She went to America and died before the war, my mother was her governess, that's how my parents met. What I meant was . . . I'm sorry if my English is a bit confused . . . that the people of Koblenz turned against us.'

'Your English is perfect.' He leaned across the table and looked into Mara's eyes, his own soft and brown and sympathetic. 'Are they still against you?' he asked gently.

Mara gave him a wry smile and drew back. 'Yes. So are you.'

'Me!'

'You, the Allies. To you, I'm German. To the Germans, I'm English.'

'How awful for you . . .' He stretched out his hand but he did not touch her although he wanted to.

The kindness in his voice brought tears to Mara's eyes. She looked down and said nothing.

After a few moments of awkward silence Alexander glanced at his watch and stood up. 'I have to go now,' he said. 'Will you be all right?'

She nodded. She was sorry he was leaving, she dreaded the thought of the empty house and the solitude which would be so much more acute for his having been there. That he disapproved of her father didn't matter to her in that instant. He had been kind and companionable. For the first time in months, in years, she'd felt like a human being and not like some dreary piece of machinery doomed for ever to hack its way through the undergrowth of life. But now he was leaving she almost wished he hadn't come, that he'd left her to her unawareness.

'Is there anything you need?' he asked.

Mara shook her head. There were of course a thousand things: food, firewood, clothes, coal. Everything.

'Can I come and see you again? I'll be back in Koblenz on Saturday.'

'Yes, yes. Thank you.' Her voice was little more than a murmur.

'Well . . . umm . . . goodbye.' He waited for her to speak, but when she said nothing he added, 'I'll see myself out. And, Miss Vogel, be sure to lock the door after me.'

Mara sat at the table listening to his retreating footsteps, the slam of the front door, the crunch of his boots outside, the distant rev of an engine. Then the silence closed back in around her.

She walked over to the window. 'Alexander Rushton, Alexander Rushton,' she repeated his name as she stared out at the dripping garden, her nose pressed against the cracked glass, her breath making a fluctuating circle of condensation on its cold surface. Lock the door, Miss Vogel! Is there anything you need, Miss Vogel! You shouldn't live alone, Miss Vogel! It seemed strange to have someone worrying about her, someone who didn't expect . . . 'But I'm not going to think about that any more,' she told herself firmly.

And slowly, as Mara watched, the rain died down and the sun came out.

Chapter 2

Alexander came back on Saturday, just as he said he would. As soon as Mara heard his car she opened the front door and stood on the steps smiling at him. She had been half afraid he wouldn't come and had been telling herself that she wouldn't mind too much. But she would have minded very much. Not only because she liked him, but because she needed him to distract her from her thoughts of Wednesday.

'Hello, there,' he called, coming towards her carrying a large brown paper bag. 'How are you?'

'All right, thank you.' Mara felt slightly embarrassed now he was here. She didn't quite know what to say to him. When he'd left they'd had a certain rapport but that seemed to have gone, they'd gone back a step.

Alexander too felt that awkwardness but he dealt with it in his own way. 'Not much to eat in here, I'm afraid,' he said, looking into the paper bag. 'Mostly firewood. But I expect you need it. And a bag of sugar. Supplies were a bit low today, they often are at the end of the week.' He chatted on as they went through into the kitchen.

'Have you always been a soldier?' Mara asked him some time later.

Alexander was stacking the firewood neatly like a platoon on parade. He glanced round to where she was perched on the end of the table. 'Yes, ever since I left school.'

'Do you . . . like it?'

'Like it!' He stared at her as though she were simple. 'Of course I do. I love it. The Army's my life.' He said this with pride and smiled at Mara who thought of Hans and shivered. 'And it's one's duty . . . I mean . . .' he blushed furiously as he remembered her father, then added quickly, 'Anyhow, I don't know what I'd do if I wasn't in the Army. Unlike my brother Herbert I'd be hopeless in business.' He had the air of someone who'd just scrambled out of a deep ditch.

Mara pretended not to notice. She asked, 'What does your brother do?'

Alexander smiled. He was on safe ground. The ditch was behind him. 'He works for my father. You'd like my father, he's a wonderful man, a real old lion. At least, that's how I always think of him, though he's really not that old, only in his late fifties, but he has a great mane of white hair so he looks older than most men of his age. And he works very hard. He still goes to the works every day. If I'd done what he's done I'd want to reap some of the benefits and enjoy myself. But he loves it.'

'The works?' This didn't fit Mara's image of an English gentleman.

'Rushton-Gaunt Motors.' He straightened up and waited for her to speak, but when she made no comment he went on, 'I suppose living in Germany you may not have heard of Rushton-Gaunt but they're one of the oldest established British motorworks and our cars have an excellent reputation. Smart too. Not heavy and ugly like the old cars were, but long and shiny and sleek. In fact, a Rushton-Gaunt is quite a status symbol.'

'Like our Benz?'

'Yes.' Then he added grudgingly, 'But we're not quite as big.'

Determined not to be outdone, Mara said, 'My father always had a Benz car. There's one in the garage.'

'Really?'

'Yes, but it doesn't work any more. That's why it wasn't requisitioned. They only took the tyres.' She paused and with an innocent smile suggested, 'Perhaps you could mend it.'

'Mend it! Not my domain I'm afraid. You need a mechanic.' Alexander was puzzled. Hadn't she understood what sort of person he was?

Immediately Mara felt guilty. Why had she had that urge to upset him? He didn't mean to be so . . . pompous, it was just his manner. And he didn't mean to begrudge praise to anything German, it was only because he was English. To placate him she said, smiling sweetly, 'Tell me more about your father and your family. Where do they live?'

'Between Oxford and Banbury.'

'Between the university and the white lady on the cockhorse.'

He laughed. 'No, it's the fine lady on the white horse and you at the cross on the cockhorse. Rushton Park is just south of Banbury. We all live there, my father, Herbert, his wife Sophia, and their twins, Damon and Atalanta.'

'Atalanta! What a lovely name.'

Alexander smiled fondly. 'She's going to live up to it. Damon, her twin brother, is very quiet but Atalanta's a bundle of fun. We had another brother called Oliver who died when I was a baby, but they say she's very like him. If you come to England you must meet them. You'd like Prince too. He's my dog – a black labrador.'

Mara laughed. She remembered her first impression of him. 'I love labradors,' she said through her laughter.

'So do I.' He nodded his approval. It was another point in her favour. 'Do you know, every time I go home on leave I find him waiting at the bottom of the drive. He knows I'm coming. Isn't that amazing, Miss Vogel?'

'Yes. Incredible. And please call me Mara.'

'Mara! That's a lovely name. Very unusual.' A pause. 'And you must call me Alexander.'

They sat in silence for some time, digesting their new-found intimacy. Mara pictured all these Rushtons, replicas of Alexander, living on their large estate where generations of Rushtons had lived before them. 'But why are your cars called Rushton-Gaunt?' she asked.

'The Gaunt is Sir Henry Gaunt, a . . . er . . . friend of my father's.' He looked embarrassed, though Mara couldn't imagine why, then said, 'I must go or I'll be late.' He stood up. 'I'll see you next week, if that's all right. Probably Thursday.'

'Yes.' Mara accompanied him to the door.

'I'll bring you a tin of Maconochie's,' he called as he crunched across the gravel to his car.

'But I haven't any beer to swop for it, nor even any Mosel.'

He laughed as he stepped into the car, waved as he set off; and then he was gone.

But before Thursday came Wednesday.

For once Mara didn't stop on the Deutsches Eck, she went straight to the Civil Affairs office, running up the steps and pushing open the heavy door, bursting into the room with her eyes shining and her face glowing as though she expected to find her father sitting on the bench waiting for her. Of course he wasn't there, just the inevitable queue. But for once there were less than a dozen people waiting, the office had been open only two minutes, the red-haired American had not yet arrived, his place behind the desk was empty, the interpreter sat on his upright chair reading a newspaper. Mara took her place on the bench, pushed her shawl back, tidied her hair with her fingers, and waited.

A few minutes later a door at the back of the room opened and a dark-haired, bespectacled American soldier came in. He walked to the empty chair behind the desk, sat down, adjusted his glasses, and called, 'Okay, come on!'

Mara stared at him in horror. Where was the big red-haired man? Why wasn't he there? Had she come on the wrong day . . . no, today was Wednesday. She knew it was. She sat on the edge of the bench, picking at the fringe of her shawl, wondering if it was worth staying. What could this stranger tell her? But then she told herself not to be silly, if the red-haired man had any information he would have put it in her file, it didn't matter who sat behind the desk, who gave her the news, just so long as she heard something.

Finally it was her turn. The soldier didn't even have to shout, 'Next!' before Mara was at his desk. 'Vogel,' she said. 'V O G E L. I'm trying to trace my father, Franz Vogel. The . . . er . . . other one, other officer, who was here last week said he would probably have news for me today.' She wished the red-haired man had been there. He would have saved her from all this.

The soldier adjusted his glasses. 'Okay, okay, not so fast. Give me the name again, miss.'

'Vogel. V O G E L. Franz Vogel.'

He began shuffling through the files, starting near the top. Mara nearly screamed, 'V is at the bottom you idiot,' but she controlled herself. Eventually he pulled out the file, laid it in front of himself and slowly opened it. He read down the first page, put it to one side and carried on down the second page. From where Mara stood in front of the desk she could make out her father's name but nothing more. Most of it was handwritten and it was all upside down to her.

When he reached the bottom of the second page, he turned it over and held it up as he read from the back of it. Then he put it down on the desk and Mara could see that there were just three lines written on it. 'I'm afraid your father is dead,' he said, looking up at her but not into her eyes. 'The prison records have now been located and his death is listed in them.'

Mara gripped the edge of the desk. 'He died in Cologne?'

'No, in Koblenz.' He glanced down at the page. 'I see that it says he was moved but my colleague, who is ill today, checked in Cologne and they had no one of that name listed. Since then we've found the Koblenz Prison records.' He shrugged his shoulders. 'I'm sorry.'

'But . . .' She swayed towards him but he didn't suggest she sit down, 'when did he die?'

He pointed to a date on the page: 3 February 1918.

Mara felt a ray of hope. 'That's not possible. My mother went to see him in prison in March.'

'Your mother saw him!'

The hope began to die. She remembered her mother answering tonelessly, 'I didn't see him.'

'Did your mother see him?' the soldier asked again. Now he understood why his red-haired friend found this job so depressing. It was bad enough having to tell them their relatives were dead without having them arguing with you.

'No, she didn't see him. They told her he'd been moved to Cologne to work on the railway.'

The soldier looked at her as if to say, 'There, you see,'

41

picked up the two sheets of paper, aligned them neatly and put them back in the file.

'But I was told he was alive last April,' said Mara in desperation.

'Who told you?' He closed the file.

'I went to the police station. They . . . they told me he was alive and in Cologne.'

He put the file to one side, not back in the pile, but to be taken away and kept with all the other dead files. Then he looked straight into her eyes and said, 'Whoever told you that was lying.'

There was nothing for Mara to do but leave. She walked slowly down the long room and out through the heavy doors. It was only now, knowing her father was dead, that she realized quite how much she'd counted on his return. She'd longed to assuage herself of the guilt of her rejection, by looking after him, by being with him, by recapturing what had once been. It seemed incredible that she had not known he was dead when, thinking about it, all the signs had been there, and that he had gone to join all those millions of people who are dead without her being aware of it. He'd been picked, as schoolchildren are selected at random to join one team or another, and he'd gone to join the bigger team while she'd stayed behind with the little one. She felt abandoned and terribly lonely, angry because the years which they could have shared had been stolen, acute despair because she would never see him again. Surely she should have sensed his death? But so long as she hadn't, he'd remained alive for her, and so long as he'd been alive for her she'd been able to face up to what she'd done with Herr Steiger.

Now the sense of martyrdom in which she had wrapped herself, and in which to some extent she had revelled, because even during the most brutal moments it had allowed her to see herself as an almost holy sacrifice, had been torn away. Wrapped in that knowledge, she had been able to put up with the German blundering on to her and into her, bruising her and tearing at her. She had suffered and hated. The pain and the humiliation had made her hate him, the sense of sacrifice had helped her to survive. And later, when Herr Steiger had become fond of her and had clumsily tried to be gentle, she had despised him, and if she ever felt her hatred was growing less intense because he no longer hurt her, she had recalled the physical pain of that first time and her humiliation when he'd said, 'He will starve unless . . .' and she was Sydney Carton again.

But Herr Steiger had tricked her. He had robbed her of the reason for submitting to his brutality: and left her only with the brutality . . . It was as if Sydney Carton, on reaching the guillotine, had been told that Lucie was happily winding wool for Madame Defarge. To pay, and all for nothing. To have the far, far better thing turned into a mockery.

Without being aware Mara had walked down to the Deutsches Eck. She stood on the point, looking down the Rhine, the wind blowing straight in her face, pushing back her shawl and buffeting her uneven hair from side to side, and suddenly she had an extraordinary feeling that she would never come to this place again, that she had gone there because it was a part of her childhood – a chapter that was now over.

Chapter 3

Mara hoped Alexander wouldn't come that Thursday. She wanted to be alone, to come to terms with her father's death. She needed to mourn, and to separate him from her bitterness against Herr Steiger, by living through all her early happy memories of him. It was essential for her to do this now, before the link between the two became so hard and fast that she could not remember one without the other. Had she been able to put off Alexander, she would have done so, but she had no way of contacting him, the telephone had been cut off when her father was arrested and in any case Alexander hadn't given her a telephone number. Perhaps, she thought, as she lay in bed staring up at the ceiling, he's afraid if I telephone him people might think he's . . . fraternizing. She rolled over on her side and watched the specks of dust dancing up a ray of pale sunlight which had found its way through the curtains.

Eventually she wandered down to her father's study. The freshly dusted books stood on their shelves and mocked her. She sat down behind his desk and stroked its dark red leather top. She closed her eyes and pictured her father sitting there. But the picture was not clear. She couldn't really let herself go, because all the time she was half listening for the sound of Alexander's car. That he might come was just as disturbing as if he were definitely coming: the time still had to be allotted to him: the mourning could not begin.

He came in the late morning, slamming the car door

and bounding up the steps, smiling broadly when Mara opened the front door. 'Here you are. Two tins of Maconochie's.'

Mara stared at the tins. She'd forgotten. 'Oh, thank you.'

Alexander stood in front of her, half smiling, waiting for her to say, 'I couldn't find any beer', or at least refer to it, and when she didn't mention it he looked dejected, as if she'd taken a small step back from him.

Had Mara told him the truth about her father's death it would all have been explained to him, but she didn't. It would have involved her in 'I know I told you he was dead but he wasn't . . . why did I tell you? . . . well, umm . . . yes, I know you could have helped trace him, but . . .' and then Alexander would have been obliged to give her his hollow sympathy while, just like the vicar, he would be telling himself what a relief it was to know the wages of sin were inadequate.

But because Mara didn't tell Alexander why she was preoccupied, he was convinced that in some way he had offended her and he followed her miserably into the kitchen, suddenly aware of how much she meant to him. 'I've brought you some bread,' he said. 'And some jam. Mr Tickler's jam. Plum and apple. It's not very good but it's all I could get.'

Mara thanked him and sat down at the table. She felt as though she were moving through a nebulous mass, a thick dark cloud, and that Alexander was talking to her from far away, almost as if he were on another planet.

'There's a song about Mr Tickler's jam' – he was trying to amuse her – 'the soldiers sing it:

"Tickler's jam, Tickler's jam, how I long for Tickler's jam;
Sent from England in ten-ton lots
Issued to Tommy in one-pound pots."

There's more but I can't remember it.'

Mara forced herself to smile. 'Who is Tommy?'

'Tommy's a nickname the British give their soldiers.' He paused. 'You're looking very pale.'

'Yes.' She stared down at her hands which lay in her lap. 'I'm not feeling very well.'

Alexander was so relieved he hadn't offended her that he went overboard with his concern. 'You need something to eat . . . I'll heat up some Maconochie's. You don't eat enough . . . no wonder you're ill.'

Mara shook her head. The thought of food made her feel quite sick.

'Then you must go to bed. I'll leave.'

She stood up. 'If you don't mind.'

'Of course not. And let me give you this.' He took a pen and a piece of paper from his pocket. 'My telephone number. If anything goes wrong, if you ever need help, you can get me here. I may be out but you can leave your name. You have a phone, don't you?'

'Yes. Thank you.' Mara didn't tell him that the line was dead, she didn't want to go into all of that because it related to her father, but as she heard Alexander drive away she admonished herself for thinking he might be afraid other people would say he was fraternizing. The word conjured up images of drunken soldiers unable to control their lust or confused young boys whose homesickness drove them into the arms of women supposed to be their enemies. Alexander was neither of these. To suggest it was offensive.

Mara didn't go to bed but into the rose garden, which was just outside her father's study and had been his pride and joy. No gardener had ever been allowed to prune the roses, only her father had touched them. Thank God he can't see them now, she thought, looking at the long stems with their shiny new red leaves shooting out in all directions. Or perhaps he can see them. She glanced quickly over her shoulder, then told herself she was being silly. Nevertheless, she went back into the house, dug around till she found his secateurs, and came out again. What had he always told her about pruning roses? Something about cutting them down to the leaf with the bud in it. She grabbed the nearest waving stem, looked for the right leaf, but couldn't see it. So she chopped it off at a reasonable height and grabbed the next stem, cursing as the thorns pricked her fingers.

An hour later there was a pile of stems on the ground and a bed full of sorry-looking bushes. Wishing she'd left them alone, Mara sat down on the low brick wall which separated the rose garden from the narrow stretch of grass between it and the house. The sun was warm on her back and suddenly she felt extraordinarily peaceful. The dark mass which had surrounded her in the kitchen had turned into something kind and protective. It was a cushion between her and what could have been acute despair. She looked at the windows of her father's study. It seemed so odd that he had lived and talked and moved in there, and that he wasn't there any more. He was somewhere else. But where? What did it feel like to be dead? Did he know he was dead?

Thinking about her father, Mara realized that there had been another reason apart from wanting to protect him why she hadn't asked Alexander to help in the search. She had wanted to hear the news at source, brutally and plainly with no comforting 'He didn't suffer,' because she would have known he had suffered and to avoid acknowledging that fact would have been a further rejection. Of him as a person and not just of his ideas.

Because in death, ideas no longer count: it is as a physical being that a person breathes their last.

She began to gather the drooping rose stems into a bundle. Only then did she remember that her father had always pruned them in the autumn. They'll probably die, she thought sadly, looking at the stunted bushes. In a funny way she hoped they would, because if they grew beautiful flowers, as they had under her father's hands, she would have robbed him of something which had always been considered his special talent. She would have invaded his territory and succeeded in setting up house on ground considered uninhabitable to all but himself. And she wanted to think of him as clever and talented, but only of his simple talents.

Alexander took to calling on Mara as often as his duties permitted. He could seldom stay more than an hour and his visits followed a strict programme; he arrived; she made coffee; they talked; he left. They would sit opposite each other at the fireplace end of the kitchen table, she with her back to the window, he with his back to the door, and they would both swing their legs round towards the warmth of the fire so that from time to time, and quite unintentionally, their feet touched. Then they would each jump back guiltily.

Mara came to know him well during these afternoons and she realized very quickly that he had no comprehension of what it was like to be without money. This irritated her but at the same time she found it oddly comforting. He faced life with the calm assurance that its necessities would be provided. She wished she could be like that.

One day he said, 'Why don't you open up the rest of the house?'

Mara shrugged her shoulders. 'It hardly seems worth it.'

'We could sit in the drawing room. It would be . . . nicer.'

'Oh, very well.'

The next time Alexander came, Mara led him into the drawing room. It ran almost the length of the house and had tall elegant windows looking out to what had been a well-mown tennis court. 'This is lovely.' Alexander turned slowly in the centre of the silky carpet and looked down at its circle of dusky pink roses and pale green leaves, entwined against a cream background. 'How extraordinary! We have a carpet like this in our drawing room.' He looked across at Mara and smiled. 'My sister-in-law Sophia chose it. I've always liked it.'

'It's an Aubusson,' Mara told him, sitting down on the sofa beside the fireplace. 'I like it too.' She hesitated, she hadn't mentioned her father since Alexander's first visit but now she felt strong enough to include him in her conversation, casually as anyone else would have spoken of their father, as Alexander spoke of his. 'My father and mother used this room a lot,' she said.

'Oh . . . er . . . yes.' He hovered for a moment before coming over and sitting down beside her. It was the most positive move he had made towards her and she was very aware of his nearness. She could sense that he was aware of her too and that the courage which had brought him over to her had now deserted him. He left shortly afterwards.

But the next time he came he took it as natural to sit next to her, it would have been unnatural not to do so.

On this occasion he said, 'I must say you're looking much better than when I met you.'

It was true. Her face had filled out. Her hair had

49

regained its sheen. Her eyes were no longer sunken. Mara patted her stomach. 'Yes, I'm even putting on weight.'

'Now you need something to do. I don't like the idea of your being alone all day. I'll speak to my American counterpart, they're requisitioning houses up here and I'm sure with your fluent German . . .'

'No.'

'But, Mara . . .'

'No. No, thank you.' She didn't want to know about the world outside, the world beyond the boundary hedge which so completely isolated her that she might have been living on an island with the sea pounding on that very hedge.

Mara was growing fond of Alexander. He had become a part of her life. It had taken her time to get used to him, to having someone around. If there's one word that describes him it's 'pleasant', she thought to herself on more than one occasion. Pleasant sounds dreadful, so . . . condescending. Or was it condensing? She always muddled up the two. But he is pleasant. And he looks pleasant. Handsome in a pleasant way. Sometimes she wondered why he wasn't more confident when he was with her: he always seemed to be afraid of saying or doing the wrong thing, and somehow he often managed to. He liked to talk about her, and was even happy to talk about her mother, but he was blind, or perhaps he wished to blind himself to the essential link which had produced Mara: that she had a father. And the more Mara came to terms with her father's death, and by doing so was able to separate him from her bitterness against Herr Steiger, the more she resented Alexander's attitude. She began to mention her father at every opportunity.

'My father was a fascinating talker,' she told him,

watching his face. 'Even those who disagreed with him couldn't help but listen.'

Alexander nodded. 'Really?'

'Yes. And not just when he spoke, when he wrote as well. But he was very fair and always put both sides of an argument.'

'Oh.'

'That's why it was such a shock to my mother when he was arrested.'

As usual Alexander switched the conversation away from her father. 'Why did your mother come to Germany in the first place?'

'Because she was living in an orphanage and my grand-father knew the man who owned it. So when he decided to have an English governess for my aunt, he wrote to this man. Luckily for my mother she was chosen for the job.' She paused. 'Of course many people in Koblenz thought that my father shouldn't have married her because she was only a governess.'

Alexander looked offended. 'Why ever not? A nice English girl.'

After he left Mara felt terribly depressed. She wandered round the house, in and out of long-closed rooms, picking up dusty ornaments, wiping them on her skirt and putting them down again. It's not Alexander's fault, she told herself. It's just one of those things. My father was not only a pacifist but he was also a German, and the Germans are Alexander's enemies. Nothing will ever make him see that just like everyone else, even his sainted English, some are good and some are bad.

She went upstairs and lay down on her bed, and sank into a mood of deep reflection. What's it all about? What am I here for? What are any of us here for? The future stretched ahead, dark and menacing: no different from the past. She thought of Herr Steiger and how he had tricked her, how he had known he was tricking her. She had been glad when she'd heard that he'd shot himself, that he had been so afraid of what would happen to him that he'd taken his own life. It had done her good to think of him being afraid. Now she was sorry. Had he been alive she would have had the chance of avenging herself on him. She thought about it: of how she would have made him suffer. She looked across at her mother's desk and thought of Hans' last letter. And suddenly she sat up. Had her mother known about her father's death? Had she been told that last time she had gone to the prison and tried to see him? Had she tried to spare Mara as she'd tried to spare her from the truth about Hans? She recalled Herr Steiger's face when she'd said, 'My mother told me he'd been moved to Cologne,' and he'd said, 'Oh, she did, did she?' He had looked surprised. She hadn't thought much about it at the time. Now she wondered. Had her mother tried to spare her, and in the end not spared her at all?

Mara lay back on the pillows and her ponderings returned to Alexander. Do I expect too much? Is that why he sometimes annoys me? Is it because I imagined that once I found a man who cared for me I should never again be bored or depressed, and now I find that I still am, I blame him? Is that it? That and . . . well . . . although he's kind and nice and really quite attractive, he's not all the other things I want . . . long for. He's not the kindred spirit my father always said my mother was for him. I don't feel for him as a . . . man. Only as a friend. A very good friend. No more. But perhaps I'll never meet anyone who means more. She sighed and dug herself deeper into the bed, and resolved to like

Alexander for what he was and not to be annoyed with him for what he wasn't.

As the weeks went by Mara realized something else about Alexander: he only wanted to know those aspects of her which fitted the image he wished to see. 'You're so courageous, so brave,' he told her frequently. 'It horrifies me when I think how you struggled on, all alone, before I came.'

After he had said this, or variations of it, on three consecutive visits until Mara felt like a fraud, she pointed out, 'I'm not the only girl in my position.'

He smiled. 'Other girls are much tougher than you.'

'Not necessarily.' Mara didn't know why she bothered to argue, when she had known few women over the past years and cared for none except her mother.

But Alexander wanted his gallantry appealed to. He longed to be able to satisfy his sense of chivalry. If he rode his white charger, then she must play the damsel in distress. 'Mara,' he spoke gently as though explaining something to a backward child, 'you don't realize that most of them survived by . . . well . . . you know.'

In a fit of exasperation Mara stood up for her absent sisters. 'I'm sure they didn't.'

'Of course they did. You, Mara, are too much of a . . . umm . . . to understand these things.'

'Too much of a what?'

'A lady.'

Mara's exasperation turned to stifled laughter. Did he really imagine she was a fragile flower? Didn't he know that only the strong survive? Her mother, her father, her brother, and even Herr Steiger, had not survived. But she had.

She got up and walked over to the sink so that he

couldn't see her laughing. Alexander watched her. She moved differently from English girls, he decided. Less as though she were practising deportment with a book on her head. She sort of prowls. Like a cat.

Mara turned round and caught his eyes resting on her. So that's it, she thought, refusing to allow herself to be disillusioned. So much for friendship! Or is it? she wondered as Alexander blushed and hurriedly looked away from her. Perhaps I'm wrong. He's so correct. Perhaps it's both. Friendship and . . . the other. She turned on the tap and filled the pan with water. But what if he tries to . . . Do I want him to touch me? No, I don't. Not really. I like him, he's quite attractive, he's tall, he has a nice face. But he just doesn't make me . . . well . . . I don't know. She turned off the tap. Yes, I do know. He doesn't make me want him like I want to want. She walked over to the fire and put the pan on the little iron ring above it, aware that his eyes had returned to her. But what if he tries? I don't want to lose him. Or the food. Or the coffee. Or the firewood. Or himself. I'd miss him. I just hope he doesn't spoil things by trying to . . . She pushed back her hair from her face and frowned. But would I, will I, if I have to?

Chapter 4

One afternoon towards the end of May Mara washed her hair in the kitchen sink and then wandered out towards the rose garden, shaking the water from the wet tangles of her hair. Poor roses, she contemplated their jagged stems and new red leaves, only seven, no, eight buds and you used to be covered in them. Poor roses, involved in yet another war! She sat down on the wall, one leg either side of it, and lifted her face to the sun. It was hot and windy in the garden and big fluffy white clouds were scudding across a clear blue sky. Watching them, Mara was reminded of other summer days: the light summer evenings of her childhood when she would lie in bed and listen to her parents and their friends playing tennis on the court below, their voices and the pit-pat of the ball coming to her through the open window: the summer before the war when she had gone to Paris with her parents, her only trip abroad: the summers during the war when she and her mother had lived through their hot, dry isolation: last summer when many suspected the war was lost but no one dared say so.

She lifted the faded blue cotton of her skirt and examined her bare knees. They were already slightly tanned. She liked to see them go brown. Very white skins, so much admired by her mother and her grandmother, had always reminded her of wet cod on the fishmonger's stall in the market. Stretching out her legs in front of her, Mara wondered if they had a nice shape. They looked good from this angle, from above, but were they nice in comparison to those of other girls? An article in one of the English newspapers which Alexander had brought her, hoping to interest her in world affairs and particularly in England and the English way of life, had described a dress-length as being 'for those with the less well-shaped calf'. Was that her? She wriggled her right leg. Should she be lowering her hems? But from what? Her childish dresses barely covered her knees and her mother's clothes were still too wide for her.

For the first time in years Mara wished she had a friend, a girl friend, with whom she could discuss these things. Someone to giggle with, someone who's . . . growing up like I am, she thought. But there was no one. She closed her eyes against the sun and drifted off into a reverie about all the clothes she would buy if she had the money: beautiful dresses with matching shoes and bags. And hats which she would wear at rakish angles. And a fur coat over her shoulders.

Her thoughts were interrupted by Alexander calling to her.

'I'm by the rose garden,' she shouted, pulling her skirt down over her knees.

He came round the corner of the house, caught sight of her bare legs and blushed furiously. 'Oh . . . er . . . hello.'

'Hello.' Mara tried not to laugh at his embarrassment.

Alexander forced himself to look at her face. 'I know I said I probably wouldn't come today but . . .' he shifted from foot to foot. 'I have some good news for you.'

'Oh. What?'

'It's about the house.'

'The house!'

'Yes.' He grinned. 'You remember I told you the

Americans were requisitioning the big houses round here?'

'Yes . . . vaguely.' What she did remember was he had had some silly idea about her working for the Americans.

'Well, yours is going to be a hospital. A sort of post-operation centre.' He spoke as if he were telling her she'd won some marvellous prize.

Mara sat up sharply, her eyes fixed on his grinning face. Good news! Her house a hospital.

Misinterpreting her silence Alexander went on, 'I knew you'd be pleased. This means you won't be on your own any more and I'll feel much happier about leaving you here. Of course the Americans can be a bit . . . rowdy, but the doctor in charge is said to be pretty tough although he's young, so I'm sure he'll keep them in order.'

Now it was Mara's turn to play the adult speaking to the backward child. 'But I don't want a hospital here. It's my house and I live in it.' She looked beyond him to her home, basking in the afternoon sun, then turned her eyes to the waving grasses of the overgrown court where once her parents had played tennis. No strangers were coming here.

'Oh, don't worry, I told them you'd have to stay. In fact, they'll be quite glad of your help because they probably don't speak . . .'

'That's not the point.' She stood up. 'I don't want anyone here. I don't want the house requisitioned. I refuse to give my permission. You'll have to tell them to go elsewhere.'

'I . . . I can't, Mara. Look . . . Be reasonable.' His arms wobbled foolishly by his sides.

'I told you I didn't want to work for the Americans. If

I didn't want to work for them, surely you didn't imagine I'd want them in my house?'

'Be reasonable!' he said again. 'Do you think I can stop them just because you don't want them? You know all the other houses have been taken over. Ask your neighbours!'

She stormed off towards the kitchen, shouting over her shoulder, 'I don't talk to my neighbours. You know I don't.'

Alexander followed. 'Mara, for goodness' sake . . .'

On the kitchen steps she turned round and stamped her bare foot. 'They're not coming here and that's that.'

Alexander was exasperated. 'Don't be so silly!'

'I'm not being silly.' She marched on through into the hall and started up the stairs.

'Yes you are being silly. I thought you'd enjoy it. When your house was under discussion . . .'

'My house under discussion!' She hung over the banisters, yelling down at him, 'How dare you discuss my house without my permission! How dare you come here and order me around! How dare you suggest I'd work for a lot of ignorant Americans! How dare you . . .'

A voice interrupted Mara's tirade. It came from the shadows by the front door. 'Captain Rushton, I'm Doctor Turner of the United States Army. We met briefly the other day.'

Alexander was horribly embarrassed to be caught with a girl screaming at him. 'Oh . . . er . . . yes,' he said, holding out his hand to the man in the shadows. 'How are you, Doctor? I'm sorry about this.'

'Having trouble, Captain?' The doctor sounded amused.

Alexander glanced up at Mara and put on his sensible adult voice, only now she was a naughty child, not a

58

backward one. 'Miss Vogel is a bit upset, Doctor. She didn't realize the house was to be taken over' – he shrugged his shoulders helplessly – 'and I haven't had time to . . . er . . . explain. I must return to Cologne.'

'That's all right, Captain. I'll sort it out. I'm accustomed to this type of thing, though usually it's old hags who don't want to go and stay with their relatives because they hate them or old men who think the war's still on. We had one a few weeks ago who said he'd report us to the Kaiser.'

Alexander smiled. He was used to this sort of talk in the 'mess'. 'I'll be going then,' he said. 'You do know that she hasn't anyone to go to?'

'Yes, it's all down here.' The doctor tapped the pocket where he kept his orders.

Alexander hesitated. He wanted to say, 'Don't be too hard on her, please,' but he didn't dare. Instead he called up to Mara, 'I'll pop in tomorrow. Goodbye. See you then.'

Mara didn't answer. She merely glanced at him.

As soon as Alexander had gone, the doctor moved forward to the bottom of the stairs, and Mara found herself looking down into a pair of incredibly blue eyes. 'Okay, miss, what's the trouble?' he demanded.

Mara answered, 'I don't want my house turned into a hospital.' She still couldn't see him very clearly, only his eyes and the white gleam of his teeth when he spoke. The rest of his face was in the shadow of the banisters.

'Well that's too bad.'

'You'll have to find somewhere else.' She wished he would move out of the shadows because she found it difficult to argue with someone when she couldn't see his face and had no idea what it looked like.

The doctor took a firmer line. 'Look, miss, there's no

point in arguing about it. Your house happens to suit our needs. We need a place high up because we have patients with respiratory problems coming, as well as the wounded.' Past experience had taught him that if the occupants were difficult it was better to treat them as sensible people and give them an explanation. In that way you usually got their acquiescence if not their cooperation. Now he'd given Mara her explanation, and he expected her to acquiesce.

But Mara had no intention of acquiescing. 'I don't care,' she said, her voice rising in anger, 'I'm not having a lot of strangers living here.'

'Really?' He took a step forward. 'We'll see about that.' He started to mount the stairs, and as he came towards her Mara saw that he was nothing like the aged family doctor of her childhood, with his short neat hair and dark suit and slow soothing manner. This doctor was young, with long athletic limbs and a shock of almost black hair which did not even pretend to be brushed back in the short fashion of the moment, as was Alexander's. And there was nothing soothing in his attitude. He was cross and tired and fiercely determined, and that determination was etched into every feature. His mouth set in a hard line, his blue eyes flat and angry, his dark eyebrows meeting above the bridge of his nose as he scowled at Mara. There was something about him which reminded her of an eagle about to attack its prey, and she ran up the rest of the stairs and into her bedroom, and slammed the door.

Once safe inside she was annoyed with herself for having run. She should have stood her ground and made him leave. Now how am I going to get him out? she wondered, hovering in the middle of the room.

She didn't have too long to think about it. The door

didn't stop Jamie Turner. To Mara's surprise he walked straight in without knocking. 'Well?' he asked as she turned her back on him. 'Come on, say what you've got to say. You have exactly two minutes.' He looked at his watch impatiently. He had hundreds of things to do and no time to waste on this obstinate girl. In the other hospitals he'd helped to set up in private houses he'd been a junior doctor, and if things weren't ready for the patients it wasn't his head beneath the axe. But this time it was different, he was in charge, and it was just his luck he had to keep the girl in the house. What had the English captain said about her? That she was shy and well brought up and had had a very difficult time during the war. I reckon the only difficult time, thought Jamie, was the time she gave other people. Shy! The man must be in love with her.

Mara picked up a towel and nonchalantly began to rub her hair dry. 'I told you this house is mine,' she said with what she hoped was great aplomb, 'and I refuse to allow you to use it.'

'Well I'm afraid you're going to have to rethink your ideas. As from tomorrow this house is going to be a hospital whether you like it or not. They'll be fifty patients, as well as myself and another doctor and various nurses, orderlies, cooks and God knows what. All I am trying to sort out with you is how we are all going to fit in so that we aren't on top of each other. I was intending to ask you to show me round the house, which is the most civilized way of doing things, but as you are so uncooperative I shall simply decide who goes where myself.' He crossed the room and positioned himself right in front of her, so that she was obliged to look at him whether she wanted to or not.

There are some people who are alive, who vibrate with

energy, who are magnetic. They can be ugly or beautiful, but that's not how you remember them. It's their vitality which comes to mind as you lie in bed till lunchtime then get up to wander purposelessly through your day. It's their energy which sweeps you along when you're with them, making you too feel vital and energetic. Jamie Turner was one such person.

But he was also something else to Mara. He was quite simply the first man, the only man, for whom she had felt that instant, overwhelming sexual attraction, that sudden inexplicable desire to touch, to feel, to seduce, to be seduced by. A stranger. An intruder. She knew nothing about him and what little she knew she did not like. But that changed nothing. It had no bearing on what she felt as she looked at him. It had no relation to that inexplicable desire.

And yet, it was no romantic dream who stood in front of her, such as she had imagined in her daydream of the ball. He was a hot, tired, irritated young man, with the crumpled sleeves of his white coat bent back at the wrists and a lock of dark hair flapping in his eyes. 'You'll have to move.' He calculated the size of the room. 'We can fit twelve beds in here. You can have one of the small attic bedrooms, I believe there are three.'

'I'm not moving anywhere.' Just because Mara found him attractive she wasn't going to let him get the better of her.

'Don't be silly!'

'I'm not moving.'

'Oh, do stop playing me up!'

'I'm not. And I'm not moving.' Ten minutes earlier she had been fighting for the whole house, now it was just for one specific room.

Jamie really didn't know why he was bothering to

argue with her. He could easily have left her to the Military Police – they would soon have sorted her out – but he needed to get the better of her if she were to stay in the house. And there was something else too. He wanted to get the better of her. 'In case you're not aware of it,' he said sarcastically, 'there are whole families living in one room in this town. One small room.'

Mara stalked over to the window and looked down on the drive. She thought of Frau Muhlhauser and all the other people who had taunted her in the past five years; all those sanctimonious old women; all those hypocritical lecherous old men. 'I don't care if they are,' she replied haughtily.

'Well you should, they're your compatriots.'

Mara clenched her fists on the window-sill. To everyone, she was always one of the others; one of the enemy.

The doctor watched her with a mixture of annoyance and amusement. She's no beauty but she's certainly got something, he decided, allowing his eyes to drift down from the nape of her neck to her hips straining against the tight childish dress, then down again to the soft backs of her bare legs. No wonder she has the wretched captain twisted round her little finger, poor guy. But she's not getting me.

'You've no right to come marching in here,' Mara told him. 'No right at all.'

He laughed. 'Is it only you, Germans, who have the right to march into other people's territories? Perhaps you now know how the Belgians felt.'

'That has nothing to do with me. I wasn't there.'

'Just like the fate of your compatriots living in one room has nothing to do with you? Well, Miss . . .'

'Vogel.'

'Miss Vogel, you're involved even if you don't like it.'
He started to walk back towards the door.

Mara glared out at the garden. What had the war to do
with her? She hadn't started it. She hadn't fought in it.
All it had ever brought her was misery. She swung round
and shouted, 'This is my house and you're not allowed to
ransack and pillage and . . .'

'Rape?'

She blushed.

He looked her up and down. 'You've no need to worry
about rape, Miss Vogel, I can assure you.' His patience
suddenly left him. What was he doing wasting time?
'Now, get moving! Clear out of here and take your stuff
up to the attic. And you're only to take one room. I
haven't been up there yet, but if I find you've taken more
I'll throw you out.'

'I'm not going.'

'You'd better.'

'You can't make me.'

'Can't I? You've exactly one hour to move your belongings, Miss Vogel.'

'I'm not going to.'

'Then I'll burn them,' he said. And he walked out of
the room, slamming the door behind him.

For some time Mara sat on the end of her bed planning
her revenge. I won't move. I'll refuse. I'll show him. I'll
. . . But that instinct for survival which, together with her
sense of personal sacrifice, had enabled her to grit
her teeth and survive Herr Steiger, and which had told
her not to disillusion Alexander by totally refusing to
play the part of unprotected damsel, told her that this
was not the moment.

She went up to the attic and chose the smaller but
nicer of the three rooms from whose slightly protruding

window it was possible to see both the drive and the rose garden. No one had used the room since her governess had left five years earlier. Mara hadn't bothered to clean the attic for her father's arrival: she couldn't remember him ever going up there: the attic was the servants' quarters. She sat on the iron bed underneath the window and examined her new home; a bare square room with just a bed, a chair and a washbasin. But with a lamp there and a cushion here . . .

For the next hour Mara ran up and down stairs, carrying armful after armful of her possessions; clothes, books, cushions, ornaments, both Persian rugs though she disliked one, even her mother's dainty desk, heaved up, step by step. Not one of her treasures did she leave, and through it all she was spurred on by the sound of hammering from the ground floor.

The last item she took upstairs was the iron box containing the letters from her father and from Hans. I haven't looked at them for weeks, she thought, not since before Alexander came. She opened the lid and looked down at her brother's neat black writing. Then she lifted the top four envelopes and stared at her father's more flamboyant writing with its right-hand slant and big loops. And then she closed the box and put it inside the desk.

It was very late by the time Mara had cleaned the attic and arranged her belongings; the rugs on top of each other, the bedspread draped double over the narrow bed, the desk, the cushions, the lamps, the ornaments. It looked, by the end of it, like Aladdin's cave – but with hardly any room for Aladdin.

Suddenly Mara realized she was hungry. It came over her in rumbling waves until she could think of nothing but food. She went out on to the landing and listened. A light shone up through the stairwell but the house was silent. Had they gone? Had he gone? She hoped so. Or did she? Yes, of course she did.

She crept down the stairs to the hall, straining her ears for some sound of life: there was none. Across the hall and into the kitchen she went, her bare feet silent on the flagstones. Luckily the light from the hall partially illuminated the kitchen, otherwise she would have had difficulty in finding her way to the larder, for the once-bare room was piled high with huge cooking pans and unopened cartons of dried food.

I bet they've eaten my bread. Anger built up inside her as she steeled herself for the discovery.

But Mara was wrong. Her solitary hunk of bread sat on its plate, grey, stale and unappetizing, just as she had left it. Despite her hunger she was almost sorry it was still there. Her anger at the way her life was being organized for her, by Alexander and by the doctor, was longing for further insults on which to feast. But she was hungry and the bread was there, so she ate it, washing the clogginess down with water, then wandered back through the hall and into the drawing room. The beautiful Aubusson carpet had been rolled back, the sofas had been pushed to one end, and the rest of the furniture was stacked beside them. Twelve iron beds stood empty and waiting. With a derisory snort Mara left the room.

The door to her father's study was closed. She stood in the hall looking at it. His books, she thought, his precious books. What would THEY care about books? Ignorant savages, they'll probably burn them. She stretched out her hand to the study door.

Jamie Turner was sitting at Franz Vogel's desk. He was ploughing through a mountain of paperwork. Lists of patients, of staff, of equipment, of supplies. Order. Counter-orders. He hated this aspect of his work, he was a doctor and his business was with the sick. In civilian life an administrator would have done all this. But in civilian life I'd have waited years before I was in charge of a hospital, he told himself firmly, even a small one like this. But still . . . He glared at the paperwork. He had to do it. He had to make a success of this hospital. He must. He would. He knew he would.

Going over the arrangements for the next day for the umpteenth time, Jamie noticed the brass door handle begin to turn. 'Come in,' he called.

Mara froze when she saw the doctor sitting at her father's desk. Just for a moment she had thought it was her father, and she had been a child again and had come to ask him some childish question.

'Can I help you?' Jamie asked politely.

Mara stood by the door, one hand still on the handle. The desk was directly opposite her and she looked at him, but didn't reply. Then she looked beyond him to the heavy green curtains, to the hunting scenes on the walls, to the bookcases crammed with books and, finally, she looked back at the doctor. He was leaning back in his chair watching her, and the light from the desk lamp, the only light in the room, cast one half of his face in shadow. Mara thought, he's not so old, not as old as I supposed, perhaps twenty-five. And he's not really attractive, I can't think why I thought he was. He's nothing more than an ignorant doctor. An ignorant American doctor. And he's sitting at my father's desk. When she eventually spoke her voice was angry and defensive. 'This is my father's study.'

Jamie rested his elbows on the arms of his chair and brought the tips of his fingers together in front of him. 'Yes, I know, and I shall be using it while I'm here.'

Mara didn't say anything. She brushed past the desk,

ignoring him, and started to take the books out of the bookcase.

'You can leave them here,' he told her. 'They'll be perfectly all right.'

'What! And have you burn them!'

He laughed. 'Don't be silly!' Then seeing she was genuinely upset, he went on more gently, 'Miss Vogel, I know your father's dead and that it's a shock for you to find me here but . . .'

Mara rounded on him. 'How do you know my father's dead?'

'Because you have to know these things.'

'Why?'

Jamie thought she was being ridiculously defensive about her father. He said, 'It's our business to know what's going on in Koblenz.'

In her mind's eye Mara saw her father's file being put to one side, to be stacked later with all the other dead files. She imagined the doctor pulling it out, leafing through it, reading the bare facts of her father's life with no more emotion than someone reading a railway timetable. Arrival: 28 November 1873. Departure: 3 February 1918. Length of journey: forty-five years. She looked down at the books in her hand. Where was she going to put them? What was the point anyhow? She began to replace them slowly, as if each book were a part of the ritual of her despair. 'I don't know why you can't leave us alone,' she muttered. 'We don't want you here. Why don't you go away?'

'Why do you think?'

Mara put back the last book and turned for the door. 'I don't know.'

'Because we won the war and you lost it.'

She walked out of the study and into the hall, calling over her shoulder, 'I didn't fight in it.'

'No,' he shouted after her. 'And God help the Allies if you had.'

All the following day Mara stayed in her room. She spent the morning lying on her bed trying to read, but her concentration kept slipping, away from the print before her to the man downstairs, his brilliant blue eyes wafting in and out of her vision, his voice, half annoyed and half amused, resounding in her ears.

During the afternoon Alexander came up to see her. He had brought her some bread. 'You won't be needing my food any more,' he said, handing it to her.

'Oh, why not?'

'You'll be eating downstairs.'

'No, I won't.'

'Mara . . .' He frowned, then began again with a breezy smile, 'They've turned the dining room into a sort of "mess" and it's really quite comfortable. Why don't we go down? Time you met everyone.'

'No.'

'Why not?'

'I don't want to. I don't like them.'

'But Mara . . .'

She longed to scream at him but she knew he wouldn't understand. He'd just be hurt and confused, and he'd put it all down to irrational female tantrums which would annoy her even more. So she glared at him and he departed hurriedly.

Some time later shouts from outside drew Mara to the window. She crouched down, munching her bread, and peered out. The drive was packed with ambulances and men. There were men carrying stretchers, men on crutches, men in white coats, all hurrying as fast as they could go. All of them directed by Doctor Jamie Turner, who strode backwards and forwards, issuing orders, more like a pirate captain controlling his cut-throat crew than a doctor with his staff and patients.

'Cut back those bushes,' Mara heard him shout. Immediately someone attacked the overgrown shrubs beside the drive. 'Bring that ambulance up here! Put that man there!'

The world outside had invaded her island. The next morning a big burly medical orderly came up to fetch Mara. 'Doctor wants you, miss,' he told her.

Mara was about to say, 'I'm busy,' but boredom and curiosity got the better of her, so she slipped on her shoes and followed the orderly downstairs.

The first thing she noticed as she left the attic was the smell of disinfectant – it permeated every cubic inch of air, growing stronger and stronger as they went down; the second was that all the rooms were now open, and as they passed she could see rows of beds lining the walls. In each bed was a man; some sleeping, some reading, some sitting up and talking. And there was something else: the noise. Doors slammed, footsteps hurried, trolley-wheels creaked, voices called out. Was it possible that this house, which now bustled with life, was the same in which she had spent all those long silent days?

Jamie was sitting at her father's desk talking on the telephone. He nodded to Mara as she was ushered in and motioned for her to sit down.

'You can't run a hospital without a telephone,' he was saying, 'so I told them to damned well get it fixed.' He listened to the response and chuckled and, but for the dark rings of exhaustion under his eyes, he looked almost carefree. 'How did I do it? Yes, I know they pretend they don't understand, but I made them understand. How? I pointed a gun at them.' There was a splutter of indignation from the other end of the line to which he replied, 'Don't worry, I didn't use it.'

An image of the scene at the telephone exchange came to Mara: the doctor with the gun: the sullen but frightened operators. And she was glad. It served them right.

Jamie looked over at Mara as he continued speaking and he thought how deceptively demure she looked. He said, still into the mouthpiece, 'Yes, language is a problem but I think we're sorted out on that score, thanks. Speak to you tomorrow. So long.'

He pushed the telephone away from him and turned his full attention to Mara. 'Settled in okay, Miss Vogel?'

Mara shrugged. She refused to rise to the bait. No, she didn't like him. He was a bully. An ignorant, rude . . .

Jamie did not seem to notice anything was wrong, or if he did he was ignoring it. 'Good. Now, I think it's time for a bit of cooperation. I've arranged for you to have your meals in the dining room with us. I've explained the situation to my staff and they don't mind.'

'Don't mind! This is my . . .'

'Okay, okay. Now let me finish. I'm very busy. They don't mind,' he went on, 'because I've explained to them you'll be working with us as an interpreter.'

Mara sat up straight. 'I will not.'

'I'm afraid you're going to have to. None of us speaks good German and we desperately need an interpreter. In fact, what I really need is a bilingual secretary.' He paused and before Mara had time to interrupt asked, 'Do you type, Miss Vogel?'

'No I do not.' She emphasized each word. 'And I'm not going to be your interpreter either. Isn't it enough that you take my house, that you force me out of my room, that you use my possessions as though they were your own?' She stood up and banged her fist hard on the desk. 'What more do you want?'

Jamie raised his eyebrows. 'I've just told you. I want an interpreter.'

'Well, find one elsewhere.' She kicked her chair out of the way and marched over to the door.

He was hot and tired and cross. 'I'm giving you an order, Miss Vogel.'

'You can't.'

'Oh, yes I can.' He spoke very slowly and very clearly. 'If you don't work you don't eat.'

'You can't do that.'

'Want to bet? Your rations are to be included with ours and until I get a day's work out of you, you starve. Do you understand, Miss Vogel?'

Unable to think of a crushing reply, Mara walked out of the room and slammed the door.

For two days Mara stayed in her room. She lay on her bed, dreaming of food. Of plates piled high with meat and gravy and vegetables. Of chocolate cakes oozing with cream. Of dry bread. Of anything.

On the afternoon of the second day she woke out of her hungry dreams to find the doctor standing at the bottom of her bed. 'What do you want?' she asked, too bemused and sleepy to be angry.

'I've come to talk to you.'

'Oh.'

'Can I sit down?'

'I suppose so.'

To Mara's surprise he ignored the chair and sat down on her bed, pushing her legs unceremoniously aside. 'Listen,' he spoke very gently, 'I know you don't want us

72

here and, believe me, we'd all much rather be at home. But we are here and we all have to make the best of it. Don't you agree?'

Mara shrugged her shoulders. She could feel his eyes on her face but she refused to meet them. Instead, she looked at his fingers which were long and tapering, and she pretended to be bored. But all the time she was terribly, terribly aware of him sitting on her bed and of his back which was touching her legs.

'You're very young to have been living on your own,' he went on, 'and I realize our being here will take a bit of getting used to, but lots of the guys have younger sisters and . . . well . . . you've nothing to worry about.'

Mara had heard every word he said, but she was thinking of something else. Of how odd it was that one could have an Alexander, a nice kind faithful friend, but one covered one's knees in front of him and washed his cup before using it oneself. Then a total stranger appears. Don't know him. Don't even like him. But one longs to press one's mouth to his, to take off his clothes, to take off one's own clothes, to do the things which could not be more intimate. With him, the stranger, the one you don't like; not with the kind and faithful friend. How odd. How inexplicably odd. She had to stop herself from stretching out her legs and nestling up to him.

Jamie pushed back the hair from his eyes and yawned. Watching him surreptitiously Mara thought, he looks exhausted, then hurriedly, serves him right.

'Well?' He gave her a questioning look. 'What do you say?' The last word disappeared into another yawn.

Mara said nothing.

Jamie stood up and yawned again. 'You must be pretty hungry. Just think of it! Lamb stew and boiled potatoes.'

Mara did think of it. She was tempted, very tempted.

And not just by the food. But the very fact of her temptation by the OTHER made her all the more determined not to succumb.

Jamie watched her. He could sense she was weakening. The day before yesterday he had thought her deceptively demure at first, and later, tough and rather haggard. Today she was warm and sleepy like a kitten. He bent down closer. 'Remember' – he gave her a wickedly disarming smile – 'I'm a doctor and if you get sick I'll have to come and examine you.'

So he thought she was giving in. Well, he had another think coming. Mara sat up and shouted, 'No, I'm not coming down. No, I don't want your stewed lamb . . . lamb stew. Leave me alone! Just because you won the war there's no need to be so condensing.'

He laughed as he walked towards the door. 'I think you mean condescending.'

He left, but she could not stop thinking about him. Wondering. Dissecting. Analysing: the way he smiled, the way he walked, his face, his mouth, his eyes, his hair, as if by studying each detail it would lose its mystery, and in the end the whole would lose its mystery, and its hold over her. But it didn't. The mystery was in her, in her wanting him, in the way she felt towards him, warm and soft. And of all the people, she thought. Of all the people!

She turned over in bed and tried to sleep, but he was still with her, next to her, beside her, in her eyes, however tightly she closed them. The pillow under her head was his shoulder, the bedclothes which lay on her body were his body, and the warmth she felt as she curled up under them was the warmth he gave her.

Hours later Mara got up and turned on the tap. To her astonishment hot water came spurting out. She wondered how they had managed to mend the boiler, and thought, how clever of them, as the hot water ran over her hand. Then she told herself, it's not clever at all; it's the least they can do in the circumstances, and she stripped off her dress and washed herself from head to toe, luxuriating in the hot flannel as she ran it up and down her body. And as the flannel touched her, she found herself thinking of the doctor again. It was his hands that caressed, his fingers that stroked. Stop it! You don't really like him. Stop it! She rubbed herself furiously with the towel, dressed herself in a furious hurry, then sat down and furiously tried to read her book. But her thoughts were of food, food, HIM, food, more food, MORE HIM: never of Alexander.

Mara had to have something to eat. She simply had to. She waited till after midnight, then she set off down the stairs, inching her way down in her bare feet. There were still lights in the wards and the odd footsteps shuffling to and fro, but apart from that, and the grunts and snores of fifty men, the house was quiet. Down, down, down she went, holding her breath each time the stairs creaked till at last she reached the bottom step. And hesitated. The study door was shut but a faint strip of light glowed beneath it. HE was in there. But would he hear her? She was almost, almost too hungry to care. Only pride refused to allow her to be caught.

She tiptoed across the hall to the kitchen and felt her way to the larder, helped very slightly by a meagre moon: it might have had the decency to shine more brightly. She was now so hungry that her hands trembled, rattling the handle of the larder door as she pulled it open, but the smell of food and the sight of the shadowy dishes piled high drove everything else from her mind. She stretched out her hand; potatoes. Dipped her fingers into a pot and licked them; stew. Felt again; sausages. Grabbed one. Grabbed another. Dipped a potato into the stew and stuffed it into her mouth, the gravy dribbling down her chin. But she didn't care. She didn't even notice. Six potatoes later she paused, noticed the gravy, wiped it off with the back of her hand, and turned her attention to the hunks of cheese. But as she stretched out her hand to them another hand clamped itself on her wrist.

'I might have known,' said Jamie Turner. 'You little thief!'

Chapter 5

With the defensive anger of the guilty Mara spun round and shouted, 'Let me go! Let me . . .' She was furious with herself for having been caught, furious with him for having caught her, her anger accentuated by the fright he had given her.

Jamie tightened his hold, 'What the hell do you think you're doing in here?'

'What do you think I'm doing?' She tried to wrench her arm away.

'Stealing.' He dragged her over to the window, to where he could see her face. 'Stealing our rations.'

'They're mine too. I've every right . . .'

'I told you' – the hazy moon behind him made him look taller and darker, a menacing shadow – 'I told you you'd get nothing to eat. Did you think I was joking?' He shook her roughly. 'Did you?' He shook her again.

Mara was determined not to be intimidated, she raised her voice to show him, and herself. 'This is my house and it's you, you who are the thieves. Now let me go!' And before Jamie could catch her free hand, she sank her fingernails into the soft underbelly of his wrist.

He released her with a gasp. Pain and surprise. His surprise gave Mara her escape. She dashed for the door, tripping over a pile of pans. They crashed to the floor, almost bringing her down with them, but she kept her balance and stumbled on, out into the hall, heading for the stairs.

Bare feet pounding on each step, Mara ran up them

with Jamie right behind. He was so close she could hear his angry breathing and feel his breath, or almost, on the backs of her legs. No need to look back, he was catching up on her. She could feel it. Sense it. His legs were longer than hers. He took two steps at a time. 'I'm going to teach you a lesson you won't forget, Miss Vogel.'

In her anger and her determination to get away from him, Mara was oblivious to the noise they made in the sleeping hospital. There were shouts of, 'What's going on? Hey, you guys, shut up!' but she didn't hear them, for mixed with her anger was panic, the pure unadulterated terror of being chased, of being the prey: the fox running for his lair. The doctor was no longer just a doctor, he was every person who had persecuted her through the long years of the war; the policemen breaking into the house, Herr Steiger pushing her towards the body, Frau Muhlhauser; he was hunger and loneliness, a culmination of all her fears let loose in the night.

Mara stumbled as she reached the top step. Jamie seized the hem of her dress. She pulled away. It tore. She ran to her room, kicked open the door, dashed inside and turned to shut it, hands fumbling desperately for the key. But she was too slow. He was too quick. Jamie wedged his foot firmly across the threshold.

She kicked at his foot. 'Get out! Get out!'

'Shut up!' He kept his voice low.

She threw her weight against the door. 'Get out! Get . . .'

'Shut up!' He eased his foot forward. 'Shut up, you selfish little bitch. There are sick men in this house.'

'I don't care if there are.' She didn't.

'I'll have you moved if you don't shut up.'

'You can't. This is my house.'

'Yes, I can.'

'No, you can't.'

Little by little Jamie was forcing the door open and as he did so Mara was being pushed back, until she was trapped between the door and the wall behind it, gasping and sobbing with rage and frustration, her nose squashed against the back of the door.

Jamie slipped into the room, his foot still against the door, Mara still in her prison. 'Now you listen to me,' he said, glaring down at her, 'I've had about enough of you and your tantrums. This is a hospital, not a kindergarten. Do I make myself clear?'

Mara tried to turn her head away, but it was impossible to make an obvious gesture of disdain when her nose was squashed against the door. Once again she was being bullied. Once again she was being used and abused.

To Jamie, Mara's behaviour was merely an obstacle to the smooth running of his hospital, an irritating nuisance wasting his precious time. He thought he understood why she objected to the invasion of her home. He thought of Mara as being enemy, though not very enemy because she spoke good English. But she was still enemy, as he felt sure he was enemy to her. Despite this, he was not prepared to make allowances for her. He treated her as he treated the girls back home who had never seen a bomb, a bullet, or a body: who had never met a Herr Steiger or had had to persuade themselves they had something in common with Sydney Carton.

'Look at me!' he said.

Mara ignored him.

'I said, look at me!' To Mara's surprise, for she had never imagined he would physically hurt her, Jamie grabbed her by the hair and forced her to turn and face him. 'I've told you before, and I'm not going to tell you again, if you don't cooperate . . .'

'Cooperate! Why should I? You ignorant American, you . . . you quack doctor, you . . .' Mara wished she knew more about him, where his Achilles heel lay, so that she could twist the verbal knife into it.

'Then you'll have to go. I don't care what your besotted captain says, but I'm not having you here if you're going to cause trouble.'

'Go? I'm not going anywhere. It's you who should . . .'

'You mean no one'll have you?' There was a knowing edge to his voice, a hint of condemnation.

Mara's face tightened. What did he know? Answer: nothing. To whom had he been speaking? Answer: no one. He didn't understand German. Nevertheless, she felt slightly sick and simultaneously full of murderous rage against all those who had, and would, judge her by their own safe uncomplicated lives. And with that rage she forgot she had ever found him attractive. If anything, that attraction compounded her dislike of him.

'Can't answer that one, can you?' He positively glowed with triumph.

'I don't know what you mean.'

'Don't you? Well, it just so happens I asked the Muhlhauser woman if you could move in with her. It seemed more suitable' – he gave a dry laugh – 'a young girl under the protection of an older woman. But you know what, Miss Vogel? She didn't think so. Fact is, she refused to have you.'

'You're lying. You don't speak German.' She was not going to be intimidated.

Jamie released the door and allowed it to swing free, as though to emphasize the lack of need for walls of wood and plaster, the wall of a hostile society beyond being quite sufficient. 'Your father's dictionary was perfectly adequate,' he said. 'The word for whore wasn't hard to look up.'

For one long minute Mara stared at him. Then she raised her hand and slapped him across the face. She hit him as hard as she could, so hard that her palm stung with the impact and red weals rose on his cheek. 'How dare you criticize me!' she cried. 'How dare you, when you know nothing. Nothing!'

Jamie kicked the door shut and grabbed her upper arms, his fingers digging deep. He hadn't meant to tell her what he knew, he hadn't meant to hurt her, but her unrepentant insolence had provoked him. He was as angry with her as he was with himself for being so weak. He shook her violently. 'Shut up! Shut . . . up, you selfish . . . Shut up! There are men downstairs who've just been through a war. Injured men. Men who've been in the trenches.'

'The trenches!'

'Yes, the trenches.'

'Do you think that's the only war – a man's war? Wearing uniforms and waving guns.'

Jamie thought of the makeshift hospital, the dying men, the mud and the chaos, and he dug his fingers still deeper into her arms. He wished he could have thrown her into a trench full of bodies and mud and stood on the edge, kicking her back into it every time she tried to get out until she cried for mercy. 'How dare you belittle the sacrifice of those men who gave their lives?' he said, shaking her again.

Mara thought of Hans. 'Other men gave those men's lives. And do you think they were the only sacrifices? What about us, the ones left behind, struggling on, never knowing when it was all going to end, never being told the truth, never seeing the glories and the victories, just the poverty and the starvation, just the trickery and the lies.'

'But not you, Miss Vogel. Don't tell me Steiger's mistress starved. Yes, I know his name. "Steiger the Sadist" is how we refer to him.' He laughed down into her angry face. 'Oh, no, I bet you never went short.'

She stared at him. 'Do you think I did it to feed myself?'

'I've no idea why you did it.'

'Do you think I wanted to be his mistress?'

He laughed again. 'I dread to think what your wants are.'

'So she didn't tell you.'

'She told me he didn't force you.'

'He did.'

'Oh, come on! Not every time. Not for six . . . eight months.'

She straightened her shoulders and raised her chin. 'Would you have let your father die? Die of starvation? Not even a nice clean bullet on a frosty morning, but a long, lingering prison death. Would you have let that happen? Would you? Would you?'

He looked at her for a moment, then his face contorted in disgust. 'You lying little tramp! Your father died over a year ago. He died *before* you became Steiger's mistress.'

'But I didn't know.' It came out of her like the cry of a wounded animal. 'I didn't know. He . . . tricked me. He said if I . . . did it my father would live. He promised. And all the time . . . all the time . . .' – her voice broke with a small dry sob – 'he was dead.'

Jamie said nothing. He knew that she had told him the truth and he was appalled with himself for what he had said to her, at what he had done to her. He had pushed her to the brink of her hurt. Her face had closed in on itself, setting hard against him and the world. 'When did you find out?' he asked.

'Two months ago.' She pulled herself free of his hold and walked slowly away from him to the iron bed, sat down on it, and leaned back against the wall, staring into space.

Jamie stood and looked down at her. He was about to say, 'Why didn't you ask to see your father first?' when he saw that this would sound futile. What chance would she have had against Steiger? How could she have insisted on anything? She had merely hoped and believed. For the first time he really began to understand what it had been like for her.

Mara looked up at him. He's going to rape me, she thought suddenly, wildly, and she drew her knees up in front of her, ready to kick out at him. Then, perversely, she almost hoped he would rape her. It would make him no better than Herr Steiger. It would give her ammunition to throw in his face: his Achilles heel: his weakness.

Jamie saw the fear and the bravado in Mara's face. And he saw too what was going through her mind, or rather the first part of it. She was like a wild animal and he had pushed her into a cage, and now she waited to lash out at him or at anyone who came near her. She was so hurt she could not differentiate between those who sought to help her and those who would hurt her. But, despite it, she was brave. It was this which touched him. Behind her barrier of self-defence he saw an ancient and embittered child, a vulnerable and fascinating young woman.

'Move over,' he said, sitting down on the edge of the bed, and leaned back against her legs, just as he had when he had come up to persuade her to eat.

Mara stiffened. She waited for him to make a move towards her, surprised when he did nothing. She knew his eyes were on her face but she didn't want to meet them, so she looked down at his hands which lay beside him on the bed. Five minutes passed. Once again Mara felt the warmth of him against her legs, only this time there was no blanket and her legs touched the tiredness of his once-crisp white coat. Slowly she began to relax, and as she did so her brittle wall of self-defence weakened. For years she had bottled up her emotions, hiding them behind a façade of indifference. She had hated and not cared if she were hated in return; at least she'd told herself she didn't care. But now, in her torrent of self-justification, some of that hatred had been swept away, leaving her weak and tired and tearful. I mustn't cry, she thought. Not in front of him. I mustn't. Not now. She bit the inside of her mouth to stop her lips from quivering, wishing he would leave but at the same time wanting him to stay.

'Mara.' His voice was gentle, it brought tears to the corners of her eyes. 'Mara, come here.'

Mara didn't move.

He touched her hair. 'I had no idea.'

She swallowed hard.

'I didn't mean to hurt you.'

She gritted her teeth.

'Your father would have been proud of you.'

Jamie watched her face crumple. He took her by the shoulders and pulled her towards him, holding her tightly against him. 'Don't. Don't,' he said. 'You couldn't help it. It wasn't your fault.'

Mara pushed her face into his shoulder. She was sitting sideways to him, her knees tucked behind his back, and he was holding her. Someone was holding her, evoking memories of a past when she had known kindness and comfort. She stopped crying and rubbed her face on his sleeve. He smelt of chloroform and carbolic, a smell of

84

hospitals mixed with his own warm human smell and a faint touch of tobacco. Did he smoke? She had no idea, she knew so little about him. She looked up at his chin. There was a vague shadow of dark stubble which stretched along his jaw. Her eyes moved up his face. There were laughter lines at the corner of his eye; she could see only one eye and one side of his face. Laughter lines, and other lines: of determination, of exhaustion. Did he get up early? Did he struggle out of bed at dawn and make his way through the silent house, so familiar to her but strange to him; a strange house in a strange country?

She looked down at the buttons of his white coat and noticed to her surprise that one was missing. He seemed too efficient to have a missing button. She wondered if he would sew it on himself and was about to offer to do so, when it occurred to her that there was probably someone whose job it was to do these things, and she felt an unreasonable jealousy towards this unknown person who was a necessary part of his life.

Jamie was almost asleep. He'd had a long and exhausting day, he'd been forced to amputate the right leg of a young soldier called Rook who'd trodden on an unexploded shell. Gangrene had set in, he'd had no alternative, but he'd hated to do it to a man of his own age. The worst of it was, the second leg might also have to come off. Rook had been unbelievably brave. 'So long to baseball,' was all he'd said.

Jamie thought of the endless paperwork on his desk. He knew he should go down and deal with it, but he tightened his hold on Mara and smoothed down her ruffled hair with his free hand.

I wonder if Mummy would have liked him, thought Mara. I think she would have. But what would she say if she could see me now, sitting on my bed with a strange man? She pictured her mother's scandalized face and giggled.

Jamie stirred. 'Umm . . . what's so funny?'

'Nothing. Noth . . . ing.'

'Come on, tell me!' He tipped her face towards him. He'd never seen her laugh and he was amazed at her resilience, that she could fight back from the depths of her despair and laugh like any other girl.

'I was only imagining my mother's face if she were to come in now. She would be . . . horrified.'

Jamie was on the point of saying, 'What if she'd known about Steiger?' but he stopped himself, angry that he could have been so thoughtless as to even think it. 'My mother would be shocked too,' he said.

'Would she?' Mara tried to imagine his mother. What did she look like? What did American mothers look like?

'Yes, she thinks I'm a nice boy. So does my grandmother. She calls me a nice wee laddie.'

'A what?'

'Wee laddie. It means a little boy – Scottish. My mother's family came from Scotland, that's why I'm called Jamie. It's a good Scottish name.'

'And are you a' – she gave him a naughty smile – 'good Scottish laddie?'

'It depends.' His eyelashes touched her cheek.

Mara knew she was encouraging him, encouraging herself, encouraging both of them, and suddenly she was afraid. Afraid of what she was letting herself in for. Of liking him too much. Of liking him and of him not liking her. Of not doing or saying or being the things he liked. Afraid, and yet unable to stop herself.

Against his better judgement, for hadn't he told the other men to stay away from the girl, Jamie nuzzled the side of her brow. I'm crazy, he thought. I should get up and go. It's circumstance, not her. I'm kidding myself she's different, kidding myself she's special, I'll regret it tomorrow. But he didn't go. He lifted Mara's face to his and kissed her on the corner of her mouth. 'You know what else I found out about you?'

She ran her hand up his arm. 'What?'

'That your' – he started to laugh – 'surname means "bird".'

'What's so funny about that?'

'Nothing.' He was still laughing. 'It's just that it suits you.' He ran his fingers through her hair, lifting it up then letting it drop slowly in soft waves about her face. 'When you're angry you're just like a baby stork with its feathers ruffled and its long legs wobbling.'

'And when I'm not angry?' She pressed her face against his.

'When you're not angry . . .' He pushed her back on to the pillow and lay down alongside her, his arm across her. 'When you're not angry you're' – his brilliant blue eyes softened – 'a very attractive little stork.' He blew into the nape of her neck, his warm breath tickling her, and he ran his hand up the inside of her leg, his fingers circling, gently, softly, higher.

There was a split second when Mara tried to call back her defences, or rather she didn't try but felt she ought to. A split second, that was all, before she gave herself up to him, her mouth to his, her face to his, feeling the roughness of his stubble on her skin and not minding it. Liking it. Wanting it. And him. And the hardness of his arms which held her to him and the hardness of his body which pressed against hers.

One by one he undid the buttons of her dress, kissing her gently, down, down, as he slid the dress below her shoulders, to her waist, to her hips. And Mara found herself responding automatically. Touching. Feeling. Knowing. It had never been like this before. She had felt nothing except hate, and every time had been an invasion of her body whose resistance she had had to force herself to overcome: for mere submission had not proved enough. But with Jamie there was no resistance. She wanted him and wanted to respond to him. The attic room was no longer a four-walled box at the top of the house, it reached far beyond and at the same time it seemed to Mara that it ended where their limbs ended, flexible and movable, hugging them in its protective cocoon. She reached up to him, soft to his gentleness, savage to his urgency, pulling him down into her, wanting to feel him deep inside her, aware of nothing else but of him: around her: above her: beneath her: beside her: things she had never done before, sensations she had never known she was capable of.

And as Jamie made love to Mara and she in turn made love to him, she had an extraordinary and frightening feeling that they were forming a link between them over which she would have no control, and which would not be severed when he left. That he was going to be a part of her life in the future as much as he was a part of her body at that moment.

Mara couldn't sleep. She was lying on her side on the outside edge of the narrow bed and the iron bedbase was digging into her hip. Jamie, on the other hand, lay on his back in the middle of the bed, sleeping the deep untroubled sleep of a child, his head tipped slightly towards Mara, his arm flung across her shoulders. And he was breathing deeply. Not snoring, but breathing loudly and just next to her ear so that she found herself counting each breath. Once, when he broke his rhythm, she waited fearfully for him to begin again, wondering what she would do if he failed to do so. Of course he did breathe again, and she sighed with relief. But then, as he obviously wasn't going to die, she wished he would find a quieter way to claim his oxygen.

Eventually she must have fallen asleep, because she suddenly found him sitting on the end of the bed, fully dressed and tying his shoe laces, bending to tie one, straightening, bending to tie the other, his shadow bobbing and bowing on the wall behind like an exaggerated courtier before an exalted personage.

'Oh, you're awake.' He smiled at her. 'I tried not to wake you but I had to get up. It's, – he looked at his watch although Mara knew he must have looked at it already – 'after four.'

'Oh.' Mara rolled into the middle of the bed, still warm from him, and pulled the covers up to her chin.

He stood up and stretched. 'Time for bed.'

'Where do you sleep?'

He looked surprised. 'Surely you must have heard us. We sleep in one of the other attic rooms. The biggest one at the other end of the corridor.'

'No, I haven't heard anyone.' At least he was close. He could come again. But who was 'we'? 'Who . . . who else sleeps there?' she asked.

'The other doctor. Durrant. Big guy with fair hair. He mostly does nights.'

Again Mara was aware of how little she knew about him. 'Do you do nights?'

'Not often. I've got the admin.'

'Admin?'

'Administration.' He yawned and bent to ruffle her hair. 'Must go. Have to start at seven. Goodnight.'

'You could stay here,' she ventured.

'And when the orderly comes to wake me . . . ?' He tiptoed over to the door, stopped, frowned, then turned back to face her, speaking with carefully chosen words. 'Look,' he said awkwardly, 'it's . . . umm . . . very important no one knows about . . . I'd be in a lot of trouble and you'd certainly be moved elsewhere.'

Mara nodded forlornly. How could he be worrying about such things already? He hadn't even left her yet. And what had he expected her to do, rush downstairs and tell everyone? 'Don't worry,' she replied, forcing herself to sound unconcerned. But this was what she had been frightened of: that she would feel and be hurt.

'Good. So it's Miss Vogel and Doctor Turner' – he opened the door, then turned to give Mara one of his wonderful half-apologetic, half-mischievous smiles – 'when you come in to breakfast with me in the morning.'

Chapter 6

It's very unfair of God, thought Mara as she picked through her mother's dresses on the following morning, discarding one after another. He might have warned me. I could easily have altered some of them if I'd known I was going to want to look . . . nice. I had plenty of time before, he could easily have let me know. She imagined herself finding a note on her pillow, yellow parchment paper and spiky black writing.

Eventually she settled on a straight skirt of dark pink silk which, by turning over the waistband several times, she managed to lift to mid-calf. With it went a silk jacket of pink and white stripes. She slipped it on and belted it. Do I look . . . desirable . . . sexy? She walked over to the mirror, the skirt whispering over her hips and the hem stroking the backs of her legs as she moved.

Her mother had bought the suit in Paris one hot day the summer before war broke out. Mara had been with her; her only trip abroad. She remembered the excitement of the journey, the strangeness of the hotel, and the long hours when she and her mother had wandered aimlessly through the sweltering city whilst her father rushed from one meeting to another. For a moment Mara was back there, walking up a cobbled street through the deadness of a hot afternoon. They were alone in the street, she and her mother, isolated as is only possible in a crowd. But the crowd was not in the street, it was above, behind closed shutters where French voices called to each other and plates clattered on unseen tables. Mara remembered how lonely she had felt listening to them and how she had been about to stretch up her hand to her mother, when her mother had suddenly seen the suit in a shop window. This suit: a memory of that summer afternoon.

It was nearly eight o'clock. Time to go down. Mara took one last look in the mirror. If only I had some stockings. Her legs were bare. If only I had some pretty shoes. A pair of flat black pumps was all she had been able to find. But still . . . She smiled at herself and herself smiled back. Thin and gaunt she might be, but there was an air about her, a sparkle in her eyes, a glow on her cheeks. She pursed her lips in an exaggerated kiss and leaned forward and kissed the mirrored lips.

At the top of the stairs, she paused. The door to Jamie's room was closed. She pictured him hurrying down these stairs an hour earlier. Had he thought of her as he'd passed within view of her door? He must have. Of course he had.

The morning had brought optimism and the morning sun those easily findable excuses. He hadn't meant to sound so harsh when he'd said their love-making must be a secret, he was thinking of her as much as he was of himself. Of course he was. He wanted to protect her.

The dining room door was open and from within came the sound of voices mingled with the scraping of plates. Mara had intended to walk straight in, at least it had not occurred to her to do otherwise. Jamie would be waiting for her. She would go in with him. But there was no sign of him, the hall was deserted. Suddenly her courage deserted her. She hovered outside the dining room, shifting from foot to foot, too hungry to go away, too shy to go in. She took a step forward and saw about twenty strange men all sitting at breakfast. Another step, she peered through the crack in the door. Jamie, at last. But not near the door, right the other side of the room, and surrounded by others. She stood watching him. He was talking excitedly, stabbing the air with his knife as he made his point, and he had forgotten all about her. 'See you at breakfast! See you . . . and everyone else,' he should have said. Mara turned away and tiptoed across the hall and into the study.

Five minutes later Jamie appeared. 'Oh, there you are,' he said casually when he saw Mara sitting in front of the desk. 'Now you must meet Sayers. He'll tell you where things are. Sayers! Sayers!'

'I'm here, doctor.' The burly orderly who had fetched Mara some days earlier now loomed on the threshold.

'Sayers, this is Miss Vogel. I think you've met.'

'Hi.'

'Hello.'

'Okay, Sayers, I'll see you later.'

At last they were alone. Mara fiddled with the hem of her jacket.

'Why weren't you at breakfast?' Jamie asked her.

'I wasn't hungry.'

'Rubbish. You'll be ill if you don't eat.'

Mara smiled. He was concerned.

'I've enough sick people without having any more.'

Her smile froze.

'You'll have lunch with me.'

She smiled again.

'That's settled. Now' – he handed her some paper and a pencil – 'make a list so I don't have to tell you the same thing twice. Ready?'

'Yes.' The pencil quivered over the paper.

'Point number one. In German. Typed if possible' – he pointed at a typewriter – 'but not if it means using up a month's supply of paper.' He thought for a minute, then began dictating, 'We regret to inform you that your house is to be requisitioned and will be used as an annex to this hospital. Accommodation will be arranged for you elsewhere.' He handed Mara a rubber stamp, saying, 'That goes at the bottom and I sign it.'

Nervously Mara asked, 'Who's it for?'

'Frau Muhlhauser.' His eyes held Mara's and he was laughing and just for a moment they were back in the attic room, then he went on hurriedly, 'I want the patients to get out in the garden. No, don't write that down. Write this down. Man to cut grass. You telephone the town hall or whatever you call it here, they'll tell you where to find one, but don't let them bully you into having someone's grandfather, I want the job done properly. Got it?'

'Yes.'

'And get him to chop down some of those bushes. I'm sorry but the place is like a jungle.'

'Not the rose garden,' Mara said abruptly. She looked out of the window at the still stunted bushes. 'It was my father's.'

'Okay. But he must do the drive. Now, next point. Get another telephone line. And get two extensions for this one. One on the first floor and one in my room. Next point. Get hold of two women cleaners. They're to do Frau Muhlhauser's house tomorrow.' Next. Next. Next. Do this. Do that. Find this. Find that. On and on he went till Mara could hardly write because her hand was aching so much.

It took Mara over an hour and four attempts to type out the requisition order, but at last, and with an immense feeling of satisfaction, she laid it on Jamie's desk and ticked off point number one. Then she picked up the telephone and dialled the town hall. A well-educated woman's voice answered.

'I'm speaking for the American hospital,' Mara began, and as she spoke on behalf of the occupying forces she felt a sickening twinge of treachery to her father's people. She couldn't help it. Nor could she bring herself to say 'we', it was always 'the hospital needs', 'the hospital wants'.

She had hardly finished saying her piece before the voice interrupted with, 'Fräulein, take my nephew. He's a good strong boy.'

So that was what Jamie had meant. No relative of such an educated woman would be used to menial work. 'Is he . . . is he a gardener?'

'Please, Fräulein, take him. Take him, I beg you.'

'Well . . . umm . . . the doctor said I had to find a gardener. Is your nephew a trained gardener?'

There was a pause, then the voice said very gently, 'Were you trained to work for the Americans, Fräulein?'

'No, of course not. They insisted.'

'Exactly. We all do what we have to in these difficult times, don't we?'

She's right, thought Mara, and it made her feel a lot better. 'Send your nephew,' she said, 'but he must pretend he's had experience.'

The woman was effusive with her thanks. 'You can't imagine what a difference this will make to us. We are six in my family and only I am working.'

'Well, perhaps you know of two women cleaners?'

'My cousins will do it.'

'I don't know what they'll be paid.'

'It doesn't matter. Food. Anything.'

When Mara gave the address and added, 'They should ask for me. Fräulein Vogel,' she heard the woman's quick intake of breath. But that was all. No mention of pacifists or cowards, just more thanks and, 'Let me know if you need anything else. My name is Hanna.'

'We all do what we have to,' Mara repeated to herself as she replaced the earpiece. But she felt a bit of a fraud. The spoils of war weren't meant to welcome the barbarian chief.

However, after that Mara would telephone Hanna from time to time, at first using some small problem as an excuse but later not bothering. It was her only private contact with the outside world, the German world, and she did it partly because she liked the sound of Hanna's voice but mostly because it meant she had not entirely forsaken her father.

Mara was thinking of Jamie. She was gazing into space as memories of the previous night flooded over her, running through her veins, up and down her arms, like a soft and sensual breeze beneath her skin. Would he come tonight? She crossed her legs and wriggled her toes. Would he? She smiled to herself and leaned forward, her elbows on the typewriter.

The study door burst open. Mara jumped guiltily. 'Come on!' Jamie called to her. 'Lunchtime!'

Mara stood up, smoothed down her skirt, wished she had time to brush her hair, and hurried out. But as they reached the dining room door Jamie suddenly stopped. 'The requisition order. What did you do with it?'

'It's on your desk.'

'Must sign it. Go in. I'll join you in a minute.'

'I'll . . . I'll wait.' How could he abandon her? It was as though he were doing it on purpose.

'Don't be silly!' He gave her a slight push and turned back towards the study.

'I'm not being silly,' she muttered under her breath.

But still she hesitated, shifting awkwardly from foot to foot. 'I'm not being silly. If you had a grain of understanding you'd . . .' On the count of three she stepped into the dining room.

The nearest man looked up. 'Jesus! Look at that!'

As heads turned the voices died into a whisper. 'It's her. It's the German girl. Look! It's her. Thought she was meant to be ugly! Well, if that's ugly . . .' Mara stood rooted to the spot. She blushed furiously and swallowed. Her knees were knocking. Her hands were shaking. All around her the men were whispering. Where was she to go? What was she to do?

Then Jamie was beside her, taking her by the elbow and saying, 'Come on, you guys, cut it out. And you, Miss Vogel, they're not going to eat you. They much prefer their lamb stew even if they do have it a bit too often.'

Laughter followed his words and the men, remembering their manners, scrambled good-naturedly to their feet. Jamie introduced them one by one, and one by one they nodded and sat down. Mara nodded back at them, far too nervous to catch a single name. Still feeling horribly conspicuous she followed Jamie over to a table. As soon as they sat down he immediately began talking to the three other men there, leaving her to sit in isolated silence. But when a plate of stew was put in front of her, she fell on it like a starving beast and no longer cared about anything else but food.

All that afternoon Mara typed and telephoned, and thought of Jamie. Often she found herself staring into space, picturing his face, his eyes, his mouth, and thinking she had only just stopped work. Then she would look at the clock and find she had been daydreaming for half an hour, and she would grab her notebook guiltily. But as the afternoon progressed into evening – she had no idea when she was meant to stop – she found it more and more difficult to concentrate. Hardly any sleep the night before, unaccustomed to working, she was quite simply exhausted. At supper she nearly fell asleep and her head kept nodding off her neck, not that anyone noticed, for again she sat in isolated silence.

As they were leaving the dining room Jamie spoke to her for the first time. 'Let me see how you got on.'

She followed him through into the study, where he sat down in her father's chair and looked at her expectantly. Mara picked up her notebook and read through the list he had given her. Jamie listened in silence, then said, 'Good.'

Mara stood in front of him, waiting, unsure if she should go or stay. Had he nothing else to say to her . . . nothing personal? 'Is that all?' she asked tentatively.

He leant back in his chair and studied her. 'There is one other thing. I think it would be better if you wore a white coat, one like this.' He touched his own. 'Just whilst you're working, of course. It would make you look more like one of the boys.'

'One of the boys?' Mara repeated, keeping her face completely deadpan.

'Yes.' He gave her a very solemn look, then slowly his face relaxed and his eyes took on a mischievous twinkle. 'Now run along, Miss Vogel,' he said very softly, 'I have lots of work to do and you're distracting me.'

That alone made up for his impersonal manner of the day. It showed he still wanted her, which was all that mattered to Mara.

* * *

Four days later Mara was in the middle of a delicious Jamie-dream when there was a knock on the study door and Alexander came in; she had practically forgotten his existence.

'So glad to see you . . . er . . . helping.' He beamed down at her. 'Knew you'd come round to it.'

Mara growled silently to herself. She longed to cry, 'Stop patronizing me! Stop giving me that "Alexander-knows-best",' but she didn't, she gave him a vague smile because she was feeling guilty about forgetting him.

'Enjoying yourself?' He was still grinning, so sure that her change of mind had been brought about by himself.

If only he knew, she thought, if only he knew. She replied, 'It's not so bad, I suppose.'

He stretched out his hand to pat her shoulder, then thought better of it and drew it back. 'Let's go for a walk in the garden. They're cutting the grass at last, I see. About time.'

That annoyed Mara too. The garden had had beauty in its wildness. 'I don't think I can go out,' she said. 'I'm meant to stay here.'

He thought she was merely being responsible. 'Oh, don't worry about that. I asked the doctor and you have a half-hour break.'

'Oh.' He hadn't bothered to ask her if she wanted to go out.

He opened the door for her. 'Nice chap, the doctor.'

'Yes, I suppose he is.' The door hid her blush.

They walked across the newly mown lawn. The air was heavy with the smell of fresh-cut grass. Out of the corner of her eye Mara saw the boy, Hanna's nephew, watching her. She gave him a slight nod and he returned it.

When they reached the rose garden Alexander pointed at the low wall. 'I must sit down.'

Mara studied him curiously. His skin was pale, almost like parchment, and he was breathing heavily. 'Are you ill?' she asked, her anger disappearing and her guilt returning.

'It's nothing. Just occasionally my lungs play up.'

'You should see a doctor. Jam . . . Doctor Turner knows about . . .'

'Oh, I've seen lots of doctors. They can't do much. All of us chaps who got caught by the mustard gas are in the same boat.' He sat down and patted the wall beside him. 'Let's talk about something more cheerful. I can't bear illness. Never been ill in my life before this.'

It was warm by the rose garden and the half-hour passed quickly. Alexander did most of the talking, he usually did, and Mara listened with half an ear. She was thinking about her father as she looked at the rose bushes and feeling glad that, although none had died, they didn't look as prosperous as when he had cared for them.

'Have you heard from your family?' she asked him.

'Yes, I had a letter from the Old Man.' He laughed and explained, 'We always refer to him as the Old Man. He said they're terribly busy at the works. Apparently everyone wants to own a car now the war's over and they can't keep up with the demand. I can believe it too. Everyone in my "mess" says he's going to buy a car when he gets home.'

She smiled vaguely. 'Oh, are they going to buy your cars?'

'I think a lot of them would like to but ours are rather expensive. The trouble is they all keep talking to me about cars as if I were an authority, but I usually know less than they do.'

She smiled again. 'What do you say? Do you pretend?'

'No, I don't even know enough for that. There was a

chap called Raymond Mays in the Grenadier Guards, he was stationed in Cologne but he's gone back now, and he knew far, far more than I did. I gather he wants to be a racing-driver but his father wants him to go into the family business. Bad luck, because if he'd been in my family he'd have had every opportunity. My father used to race. He'd be delighted if one of us wanted to.'

'Wouldn't you like to?'

'Heavens no, I don't have the nerve. It's jolly dangerous.'

'Wasn't it dangerous for your father?'

'Yes, but he lóved it. He raced right up to the beginning of the war, although he was a bit old for it by that time. But when I was younger he used to win a lot. He was quite a hero. All my friends were longing to meet him.'

Mara had never seen a motor-race although she had sometimes heard her parents mention them. She wondered if she would have the nerve. 'I'd like to learn to drive,' she said. 'I'm sure I'd like it.'

Alexander smiled at her. 'I don't know that women make very good drivers.'

'Why not?'

'They tend to dither about in the middle of the road and cause accidents. Not all them, of course, there are a few very good women drivers. But most of them aren't much good.' He stood up. 'I'd better be getting back.'

As they walked towards the house Alexander seemed to notice Mara's white coat for the first time. 'I must say, you look most attractive in your . . . er . . . uniform.'

The doctors' coats had all been much too big for Mara, but she had taken the smallest, wrapped it tightly round herself and secured it with a wide red belt. She waggled a bare leg at him. 'Doctor Turner thought I should look more like one of the boys.'

'Really?' He looked down at her legs. 'You don't, you know, and it is very . . . short and' – he eyed the red belt – 'not exactly shapeless.'

'No.' Mara had made sure of that.

Alexander frowned. 'You haven't been having any trouble, I hope? I know what the Americans are like where women are concerned. They don't bother you, do they?'

Mara laid a reassuring hand on his arm and smiled innocently up at him. 'No, they've all been perfect gentlemen.'

It came to Mara that evening as she watched Jamie over the supper table that what she had been frightened of was happening. Her feelings were growing beyond her control, and there was nothing she could do to stop them. It's been four days, she thought. Doesn't he want me any more? Doesn't he think about me . . . like that? Did he only do it because he felt sorry for me? That idea, more than any other, upset her.

She listened as he discussed the finer details of some treatment he had ordered for a patient. Will he come tonight? Will he ever come again? Does he ever think about anything but hospitals and medicines and ill people? I don't think he does. Perhaps momentarily, but that's all. She watched him lean forward eagerly to expound his argument. Does he know how I feel about him? Why do I feel what I feel? Why do I have to feel it about him? Mummy used to say men are different from women because they have other things in their lives apart from love. I suppose some women do too. Clever women. At the thought of smart, clever, busy women Mara felt a curious rush of inadequacy. She was so ignorant, so uneducated. It wasn't her fault, but she was. Perhaps she

102

should study something. But what? And honestly, when it came down to it, she lacked the inclination. I only have Jamie, she went on to herself. And Alexander. But he's different. I don't . . . want him. I only want Jamie.

Once again Jamie dismissed her as soon as they had gone through her work, this time without even a trace of intimacy. Mara had no alternative but to go up to her room. There was nowhere else for her to go. The men were either on duty, asleep or in the dining room, and in any case they didn't want her company. She went up to the attic, to bed, trying not to let the loneliness invade her. Closing her eyes she pictured Jamie coming into her room and sitting on the bed . . . no, lying on the bed. And would she? Should she? Or should she be cool and distant, a touch of his own medicine? Very appropriate, she decided. A touch of his own medicine. She pictured him trying to kiss her and herself pretending not to want to. That was right. She mustn't give in – not too easily. She must make him beg for it. The only trouble was, Mara couldn't imagine Jamie begging for anything. That was part of his attraction.

Mara was just trying to work out exactly what she would say as she pretended she didn't want Jamie, when there was a light tap on the door. Pretence forgotten, she called out in a voice squeaky with excitement, 'Who is it? Come in!'

The door opened and Jamie came in. 'It's me. Who else were you expecting?'

'No . . . no one.'

He flopped down on the bed. 'Thought I'd come and see how you are.'

She smiled at him, she couldn't help herself. 'I'm fine. A bit tired.'

He yawned, then leaned across and ruffled her hair. 'Does you good. Stops you being a naughty Stork.'

Stork was no romantic endearment, but Mara loved it when Jamie called her Stork because it was his special name for her: perhaps she even loved it more because it was ugly. She linked her fingers through his and said, 'I don't have much time for being naughty.'

'Complaining already?' He gave her a wickedly speculative grin. 'You'll never again work for someone as kind and considerate as I am. Why, I'm an angel in disguise.'

Mara laughed. 'I'd never have known. The disguise is excellent.'

Their eyes met. 'I think I'll have to teach you a little more respect for your boss.'

'Really?' She ran her foot up and down his calf, then hooked her toes underneath the bottom of his trousers and twiddled them against his ankle.

'Yes.' He pushed her backwards and rolled over on top of her, trapping her underneath. 'This is lesson number one.'

Mara slid her arms up round his neck. 'But I don't have my notebook.'

'That means' – he blew into the nape of her neck – 'I'll have to tell you everything twice.'

It was then that Mara remembered she had intended to make Jamie beg, but by then it was far too late.

The routine of working was what Mara found hardest to accept. She wasn't used to getting up early and at the same time each day, or sitting behind a desk for the prescribed hours, but after a couple of weeks she grew accustomed to it and even began to enjoy it. Or was it that she enjoyed working for Jamie, enjoyed doing anything for him and with him? Not that he was very easy to

104

work for: although a good delegator and organizer – he gave his instructions clearly and didn't hang over her watching her every move – he was impatient, quick to criticize and seemingly inexhaustible, demanding of others the same dedication to their work as he gave to his own. But his saving grace, what made everyone strive to please him, was that when praise was due he gave it unstintingly. On the occasions he praised Mara she glowed for days in the aftermath of it: a small compensation for the fact that when the hospital was busy, which it usually was, she saw little of him. Days passed when he scarcely spoke to her except to give her instructions, nights passed when she lay in bed waiting in vain for his light tap on the door. The trouble was, when he did come she was so pleased that she clung to him and did her best to detain him long after she knew he wanted to go. And not only that, she was caught up in that fateful circle where she no longer said what she thought, only what she thought he wanted her to say. And she despised herself for doing it.

Once he said to her, 'I think the Rhineland should be permanently demilitarized.'

Mara wanted to say, 'That isn't fair! Why should Germany have to pay for her defeat for ever? Why should you, the Americans, come and tell us what to do? That's what's wrong with the world, one country dominates another, one person dominates another.' But she merely nodded and said, 'Yes, you're right.'

And the less Jamie came to her the more submissive and clinging she became. She blamed his absences on work. How she resented it. And the other men. And the patients. Anything which occupied his time: time stolen from her. Work. Not another woman, but an irreproachable and therefore unbeatable rival.

One night she berated him, she knew she shouldn't but she couldn't stop herself. 'You're always busy. Too busy.'

'I know.' He flopped across her bed as usual. 'But what can I do? All these poor guys who've been in field hospitals are being brought in and they've had a helluva time out there.'

'I thought some of them were being sent home.'

'Anyone fit to travel, yes. Ours can't travel. On top of that, we're now getting those who've become sick since the end of the war. Appendicitis. Broken legs. You name it.'

Mara picked at the blanket. Nervousness made her pick at things. 'I hardly ever see you,' she complained.

He yawned.

'You only come when you . . . want to.'

He looked at her and laughed. 'Well, you don't expect me to come when I don't, do you?'

It came out before she could stop it. 'Oh, so sometimes you don't want me?' She loved him so much, why couldn't he love her? There was never a night when she did not wait, when she did not want him. Never.

Jamie yawned again. 'Don't be a bore, Mara! What's the matter with you? You used to be such fun. Now, if I don't talk to you you look miserable and if I do, you agree with everything I say. I might as well be talking to myself.'

'I'm not a bore.' She turned away so he couldn't see how hurt she was.

He frowned. 'Yes you are. You're turning into a limpet.'

'What's a limpet?'

'A little animal that clings to rocks.' He got up and walked over to the door. He'd only been there ten minutes and he hadn't even kissed her.

Mara watched him. She mustn't cry – not till he'd gone. 'Are you . . . going?' she asked falteringly.

'Sure I am. The last thing I need at the end of a long day is you giving me a hard time.' He put his hand on the door handle, then hesitated. 'You know what's the matter with you,' he said, looking back at the corner where she sat shivering and miserable. 'You don't talk to anyone except for the captain and me. You need company. Go and talk to the others instead of sitting up here moping.'

'They don't want to talk to me.'

He groaned. 'They're just a group of ordinary guys who've suddenly found themselves stuck in a strange land. If you were a little less reserved . . . I mean . . . you're always glaring at them, so what do you expect?' He suddenly began to laugh.

'What's so funny?' Mara could see nothing funny at all. The man she loved, yes, she admitted she loved him, had told her she was a limpet and a bore.

'I was just remembering that when we came I told them to stay away from you. I had visions of them creeping up here every night and now, here I am, telling you to be more friendly.'

He was still laughing when he left the room.

Mara lay in bed listening to his footsteps, the creak of the other door, the click as it shut, more footsteps; then nothing. He'd gone: her chin wobbled. He'd called her a bore: she bit her lip. A limpet: she rolled over and buried her wet face in the pillow.

Of course Mara couldn't sleep that night. When the tears stopped, she lay thinking about what Jamie had told her, turning his words over and over, analysing them, dissecting them, putting them back together again. No longer was she Mara Vogel, an entity. Obsessive love had bound her to Jamie so that she didn't function as a person, as an individual. Her emotions had become a part of his, see-sawing up and down with his moods and availability; a Siamese twin; the weaker twin; a limpet.

At dawn Mara was still awake. She knelt in front of the window and watched the ghostly fingers rise up from the east to stroke the night away. A new day. Midsummer's day. I'm going to lose him, she thought. I'm a bore and I cling. I used to be fun. Was I fun? What was I like when I was fun? How can I be fun again? How can I be me again when I love him so much and I'm so afraid of losing him?

The ghostly fingers had been replaced by a solid mass of blue and red, like a pile of blankets with the darkest blue on the top. He doesn't want me. She picked up a hand-mirror and saw that her eyes had almost disappeared into the puffiness of her crying. And he certainly doesn't love me. And yet, she lifted her hair high above her head, then released it into a cascade of shiny streaks, he could. I know he could.

Chapter 7

To be the old Mara, that was the solution. To smile. To joke. To recapture whatever it was he had liked in her: the aggression, the person she had been. But it wasn't easy when inside she was sick with hurt.

At lunch next day Mara steeled herself to make conversation with Sayers, who was sitting opposite her. Jamie was on her left, in deep discussion with Durrant. She was about to ask Sayers where he lived in America, when one of the nurses, they were all men, burst into the dining room yelling, 'I say, you guys, have you heard about Scapa Flow? They've scuttled their fleet, the bastards! Von Reuter ordered them to open the sea-cocks. Forty-eight ships sunk in an hour!'

The dining room was in an uproar. There were shouts of, 'Why? Why?'

'Because the Kaiser'd once told him not to surrender.'

'The Kaiser's abdicated.'

'Too right! But he still stuck to his orders. What do you expect from the . . .' he stopped as he caught sight of Mara.

It was most unfortunate that Admiral von Reuter chose that day on which to scuttle the German Fleet; it was now impossible for Mara to talk to Sayers or anyone else. If she'd had the courage she would have left the dining room, but she was afraid to draw attention to herself, so she sat with her head bowed miserably over her plate.

I mustn't give up, she told herself that evening. I'll be friendly to them individually before I try to talk to them in the dining room. And I'll be nice to Alexander when he comes tomorrow. Very nice. Particularly if Jamie's around.

At first Jamie didn't seem to notice any change. He was still busy, still brusque. All this hard work for nothing, Mara thought despairingly. Face stiff with smiling. Throat sore with saying, 'Good morning. How are you? Thank you. How kind.' Brain tired with thinking of things to say. And he doesn't even notice. But she didn't give up; she renewed her efforts. Perhaps I do have a vocation, she concluded one day. An actress!

Finally, one evening as they were going through her wretched list, Jamie said, 'You're beginning to get the hang of things, Mara.'

'Oh, am I?' She blushed with pleasure and took a step towards him. Then a little voice warned, 'Come on, Mara, don't collapse into a heap at his feet! You haven't won yet,' and she forced herself to smile brightly and say with great enthusiasm, 'I'm so glad. It has taken me a bit of time but I'm rather enjoying it now. I never knew a hospital could be so interesting.'

'I knew you'd do well.' He was pleased, but only vaguely. His eyes kept drifting down to the papers in front of him.

The temptation to stay with him was overwhelming, but she made herself walk to the door and wish him a cheerful, 'Goodnight.'

Never again would she give him reason to call her a limpet.

Several evenings later Mara was sitting on her bed towel-drying her hair when there was a light tap on the door and Jamie came in. He was carrying a cup of coffee. 'Thought I'd come and have my break with you.' He put

110

the cup on the floor and flopped down on the bed. 'I'd have brought you some only it might have looked a bit strange if I'd come up here with two cups.'

To give herself time to recover Mara carried on rubbing her hair, but against its wet tangles her face was hot with embarrassment. Had he forgotten about . . . bores and limpets?

Jamie grinned at her. 'Want a hand? I'm an excellent dryer of hair.'

'No, it'll dry itself now.' She tossed the towel on to a chair. It was just as though nothing had happened. But then, she told herself, he doesn't know about my games; my silly, necessary games. She peered at him through the tangles of her hair. He's no idea how I've schemed and planned. The brute!

Jamie leaned back against her legs. 'Umm, that's better.' He ran his hand up her blanket-covered knee and squeezed it, and Mara found herself smiling at him, responding to him, stretching out her legs so that his hand could reach higher and higher. She could not help it. How could she when she loved him so much? How could she when all she wanted to do was to pull him down to her? That feeling which he alone could arouse in her. It was all very well, when he wasn't there, to say she'd be cool and casual, but quite another when he was lying across her.

Jamie yawned and stretched. 'What a night!'

'Are you on night duty?'

'Wasn't meant to be but there's a problem.' He looked at his watch. 'Have to get back in a minute.'

'Oh, what's wrong?'

'It's Rook, the man on the first floor whose second leg was amputated ten days ago. He's developed complications.'

Mara never thought of the patients as being individuals; just as names on lists, or bed numbers. She didn't see them, except as blurred bodies on beds through half-open doors and she always experienced momentary surprise to hear a patient talked of as a real person. 'Is he going to die?'

'I don't know.' A wave of exhausted despair swept over him. 'I really don't know.'

Mara, whose emotions were so tied to Jamie's, also felt the draining effect of his despair. She sank back against the pillows and watched him through half-closed eyes.

'He has pneumonia.' Jamie picked up her hand and played with her fingers. 'It often happens after an operation.'

'And there's nothing . . .'

'No. No, there isn't. Can you imagine what a shock it is to the body to have both legs cut off in one month?'

Mara wriggled her own legs. She could almost feel the knife cutting through them. 'Yes, yes, I can.'

He laughed and stroked her thigh. 'Don't worry! I'm not about to cut yours off.'

'I'm glad to hear it.'

'Would be a pity.' His hand moved up her thigh. 'You've got nice legs – apart from your knobbly knees. Still, I suppose they're not bad for a stork.'

She kicked at him playfully. 'What do you mean, knobbly knees? I have beautiful knees.'

He stretched up along beside her. 'I could improve them with my knife.'

She nuzzled his face. 'No thank you, doctor.' She was sure of him now. Sure for tonight, at least. She pushed the blanket down and turned sideways to him, nibbling at his neck and his jaw, her long legs entwined with his.

But suddenly Jamie rolled on to his back and although

he didn't push Mara away, which was something, it was obvious his mind was still on work. 'The trouble is,' he said after a minute, stroking her hair and kissing the top of her head which lay on his chest, 'after such a big operation the patient has to stay in bed. Of course he does. And, as I say, they frequently catch pneumonia . . .'

'And die?' Mara was trying to show an interest in his words, when all she really wanted was his body.

'Exactly. Now, pneumonia affects the lungs and I can't help feeling if one could only get Rook up . . .'

'But he hasn't any legs.'

'I mean, if we sat him up. We could even carry him around. Just get him moving. Anything. It might help to clear his lungs.'

'Why don't you?' By trying to show an interest Mara found she really was quite interested.

'Because it might kill him.'

'If he's going to die anyway . . .'

Jamie smiled down at her. It was neither an intimate smile, nor the brief smile of the vaguely amused, it was a smile of confidences shared, and it went straight to Mara's heart. 'I'm a very junior doctor. I only qualified two years ago.' This was something he had never told her before. 'It's a miracle I got this post. If they'd had anyone more experienced, I wouldn't have. I'd done a year specializing in lung diseases. That stood me in good stead. But it's a miracle. A hospital all to myself at my age . . .'

'How old are you?' She had been longing to know.

'Twenty-five.'

The same age as Alexander, she thought. But Alexander seemed much older. He lacked the drive of life.

'So, you see,' Jamie went on, 'this is my first responsible post and if I kill Rook by trying out something not strictly by the book, it'll be my last.'

Mara kissed him on the cheek. 'Yes, but if you believe.'

He thought for a moment. 'I do believe.'

There was no sign of Jamie next day. Mara wondered if Rook was still alive, if Jamie had got him up, or if in the end he'd followed the rules. Although she had never seen Rook, it mattered very much to her that he was living, and it mattered too that his survival had been due to Jamie. If Rook lived, she felt in a funny way she would have had a part in his living; a small part, a supportive part. But still a part.

She decided to ask Sayers at lunch. Of all the men he was the most friendly to her, the one she knew the best. Most of the others she had never even spoken to beyond her recent 'good mornings' and 'good nights'. Feeling very conspicuous she approached Sayers. He was sitting with the other orderlies and did not see her coming. 'Mr Sayers,' she said hesitantly.

He looked up with surprise. 'Yes, miss?'

'I was wondering if you knew how Rook is. Doctor Turner told me he was very ill and I . . . umm' – everyone seemed to be watching and listening – 'I had not heard.'

For a moment Sayers looked at her blankly, then his broad face broke into a smile. 'Well, that's mighty kind of you to ask, miss.' His voice boomed out and Mara had the impression he wanted to show everyone, perhaps those who still resented her presence, that she wasn't so bad. 'I gather Rook's pretty sick but not dead yet.'

'I'm so glad. It must be terrible . . . no legs.' Mara smiled nervously and turned away to look for an empty table.

But Sayers called her back. 'Miss, would you like to sit with us?'

'It's very kind of you but I don't want to . . . intrude.'

114

'It'd be a pleasure. Sit yourself down.' He pointed to an empty chair. 'Do us good to talk to someone new, wouldn't it?' He looked at his companions, who nodded. 'Got two daughters of my own. A bit younger than you, I think?'

Mara had known the men resented her at first, but she hadn't realized how curious they were about her. Isolated as they were in their hospital world, she had been an endless source of speculation. 'I'm seventeen,' she said, 'but I'll be eighteen in August.'

Sayers nodded. 'My youngest's birthday is the tenth.'

'Really? Mine's the first.'

'You speak very good English,' one of the others told her.

'My mother was English.'

'She's not here, is she?' The questions came from all directions.

'No, she's dead.'

'And you've been here all on your own?'

'Yes, since my mother died.'

'A long time ago?'

'During the . . . a year ago.'

There was an ominous silence. The word 'war' loomed before them. It was my fault, thought Mara, I said it, or nearly did. It's up to me to repair the damage. If I don't do it now it'll always be there. And she turned to Sayers with a smile, saying, 'I've never been to America but I've always wanted to go.'

After that, all she had to do was to sit back and listen to what life was like on a small farm in the Mid West.

Rook survived.

'Did you do it? Did you get him up?' Mara asked Jamie next time they were alone.

'Yes.' He threw his arms around her and hugged her tightly to him. 'Yes, I did and it worked. It worked, Stork.'

One day followed another. Hot summer days with long light evenings, days with little to distinguish them except that for Mara they were the happiest in her life. She had Jamie. Not all the time, not every night, but he was there. He was in the house, she could hear his voice. He crossed the hall, she recognized his footsteps. He was a part of her and she was a part of him. Not the only part, not even the most important part – that she recognized, that she tried to come to terms with. She would never possess Jamie, not as she would have let him possess her had he wanted to, but then that was Jamie. Somehow it made her love him all the more.

The hospital had become a unit and those who worked there united. Communal living and shared exhaustion bound them together like a large family, and Mara loved it. She no longer thought of the house as her parents' home, the stark wards bore no relation to that chapter of her life. It was as if the Americans had always been there and she was an only daughter amongst many brothers, overprotected and spoilt just as Hans had spoilt her, and just as he had, they teased her. Only about Alexander, whom they called 'The Courting Captain', but never about Jamie – although Mara was sure they suspected – because Jamie was sacred to them. He personified all those qualities of leadership other men so admire and in their eyes all he did was admirable, even if not fully understandable.

And because Mara loved Jamie and their love included all that was physical and emotional, at least on her part, she did not really believe, despite the teasing, that

Alexander's intentions were serious. He was fond of her, of course he was. He found her attractive, she knew he did. But he never made a move in her direction, never tried to kiss her or hold her hand, so she presumed, because she wanted to, that he realized she was not interested. To Mara, Alexander was a surrogate brother, someone of whom she was very fond, someone on whom she knew she could depend: a friend.

One day Alexander came to see her and he was smiling and laughing.

'I've never seen you so happy,' she said, laughing with him. 'What's happened?'

'One of the big nobs from High Command is coming to lunch tomorrow and I've been asked to sit at his table,' he said. 'The colonel told me yesterday. It's a great honour and it'll do my career a lot of good.'

'Will you be a colonel one day?' Mara asked him.

'I don't know. We'll have to wait and see.' He left almost immediately, he had to get back to Cologne, and Mara went back to her work, happy for Alexander although she couldn't quite see why one lunch could do a career such a lot of good.

Although Jamie, and most of the Americans because he had told them, knew that Franz Vogel had been a pacifist, he had never questioned her about her father's views. In fact, he never mentioned her father unless Mara did first, and as Mara still found the subject was very painful, they hardly ever spoke of him. But a few days later he came out to the rose garden where Mara was sitting on the brick wall relishing the last few minutes of her lunch hour, and sat down on the grass nearby, saying, 'Tell me something, why didn't your father believe in war?'

She looked at him with surprise. 'My father? I don't really know.' She thought for a moment. 'I think he felt that it wouldn't solve anything, and that whoever won wouldn't really win, because in war everyone is a loser in the end.'

'Did he think that about this war or all wars?'

'All wars, I think.' She frowned. 'But you see, I was twelve when he was arrested and although he talked about it to my mother and my brother . . .'

'You have a brother!'

'He's dead. He was killed in the war.'

'So he wasn't against fighting?'

'He had to go. But, no, he wasn't against it.'

'What did you father feel about that?'

'He was in prison by that time. Why do you want to know these things?'

'I'm curious. Do you mind?'

She hesitated. 'No.'

'What did your mother feel about your father's views?'

'I don't think she really understood, but she loved him so she supported him in whatever he did. She had been poor when she was young' – she thought of her mother's gentle fatalism – 'and she felt it was her lot to be poor again. She saw it as the natural way of the world.'

Jamie picked at the grass. 'You've had a hard time but you don't think that's your lot, do you? Despite . . . everything.'

Mara looked at the rose bushes. A number of flowers had actually appeared but they had nothing of their previous splendour. 'No, I don't,' she replied, thinking of Herr Steiger. It was inconceivable that she should let herself be tricked again.

Jamie watched her face close in and he knew what she was thinking about. He wanted very much to help her,

118

and when he saw her hurt, it made him realize how fond he was of her. But he was sure that although it might hurt her it did her good to talk about the past, to exorcize it from herself. Only in that way could she come to terms with it. 'Do you believe in God?' he asked suddenly.

'I don't know. I did. But I'm not sure any more. If there is a God why did he let all this happen? Do you believe in him?'

'I don't know either. I used to, then I didn't for a bit, but now I think I do again.'

Mara thought for a few moments, then asked, 'Why did you ask me that question?'

'Because if there is a God, perhaps it was his way of doing things. What happened to you was inevitable but the timing could have been much worse. Don't you . . .'

'Worse!' she interrupted him. 'How could it have been worse? If I'd known about my father, I wouldn't have . . . have . . .'

He held up his hand. 'Let me finish. Mara, even if you had known about your father, if Steiger had wanted you he would have taken you just the same. Okay, I know he might not have seen you, but if he had, and you'd refused, he'd have raped you.' She tried to interrupt him again, but he silenced her. 'No, listen! Isn't it better that you thought you were doing it for a reason? That timing gave you a reason. Just as timing gave you hope during those months after the war, when you were here alone.'

'You don't under . . .'

'When did the captain turn up?'

'March. But . . .'

'Listen to me. When did you know about your father?'

'A week later. But . . .'

He carried on talking over her protests. 'There, you see. Perhaps it was meant to be that way. I know it's no compensation, but it was better for you like that.' He paused, then added, 'Better in all ways but one.'

Mara looked down at the grass by her feet. 'But he tricked me,' she said flatly.

'I know. That's what I meant by better in all ways but one.' He spoke very gently to her, it was as if he were holding her in his arms and comforting her, only he couldn't do that, not in the garden in full view of the house.

'And he went on tricking me.' Mara didn't look at him.

'And you had to do what he wanted, didn't you?'

Her mouth trembled. 'Yes.'

'And you had to pretend, didn't you?'

'Yes.' She pushed back her hair and looked him full in the face. 'After the first few times he said he wasn't going to come any more unless I was more . . . responsive, and that if he didn't come any more my father would die. So I pretended, I did what he wanted.' She swallowed hard. 'Everything. That's why I'll never stop hating him. He didn't just trick me once, he tricked me over and over and over again.' She stood up and walked towards the house, her shoulders straight and her chin up.

Jamie followed her. She went up to her room and stood staring out of the window. He came up behind her and folded her in his arms, rubbing his face against her cheek. He had never felt so close to her as he did at that moment when she was at her most brave and her most vulnerable.

Gradually Mara was growing confident in her relationship with Jamie. She loved him and her love for him filled every aspect of her life, but she now loved him as an entity, both part of herself and separate from herself. She was no longer the weaker twin, a limpet, but a person in

120

her own right. The barriers of self-defence had gone and with them her reserve. She regained the laughter which she had known as a child. She admired Jamie for what he was and for what he was trying to do but, unlike the early days of their affair, she no longer talked to him as though he were a god whose whims she must placate, she teased him and he teased her back. They were lovers and friends and happy puppies together.

Once when she passed him on the stairs, she winked at him and flicked her white coat up to her thighs.

'If you do that again I'll do something unspeakable to you,' he muttered, keeping his face deadpan.

'Promises, promises.' She flicked up her coat again.

'I will.'

She went on down, laughing to herself, collected her cup of coffee from the kitchen, and took it into the study. A few moments later Sayers came in and told her the doctor wanted her to tell the gardener to trim the grass verges.

When Mara came back from the garden, she settled down with her cup of coffee. But when she took her first sip, expecting the delicious sweetness of well-sugared coffee, it was revolting. There was salt in it. She spat the mouthful back into the cup and thumped it down on the saucer. Only then did she notice the note on her typewriter.

'I warned you I'd do something unspeakable!!'

On Mara's eighteenth birthday she came down to breakfast to find the dining room full, even the cooks were there, and a huge box carefully wrapped in army-issue writing paper sitting on the table in front of her place. She looked from the box to the upturned faces watching her. 'For me?'

121

The men laughed, and someone shouted, 'One, two, three, happy birthday to you, happy birthday to you.' They all joined in, some singing, some shouting out the words and banging on the tables with their forks. 'Open it! Open it!' they cried at the end.

Inside the box was a beautiful silk shawl. Slowly Mara lifted it up and stroked the flowers and butterflies embroidered in subtle greens and pinks across it. 'It's beautiful. Thank you! Thank you.' She went round the tables, hugging each man, her face glowing with pleasure. 'But how did you know it was my birthday?'

'You've Sayers to thank for that. He remembered,' said Jamie.

'Oh, yes.' She recalled her conversation with Sayers about her age and her birthday. 'It's gorgeous.' She draped the shawl around herself, flicking the ends up over her shoulders. 'Thank you so much.' She pirouetted before them, and the silky fringes swirled out about her, and the flowers and the butterflies chased each other across the silk, a mixture of the Orient and the gypsy campfire. And to each man she was the wife, the sister, the lover or the child to whom he would normally give a birthday present. They sat there smiling and watching her and thinking of their loved ones.

Mara's birthday did not end at breakfast. There was a cake with eighteen candles for tea, and there was Jamie coming late to her room with his own special present, a heart-shaped locket on a thin gold chain. 'You can keep your juicy secrets locked up in it,' he told her, hugging her to him. 'Then I shall come along and read them. So remember to write clearly, not your usual scrawl.'

'I shall write in code so you can't understand.' She snuggled up to him. 'I'll list all my hundreds of lovers with scores beside their names.'

'Will you? Well, I'll soon break your code. I have my ways' – he pinched her right nipple – 'and my means' – he pinched the left one.

Mara started to tickle him, he was very ticklish, and all the time she was thinking, a heart means love, even if he doesn't say so.

But in spite of her happiness, from time to time Mara was plagued by insecurity. Were these halcyon days merely borrowed or were they hers for life? Would Jamie take her with him when he went back to America? He had never mentioned it. In the night, lying awake after he had left her, or in the sultry heat of an early afternoon when she would walk alone through the garden with the grass trailing at her bare ankles, her fears would rise up and she would see herself standing by the front door waving goodbye to the Americans, listening to their soon-to-be-forgotten promises to write, watching as the last car disappeared down the drive, then turning back into the silent house. But surely Jamie wouldn't leave her behind.

When Alexander heard that Mara had had a birthday and the Americans had given her a present he was mortified. 'Why didn't you tell me it was your birthday?' he asked her.

She laughed. 'Then you'd have had to give me a present.'

'But I wanted to give you a present.'

A few weeks later he turned up with a parcel. 'Happy birthday,' he said, handing it to Mara who was sitting on the grass near the rose garden.

She opened it quickly, she loved surprises. Inside was a pale blue cashmere cardigan. 'It's beautiful.' She rubbed the soft wool against her cheek and ungratefully wished it could have been bright blue or red or bright yellow.

'I thought you'd like it.' He sat down beside her. 'It'll keep you warm. I asked Sophia to choose it.'

Mara thought of Jamie's locket and of the shawl, both so wonderfully impractical. 'You'll make some girl a very good husband,' she told him.

He chuckled. 'That's what Sophia says, she's always trying to find me a wife but so far she hasn't succeeded. She says I'm too fussy. So does her aunt, Lady Henrietta Stone. Between them they know lots of suitable girls, particularly Lady Henrietta who moves in . . . er . . . very social circles. She brought Sophia out.'

'Out where?'

'It's an expression. It means Sophia was a debutante and Lady Henrietta introduced her to all the right people and got her presented to the King. That sort of thing.'

'Oh.' Balls and white fluffy dresses and an ageing monarch sitting on a gold throne. 'Were you brought out?'

'Oh no. Men aren't. Anyhow, my family weren't like that, not till recently, not till . . . but Atalanta will be.'

Mara tipped her head to one side, her big grey eyes laughing up at him. 'So they introduced you to lots of girls?' She was fascinated, they'd never talked about this sort of thing before.

'Oh, hundreds.'

'Don't you like any of them?'

Alexander looked at her. 'Well . . . er . . . not really.' He hesitated. 'I'm glad you like the cardigan, so clever of Sophia to choose that pale blue, I knew it would suit you as soon as I saw it.'

The hot summer gave way to a golden autumn. From her bedroom window Mara watched the leaves collect on the drive, waiting for Hanna's nephew to clear them up.

Usually she hated the autumn because it was like the approach of death, but this year she didn't mind, she even enjoyed it: she had Jamie. The cosiness of the nights when they sought each other's warmth was just as beautiful as the long and languid hours when they had kicked off the sheets and blankets and lain uncovered on the bed.

Mara saw less of Alexander during this period, although in all honesty she hardly noticed. He had been ill, he was often ill, and this meant he did not come to Koblenz for weeks at a time, but he sent her notes and she wrote back, when she had time.

Things were changing in the hospital. Most of the wounded had gone home and the patients were now those who had become ill since the occupation, mainly with tonsillitis, appendicitis or broken limbs. And the conversation in the dining room was no longer about the war, it was about going home.

'I just hope I get there before these puritans ban liquor,' said Sayers. There were shouts of agreement and, 'Damn me if I have to celebrate my homecoming with a cup of tea!'

At the end of October Rook's wooden legs arrived and every day he practised walking on them, cursing at anyone who got in his way. 'I'm booked to go home next month,' he told Mara. 'Must be able to walk by then,' and he staggered off across the hall.

When the time came for him to leave, everyone who could do so got out of bed to wave him off. He was a great favourite and his going made the other patients feel restless. But he also gave them hope. If Rook could lose two legs, survive pneumonia, and still go home, then they all could.

'Look me up if any of you guys find yourselves in

Brooklyn,' he called as he made his unsteady way towards the ambulance, 'and you too.' He turned to look at Mara, almost falling over as he did so. 'I'll get Ma to cook you some sauerkraut.'

They all laughed as Mara, who was standing by the front door, pulled a face. 'It's only because you hope I'll bring some of our good Mosel wine with me, isn't it?' she shouted after him.

He waved his hand and nearly fell over again. 'And we'll be drinking it out of Ma's teacups if those old bitches from the Anti-Saloon League get their way.'

They watched him being driven off, and suddenly it seemed that winter had come. Mara went into the study and looked out at the rose garden. When the buds grew again it would be a year since she had known about her father. She still thought of him, though not as often as she had once done, and she still hated Herr Steiger, that feeling had not been muted, but her months with Jamie, during which their fondness for each other had grown, although he never spoke of these things, had done a great deal to lessen her insecurity. Only occasionally did she worry about the future, she was now so sure Jamie would take her with him.

In preparation she learned all she could about America, reading the Americans' newspapers and asking them questions like, 'Are American girls very different to us . . . to me?' to which they replied, 'To you? Sure.' But when she asked them why, their explanations of, 'I don't know, they just are,' were most unsatisfactory.

She had already gleaned from Jamie that his parents lived in New Haven which, he told her, was just north of New York, and that his father was a lawyer and that he had an older married sister with whom he had little in

126

common. 'Will you live with your parents when you go back?' she asked him.

'I shouldn't think so, I hope not. I'm very fond of them but living at home . . .'

This seemed all to the good. She wouldn't want to live with her parents-in-law. 'Do you have a lot of friends in New Haven?' she asked.

'Umm, yes, I suppose I have. But more from medical school because we're interested in the same things.'

What Mara really wanted to know, but what she could never get out of him, was how many girls he had had and what they were like. She would have hated to meet a girl he had made love to, but at the same time she would have had a morbid curiosity to know all about her. To find out about other girls, Mara said things like, 'America's a much freer country, isn't it?'

'How do you mean?'

'Well . . . girls and things like that.'

He laughed. 'Of course it is, we've all had at least a hundred lovers by the time we're ten.'

One afternoon in early December Alexander came into the study. Mara looked up from her work and smiled at him. 'Hello. I didn't expect to see you so soon. I had your note last week and you said you were ill again. How are you?'

'I'm a bit better.' He hesitated, shuffling from foot to foot. 'Will you come for a drive with me, Mara? I've asked Doctor Turner and he says it's all right.'

Mara felt like saying, 'Please don't organize my life,' but she bit back her words because she could see he was agitated and she was genuinely pleased to see him. She was also surprised about the drive, he had never taken her out before, he was so conscientious about not wasting petrol. 'I'd love to go,' she said, and she meant it.

'You'll need a coat. It's very cold.'

She ran upstairs for her coat, the same old grey coat, and hurried down again before he could change his mind about the drive. 'Do you know,' she told him as they turned into the road and headed away from Koblenz towards the forest on the hills behind, 'I haven't been up here since before the war. We used to come here and have picnics when I was little.' She looked out of the window at the rows of tree trunks. 'I wonder if people will come here to picnic again.'

'Would you like to get out more, to travel?' he asked, turning down a narrow road to the right.

'Oh, yes.' She thought of America and hoped she wouldn't be seasick on the way over. Then she remembered that Alexander had been ill and she hadn't shown much concern. 'Are you really better now? You don't look very well.' His skin looked yellow and parchmenty.

He slowed down as they came to the edge of the forest and the road began to drop to the valley below, where the Mosel wound its way down to the Deutsches Eck. 'Actually,' he said, 'that's what I want to talk to you about.'

'Why, do you need some medicines?'

'No, it's not that.' He stopped the car at the side of the road. 'I've been invalided out. I'm going home.' He spoke as if it carried a stigma of disgrace.

'Going home! To England!' Mara's first reaction was one of purely selfish panic. He was her friend and he was deserting her. 'Surely you're not that ill.' Then, horrified at her own selfishness, she added quickly, 'I'm so sorry.'

Alexander was sitting with his hands on the steering wheel and his eyes gazing blankly ahead. 'It's my lungs.' He sighed. 'They say I need the comforts of home. Good food and rest.'

'And if you don't go?'

'They will . . . may get worse.' He drew a deep breath and forced a smile. 'Anyhow the war's over.'

'Yes, yes, of course it is.'

'I'd just like to have seen my job through, I feel a bit of a rat as far as the other chaps are concerned, leaving them here and all that.'

Mara thought, fancy caring what a lot of stupid soldiers think, but she didn't say so. She patted his arm and said, 'I'm sure they understand. You've been very brave to have carried on as long as you have. Most people would have jumped at a chance to go home.'

He smiled gratefully. 'That's what they all said.'

'Are you going soon?' Mara began to have an inkling of how much she would miss him. Jamie might be her life but Alexander was its support.

'In three days' time.' He drummed his fingers nervously on the steering wheel and his nervousness communicated itself to Mara, who wished he would either tell her what was troubling him or take her home. Anything but this nervous drumming.

Eventually he did speak. 'Mara,' he said, turning towards her, 'you know I'm very fond of you, don't you?'

She nodded apprehensively. Was this what all the drumming had been about?

'And I would like to think you're fond of me.'

'Yes, I am. Of course I am.' For a moment she had been afraid he might try to kiss her. Now she decided that all he wanted was a promise she would write. Of course I'll write, she told herself. I really will . . . when I have time.

'Mara.' He was searching her face for some clue as to her response. 'Mara, will you marry me?'

'Marry you! Marry . . .' How could he want to marry

her when they had never even kissed, when they had never touched or held each other, or loved?

'Yes, Mara.' Gingerly he took her by the shoulders and turned her face to his, tentatively he pulled her closer as though his nearness might affect her decision. 'Marry me and come back to England with me. I've already made inquiries and the British Consul in Cologne will marry us.'

She tried not to pull away from him, because she did not want to hurt his feelings. He was good and kind and honourable, all the things she wished she was, but even without Jamie marriage to Alexander would be a mistake. She saw that with unbelievable clarity. They were different, far too different. He saw the world in black and white while she saw it grey. 'I can't,' she said, more abruptly than she meant to.

For a moment he looked downcast. Then his face lit up. 'If it's because you're German, don't worry. I explained about your mother and, anyway, I shall be discharged by then.'

She was too sorry for him to be cross this time at the way he tried to organize her life. 'No, it's not that. It's just that . . .'

'You don't love me?'

'Yes.'

'I didn't think you did, not like I love you, but with time I think . . .'

'No.'

He released her and his hands fell to his sides, and all the tenseness drained away to nothing. 'I love you very much,' he said quietly. 'I loved you from the first day I saw you and I suppose I've always hoped . . .'

Mara nodded to the unspoken end of his sentence. If only he were Jamie, how different her answer would be!

130

'I'm very fond of you,' she said, 'I really am.' She put her hand to her breasts and touched Jamie's locket. 'And I'll miss you.'

He waved her words away with his hand. 'It's all right, Mara, say no more.'

They sat in silence, both staring straight ahead at the distant hills on the other side of the Mosel, and Mara wished he would take her home, back to Jamie. In her mind's eye she saw herself telling Jamie of Alexander's proposal and in her fantasy Jamie replied, 'You can't marry him. You're going to marry me.' Perhaps this was all she needed to make him say it. Doctor and Mrs Turner. Doctor and Mrs Jamie Turner. Mara Turner. MT.

Alexander interrupted her reverie. 'Even if you don't want to marry me, I'd still like you to come to England with me.'

Mara opened her mouth to say no, when he raised his hand to silence her. 'I mean as a friend, of course.'

She shook her head.

'What will you do? The Americans will be gone in a year or so, maybe less, and when they leave your situation will be as bad as before. Look, come with me to England and you'll be safe. You can always come back here later but at least you will have a home with my family. As I think you . . . er . . . know we are quite . . . er . . . well off, in fact very well off.'

'I can't live off your family.' Once it wouldn't have worried her.

'Then you could find a job. A good job. You could train to be a' – he tried to think of a suitable occupation for a young lady – 'a nursery school teacher.'

Mara had to laugh at that.

'Well, whatever,' he added hurriedly.

She shook her head. 'I do appreciate your concern, I really do, but I've already decided to look for another job here when the Americans go.' Of course she wouldn't, she'd be going with Jamie.

'Mara' – Alexander touched her arm – 'there'll be no jobs. Germany's on her knees.'

'But I can't leave. I can't . . .'

'Why not? Are you afraid I'll . . . pester you to marry me?'

'No, not at all.' She had to give him a reason, everything for Alexander had to have a reason. 'Koblenz is my home,' she said, feeling a terrible fraud: when Jamie asked her she would abandon it without a backward glance. 'I was born here . . . brought up here.'

'England could be your home. After all your mother was . . .'

'My mother! What does she have to do with it?'

'She was English.'

Mara felt as though she were standing on one side of an ever-widening void between herself and Alexander. 'But I'm not English.'

He sighed. 'I don't mean to press you, I'm just so worried about you.'

Mara gave him a rueful smile. 'Don't be! I'm a mongrel and mongrels survive in the wild.'

It was hard not to cry when he left her.

Mara did not see Jamie alone until the following night, and it was in that precious time after their love-making, when each minute longer he stayed was stolen and tinged with fear of discovery, that she told him, 'Alexander's leaving tomorrow. He's been invalided out.'

'His lungs, I suppose.'

'Yes. How did you know?'

132

'By the look of him. And he told me.'

'He did?' She felt excluded. When had they talked?

'Yes. Poor guy.' Jamie looked at his watch. 'My God, it's nearly four. Must go.' He clambered over her and out of bed.

'Alexander said . . . asked . . .' She picked at the fluff on the blanket.

'Have you seen my other sock?'

'It's on the chair.' She sat up. 'Jamie.'

'Umm.' He began to tie his shoe laces.

'Alexander asked me to marry him.'

He stopped tying his shoe laces. 'What did you say?'

'I said no, of course. How could I marry him? I don't love him.'

'Quite right.' He carried on with his laces.

Mara waited for him to speak but he said nothing. Nothing about, 'You can't marry him, you're going to marry me.' Nothing. So eventually she said, 'Then he offered to take me to England with him, to live with his family.'

'And?'

'I refused. I said I couldn't live off his family.'

'Right.' He put on his jacket.

'Then he said if I didn't want to live off them I could train for any job I liked.' To emphasize her sacrifice, she added, 'They're very rich.'

'And you accepted?'

'No.'

'Why not?'

'Because I don't want to go.'

Jamie was now fully dressed and standing at the bottom of Mara's bed. 'You must be out of your mind, Stork. This is a wonderful opportunity for you. Goddamit, you must be crazy.'

Mara stared up at him in miserable silence. She couldn't believe he meant what he was saying.

'After all,' he said, 'we'll be gone sooner or later. I'm definitely going back to the States in August.'

'Are you?' He hadn't told her.

'Yes. I heard last week I've got a place to specialize in respiratory problems and I start in September. After that I may go to England for a few years, they're very advanced in that field' – he smiled at her, – 'so if you're there we'll be able to see each other.'

She felt physically sick as she listened to him. 'But I don't want to leave here.'

'Don't be silly! What'll you do when we leave? Starve?'

'Can't I . . .' She swallowed hard. 'Can't I come with you?' She hated herself for asking and him for making her ask.

'Come with me!'

'Yes.'

'To America?'

'Yes.'

'To do what?'

'I . . . don't . . . know . . . but . . .'

Jamie looked down at her for a moment, then he gave an awkward laugh. And in his awkwardness and his laugh was her answer.

Jamie had used Mara, she saw that in the grim hours of the night. He had used her just as much as Herr Steiger. No, more, much more so because he had tricked her not only out of her body but out of her mind. He had led her to believe he cared for her, and she had loved him. She relived their hours together, the way he'd talked to her about her father and she had thought he was trying to help her, the way they'd laughed and whispered to each other: the little things which had meant so much to her but had meant nothing to him. In August he would have left her, he'd never intended to take her with him. She was convinced that he hadn't told her he was going then so as to keep her till he no longer needed her, to trick her as Herr Steiger had tricked her. And she hated him for it, and for the mockery he had made of her love, and she could see only one way of getting back at him.

The house was just stirring early next morning when Mara went down to the study. Inside, she paused for a minute and stood by the window, looking out at the rose garden and the early-morning sun which shimmered on the hapless rose bushes. Cold winter. Poverty. Loneliness. She picked up the telephone and asked for Alexander's number in Cologne.

It took Mara three hours to pack. Alexander had said she could take only two suitcases. 'Don't worry about clothes,' he told her. 'We'll buy everything you need in London. If you want any furniture sent on later . . .'

'No, no I don't.'

'I could organize it. I could try.'

'No. Nothing.' She wanted no memories.

By half-past eleven she was packed and ready. Feeling like a sacrificial lamb she sat down on her bed. Of Jamie she had seen nothing. It was better that way, she told herself, but nevertheless she couldn't help hoping.

The time passed slowly, too slowly. 'Come on, Alexander!' she murmured. 'Come on before I change my mind. Hurry up for my sake, for your own sake.' She touched Jamie's locket nestling between her breasts. Soon she would be far away, but not with the man she loved, with another man. She tried not to think of what this would mean.

135

She went over to the larger suitcase, undid it and drew out the iron box. Lifting the lid, she looked down at the yellowing paper and the black writing. Of all things these letters carried her most poignant memories, but she couldn't leave them behind, that would have been a rejection not only of her father but of her mother. She put the box down, took off the chain with Jamie's locket, and laid it on top of the letters. Then she closed the box and put it back in the suitcase.

There was a tap on the door. It was Sayers. 'Captain's here, miss. Says you're leaving us.'

'Yes, I'm going to England.' She couldn't meet his eyes. She knew he was offended she hadn't told him she was going.

'Very sudden?' He picked up her suitcase.

'Yes. I only knew this morning.' Was she going to have to go through this with each person?

Sayers smiled. 'Well, I sure am sorry to see you go but it's for the best. We were all mighty worried about leaving you here when we go.'

'Yes.' There was nothing else to say, and Sayers hurried off down the stairs.

She turned to look at the room one last time, but when she turned back she was not alone: Jamie was standing in the doorway.

'Weren't you going to say goodbye?' he asked.

'Yes, of course I was.'

'I'm glad you've come to your senses.'

'Yes.'

He took a step forward and smiled sympathetically, saying, 'Look, I know I sounded a bit tough last night but . . . well . . . you'll be better off in England.'

She gritted her teeth. 'Yes.'

'You will write to me, won't you?'

Mara's chin began to wobble. How could she write?

'Won't you?' He touched her cheek.

Before she could answer, feet pounded on the stairs and Alexander burst into the room. He looked from Mara to Jamie, then back at Mara, a bright smile of possession on his face. 'Sorry, darling,' he said, 'but we mustn't be too long.'

Darling! The word froze on the air.

Happily oblivious, Alexander held out his hand to Jamie. 'Goodbye, doctor. Do come and see us if you're ever in England.'

Automatically Jamie shook hands, mechanically his voice said, 'Goodbye.'

'I'll be downstairs.' Alexander gave Mara a loving look.

'I won't be long.' She had to force out the words.

They waited till his footsteps reached the floor below, the silence around them petrified as the air before a storm when the leaves on the trees whisper their apprehension.

'Darling!' Jamie's voice was scarcely audible. 'Darling!' It was no endearment.

Mara could not bear to look at him. She couldn't bear to see what she knew she would find. She walked slowly towards the door, her legs and arms ungainly with emotion.

But Jamie took her arm. 'What does he mean by "darling"?'

She stood there with his hand on her arm, even now his touch affected her, she could not help it; she wanted him. She could have let him take her then and there, with Alexander and Sayers and everyone waiting downstairs to say goodbye, had he tried. And she would have given up England, everything, had he asked her. Even at that last moment. She stood there, knowing all this. But then she

137

remembered his awkward laugh of rejection. 'What do you think he means?' she snapped.

'Don't tell me you're . . .' He tightened his grip.

'Going to marry Alexander? Yes, I am.'

'You can't.' He said it flatly.

'Why not?'

'Don't be a fool!'

She laughed, but without amusement. 'Last night I was silly because I wasn't going, now I'm a fool because I am.'

'That's not what I mean and you know it. Go to England with him but don't marry him. You said he'd arrange for you to do a training. Well, do it! Do something worthwhile!'

'You mean, be a doctor?'

'No. Anything. But stand on your own two feet. You're not stupid, in fact you're quite intelligent. You don't need to lean on someone, you've proved that these last months. Don't throw it all away! Do something with yourself! Get a job!'

Mara thought of the sort of jobs women had done before the war: shop assistants, nurses, or governesses like her mother. But they were hard jobs and the women who did them were regarded as unfortunate: fortunate women were kept by their husbands. Did Jamie want her to be unfortunate, had he hoped to leave her to face a life of hardship, was he angry because she was not only escaping from him but was marrying a wealthy man? She hoped he was. 'I'll have a job,' she said. 'It's called marriage.'

Jamie released her arm and grabbed both her shoulders, shaking her violently as though by doing so he might dislodge the pattern of her thoughts. 'You don't love him. You know you don't. You said so.'

138

She didn't deny it. Perhaps even now he'll realize he loves me, she thought, and she leaned very slightly towards him.

But Jamie did not say what Mara wanted him to. Instead he tried to reason with her. 'You can't marry a man you don't love. For God's sake, Mara! One day you'll meet someone you do love and what will you do then? Get a divorce?'

She longed to cry, 'I have. I love you,' but she knew he would merely laugh that awkward laugh as he had the night before. So she looked up at him, straight into his eyes, reminding herself of his rejection, and all the softness and indecision disappeared from her face and all the clumsiness from her movements. She was, once again, a survivor, and she was graceful and cold. But for her own sake she still had to repel him, to put him far beyond her reach so that he would never tempt her again and, if tempted herself, he would still be so disgusted by her that he would repudiate any advance she might make. She had to do it or she was lost. 'I'm not marrying him for love,' she said.

'Then what are you marrying him for?'

'Money.'

Jamie dropped his hands and took a step back. 'I might have guessed.' He spoke slowly, separating each word into its own pocket of disgust. 'Yes, I might have guessed. And I really thought you were something, but you're nothing but a little parasite.' He laughed drily. 'Well, I just hope the worthy captain knows he's buying second-hand goods.'

139

Chapter 8

Mara stood in the middle of the entrance hall of the Ritz, waiting while Alexander signed the register. She was still wearing her shabby grey coat, there had been no time for her to buy clothes, and she felt horribly conspicuous. All around her bustled the early-evening life of a smart hotel, men in tails with their hair like Alexander's, slicked back and with a centre parting, women exuding confidence as they flirted with their ostrich feather fans and twisted their bare shoulders to show off their fashionable tubular dresses. She knew they were looking at her curiously, wondering why she had been allowed in, as if she were a beggar who might suddenly embarrass them all by asking for money.

She wished she had stuck close to Alexander but somehow they had been separated when he went to the reception desk. A group of people now stood between them and Mara didn't have the nerve to push past. She tried to distract herself by looking at her surroundings but the luxury of the massive chandeliers, whose light picked up both the jewellery of the other women and the bare threads of her coat, and the ornate gilt-edged mirrors in which she saw herself standing like an unbegowned Cinderella at the ball, made her feel more conspicuous than ever.

A hand touched her arm. 'Can I help you, madam?'

She turned smartly to find a porter giving her the firm but polite smile with which, she imagined, he intended to evict her. 'I'm waiting for my . . . husband,' she stammered, picking nervously at her grey coat. 'He's signing the register.'

The porter masked his surprise. 'You may sit down if you like, madam.' He pointed to an elegant gilt chair with a dusky red velvet seat, but his tone suggested that he preferred she didn't.

'No, no.' His manner made Mara worse. She sensed that her hesitation in saying 'my husband' had made him suspect that she and Alexander weren't married and she felt sure he must be wondering why any man who didn't have to should bring a girl like herself to the Ritz. She looked to Alexander for help but he was standing at the desk with his back to her. He glanced up and caught sight of her anxious face in the mirror behind it. 'One minute,' he mouthed.

Mara nodded and shifted from foot to foot, trying not to think of Jamie sitting at her father's desk and of all the times when they had been together, when she had felt cherished.

'Here I am, darling.' Alexander slipped an arm round her waist. 'We're on the first floor,' he said cheerfully, steering her towards the stairs. 'The Old Man's certainly come up trumps this time. He's booked us a suite overlooking the park.'

They went up the long curling flight of stairs. Mara resisted the temptation to stroke the gleaming brass hand rail. Above her she could see two circles of black rails and above them an enormous glass window to the sky. 'It's very big, isn't it?'

Alexander squeezed her arm. 'Not nervous, are you?'

'A bit.'

'Well, you'll feel better once we've had dinner. The restaurant here is excellent.'

141

Mara thought of all the women in their beautiful dresses. The only vaguely smart thing she possessed was the pink and white silk suit which she had worn that first day when she had worked for Jamie, the day after . . . 'Do we have to go down to dinner?' she asked. 'Can't we eat in our room?'

'But, darling . . .' He looked beyond her. 'Ah, good, here comes our luggage.' They followed the porter to a nearby door and were ushered into a huge sitting room whose walls seemed to be entirely covered with ornate gilt mirrors and whose windows were hidden by dusky red velvet curtains which reached from the high ceiling right down to the carpet, cream with a discreet pattern of green leaves and roses in the inevitable dusky red. It reminded Mara of the carpet in the drawing room at Koblenz, but it wasn't as beautiful, it wasn't an Aubusson, it didn't have that silky finish.

The porter said, 'Please ring the bell when you wish the fire to be stoked, sir.'

Alexander said, 'Yes, of course.'

Mara hadn't noticed the fire, she had been thinking about the carpet and Koblenz, but now she walked over to it and she felt a little happier as she looked down at the flames: they were something natural and normal, even if you did have to call some stranger to stoke them for you.

'The bedroom is in here, sir,' said the porter, opening a door and showing them into an elegant bedroom, again with plenty of mirrors and dusky red. 'And the bathroom.' Mara glanced through the door. She had never seen such a large bath or such enormous brass taps.

She waited while Alexander tipped the porter, and when the man had gone, she said, 'Please can't we eat up here?'

'But Mara, why?' He walked towards her across the great expanse of the sitting room carpet and stood in front of her, looking disappointed.

'Because I haven't anything to wear,' she wailed.

He put his hands on her shoulders. 'I'll buy you lots of things tomorrow.'

'I meant for tonight.'

'What about that nice pink and white suit?'

'It's not smart enough.'

He sighed. 'If you really don't want to go down we won't, but I did want to treat you to a proper dinner on our first night here.' He paused and smiled tentatively at her. 'It would mean a lot to me.'

Mara thought, how can I refuse him and, anyway, who's going to know me? I'm just being silly. Silly and vain. She looked at Alexander. He was just like a small boy wanting to play with an uncooperative child – he reminded her of herself when she had wanted Hans to play with her, and of how disappointed she would be when he told her to go away because he was busy. 'All right,' she said, forcing herself to smile. 'I just hope you won't be ashamed of me.'

'Ashamed of you!' He hugged her. 'You're the most beautiful girl in the whole hotel, you don't need smart clothes like the others.'

She closed her eyes and leaned against his chest. Then she drew away. 'I'd better go and have a bath and wash my hair. I can at least be clean.'

He kissed her on the cheek. 'Shall I ask them to send up a woman to help you with your hair?'

'Oh, no.' The idea of some smart efficient woman censuring her badly cut hair was horrifying. 'No, I'll dry it in front of the fire.'

She went into the bathroom and closed the door. The

bed was enormous. She looked apprehensively at it as she took off her clothes. 'It's not as bad as all that,' she told herself. For a moment she stood looking down at the embroidered bedspread and thinking of another bed, the little iron bed in the attic. She remembered what Jamie had said about second-hand goods. That problem had worried her during the two days prior to her marriage when she had been a not-very-welcome guest of a member of the consular staff and his wife in Cologne; they had been kind but had clearly disapproved of an English ex-officer marrying a German girl, even if the girl's mother was English, but to Mara's relief there was no problem. Alexander had believed her because he wanted to: a dark night – a deserter – rape. If anything it made him love her all the more.

For nearly an hour Mara lay in the bath, twiddling at the brass taps with her toes and adding more and more hot water. All around her the steam rose up, scented by the bath salts provided by the hotel, and every so often she submerged herself in it, so that her hair spread out about her.

Alexander knocked on the door. 'Darling, are you all right?'

She sat up. 'Yes.'

'You've been in there for ages. I thought you'd drowned.'

'I'm getting out now.' She stepped out and wrapped herself in a huge bath towel, rubbing her face against its soft pile. 'Do you think the water here ever runs out?' she asked anxiously as she came out of the bathroom.

He was sitting on the end of the bed undoing his shoe laces. 'No. Why?'

'I've used an awful lot.'

He laughed. 'Don't worry. I won't say anything if we

144

find the place in an uproar because nobody else could have a bath.'

Mara put on her dressing-gown quickly. They were self-conscious about each other's nakedness but, although she didn't look at Alexander, she sensed he was watching her while pretending not to. 'I'm going to dry my hair,' she said, going through into the sitting room. As she passed a small round table the telephone on it began to ring. She stopped and stared at it, not daring to pick it up.

'It'll be my father,' said Alexander, padding through in his socks. Mara wandered over to one of the tall windows and peered out between the heavy velvet curtains, but she couldn't see the park, just the twinkling lights of some houses to her right and the dull red glow which hangs over a city at night. Behind her she could hear Alexander saying, 'Yes, thanks, everything's perfect. No, I'm not overdoing things. Yes, we'll be down on Christmas Eve. Will you send Owen with the car? . . . Eleven will be fine. No, she's fine.' He looked over at Mara who had her back to him. 'We're a bit tired, the crossing was quite rough but it didn't last long . . . The Dower House! That's marvellous news . . . See you then. Can I speak to Sophia for a moment?' A pause while he waited for his sister-in-law to come to the phone. 'Hello, Sophia, how are you? . . . And the twins? Good. Look, I wanted to ask you where Mara can get some clothes. She's had to leave practically everything behind . . . Where? . . . Madame Cecile. Bond Street. Could you ring her and tell her the sort of thing Mara's going to need? Thanks so much.' He replaced the earpiece and said to Mara, 'They all send their love and they're longing to meet you.'

She turned away from the window and smiled, thinking,

I bet they are. I can just imagine what they're saying. 'Why did dear Alexander have to marry this German girl when there are so many decent English girls to choose from!'

'Sophia's given me the name of the woman she buys her clothes from, a Madame Cecile. She's going to make an appointment for you tomorrow morning, she'll tell her the sort of thing you need.'

Mara smiled. 'Thank you.'

'And the best bit of news is that the tenants who have the Dower House are leaving in the middle of February so we'll be able to have it.'

'Where is it?' She had a wild hope that it might not be too near his family. The prospect of living with a lot of strangers who might disapprove of her was one she'd been trying to push to the back of her mind.

'It's only two miles from the Park but it's much nicer, at least I think so, but then I'm biased, I was brought up there, it was our home till I was fourteen.'

'Why did you move?'

'Because the old recluse who owned the Park, it's now called Rushton Park, died and his family were going to sell the place. We'd already bought the Dower House from him ten years earlier but he wouldn't sell us the land round it, that belonged to the Park. So if we hadn't bought the Park, the land all around us would have gone to strangers. Anyhow, Herbert and Sophie were about to get married and there wasn't room for us all at the Dower House. It's much smaller.'

'Why didn't Herbert and Sophia stay in the Dower House? Didn't they prefer to be alone?'

Alexander shrugged. 'Herbert likes living at the Park.' He took out his fob watch. 'Oh, nearly seven. I'd better go and have a bath. I've booked a table for eight and I've also asked the maid to take your suit to be pressed. It was on the top of your case.' He hurried off into the bedroom, missing Mara's look of horror. The hem of the skirt was tacked up with big stitches, the jacket cuffs were frayed, a button was missing at the waist. The whole hotel will know how poor I am, she thought miserably, wandering back to the curtains and wrapping one of them round her body, rubbing her face against its velvet pile.

Suddenly there was a sharp knock on the sitting room door. Mara called to Alexander but he didn't answer, he was in the bath. She hesitated, staring at the door. There was another knock. Straightening her shoulders, Mara called, 'Come in!'

The door opened and a middle-aged woman in a black uniform came in, carrying Alexander's tails over one arm and Mara's suit over the other. 'Good evening, madam,' she said, pretending not to notice Mara's wet hair and shabby dressing-gown, 'would you like me to hang these up?'

'Er . . . no, I'll take them.' Mara held out her arms.

'Will there be anything else, madam?'

'No, thank you.' She's waiting for a tip, thought Mara in panic, and I haven't any money. 'My husband will . . . er . . .' she stammered.

'Of course, madam.' The woman turned abruptly. 'Good evening, madam.'

As the door closed Mara sighed with relief and laid Alexander's tails over one chair and her suit over another, then sank down in front of the fire, trembling as she stared at the flames. What a nightmare! She felt as though she were being buffeted from one humiliation to another: as she rebounded off one scene it pushed her straight into the next, and every time she would cope less well and her humiliation would be more obvious. But gradually she

147

began to calm down. Drying her hair in front of the fire reminded her of her childhood, of simple normal things.

'Oh, she brought them back I see,' said Alexander coming out of the bedroom. 'Will you be ready soon, darling?'

'Yes, in about five minutes.' Darling! Darling! She was now Alexander's to call darling. Jamie had never called her darling, he'd only called her Stork. She couldn't imagine him calling anyone darling. She would hate it if he were to call her darling, a word used by countless others to countless others. But what am I thinking, Jamie's never going to call me darling or Stork because I'm never going to see him again. And I don't want to either. She stood up quickly. 'I'll go and dress.'

As she straightened the seams of her stockings she wondered if all married couples did this little dance around each other to avoid being seen naked, or if the natural way in which she and Jamie had enjoyed each other's naked bodies was the exception.

The supercilious maid had done wonders with the suit, Mara saw as she caught her reflection in a long mirror at the top of the stairs, but even so, compared with everyone else she looked poor and downtrodden. Her hair hadn't had time to dry properly, it fluffed up around her face and bunched on her shoulders and, unlike the other women who swept past, she hadn't any make-up, not even any lipstick. They probably think I'm an unfortunate cousin Alexander's forced to look after, she thought, deciding that he really was good-looking particularly with his snow-white stiff collar close round his neck and the long lines of his black tails. Poor Alexander, he must be ashamed of me.

They set off down the stairs and this time Mara surreptitiously stroked the gleaming brass rail. It felt cool and rich and expertly cared for, just as everything else looked rich and expertly cared for.

'We just have time for a quick drink in the Rivoli Bar,' said Alexander, steering her down a second set of stairs and into the basement. 'You'll like it down here. Plenty of atmosphere.' He took her to a table and a waiter held her chair for her. 'What would you like to drink, Mara?'

'I don't know.' Before the war she had been too young to drink, except for the odd glass of wine on special occasions. Since then, the only drink she had tried was the beer the Americans loved so much, and she didn't like that. Anyhow, she sensed that beer was not a drink for ladies or for the Rivoli Bar.

Alexander said, 'Sherry, I should think.' And to the waiter, 'Make that two. Dry.'

Mara smiled at him, grateful that he had diverted an impending humiliation, then she turned and looked around her. The bar was full of people, the women glamorous, the men smart. They were all chatting and laughing and smoking; even some of the women, the more raffish-looking ones, were smoking. 'I've never seen a woman smoke in public before,' Mara whispered to Alexander.

'Don't you start. It's a revolting habit.'

Mara laughed and turned again to watch the people. They fascinated her with their confidence and their elegance. She wondered if she would ever be like them. The waiter brought the sherry and she sipped at it.

'Like it?' Alexander touched her arm.

'Yes,' she took another sip, 'it's nice.'

At that moment a man came down the stairs. What first caught Mara's eye was the rhythm in his movement but then when he turned to face her, she saw the colour of his skin. He was black. Mara had never seen a black man before. Like countless other children she had sobbed over Uncle Tom – but this man hadn't stepped from any cabin. He was wearing full evening dress and he seemed perfectly at home in the Rivoli Bar. Mara watched him raise his hand in greeting to a girl who was the centre of attention, who immediately detached herself from her group and hurried over to him, linking her bare white arm through the crook of his elbow. They stood and whispered to each other, then the man laughed and walked over to the piano at the other end of the bar: the girl went back to her group, a possessive smile on her face. The man sat down at the piano, ran his fingers up and down the keys, and began to play: not the sort of tune Mara's mother had played, waltzes by Strauss or concertos by Mozart, but a honky-tonk sound which was both haunting and rhythmical.

Mara leaned towards Alexander. 'What sort of music is this?'

'I think it's called jazz or Dixieland, I'm not quite sure, but one of the chaps in the mess saw the Original Dixieland Jazz Band when he was on leave, and kept putting their record on the gramophone.' He pulled a face. 'Not my sort of thing but he was mad about it.'

'I like it. At least I think I do.' She was beginning to relax, although she wasn't sure if it was because of the strange music or the sherry.

'I think we ought to go up to dinner,' he said when she had finished her drink. 'You must be quite tired, I know I am.'

'Oh, are you all right?' She felt guilty because she kept forgetting he had been unwell and she knew that had she been in love with him, she would have constantly worried about him: as it was, she didn't, she forgot.

He squeezed her hand affectionately as she walked

beside him to the stairs. 'Yes, I'm fine. I feel better than I have for ages,' he smiled down at her, 'and happier than I've ever been. Are you happy, Mara?'

'Oh, yes.' She made herself look up at him and smile.

He patted her hand. 'You'll soon get used to everything.'

'Yes.' There was something in his tone which made Mara think that, although he didn't want her to worry because then she might be unhappy, to some extent her lack of confidence added to his. It made him feel protective towards her: he was the white knight and she the damsel.

They walked through the wide gallery which ran the breadth of the Ritz and which was still full of people. She stuck close to Alexander, her eyes fixed ahead, but even so she was aware that a number of the men they passed looked curiously at her.

When they reached the dining room the maître d'hôtel hurried to meet them. 'Rushton, yes, of course. A table for two. Please come this way, sir . . . madam.' He led them to a table by the windows, saying, 'As I expect you know, in the daytime the view over the park is wonderful from this room.' It was a secluded table and Mara wondered if the word had reached him that Mrs Rushton wasn't properly dressed.

'Well, what would you like?' Alexander asked after she'd been studying the menu for over five minutes and the waiter had come and gone twice.

'I'm not sure.' She stared at the list: *Boeuf en Croûte*; Duck *à l'Orange*, Casserole of Venison, Trout with Mushrooms and Wine Sauce, and many others. She wanted to try them all, she couldn't bear to think she might miss something. 'I'll have the . . . er . . . beef,' she said, casting longing eyes at all the others.

'And to start with?' The waiter had come back and they were both looking at Mara. Alexander added, 'I'm having the vichyssoise.'

'I'll have the same.' She closed the menu reluctantly as Alexander ordered a bottle of Château Margaux.

Mara leaned back in her chair and listened to Alexander, hoping she had the air of someone who dined frequently at the Ritz. But underneath the table she squeezed the thick white damask tablecloth, and trusted that no one could see. Nor, she hoped, could they see how she longed to stroke the curtains beside her and wrap herself in them, or how her finger itched to trace the stiff gold threads which ran through the brocaded tie-backs hanging loose behind her chair.

'We'll go to this dressmaker of Sophia's in the morning,' Alexander was saying. 'I don't know anything about women's clothes so I'll leave you there and pop down to my tailor in Savile Row. The dressmaker's in Bond Street so they're not far apart. Then, if we feel up to it, we might go to see a show in the evening. Would you like to go to the theatre, darling?'

Mara came back from her contemplation of her surroundings. 'I'd love to. What are we going to see?' She smiled as she remembered her daydreams of the theatrical manager who would whisk her off to Broadway.

'We could see *A Southern Maid*. I believe it's very good. José Collins is in it, all the chaps in Cologne who'd seen her in *Maid of the Mountains* were mad about her. One had seen it three times in a two-week leave!' He smiled sadly and once again Mara knew he was thinking of his life in the Army. She laid her hand on the crook of his arm and he laid his hand on hers.

The wine was uncorked and the soup put before them. Mara tried not to attack her food too obviously, but suddenly she was starving and the earlier humiliations receded as she lifted the first spoonful to her mouth. It was delicious. So was the wine! Red and fruity but dry, very different from the light Mosel wines she had drunk before. By the time Mara had finished her soup she had already drunk two glasses.

'Everything all right, darling?' Alexander smiled at her.

'Oh, yes, lovely.' She smiled back. She was feeling warm and contented and a little light-headed; the restaurant no longer seemed so imposing, the waiter seemed almost friendly, even the maître d'hôtel didn't frighten her when he came to ask if they had all they needed.

The beef was as delicious as the soup and Mara ate everything on her plate: meat, pastry, potatoes, carrots, cabbage. Everything!

'How about a pudding?' asked Alexander, looking at her plate with amusement.

'Oh, yes, please.' She finished her wine.

The waiter brought the menu. She chose a chocolate pudding which sounded just like Black Forest Gâteau and she wondered if it was, and if the hotel had changed the name because it sounded too German. So far no one had said anything to her about being German or remarked on her accent which, though not pronounced, was certainly teutonic. She glanced at Alexander and wished she could ask him if people minded her being German. She felt sure they did, but she didn't feel she could talk to him about it; he would deny it or tell her, as he kept doing, that everyone would love her.

When she had finished her chocolate whatever-it-was, Alexander said, 'Would you like anything else?'

She hesitated. 'Could I have another chocolate pudding?'

'Yes, of course, but won't it make you ill?'

'No. I loved it.'

He called the waiter over and they smiled together at Mara's request, as if she were a little girl who'd asked for a second helping of ice cream.

'Do you want another one?' he asked when she had finished.

'No.' She was beginning to feel a bit sick.

'Coffee?'

'No thanks.'

'I don't want any either. Shall we go? I'm very tired.'

'So am I.' Mara stood up. She didn't add, 'And I'm a bit drunk.'

As soon as they reached their rooms Mara flopped down on the bed. It was the first time she'd been relaxed enough with Alexander to do so. He came and stood beside her and laughed. 'I didn't like to tell you,' he said, 'but Château Margaux is a bit heavier than your German wines.'

Mara kicked off her shoes and curled her legs up under her chin. Alexander stroked her cheek. 'Don't go to sleep with your clothes on.'

'No, I'm all right. I've just eaten too much. I'm going to bed.'

Alexander nodded and went back into the sitting room, closing the door behind him.

Alexander was still asleep when Mara woke. She lay for a few minutes listening to him breathing, then she put on her dressing-gown and went to the bathroom. When she came back he was awake. 'How are you feeling?' he asked.

'Very well.' She added hurriedly, 'What about you?'

'Couldn't be better.'

'Can I draw the curtains?'

'Of course.' He rolled over to watch her.

Mara drew back the heavy curtains and looked down on the leafless trees of the park below. 'What's this park called?'

'Green Park. If you look to your right you'll see Piccadilly. The Circus is at the end of it. You can't see it from here, but we're going up that way this morning.'

'Where does the King live?'

'I'll show you.' He came behind her, linking his arms round her waist. 'Buckingham Palace is over there, to your left.'

'Can we go and see?' She leaned back against him. His blue and white striped pyjamas felt warm and soft, as he did.

'When we've sorted out your clothes problem.' He blew down the back of her neck. 'Mara,' he whispered hoarsely, 'why don't you come back to bed?'

She wished she could have stayed at the window, looking out, she was even happy to have his arms around her and for him to kiss her neck, but she didn't want him to make love to her.

But how could she refuse him?

It's not so bad, she thought afterwards, it really isn't, it's just that it isn't . . . She sat up abruptly. 'Shall we have some breakfast now?'

He rolled over and clasped her knees in his arms. 'Yes, I can't wait to taste some decent marmalade.'

'What was that funny rhyme you told me about Mr Tickler's jam?' she asked, wanting to compensate him for what was missing between them. 'Tell me again. Let me see if I can learn it.'

Whatever Madame Cecile, manageress of the *haute couture* business patronized by Sophia Rushton and many

155

others, thought of the new Mrs Rushton's appearance, she hid it well. Her only remark about the grey coat, as she whisked it away, was, 'A pre-war model, I believe.'

Mara looked uncertainly at Alexander. She was standing in her even shabbier brown wool dress in the middle of a long room behind the main shop. All down both walls were mirrors, built on hinges so they could be swung round to view a garment from every angle. 'Will you be all right, darling?' he whispered. He felt intensely awkward in such feminine surroundings.

Mara nodded. 'I hope so. Do you think she knows what I need? I don't.'

At that moment Madame Cecile came back. She gave Mara a reassuring smile, which immediately transformed her from a highly sophisticated and rather terrifying woman into a fairy godmother who knew exactly what a young lady should or should not wear. 'Mrs Rushton telephoned me early this morning,' she said. The French accent softened her voice and she gave Mara another of her smiles. 'And Lady Henrietta Stone rang a few moments ago.'

'She's not coming too, is she?' asked Alexander.

'Yes sir, she is.'

Alexander touched Mara's arm. 'Lady Henrietta is Sophia's aunt. You remember I told you about her?'

Mara nodded. She remembered him talking of a very social relation who wasn't quite a baroness. 'Are you going to stay and see her?' she asked, hoping he would.

'No, I'll be back later.' He pecked her on the cheek. 'You'll be much better off with Lady Henrietta and Madame . . . er . . . Cecile.'

When he had gone Madame Cecile led Mara over to a chair. She pulled up another one for herself, saying, 'Now, let's enjoy ourselves, shall we? Choosing your clothes should be a pleasure, most of my clients find it is. It's their husbands' – she winked at Mara – 'who aren't so happy when the bill arrives.'

Mara laughed. When she laughed her face lit up, the colour came to her cheeks and her big grey eyes shone luminously. She was no longer a forlorn little girl dwarfed by the glamour of her surroundings, she was a beautiful picture hung frameless on a plain dark wall, and Madame Cecile was the picture-framer who had been called in to enhance it. The manageress studied Mara and mentally put aside all her more conservative designs, those which Mrs Herbert Rushton might have chosen.

It was at that moment, with Mara still laughing, that Lady Henrietta Stone sailed in like a battleship at full steam. 'Ah, there you are,' she boomed, handing her mink to a salesgirl who had materialized from the back of the showroom. 'Good morning, good morning. So this is Mara!' She looked at Mara. 'No, don't get up, my dear.'

But Mara was already up and holding out her hand. There was something about Lady Henrietta, tall, imposing, grey-haired and smartly dressed, which would have drawn even the most ill-mannered man to his feet. 'And what do you have for us, Madame Cecile?' she said, sitting herself down in the chair vacated by the manageress. 'I've only half an hour, so let's get on with it.'

The manageress's manner was deferential. 'I'll have my girls put on . . .'

'Oh, let's not bother with all that! Just because something suits one of your girls, there's no reason why it should suit Mara. Let's put the child into a few things and then we can all see what looks good on her.' She patted Mara's knee, and although Mara was rather frightened of her she couldn't help liking her.

Mara was led through into another back room. 'I think this first,' said Madame Cecile, producing a deep blue dress, made of very fine wool, which folded into a low waist then was draped down over the hips in the same calf-length tubular skirt as Mara had seen on all the smart women at the Ritz. 'And a hat. These small turbans are going to be all the rage.' She produced a little turban made of the same material,

Mara undid the buttons of her brown wool dress and hesitated. She wasn't embarrassed about undressing, she was embarrassed about her plain white cotton underwear.

But Madame Cecile knew enough to realize that anyone who wore a shabby dress was hardly going to be sporting beautiful silk lingerie. 'I expect you'd like to see some pretty undergarments,' she said.

Mara smiled gratefully. 'Yes please.'

'There's a lingerie shop near here. I'll send one of my girls for a selection. Anything else?'

'Some shoes.' She looked down at her scuffed black pumps.

The manageress patted her arm. 'Don't worry, we'll soon have you with more things than you need. There's a shoe shop opposite here. When you've decided which clothes you like, I'll pop over for some shoes to suit them. Now, I'll leave you in peace.' She went out of the room and closed the door. Through the wall Mara could hear the manageress's soft tones. They were followed by the higher-pitched voices of several girls. She was glad these girls couldn't see her, she would have been plunged back into her awkwardness by the curiosity of girls of her own age, particularly those with the critical eyes she imagined anyone working in a place like this would have. She slid the fine blue wool over her head and then, taking a deep breath, opened the door and went back into the showroom.

Lady Henrietta and Madame Cecile were talking as Mara came in. They stopped and looked at her. 'Well!' exclaimed Lady Henrietta. 'My dear you look quite different! But the hat needs to come down to the eye-brows, doesn't it, Madame Cecile?'

Madame Cecile hurried over to Mara and adjusted the turban. 'That's better. Now, turn round and let's have a look at you.' She stood back and smiled.

Mara examined herself in a long mirror as she turned slowly in front of the two women. She hardly recognized herself. The blue enhanced the greyness of her eyes, the soft drapes of the material clung to her body, and the little turban gave her an air of sophistication touched with a certain youthfulness.

'That's a definite possibility,' said Lady Henrietta. 'How clever of you, Madame Cecile, to choose that one first. It's so depressing when the first garment makes one look like a sack of potatoes. Now, let's see something else.'

Mara went back into the small room and this time she tried on a dress of soft black slinky velvet with a cheeky little beaded beret. 'That looks wonderful,' enthused Lady Henrietta, settling back in her chair and warming to her task. She had imagined herself spending a boring half-hour attempting fruitlessly to add a bit of class and elegance to some unsuitable hussy, and here she was watching a girl change from a scruffy but not unattractive creature into a beautiful, fashionable young woman. She has style, she thought, as Mara appeared in a grey and pink silk evening dress which, like everything else that year, had a tubular skirt and which, like all the evening dresses, had a low straight neckline and thin straps to show off bare shoulders. Around Mara's head was a grey velvet headband pulled well down in the front. She looked like the mistress of an extremely successful painter temporarily abandoning Bohemia to attend the opening of his latest and much-publicized exhibition.

'They all suit you,' said Lady Henrietta when Mara came in to choose her underwear. 'I've never known anything like it, have you, Madame Cecile? The child looks a picture every time.'

'She certainly does,' agreed the manageress, smiling broadly. 'I wish I could find girls who had such an instinct for wearing clothes.'

'But we must do something about her hair.'

'I agree.'

'There's a good woman at the Ritz. I'll take her to her myself.'

'And a little make-up.'

'Elizabeth Arden will know what's right for her.'

Mara stood between the two women while they discussed her finer points as if they were two horse-dealers and she a race horse.

'I think we have enough,' said Lady Henrietta eventually. 'How many evening dresses have we chosen?'

'Three. Two to take away and one to be altered and sent on.'

'And day dresses?'

'Four. All with matching hats.'

'And two coats. The black velvet for evening and the pale grey for day . . . and that heavenly dusky pink cape.' Lady Henrietta laughed. 'Poor Alexander! Oh, by the way, what's happened to him?'

Guiltily Mara realized that she'd forgotten all about him. She'd had such fun trying on all the clothes, she'd forgotten that she had a husband or that he was going to pay for the huge pile which they had selected between them. 'He's gone to his tailor. He'll be back soon.'

'Not too soon, I hope.' Lady Henrietta and Madame Cecile exchanged a smile. 'It's a bad thing to have one's husband hanging over one when one's spending his money. Now, let's choose some of this lovely underwear for you. And Madame Cecile, you go and fetch her some shoes. Quick, before he comes back.'

Mara laughed, but she did feel a bit sorry for Alexander. She was sure he had no idea she would end up with so much, and had she been left to her own devices she would only have chosen a couple of things. She was so unused to buying clothes that even one new dress would have seemed like extravagance, but she settled down happily with a pile of lacy underwear in front of her.

'You look absolutely beautiful,' Alexander told her proudly, later that afternoon when they walked across Green Park to Buckingham Palace. 'Did you enjoy yourself this morning?'

'Oh, yes.' Mara linked her arm through his and stretched up her other hand to touch the little blue turban. 'I'm afraid I spent an awful lot of money,' she confessed anxiously. 'I've no idea how much. She didn't tell me and I didn't like to ask.' The brown dress and the old grey coat seemed a long way behind her.

Alexander squeezed her hand. 'That doesn't matter so long as you're happy.' He paused. 'You are, aren't you?'

'Oh, yes.' She wished he wouldn't keep asking her if she was happy. 'Is this it?' she said, as they came to the edge of the park at the bottom of Constitution Hill. There they stopped and looked across at the pàlace, and as they watched the daylight faded and lights appeared in some of the windows. It made Mara think of a rather grand and somewhat isolated Christmas tree. 'Do you think the King and Queen are there now?' she asked.

'No. The flag's not up.'

They turned away from the palace and walked a little way up The Mall before turning again, left up St James's and back to the Ritz.

'I've booked tickets for *A Southern Maid*,' Alexander said as they went in through the revolving doors. 'You'd like to go, wouldn't you?'

'I'd love to.' She smiled at him, and walked straight into the porter.

'Excuse me, madam,' he said, and he looked from Mara to Alexander, then back to Mara, his astonishment barely concealed when it dawned on him that she was none other than the waif who had stood in the entrance hall the previous evening.

Mara loved the theatre. She loved the anticipation before the curtain went up, the music and the singing and the story, of which she felt a part; but almost more than anything she loved sitting amongst all the elegant people and knowing she looked as smart as they did. She was aware of men staring at her, not out of curiosity because she was unfortunate, but because they admired her and found her attractive. She smoothed down the silky velvet of her black dress and raised her hand to the little beaded beret.

'Enjoy it?' Alexander asked her as the final curtain fell.

'It was wonderful. I can see why all the men like José Collins, she's just like a gypsy queen with her lovely black hair.'

Alexander hugged her to him as they squeezed through

162

the foyer and out on to the pavement. 'She's not my type,' he murmured against her beaded beret. 'I like my girls to have tawny hair.'

Mara laughed. 'Let's walk back, shall we? I want to see London by night. It all looks so exciting. All these people . . . all these lights.' She watched the theatre crowd spill out into the street and mill around, shouting for taxis and calling to each other, telling each other where they were going to dine and at which nightclub they'd meet later. Mara wished she and Alexander could go to a nightclub, she'd never been to one, but she didn't like to suggest it.

Alexander looked down into Mara's shining eyes. 'Yes, I suppose it is exciting, but I hope you're not going to be disappointed when we go home. Oxford is very social because of the university, but we're a good ten miles north of it, if not more, and right out in the country. Of course we know a lot of people, but living in the country isn't quite the same as living in London.'

Mara nodded but she wasn't really listening to him. She wasn't thinking about the future, she was living in the present, in London, in the Ritz; a pretty girl wearing her first new dress for over five years.

They stayed at the Ritz for ten days, by which time Mara felt perfectly at home there. She swanned in and out of the entrance hall where she had once stood like Cinderella, she ate in the dining room and knew what to choose, and didn't eat too much, and she spoke to the porters and the maids in the same polite but superior way all the other guests used when speaking to them. From time to time she wondered if they remembered her as she had first been and if they were amused by her sudden change, but they were far too good at their jobs to show if they were, and in any case Mara was too exhilarated by her new-found confidence and by the veiled attention she was receiving from other men to notice much.

On their last afternoon in London they went to Harrod's to buy Christmas presents. Mara only had Alexander's word to go on: she bought a silver paperweight for her father-in-law, a book on great country houses for Herbert, a silk shawl for Sophia, a pink fur muff for Atalanta, and a train set for Damon. 'Are you sure they'll like them?' she asked him.

'Of course I am, darling, I know my family.'

'And what would you like?' It seemed funny to ask him what he wanted and then buy it with his money. When she was a child she'd bought her father presents with his money, but that had been different, she'd been a child.

'What I'd really like,' he said, 'is a cigarette-case.'

'But you don't smoke!'

'I ought to have one in case other people want to smoke.' He pulled a face. 'Disgusting habit!'

Mara found the whole thing extraordinary, but she said, 'If that's what you'd like,' and they made their way through into the right department. She would have liked to spend more time in Harrod's, it all looked so exciting, but Lady Henrietta was expecting them for tea.

After they had had tea, Alexander suddenly stood up and said, 'Do you mind if I leave you here for a short while, Mara? I have to collect something.'

She smiled up at him and smoothed down her emerald-green cashmere skirt, another of Madame Cecile's creations. 'Not at all.' What a difference a week made!

'You run along, Alexander,' said her hostess. 'I want to talk to your wife about being presented. We'll have to do something about it if she's to appear in society, though

164

I'm not sure what. I'm afraid, my dear' – she patted Mara's arm, – 'we may have to leave it for a year until some of this anti-German feeling's died down.'

'Surely none of that will . . .' Alexander hovered above them.

Lady Henrietta interrupted him. 'Run along! You must be back by five because I have to go to a committee meeting. My East End soup kitchen charity.'

When Alexander had gone Mara said, 'Do you think I will have any trouble?' It was the question she hadn't been able to ask Alexander.

'You may have. If you do you mustn't lose your temper. My dear, there's no getting away from the fact that a great many people, almost everyone, lost someone close to them, and they're not going to welcome a German with open arms. What you have to do is to make them like you in spite of the fact you're German. It's up to you.'

Mara asked, 'Do you think people know when they hear me speak?'

'They certainly know you're not English. Try to make your "w" sound less like "v". Say week.'

'Vweek.'

'No. Week. Wwwwweek.'

'Wwweek.'

'Yes, that's much better. Of course Alexander's not going to be much help.'

'Why not?'

'Because he's much too besotted.'

Their conversation was cut short by Alexander's return. He came into the room carrying a large cardboard box. 'A present for you, darling,' he said to Mara, giving Lady Henrietta a conspiratorial wink.

Mara stood up. 'What is it?'

'Open it!' He handed her the box.

Mara took the box from him, laid it on the floor and lifted the lid. Inside was something black and soft. She picked it up. It was a beautiful black sable coat. With Alexander's help Mara slipped her arms into it and drew it up around her neck, wrapping the folds of fur about her. 'It's beautiful!' she gasped, 'absolutely beautiful,' and she hugged him, glowing up at him, her face framed by the black fur of the collar. In the taxi on their way back to the Ritz Alexander said, 'You seem to get on very well with Lady Henrietta.'

Mara smiled. 'I was a bit frightened of her at first but now I like her very much.'

He squeezed her hand. 'She certainly seems to like you.'

Mara had the feeling she had passed a test which even Alexander had expected her to fail.

As they went into the entrance hall he said, 'I'll just tell the porter we're expecting the Old Man's chauffeur at eleven. Do you want to go on up?'

'Yes, I'd like a bath.' Alexander went to the porter's desk and Mara walked slowly up the stairs. She had just come to the big right-hand curve when Alexander started after her.

'I'll book a table for dinner from the room,' he called up to her. 'They're a bit busy at the moment.'

Mara nodded. 'Very well.' But she saw he hadn't heard her, so she said it louder and somehow, perhaps because she raised her voice, the 'v' came out as an 'f' and the 'w' as a 'v'. Fery vell! Nothing could have sounded more German. She turned to carry on up the stairs and found two women blocking her way. They were looking at her oddly.

One of them, the older of the two, a horse-faced woman

in her late sixties, was carrying a folded newspaper. 'May I ask what nationality you are?' she said to Mara.

Mara felt that hours passed before she heard her own voice say, 'I'm German.'

The woman smiled triumphantly at her companion. 'I told you so when I heard her talking in the restaurant yesterday.' She looked at Mara, then at Alexander who had come up the stairs and was standing silently behind her, then back at Mara. 'Look at this!' she squeaked indignantly, unfolding her newspaper and waving it under Mara's nose. 'What do you think of that?' She pointed to the bold black heading. '"Hang the Kaiser!" If you ask me all Germans should be hanged.'

Mara stared at the woman's contorted face. She was numb with shock at the suddenness of the incident and couldn't think what to say or do, trapped there between the women, the brass rail and Alexander, who did nothing to defend her. She had a horrible feeling that other people were watching, that soon everyone in the entrance hall would be drawn to the commotion on the stairs. She was about to push past the women and run up to her room, when she remembered Lady Henrietta saying, 'You mustn't lose your temper . . . Alexander's not going to be much help . . . it's up to you,' and she straightened her shoulders and said, 'I appreciate your feelings. Now, may I pass?'

Astonished by her calmness, the women stood aside and let her go and Mara carried on up the stairs, head held high, forcing herself to walk slowly. Alexander followed dejectedly.

'Darling, I'm so sorry,' he began once they were out of earshot, 'it was so sudden I didn't know what to do. I never expected anything like that, not here, not in the

167

Ritz. Oh, Mara . . .' He touched her arm as she went past him into their sitting room.

'Darling . . .' He followed her across to one of the tall windows and hovered behind her as she stood looking out at the park. 'Darling, I know I should have said something to her but I didn't know what to say and I thought it better to keep quiet.'

Mara shook her head. 'It doesn't matter.'

'But it does. I should have . . .'

'Don't worry.'

'But I do, I should have . . . done something.' He looked helplessly at her stiff back. After a few minutes he said, 'Shall we have dinner up here?'

'Yes.' Standing by the window looking out at the dark, Mara saw that although Alexander was able to provide her with the smoothness of life, he was unable to defend her from its roughness: that she would have to do for herself.

Chapter 9

Mara was glad to leave the Ritz. She'd been happy there, but now the incident on the stairs hung between herself and Alexander, although they didn't talk about it. But it was with them as they walked down the stairs in the morning, both of them terrified there might be a repetition, not so much of the incident but of his inability to defend her against it. She knew he longed for her to reassure him that he had done all he could, but she couldn't because he hadn't. They both knew he hadn't.

She was relieved when they got out of the hotel.

'There's Owen,' said Alexander over-cheerfully, pointing to a small dark man in a dark green uniform standing on the pavement just outside the hotel doors. 'Hello, Owen. Good to see you again.'

'Hello, sir, it's good to have you back.' The chauffeur had a slightly sing-song voice, and merry brown eyes which he turned on Mara.

'This is my wife, Owen,' Alexander introduced her. 'Darling, this is Owen. Well, are we ready? Shall we go?'

He turned and thanked the doorman, handing him a florin, then marshalled Mara across the road to a large, shiny car, dark green like Owen's uniform. 'Your first Rushton-Gaunt, Mara.' He touched the gleaming bonnet. 'Beautiful, isn't she!'

'Yes, lovely.' Mara stepped up on to the running-board, twisted and sank back against the brown leather upholstery, drawing her sable around her. A poorly-dressed shopgirl was watching her enviously from the other side of the street and Mara, adjusting the blue turban on her head, felt a warm glow of confidence. And yet when they drove off she was not sorry: she knew what it was like to want, to stand on the outside looking in.

'This must be the new model,' said Alexander, patting the seat between them. He leaned forward and shouted down the speaking tube, 'Owen, is this the new saloon?'

'Yes,' came the muffled reply.

'Well, you'd better tell me what the differences are so my father doesn't think I'm not interested.'

Mara was staring out of the window, watching the houses as they became less and less smart. When they had arrived in London on the boat train from Dover to Victoria, it had been dark and since then all she had seen were the elegant white houses of Mayfair and the West End, where black railings prevented the pedestrian from squashing his nose up against the windows and seeing the splendours inside. Now, as they drove north-west from Hyde Park, she saw buildings built in a similar style, only these were dilapidated, with broken windows and peeling paint. They reminded her of her house in Koblenz before Jamie and the Americans came.

'Ever been in such a luxurious car?' Alexander touched her hand tentatively and gave her a breezy smile when she turned to him.

'No, I don't think I have.' She smiled back at him because she felt sorry for him. Immediately he relaxed and squeezed her hand, and Mara saw that for him the incident on the stairs was relegated to the past. She looked down at his big hand covering hers and wondered if all this was real. Was she really married to this man? Was this really her? England. The fur coat. The car. This man, her husband. She felt as though she were acting in a

170

play, or rather that she had been dreaming of acting in a play, and had suddenly woken up to find herself on stage playing the part of a rich man's wife. Only it wasn't a dream or a play. She was a rich man's wife: she had married Alexander. It seemed incredible that she should have taken such a step and yet, what else could she have done? 'When will we move into the Dower House?' she asked by way of making conversation. She wanted very much to recapture the companionship of the past week, for how could she face all these strangers if Alexander were also a stranger?

'Probably not for four or five months,' he replied. 'It's not free till mid February and then it'll need redecorating. And we'll have to buy some more furniture, there's some in the attic at the Park but not enough. Sophia will help you, she's frightfully good at that sort of thing.'

Mara listened to the muffled purr of the big engine. They had now left London and were well on their way, climbing steadily through bleak drizzling countryside.

'Nervous?' he asked.

'A little.' Of course she was nervous.

'Nothing to worry about. They'll all love you.'

Suddenly Alexander began speaking in a resigned voice. 'There's something I ought to tell you,' he said, clutching her hand as if he were afraid she might disappear on hearing what he had to say. 'You're bound to hear it eventually so I'd rather it came from me.' He paused. 'You remember I told you about my father's . . . friend, Sir Henry Gaunt.'

'Umm . . . oh, yes, Rushton-Gaunt.'

'Well, he's a very good friend now but he used to be my father's . . . er . . . employer.' He clung to her hand. 'You see, my father was born into a . . . er . . . he used to look after Sir Henry's cars.'

Because she couldn't think what else to say, Mara said, 'Oh.' She wondered what lay behind Alexander's awkwardness. It was obvious he felt he had misled her. Serve me right if he has, she thought wryly.

Alexander began to gabble, increasing Mara's apprehensions. 'Of course that was years ago and cars were already breaking down then, far worse than today, and no one knew how to mend them, most people had never seen a car, the whole of Gaunt used to come to a standstill . . .'

'Gaunt?'

'The village. We're about three miles from it, and Sir Henry lives at Gaunt Hall which is sort of between us and the village,' he carried on quickly before Mara could interrupt again. 'But the Old Man was brilliant, he always managed to get them going. Of course he wasn't old then.'

Mara was still wondering what lay behind all his ramblings. If Alexander's family was as wealthy and educated as he was, and as Lady Henrietta was, what did it matter if they hadn't always been? She remembered what he'd once told her about 'coming out', about how his family hadn't moved in those sort of circles but that Atalanta would 'come out'. The Vogels hadn't moved in the upper echelons of society either, they had been well established and well to do, but Mara's father had been so entirely unfettered by conventional thought that he had had friends from all creeds and classes, his only criterion being that they should be interesting. This liberal and unprejudiced attitude had rubbed off on Mara: Alexander's father interested her. 'So what happened?' she asked.

'He was convinced he could design a better car, one that didn't keep breaking down, but he couldn't afford to

172

build it. My mother died six months after I was born so he had to pay a woman to look after us, three of us. You remember I told you I had another brother who died?'

'Yes, Oliver.'

He was pleased she remembered the name. 'But luckily Sir Henry was just as mad about cars as my father and he insisted on putting up the money. He even gave the Old Man a field to build the works on. It's only a mile from the Dower House.' He paused and squeezed her hand again. 'I just thought you ought to know we haven't always moved in the social circles in which we now move. Not that it matters,' he added hurriedly.

They drove past some children who were playing in the road outside a stone cottage, and she drew her sable tightly around herself. 'Sir Henry must be a very good man,' she said.

Alexander smiled. 'He certainly is. The Old Man says no man could owe another what he, and all of us, owe Sir Henry. Everything we have is due to his having believed in the Old Man. Me for instance. I would still have had to go to war, but as an ordinary soldier not as an officer. I wouldn't have had the education . . . or the background.' He stopped abruptly as though afraid he was going to say too much, and Mara was left feeling a fondness towards him for his personal honesty but strangely dissatisfied by his overall explanation.

'You must all be very grateful to Sir Henry,' she said, linking her fingers through his to assure him that whatever it was that worried him she didn't mind.

'Er . . . yes, we are.'

Mara was puzzled by his hesitation until she remembered Herbert. Herbert was . . . what . . . thirty-six? Twelve years older than Alexander?

173

'How old were you when your father began Rushton-Gaunt?' she asked.

'Oh, I was just over a year old. Apparently he had quite a struggle to begin with, but of course I don't remember any of that. One of my first memories is standing under the big oak tree in the Dower House garden and hearing my father tell Herbert that if the old recluse at the Park hadn't been so hard up and so unpleasant to his relations, he was sure they'd have clubbed together and given him an allowance to stop him selling off the Dower House for so little. I remember it very clearly because, although I don't remember anything about the house we'd been living in, I do remember thinking that the Dower House was enormous and wondering why anyone needed another house as well.' He laughed. 'I must have been about three and a half at the time.'

Mara laughed too, but she was thinking about Herbert. He must have been fifteen when the family fortunes dramatically increased. Fifteen and too old to benefit. On the other hand, she thought, remembering Lady Henrietta, they can't have been too . . . lowly beforehand or they wouldn't be related, even by marriage, to such a woman. She turned her attention back to the countryside and decided that Alexander was probably what her father had called 'class-conscious'. So long as I'm not going to live in a hovel, she thought, and I'm obviously not. She stroked her sable.

It was almost dark now and as far as she could see they were on a sort of plateau. The edges of it were obscured by darkness and distance, but the feeling was of height, and that not far away the land dropped. They came into a grey stone town. 'B i c e s t e r,' Mara read the name above the post office.

174

'Bicester, darling, it rhymes with sister.' He looked out of the window. 'Good hunting country round here. We hunt with The Banbury. Must get myself a couple of hunters now I'm back . . . and a nice little mare for you.'

'But I can't ride.'

'Can't ride? Oh, not to worry, you'll soon learn, you can have lessons with the twins.'

The land on either side of the road was now slightly undulating and Mara pictured herself galloping across it, clinging on to her horse for dear life. 'I think I'd rather learn to drive.'

Alexander laughed but made no comment.

After some ten minutes, Mara asked, 'How much longer?'

'Less than half an hour. And sit well back, darling, it becomes very hilly.' He wanted to say, 'Come here and let me hold you and protect you,' but since that horrible woman had attacked Mara she had been distant: friendly but still distant. But what could I have done, he asked himself for the hundredth time? What should I have said? What could I have done and said that would have been better than what Mara did and said? He glanced sideways at her hands folded firmly in her lap, and he wished they were back at the Ritz on their first evening, when she had been so unsure of herself and her unsureness had made him feel so confident and protective.

Mara was thinking, just a few minutes and I'll be there. Under her breath she imitated their English voices saying, 'But how could dear Alexaaaander pooorrrsibly have married a German?' She began to wish very fervently that they had stayed in London. It might not have happened again, she told herself, not everyone is as bitter as that woman. No one else said anything to me. We could have had fun. We did have fun. I could have had more fun if it wasn't for Jamie.

Jamie: was it really three weeks since she'd seen him? It seemed longer. A lifetime. Another world. And yet it seemed like yesterday. If only she could see him again. If only he could see her now, in her elegant dress and her neat little turban and her beautiful, beautiful sable. She blew on the collar and the tips of the fur shivered. Fur coat. Fast car. Adored and adorned. If only Jamie could see her and want her. She closed her eyes and she was back in Koblenz, in the attic bedroom with Jamie. Her legs moved up and down against each other, touching and caressing, her silk stockings gentle against each other. If only he could see her and want her, how she would laugh in his face. But would he want her, or would he take one look at her and laugh that awkward laugh?

'We're there, darling! Wake up!' Alexander shook her gently.

Mara opened her eyes as the car turned under the arch of a stone gatehouse and began its long slow prowl up the drive. She looked out of the window, it was still raining and the stone walls on either side of the drive shone black and sweaty in the headlights. Beyond the walls she could see miles of grassy parkland dotted with trees stretching away to distant hills, dark against the closing sky of a winter's evening. Never had she seen anywhere quite so bleak and forbidding.

Alexander leaned forward eagerly. 'There's the house. Look!'

Over the chauffeur's shoulder Mara could see two long rows of identically sized oblong lights, one above the other, shining out into the drizzle. They reminded her of a picture of an ocean liner she had once seen, it might have been of the doomed *Titanic*.

The car drew closer. The house grew bigger. The car turned in to the gravel circle in front of the house. The house was enormous. The car stopped at the bottom of a flight of steps, so well-scrubbed that Mara knew the orderliness of the house without yet having entered it.

Owen opened the car door for her. 'We've arrived, madam,' he said. 'Welcome to the Park!'

She stood beside the car and gazed up at the massive grey stone building. She could not help being impressed, she had expected something big but not as big as this. Her home in Koblenz had been spacious, Rushton Park was a mansion. It was at least twice the size. But as Mara stood there, looking up at it, seeing the endless windows cut deep into the stone and imagining the endless rooms behind them, she felt no surge of excitement at the thought of living in such a place, for the great oblong plates of glass, staring out over her head to the South Lawn and the parkland beyond were as impersonal as the sightless eyes of the blind, and the house, so perfect in its lineal symmetry, was as cold and lifeless as the tomb of its long-dead architect.

Alexander took her by the elbow and steered her up the steps. But long before they reached the top the front door opened and a stately old butler appeared. He was pushed aside by a fat, sleek black labrador which bounded down the steps and threw itself at Alexander, barking and slobbering with excitement.

'Hello, Prince old boy.' Alexander patted the dog's head. 'Darling, this is Prince. And hello, Mortimer,' he said to the butler. 'Do come and meet my wife. This is Mortimer, darling. Without Mortimer, Rushton Park would collapse.'

The butler inclined his head to Mara and murmured

his welcome. He might have been a courtier at Versailles, not the butler of an automobile tycoon.

A pretty little girl dashed out of the lighted hall and came down the steps to meet them. 'Uncle Alexander! Uncle Alexander! Did you bring me a present? Did you?' She jumped up and down in front of him, tossing her head so that her long, dark curly hair, which someone had fruitlessly attempted to control with pink ribbons, danced around her pretty upturned face. A child of about eight years old, but a miniature woman with all the age-old womanly wiles.

'Of course we brought you a present.' Alexander emphasized the 'we'. 'Aunt Mara helped me choose it.'

'Oh.' The eyes, brown like Alexander's, flickered over Mara, who nearly laughed to see the furious rivalry in the childish face, but somehow stopped herself, forced a smile, and said in her most aunt-like voice, 'Hello Atalanta. It is Atalanta, isn't it?'

'Yes, I'm Atalanta.' The girl curtseyed with a savage politeness. 'How do you do, Aunt Mara.'

It was then that Mara noticed a boy watching her from the shadows of the doorway. 'And is that Damon?' she asked.

Atalanta spun round. 'Yes, that's Damon.' She began to jump up and down chanting, 'Damon, Damon, Damon.' But when her twin brother moved forward she stopped and giggled nervously, covering her mouth with her small hand; it was obvious she was in awe of him.

Of his own accord the boy held out his hand to Mara. As he did so, he moved into the light and it caught his face, and Mara saw him clearly: his disturbing beauty, the paleness of his delicate features, his light brown Byronic curls, and his eyes, brown as all the Rushtons

178

seemed to have, but not kind like Alexander's or mischievous like Atalanta's, but solemn and thoughtful, not unlike her own. And when Mara took his hand she found it cool and impersonal, like the house – except that, unlike the house she liked him and sensed he liked her. They were misfits, both of them, and they recognized that quality in each other. But whereas his sister, the dark and pagan Atalanta, showed her every thought and emotion, Damon showed nothing.

'They're not very alike for twins,' Mara said to Alexander.

'No, I suppose they're not.' He looked at his niece and his nephew as though he were seeing them for the first time.

With Prince bounding at their heels they stepped into the hall, which was like a huge white-marble mausoleum, brightly lit by two enormous chandeliers. They reminded Mara of a conglomeration of diamond earrings swinging in the breeze, and the light they gave, a little too bright, bounced off the marble floor and the cascading marble staircase, both of which were just a little too white. Just as the frames of the pictures hanging on the walls – hunting scenes not family portraits because no Rushton ancestor had ever been painted – were a little too clean and lacked the black shadows which gold leaf acquires with age.

Atalanta scuttled across to an enormous Christmas tree. 'Look!' She pointed at the decorations. 'I helped do it, I really did . . .' She fell silent as a great bear of a man appeared at the top of the stairs.

'Ah, there you are,' he boomed down at them. 'My baby brother home from the wars at last.'

For one terrifying moment Mara thought it was Herr Steiger. She stared in horror at the man who came bounding down the stairs. He had the same red, bulldog face, the same thick, unhangable neck, and the same big burly body. But of course it wasn't Herr Steiger, although at first Mara could see no resemblance between her husband and his brother. But as she studied them she saw that they were alike, except that fate had dealt Herbert a cruel hand. He was a gross caricature of his younger brother and, notwithstanding all the trappings money could buy, he would always look more at home at the seedier end of a race-track than in a mansion such as Rushton Park. And he knew it.

'Ah, the bride.' Herbert turned his attention to Mara.'How do you do . . . er . . .'

'Mara,' said Alexander.

'Yes, of course, Mara. Such an unusual name I'd forgotten it. Sorry, my dear.' He crushed Mara's hand in his massive grip with every show of welcome though she knew very well he had not forgotten her name.

'Where's the Old Man?' asked Alexander.

'At the works. Where else?'

Alexander tried to hide his disappointment. 'Of course.'

'I'm afraid not even your return could keep him here, not when that hot-head Mark Hatton is around.'

Alexander looked surprised. 'Is Mark a hot-head? I always thought he was meant to have nerves of steel. After all he was in the Royal Flying Corps and he is going to race Rushton-Gaunts.' He hesitated before asking, 'He's not staying here, is he?'

'No, at Gaunt Hall. So you can imagine the three of them, on and on about revs and pistons.' The two brothers looked at each other and laughed. 'But at least the new saloon is doing well. In fact, we've so many back-orders we won't clear them till Easter. Mind you, everyone's in the same boat.'

180

Alexander nodded. 'Yes, I can imagine. Every chap out in Cologne says the first thing he's going to do when he gets home is buy a car.'

'I'd like a car too.' Atalanta grabbed at Alexander's trouser leg.

Herbert appeared to notice his children for the first time. 'What are you doing down here?' he demanded, scowling not at Atalanta but at Damon.

Atalanta's face puckered. 'Mummy said . . .'

'I don't care what Mummy said. Go upstairs! Both of you.'

The children slunk off and Mara was left feeling slightly guilty, as though it were her fault they had been sent away.

'I believe in old-fashioned discipline,' Herbert said with a breezy smile. 'Now, where were we? Yes, come along and see Sophia.' He waved to Mortimer to take Mara's coat, adding for her benefit, 'My wife isn't well so she stayed in the drawing room.'

Suddenly everyone seemed to be talking at once, like a lot of actors with differing scripts. Alexander was saying, 'I'm glad Mark's not staying here, I like him, but I wanted this to be a family occasion,' and Herbert was saying, 'I'm fed up with him. Thank God he's going away for six weeks. The Old Man treats him better than he treats me . . . us,' and Mortimer was saying very firmly that the new Mrs Rushton must meet the staff and asking if she had her own maid or if he should find one for her.

To her surprise the old butler got his way. She was soon to discover he nearly always did; the Rushtons were too recently arrived at elegant living not to obey their butler. But even as the servants trooped in, the house-keeper, the cook, the footmen, the nanny, the maids, she could still hear Herbert and Alexander discussing Mark

Hatton. They went on and on, and it was mostly Herbert, whose grievances had obviously been building up in anticipation of Alexander's return. 'All right, so Rushton-Gaunt ought to get back into racing and I agree the publicity's good, but it takes up a lot of time and money and we're not just here for the racing, we're in business. It was all very well when the Old Man raced but if we've got to have Mark hanging around the place all the time . . . The Old Man's living in the past, Alexander, he doesn't understand that things are different since the war. You should have heard him when I suggested going for a mass-produced small car. He said I'd be the ruin of Rushton-Gaunt. And Mark agreed with him. Well, of course he would. Knows which side his bread's buttered. Caviared, I'd say.' On and on went Herbert's rough voice as Mara tried to remember the names of the bobbing faces before her.

'Now to meet my wife.' Herbert steered Mara towards the door. 'And I suppose we'd better wait for the Old Man before we have a drink, eh, Alexander? Mind you, if we lived in America we soon wouldn't get one at all. They're going to ban the stuff!'

It was perfectly obvious to Mara that Herbert had had no hand in the drawing room, for it was exquisitely elegant. As Alexander had said, the carpet was much like the one in Koblenz, though secretly Mara thought it wasn't quite so beautiful. But the furniture could not be faulted. It was just the right mixture of antique and modern, each piece complementing the next but not overshadowing it. Nothing bore the vulgar label of money although the effect could not have been achieved without it. Everything was delicate, a little too delicate for Mara, but in perfect taste, just like the youngish woman who lay on a chaise-longue near the fire, holding out a white, lifeless hand to her and saying, 'I'm sorry I couldn't come to the door, but I'm so glad to meet you . . . umm . . .'

'Mara.' Alexander supplied the name as he kissed his sister-in-law's pallid cheek.

'Yes, Mara.' Sophia smiled weakly at Mara, who smiled back and shook the proffered hand.

'I'm so sorry you're not well,' she said, wondering how this woman could possibly be the mother of such a healthy, vigorous girl as Atalanta. Of Damon she could understand, for he had his mother's fine features, except that where he was delicate and beautiful she was delicate and far, far too thin.

'I'll be all right in a day or two.' There was bravery in the sad smile. 'I feel better already, seeing you again, Alexander. We've been so worried about you and we've all missed you, especially Atalanta. She was so excited last night she could hardly sleep. You know' – she looked at Mara with a sort of vague surprise as though she had half expected to find her gone – 'Atalanta always used to say she was going to marry Alexander when he came home.'

Mara laughed. 'She's a bit young.'

'Oh, she'll grow up soon enough,' said Alexander nudging her towards a chair near Sophia. 'Do sit down, darling, you're at home now.' He glanced down at the floor. 'Look! Remember what I said about the carpet? Mara's mother had a carpet like this, Sophia. You know Mara's mother was English?'

Sophia nodded. 'Yes, you told us in your letter.'

'Oh, so I did.' He yawned and took himself off to a big armchair on the other side of the large room, sat down, picked up a magazine and leafed through the pages, saying to Herbert, 'How are The Banbury doing this season? I see we still have the same Master. Mind you,

183

he does a pretty good job. Have to find myself a couple of hunters. Alison Taylor will know of some. No, never too ill to hunt. It'll do me a power of good. And we must get in some shooting too, eh, Prince?' He nudged the dog lying at his feet.

Sitting beside Sophia and listening to Alexander, Mara thought angrily, how could he abandon me! It may be his home but it isn't mine. I suppose he thinks Sophia and I are bound to have lots to talk about, being women, you-know-what-women-are-like and all that. She glanced apprehensively at her sister-in-law, who was gazing vacantly into the fire. 'I met your children in the hall,' she began.

'Did you?' The pale blue eyes lit up and for a moment Sophia was almost pretty. The transformation from the waxy invalid to the vestige of what she had obviously once been, a pale English rose, surprised Mara but it also made everything more logical. Alexander's talk of the social young woman who, together with her aunt, produced endless suitable young girls, had been incongruous in the invalid.

'They're very beautiful,' said Mara. 'Very different too.'

'Oh, yes.' The lifeless hand reached up and patted the lifeless reeds of hair, she said nothing more than that, 'Oh, yes,' and Mara was left to sit in awkward silence again.

If I were in love with Alexander I'd be happy just to be in the same room as him, she thought looking about her. I'd be happy here, saying nothing, just being in this house which is a part of him and with his family, and I'd want to know all about him before I met him, as a child, as a boy. I'd be looking round for old photographs and trying to recognize him in them. If I were in love. But I'm not,

184

so all that's missing. I'm just left with the awkwardness of meeting strangers and knowing I have to get on with them.

Eventually she said to Sophia, 'This is a beautiful room. Did you choose everything?' She stretched out her hand to stroke a plush velvet cushion, feeling her fingers absorb its richness and its wealth.

Sophia smiled. 'Yes, I love this room too. Herbert was very kind.' She glanced at her husband but he was deep in conversation with Alexander. 'He let me choose exactly what I wanted. You see, I wanted it to look like the drawing room in the house I was brought up in, my old home.' Again there was that animation in her face and she was pretty.

'Where do your parents live?' asked Mara, more to continue the conversation than out of curiosity.

'Where we used to live. My parents are dead.' Sophia lowered her voice. 'They died after the house was sold. I think that's what killed them . . . selling it. Poor Papa, it needed so much doing to it. The roof. The stairs.' She seemed to feel a need to justify the shame of the sale. 'But he couldn't afford to . . .'

Herbert cut her short. 'Now you mustn't upset yourself, Sophia, and I'm sure Mara doesn't want to hear about all that.'

Mara opened her mouth to say she did, but Sophia spoke first. 'No, you're right. I'm sorry.' She lay back and closed her eyes, and all the prettiness drained away from her face.

Mara was appalled. She waited for Alexander to say something kind to Sophia, but when she looked at him he merely smiled benignly, so she turned away and watched the fire and thought of Sophia: a lonely little girl wandering through the crumbling house for the last time, perhaps visiting some secret place in the garden, a place where she used to sit and dream.

Mara was thinking about all this when there was a commotion outside in the hall and a fierce white-haired lion of a man burst into the room. Immediately Herbert and Alexander stood up and Mara found herself standing up as well and she noticed that, sick though Sophia was, she sat up straight on her chaise-longue. It was an automatic response to the power of the man who had founded Rushton-Gaunt. Grown up though his sons were, before their powerful father they stood like naughty children.

He walked slowly across the room, ramrod straight and terrifying, his thatch of white hair reminding Mara of a mad eighteenth-century musician. And yet, and she could hardly believe it in such a man, there were unashamed tears of happiness in his eyes as he looked at Alexander, and there were definite signs of tears on his granity cheeks, as though he had cried with happiness all the way home. 'My son!' He put his arms around Alexander. 'My son! Home at last. And my new daughter.' He studied Mara who smiled nervously and tried not to wriggle. 'Welcome to our family, Mara.' Suddenly she found herself enfolded in his strong arms, her face pressed against his wet cheek.

Samuel Rushton was the only one to have remembered Mara's name and for that alone she knew she was going to like him.

186

Not one of those who attended that Christmas morning service at the ancient church in the village of Gaunt could have truthfully said that he or she did not have a good look at the new Mrs Rushton. Most of them did so during the sermon, Christmas sermons being predictable. Afterwards opinion would be divided as to whether she was beautiful though not pretty, or far too thin and really rather plain. However, it would not be divided on her clothes; the sable was a coat to be envied, the dark red dress with the little matching helmet moulded to her head was a creation to be copied.

Mara knew they were watching her. At first she was self-conscious but after a bit she found it quite amusing. Every so often she would glance round surreptitiously and when she found a pair of eyes fixed on her, she would pretend not to notice and revert her own to the front, to the portly vicar and the warbling choirboys. But after a few minutes she would be drawn to check if she were still being watched. Once, her eyes met those of a woman sitting some three rows back on the other side of the aisle and Mara wondered how she hadn't noticed her before because, even to Mara who didn't know England, this woman looked out of place in a country church. Her clothes were bizarre: a black cape edged with turquoise, a turquoise turban edged with black. They would have looked ridiculous on anyone else, but not on her. Her face was striking: white and angular with a hard stare from brilliant green eyes. Her hair, shoved carelessly up into the turban, was black with the odd streak of grey. She was probably in her late thirties, though she could have been older, and there was something slightly decadent but infinitely fascinating about her.

At the end of the service the Old Man, who had been sitting in the aisle seat, stood up. Simultaneously, on the other side of the aisle, another man stood up. They looked at each other, nodded, then stepped into the aisle, and side by side they walked down to the door whilst the whole congregation waited respectfully in their seats. Mara turned to watch the two men: her father-in-law taller and more powerfully built, his white hair as wild as ever, the other man older, shorter and thin as a whippet, but with such an air of authority that she already sensed who it was. 'Is that Sir Henry Gaunt?' she whispered to Alexander.

'Yes. He and the Old Man always go back to Gaunt Hall after church.'

Mara watched the narrow straight back disappear out into the graveyard. So that was the man to whom Samuel Rushton owed everything he had.

At the church door Mara was introduced to the vicar who said, 'Charming, charming,' to the schoolmistress who said, to everyone's embarrassment, 'I must practise my German,' and to one of the whippers-in from The Banbury who said, 'Hunt?' and when Mara replied, 'No, I can't ride,' he gasped, 'Good God! . . . er . . . sorry, vicar.'

'You'll have to learn,' murmured Alexander as they walked out into the graveyard. 'Everyone rides, except for the Old Man, and he's different.'

Mara was introduced to a number of people, all of whom were curious and some of whom had to make an effort to hide their hostility, but she wasn't introduced to Sir Henry.

'You'll meet him later,' said Alexander. 'He's coming to dinner.'

Nor was she introduced to the angular woman, although she asked Alexander about her.

'Oh, you mean Mrs Harris. Why do you ask?'

'She looks . . . different.'

'Yes, and she is. We know her of course, I mean, we say hello. But we don't call.'

'Why not?' At that moment the woman swept past them, turbaned head in the air, turquoise cape floating.

Alexander lowered his voice to explain. 'She's a divorcee. A painter. Very bohemian. Smokes in public. Completely beyond the pale, darling.'

Mara watched Mrs Harris cross the street. At that moment her father-in-law's car drew away from the church. Was it in her imagination that as it drew level with Mrs Harris it slowed down?

It was a strange day for Mara. She was never quite sure where she was meant to go and what she was meant to be doing. Things suddenly happened. The presents were given and Alexander produced her sable for everyone to admire.

'Thank you for the train set.' Damon gave her a solemn, polite smile.

Mara longed to say, 'If I'd met you first I'd never have chosen it.'

'And thank you for the pink muff,' said Atalanta, tucking her small hands into it. 'What did Mummy and Daddy give you?'

'A travelling vanity case. It's beautiful.'

Atalanta giggled. 'Are you going away? Is that why

189

they gave it to you?' There was something in the child's tone which made Mara suspect she had overheard people saying they hoped the German wouldn't stay too long.

Then nothing happened and Mara sat around the drawing room until tea, when a middle-aged couple called Taylor and their horsy daughter Alison came to see Alexander and to inspect his bride. The Taylors and the Rushtons talked endlessly and tediously about people Mara didn't know, while she fiddled with her cup and tried not to yawn. Alison's passion was horses and she was far more interested in their appearance than in her own. Her round face was untouched by make-up and her pretty fair hair was twisted up into an old-fashioned bun. Mara suspected that Mrs Taylor was beginning to despair of her daughter, who was unmarried and nearly thirty, but Alison didn't seem to care. She and Alexander gossiped about the hunt until Mara almost screamed with boredom.

As soon as the Taylors left the Old Man said, 'Now it's time to give the servants their presents. Come along!'

They went through the back of the house and down into the large basement room, the servants' dining room, where they and their families sat at long trestle tables. They were all laughing and talking and calling to each other across the room, and it struck Mara that they were having much more fun than the Rushtons. Followed closely by Mortimer, who was carrying a sack, the Old Man went slowly round the tables, shaking each employee by the hand, wishing him happy Christmas, then handing him a sealed envelope produced from the sack by Mortimer. Behind them came Herbert, then Alexander and Mara, and finally the twins. Sophia was still unwell and had remained in the drawing room.

'This is my wife,' Alexander told each person, and Mara held out her hand and smiled nervously.

But by the time they had done three tables, she began to relax. Work-worn hands clasped hers and admiring giggling children stretched out their fingers to touch her deep red dress. It was real lady-of-the-manor stuff.

They were on the last table, with only two more people to go, when instead of finding a proffered hand, Mara was confronted by an angry young man who stood up, pushing his chair away from the table, and shouted, 'No, I'll not be shaking the hand of a German.'

Mara froze, her hand held out to his rejection. She hadn't expected to find herself entirely welcome in England and she had sensed the thinly veiled hostility whenever she spoke, but this was different. It was different from the incident on the hotel stairs because it came from within. Lowering her outstretched hand she stood there helplessly, listening to the happy chatter die to whispers.

The young man's face was red with indignation. "Ave you all forgotten my brother Fred?' he demanded, looking at the other servants. "Ave you forgotten my brother was killed by Germans? 'Im an' all the others like 'im.' His voice was sing-song like Owen's.

Mara was aware that her father-in-law had come to stand beside her and that Alexander was looking to his father for help. 'No, Bonner, we haven't forgotten Fred,' said the Old Man gently, 'but my son has married this young lady and she is now a member of my family.'

'Well, you can throw me out if you want to, sir, but I'm not shaking the 'and of no German, not when they killed my brother.'

Mara felt her strength returning as she looked at the young man. She saw the bitterness in his ruddy face and

191

she understood how he felt. 'My brother was killed in the war too,' she said quietly, 'and I know how it feels to lose someone. I'm very sorry that your brother was killed by Germans.' The young man gaped at her and she moved on to the next person, an elderly man who held out his hand automatically. He was too stunned by the calmness of her reply to do otherwise.

'You'll have to get rid of Bonner, Papa,' said Alexander as soon as they reached the drawing room. 'You can't keep him. How dare he speak to Mara like that!'

Herbert laughed. 'What are you trying to do? Cause a riot? Bonner and Owen are cousins, we'd lose a chauffeur as well as a groom.'

Alexander frowned. 'It's not funny! Papa?'

'I'm not sacking a man whose family I've known for years just because he loved his brother,' said the Old Man.

'But, Papa . . .' protested Alexander. He was outraged that a servant should be rude to his wife and he was convinced if he didn't insist the youth was removed then he was failing to defend her.

Mara, who had been standing between them, turned to her father-in-law and said, 'If you throw him out they'll all hate me. It's I who have to make them like me in spite of my being German.'

The Old Man looked at her in surprise, then his leathery cheeks creased in a smile. He didn't say anything but Mara felt that he was reappraising her.

Dinner that night was a sumptuous feast. It was Christmas dinner and Alexander's homecoming. Even the twins were allowed to stay up for it, although Sophia excused herself and retired to bed early. No one mentioned the incident in the servants' hall but the Old Man was particularly kind to Mara; they both knew she had a long hard battle ahead of her, and one which only she could fight – and win.

When Sir Henry arrived Samuel Rushton put his arm around Mara's shoulders, saying, 'This is my new daughter. Isn't Alexander a lucky man!'

'Indeed, indeed.' Sir Henry took Mara's hand in his clawlike grip and gave her a fierce smile. Because he moved stiffly and had slightly bent knees and a very straight back, he made Mara think of a cavalry officer temporarily without his horse, and she half expected him to open her mouth, examine her teeth and say, 'Eighteen or nineteen.'

'As the bride, you sit on my right,' the Old Man told Mara as they went in to dinner. 'Damon can sit next to you. Brides always sit on my right, don't they Mortimer?'

The butler inclined his head. 'Yes, sir.'

'And after that they become just another married woman, so make the most of it my dear, I certainly shall.'

Mara smiled at him and sat down. She was thinking how nice he was; all of Alexander's best qualities and none of his pompousness, a touch of Herbert's ruthlessness and none of his hinted dishonesty; in fact, not unlike Jamie. Or rather, not unlike what Jamie might be in years to come once he, like Samuel Rushton, had fulfilled his ambitions. But I must stop thinking about Jamie. I must stop linking everything and everyone to him. She smiled again at her father-in-law and without thinking stretched out her hand and stroked the edge of the polished mahogany table. It was cool and soft, a bit like silk. A bit like Jamie's back where the muscles of his shoulders joined his spine.

'Admiring the table, are you?' Her father-in-law was watching her.

'Yes.' She blushed, she had been thinking forbidden thoughts. 'Yes, it's lovely.' It was true: and not only the table: the silver, the glass, the twinkling chandelier, the gilt directoire chairs, the uniformed footman standing behind each person, and not least the oak-panelled walls. It was lovely. It was luxurious. Was it possible that on the same planet people were starving?

'Now, tell us all about yourself,' said her father-in-law, 'and don't worry about them.' He waved his hand at the footmen. 'We're all longing to know about you and at least they'll be able to tell the truth to the rest of the household. Save us all from a lot of ill-informed gossip, won't it Mortimer?'

'Yes, sir.'

'Come along, Mara. Where were you born? Have you any family?' The Old Man gave her a fierce smile.

'Well, I was born in Koblenz. I haven't any family now. They're all dead. Until I became a . . . er . . . Rushton,' she smiled at Alexander, 'I was the last of the Vogels. Our branch, anyhow.'

'Of the what?'

'Vogel. That was my surname. It means bird.' She tried not to think of Jamie.

'And what did these birds do with themselves?'

'They owned a newspaper. My father's family had owned it for generations.' She paused. 'It's closed down now, it closed down at the beginning of the war.'

'Why?'

'My father was . . . er . . . arrested when war broke out.' Mara waited for someone to say something, but when no one did, not even Alexander, she went on, 'He didn't believe in fighting. He was a pacifist.'

Atalanta was watching Mara with reluctant fascination. 'What happened to him?' she piped up.

'Be quiet,' Damon hissed at his sister. 'You don't ask things like that.'

Herbert silenced his son. 'Why shouldn't she ask? What I can't understand is why you told us so much about Mara but not this,' he said, looking at Alexander with a touch of triumph in his eyes.

'I . . . er . . . forgot I suppose.'

It infuriated Mara that Herbert should mock Alexander and that Alexander should allow himself to be mocked. 'My father died in prison,' she said loudly. 'He died . . . eight months before the war ended. And my mother died shortly after he did.' It came back to her as she said it: had her mother spared her from the truth about her father – and about Hans?

The Old Man nodded. 'I believe your mother was English.' He said this loudly and Mara knew he wanted it to be passed down to the servants' hall.

She answered him very clearly. 'Yes, she was brought up in Kent' – a bowl of soup was placed before her – 'but I don't have any family there, she was an orphan and an only child.' She looked down at the array of cutlery beside her plate and hesitated for a moment before picking up a silver soup spoon.

The Old Man had been watching her. 'That's right,' he boomed. 'Outside in. That's what Mortimer taught me and he's the expert.' With that, he tucked his napkin under his chin and Mara had to stifle a giggle when she saw Mortimer's look of pained disapproval. But the butler said nothing. He knew very well that the master of Rushton Park didn't appreciate unsolicited advice.

Chapter 11

It was nearly midnight by the time Alexander fell asleep, his hand across Mara's bare stomach, his breathing deep and satisfied. But Mara couldn't sleep although she was tired. She lay on her back staring up at the mouldings, roses and leaves picked out by a shaft of pale moonlight which had somehow escaped the heavy satin curtains.

The events of the day were going round and round in her mind: the polite curiosity and veiled hostility of the people in church: the sound of Alison's voice battering on about horses: the red-faced young man in the servants' hall: the Rushtons.

With increasing irritation she listened to Alexander's deep breathing, just as some six months earlier she had listened to Jamie. She wished she could turn on the light, but she couldn't, she would wake him, or go downstairs but she couldn't, it wasn't her house. So she lay there, rigid with anger because she was so tired but couldn't sleep.

Somewhere, possibly from the village church, a clock began to strike. One, two, three . . . ten, eleven, twelve. Midnight in England. One o'clock in Koblenz. Jamie. What was he doing now? Was he working? She pictured his strong face sweating under the hot lights in the operating room. Was he talking? She pictured him stabbing the air to make his point. Was he sleeping? She pictured him lying on his back, his face calm and boyish. And I bet he's breathing deeply, damn him!

Carefully removing Alexander's hand from her stomach, she slid out of bed. It was freezing, the fire had died right down, and she shivered in her silk chemise. But she couldn't stay in bed any longer, Alexander might wake up and want to make love again, and she couldn't, not just now, not with Jamie so clear in her mind. It would seem like infidelity, although she wasn't quite sure to whom. But if Alexander woke and wanted her, she couldn't deny him. Nor could she deny that that night, for the first time, she had quite enjoyed it. It had been more than not so bad. But she wished it could have been more exciting, that she could have been transported to wherever it was that Jamie had always managed to take her. That would have been a real kick in the face for Jamie.

She pushed her head between the curtains and looked down at the Box Garden, with its neat tramlines of box hedges, then beyond the garden wall to the rolling parkland dotted with trees. A path led from a gate in the wall, across the grassy park, to the distant woods. It shone like a silvery ribbon in the moonlight and in a funny way it seemed to be beckoning to her.

'Mara, what are you doing?'

She spun round. Alexander was sitting up in bed watching her. 'I couldn't sleep.'

'Was I snoring?'

'No, not really. Just breathing deeply. I'm sorry I woke you.'

'Don't worry.' He smiled reassuringly. 'It must be late. Aren't you cold?'

'A bit. It's just after midnight. I heard the clock.'

'The church clock.' He put on the bedside light and checked his own watch. 'Twenty past twelve. Did you enjoy your first English Christmas, darling?'

'Yes.' She turned back to look at the park. The wind had picked up and the trees were moving from side to side and, as Mara watched them, they seemed to take on the shape of men, their leafless branches arms, their waving twigs hands. Hands waving rifles far above their heads. Men staggering through a moonlit no-man's-land.

'Christmas Day,' she whispered to herself. 'Hans.' Hans died on Christmas Day. I haven't thought about him once. I didn't even pray for him. Five years ago this morning Hans was eating his last breakfast, living his last morning. His last nine o'clock. His last ten o'clock. She leaned her head on the cold window pane, and wished she were alone. Poor Hans. Had he known he was going to die that day? Did anyone know?

'Mara, is anything the matter?' Alexander's voice was full of concern.

'I was just remembering my brother. He died on Christmas Day.'

'Did he? I knew he'd died but I didn't know when. I . . . I should have asked.'

'Why? Why should you have asked?'

'No reason at all,' he said hurriedly. 'How long ago was it?'

'Five years.'

'You mean, that Christmas Day? The day I met him?'

'Yes.'

'How did he die?' There was an inexplicable urgency to Alexander's question and he leaned forward to hear her answer, but Mara did not notice. She was too wrapped up in her thoughts and her guilt at forgetting Hans, today of all days. 'He was shot,' she said dully, promising herself that tomorrow she would find time to read his last letter again.

'I see.' Alexander sank back against the pillows and

198

closed his eyes. 'I see.' His handsome face fell into lines of heavy despair. He was no longer the returning hero lying in his bed at Rushton Park, he was a very inexperienced subaltern crouching on the rim of a trench at Ypres watching the Germans wend their way back across no-man's-land to their own side. Then suddenly his colonel was behind him, shouting, 'What the hell's going on here, Rushton? Why aren't your men firing?'

And he was answering, 'There's a truce, sir.'

And the colonel: 'Truce! What truce? There's a war on, Rushton. Good God, man, now's your chance to kill a few Huns.'

Still Alexander had hesitated, and all along the trench his men had listened and waited. The colonel's face had turned white with rage. 'Do you want to be court-martialled, Rushton?'

Court martial equalled disgrace. Disgrace equalled shame. 'No, sir. Of course not, sir.'

'Then set an example to your men.'

'Yes, sir.'

Lying in bed Alexander gripped the bedclothes and squeezed. But it was not the bedclothes he was squeezing, it was the trigger. And Mara's anxious voice saying, 'Alexander, are you all right?' was not his wife speaking, it was the distant cry of the man he had shot, in the back: a man whose hair, fair like Hans Vogel's, had caught the late afternoon sun as he fell on that Christmas Day five years earlier. Had it been Hans Vogel? How often over the years he'd asked himself that question. For what other reason had he gone looking for Hans in Koblenz and then, on hearing he was dead, been afraid to ask the ultimate question: when? And why had he been afraid? Because he had met this girl and wanted her, and known that if she were to discover he had shot her brother, in

199

the back, like a dog, he would never have been able to face her. So he had chosen not to know if he were her brother's murderer. I'll make it up to her, he promised himself. I'll make her happy. I'll give her everything she wants.

Chapter 12

There was a timelessness and a sameness about days at Rushton Park, as Mara soon discovered. Fires blazed in each room, curtains whispered on well-polished floors, and servants scurried beneath the critical eye of Mortimer, whilst outside, day after day, a cold grey drizzling mist hung over the cold grey parkland. And there was a timeless, mindless sameness to Mara's days.

Alexander didn't start work until the New Year and every morning he would go down to breakfast at nine, leaving Mara to follow him. Fifteen minutes later she would walk determinedly along the wide corridor which led from their room to the top of the stairs, and there she would come face to face with two housemaids.

'Good morning,' she would say, forcing herself to smile at them.

'Morning,' they would mutter, exchanging mutinous glances.

Without fail between the bottom of the stairs and the breakfast room, which lay beyond the dining room, she would meet at least another three mutinous mutterings. Mara felt like grabbing them by their necks and screaming, 'How dare you mutter at me, you stupid little English girls?' Fervently she wished that each one of them could meet her Herr Steiger. All through breakfast she pictured what he would do to them, how they would cry and beg for mercy, how he would force himself into them, slapping their well-scrubbed faces when they wouldn't submit to his demands. And how they, just as she had, would have to pretend to enjoy it.

On the Saturday before Alexander started work The Banbury were meeting in Gaunt. 'Let's go,' he said to Mara after breakfast. 'We could take the twins and it will be nice for you to see a typically English scene. Fetch your coat, darling, and I'll send for Owen.'

They piled into the back of the car and Owen drove them through the narrow country lanes to Gaunt. On Christmas Day, when they had come to church, Mara had been too bemused to notice the village but now she saw that, unlike the grey stone villages they had passed on their way from London, Gaunt was of a yellowish stone which, despite the overcast sky, gave the houses a warm and friendly glow.

'Sir Henry lives over there,' said Damon, pointing to the right, to the south of the village. 'You can't see it because of all those trees.'

'It's not nearly as nice as the Park,' said Atalanta. 'Our chandeliers are much bigger and newer.' She looked from Mara's pale grey coat to her own bright blue one, and crossed her chubby legs at the ankles.

They drove up through the village, past the church, and then up between low thatched cottages built right on the edge of the narrow street.

'Here we are,' said Alexander as they came to a fork in the road and drew to a halt beside the village green, where the meet was already in full swing. They left the car and Mara found herself engulfed by big brown and white dogs, all yelping and wagging their tails.

'Come on, darling.' Alexander took her arm. 'And you two' – he grabbed Atalanta's hand – 'come here. Damon, hold Atalanta's hand!' He led them over to where some forty or fifty riders sat on their horses, drinking sherry and talking loudly. 'Good morning!' he called to everyone they passed, or so it seemed to Mara.

'Good morning, Alexander, good to see you! Good morning,' they shouted back, too polite to stare openly at Mara. But as she walked on she sensed the raised eyebrows and the disapproving glances.

'Why do some of them wear red jackets?' she asked.

'Not red jackets, darling, pink coats! Ah, here's Alison. Hello, there! Fine-looking animal you have.'

Now Mara found herself surrounded not only by hounds but also by large horses, champing their bits and swishing their tails. She looked around while Alexander talked to Alison. Almost half of the riders were women, the older ones riding side-saddle and wearing skirts and top hats, the younger ones like Alison riding astride and wearing jodhpurs and bowler hats. But they all wore veils, fine black ones which came right down over their faces. They look very elegant, she thought, deciding she might after all quite enjoy it.

Suddenly the huntsman blew his horn and the hounds all began to yelp madly. Alison's horse stamped its feet and did a little dance, its hindquarters swinging round and banging into Mara.

'Watch out!' shouted Alison.

Mara jumped to one side feeling stupid and clumsy. 'Are we going to follow the hunt?' she asked Alexander, hoping they would. She longed to join in the excitement, of the horses raring to go and the hounds circling the village green, not to go back to the Park where she would sit in the drawing room looking at magazines while Alexander read *The Times*.

'I think not,' said Alexander. 'We mustn't be late for lunch.'

Mara was about to say, 'Lunch isn't for another two

hours,' when Alison said, 'Hounds! One always says hounds, not hunt.' She gave Alexander an apologetic smile, adding, 'You'll have to tell Mara these things.'

But when they returned to the Park, Herbert said, 'Back already? I thought you were going to follow the hunt.'

That night at dinner the conversation soon turned to cars, and in particular Rushton-Gaunt's next model, a two-seater sports car to be called the Rushton Roadster. 'Work's been going slowly because of all the back-orders on the saloon,' said the Old Man, 'but now we have you with us, Alexander, we'll soon get things moving.'

Herbert looked hurt, and for the first time Mara felt a twinge of sympathy for him. He'd had none of the benefits of a good education and had spent all his adult life working for his father, and yet his younger brother, who knew nothing about cars, was joining as an equal.

The Old Man went on, 'With a bit of luck the Roadster should be ready for Mark to test at Brooklands in the summer.'

'Not race?' said Herbert. 'I thought the whole point of all this . . . extra expenditure was that Mark would race the Roadster and we'd get some publicity.'

The Old Man frowned. 'We've talked about this before. We're not racing the Roadster till I'm satisfied she's a winner, and that won't be this year. If she's ready, and only if she's ready, I might let Mark enter her for the Shelsley Walsh.' He turned to Mara. 'Shelsley Walsh is a hill-climb. That means you take it in turns to drive up the hill and see who can do it in the fastest time.'

She nodded and tried to look interested.

'And we'll have to take you over to the works,' he went on. 'They'll be expecting to meet you. Alexander and I will take you. Introduce you to the men.' He smiled at her. 'It's no great ordeal. We'll take the twins and make an expedition of it. Good for them to see where our money comes from. We might wait till Mark comes back in February. You'll like Mark, Mara.' He picked up his napkin and tucked it under his chin, and so missed the glances passed between his sons. But Mara didn't, and not for the first time she wondered what Mark Hatton was like.

'Tell me about Mark Hatton,' Mara asked Alexander as they were going to bed.

'Oh, he's Eton, Oxford, Royal Flying Corps, that sort of thing. We got to know him just before the . . . er . . . when he was at Oxford because he's mad keen to race Rushton-Gaunts and he came up to see the Old Man.'

'What's Eton?'

'A public school. They're called public but they're anything but.'

'Like Tom Brown's school?'

'Rugby. Yes. But Eton is said to be the most exclusive . . .'

'Did you go there?' she asked, settling herself down into the bed.

'No, but Damon will.'

She nodded but she still didn't know what Mark Hatton was like, except that his benefits obviously began much earlier than the Rushtons'.

The twinge of sympathy Mara had felt for Herbert did not last long.

The next day, when they were waiting to go in to dinner, Herbert said to Alexander, 'You still haven't told me what you think of the new saloon.'

Alexander twiddled his sherry glass. 'I . . . er . . . thought it was very good. Very smooth.'

Herbert glanced at the Old Man who was reading the paper. 'Did you notice the difference in the length?'

'Er . . . yes. I suppose it's a new chassis.'

'No, the same but extended. Didn't you read the information I sent to you in Cologne?' He raised his voice to make sure his father could hear.

'Er . . . I looked at it but I was very busy and I decided I'd learn more about it when I started work.'

'And of course you weren't well,' said Sophia timidly.

Herbert glared at his wife. 'You're the only one around here who's always ill.' Sophia went whiter than white and twisted her hands nervously in her lap. 'But I suppose Alexander was quite busy.' He let his eyes fall on Mara who was sitting on the sofa beside her father-in-law.

There was silence. The Old Man put down his paper. 'Alexander will learn all he needs when he starts work next week,' he said firmly. 'Now, may we go in to dinner' – he stood up and beckoned to Sophia to take his right arm and to Mara to take his left – 'and can we please talk about something other than the works?'

Mara laughed to herself as she took her father-in-law's arm. When he wanted to talk about something they talked about it, and when he didn't they didn't. He was just like Jamie.

After Alexander started work Mara continued to get up for breakfast, only now she found this meant she had all morning on her own with nothing to do; Sophia never appeared till midday. It was these mornings which made Mara feel most like a poor and unwelcome relative who had been foisted on the family. She would sit in the drawing room, a magazine on her lap, staring at the rain sliding down the window panes or, when she became a little more adventurous, she would wander from room to room, steeling herself against the hostility of the servants and smiling politely at their sullen faces.

Her first impression of the exterior of the Park proved true of the interior. Each room on the left of the hall was the exact replica of its counterpart on the right. The same appeared to be true of each floor. It was all efficient and methodical.

Beyond the drawing room lay another reception room, apparently never used, and beyond that another staircase. One day she heard the uneven tinkling of a piano coming from one of the rooms on the other side of these stairs. She tapped lightly on the door.

'Come in!' called a woman's voice.

Tentatively Mara opened the door. The vicar's wife was standing beside a grand piano berating Damon, who was sitting on the piano stool. 'There are two bars not three. I've told you that before,' she was saying.

'May I listen?' asked Mara.

The vicar's wife answered her stiffly. 'I'm giving Damon a lesson but of course you may listen if you wish, Mrs Rushton.' She looked across the room to Atalanta who was sitting on the window-sill sucking her thumb. 'Atalanta! Stop doing that!'

Music, Mara thought as she listened to Damon play, is like painting: you're either good at it or you're not. Damon was good at it. She was surprised at the end when the vicar's wife said, 'And you'll go on playing Mozart's Allegro in B Flat until you stop fooling around with it. If Mozart had wanted to add another bar, he would have done so himself and he doesn't need Damon Rushton to do so for him.'

As soon as the lesson was over and the vicar's wife had

left, Damon played the piece again, this time with not one extra bar but three: even Mara could tell that. Then he closed the piano and spun round on his stool, saying to Mara, 'Why should I play it her way, Mozart's dead, what does he care?' He laughed and threw back his head.

Atalanta walked towards Mara and stood looking at her with a mixture of fascination and resentment. 'Is it horrid being a German?' she asked in a voice which was both childish and adult.

'Germans are just like anyone else. There are good ones and bad ones.'

Damon came over and stood next to his sister.

'But there can't be any good ones,' said Atalanta, 'otherwise everyone wouldn't wish they were all dead.'

'Shut up!' Damon dug her in the ribs with his elbow. 'Shut up, you sound like Daddy when you say things like that.'

Atalanta's face puckered and tears came into her eyes. 'You hurt me, you pig! You don't like Daddy because he likes me best.'

'What do I care? I hate him.' Damon grabbed a handful of her long dark curly hair and twisted it till she cried out.

'Stop it!' shouted Mara.

He released Atalanta and she ran screaming from the room.

'You shouldn't do that,' Mara told him. 'Don't you like your sister?'

'Of course I do, I just don't like her when she behaves like HIM.' He frowned. 'Where are the grown-ups?'

Mara had to smile. 'Aren't I a grown-up?'

He smiled back at her and she saw that he was even more beautiful than she had first thought: if anything, too beautiful. 'No, you're different.'

'Why?'

He shook his head and went back to the piano and began to play Mozart, but not as Mozart had written it.

Another day Mara's wanderings took her in the opposite direction, through the dining room on the other side of the hall, through another room which she saw could be opened up to make one enormous dining room, until she came to another set of stairs. She opened a door which corresponded with the music room. It was a study. She closed it hurriedly.

She opened another door. It was the library, one of the few rooms which hadn't been touched by the Rushtons, and was just as the recluse had left it. Old copies of magazines dated 1909, the year the recluse had died, were still piled on the centre table, while the books he had presumably been reading at the time of his death – Darwin's *On the Origin of Species by Means of Natural Selection* and Einstein's *Theory of Relativity* – lay on the floor beside a button-backed leather chair, whose seat was so badly in need of re-upholstering that it still bore the shape of its last occupant: the recluse.

Once when Mara went to the library she found Damon standing on a chair reading the titles of some books on a high shelf.

'Are you looking for something to read?' she asked. 'Aren't they all a bit old for you?'

He looked down at her and answered very seriously. 'I only read the titles. It makes them feel wanted. If I tried to read a whole book, only that one would feel wanted. This way they all do.' He turned back to the books and twisted his small head to read off their spines, his lips moving over the difficult words.

One day Mara went to the music room and found

Sophia playing the piano. 'You play very well,' she said, not adding that she'd never listened to so much piano playing as she had since she'd come to the Park.

Sophia smiled vaguely. 'I used to play every day when I was a child.'

'Damon plays well.'

'Yes, he does. I'm afraid the vicar's wife is not really good enough to teach him. I should but it makes me so tired.'

Remembering the black man in the Rivoli Bar, Mara said, 'When we were at the Ritz we heard some strange tinny music, Alexander said it was jazz or Dixieland or something.'

'Jazz.'

'Can you play it?'

'No. It's American and very new over here, I've only heard it once, on a gramophone record, and I didn't like it.' She folded her music carefully. 'Herbert didn't like it either.'

To keep the conversation going, Mara asked her, 'Do you have a gramophone?'

'No, we prefer the piano.' She closed the lid. 'Have you met the twins' governess, Miss Pinner? She came back from her holiday yesterday afternoon.'

Mara recalled the stern grey-haired woman who had introduced herself on the stairs. 'Yes, I met her.' She walked over to the window and looked out at the rain-swept garden. 'Is there anything for me to do?' she asked.

'Do?' Sophia looked puzzled. 'Oh, we'll have lunch in a minute.'

For the first three weeks Mara didn't have a maid of her own; a variety of sullen girls looked after her and she suspected, although no one said so, that Mortimer was having difficulty in finding anyone to work for her. But gradually through her own supreme efforts at being polite and undemanding, the maids became less sullen and this coincided with Mortimer saying to her one morning, 'This is Rachel, madam, I think she'll suit you very well.'

Rachel was a fresh-faced dark-haired country girl with big blue eyes, and Mara took to her immediately, though she had a feeling it was the combination of dark hair and blue eyes, not quite as brilliant as Jamie's but almost, which attracted her. Now she had breakfast in her room and spent her mornings lying in bed looking at fashion magazines and chatting to Rachel, from whom she gleaned that the servants disliked Herbert, felt sorry for Sophia, loved the Old Man, and couldn't do enough for Alexander. But of the twins she was sorry to discover they preferred Atalanta to Damon.

Having Rachel made an enormous difference to Mara. Although there was between them the natural distance of mistress and maid, she had someone to talk to, someone who laughed and chatted and didn't make her feel like a child who might at any moment disgrace itself. She no longer hung around downstairs in the mornings but only appeared in time for lunch. This she had with Sophia and the twins; the men had theirs at the works.

After lunch came the inevitable calls or, if it were Wednesday, being 'at home'. Calling, Mara decided, was worse than being 'at home', because it meant sitting primly in some strange drawing room whilst her hostess did her best to hide her hostility. Even when she knew the people they called on it was almost as bad. Every other Tuesday they went to the Taylors and Alison gave Mara a blow-by-blow account of the previous Saturday's meet.

In the evenings the Rushtons usually dined at home,

211

their most frequent guests being Sir Henry and the Taylors, although occasionally they dined at other people's houses. This wasn't quite as bad as the afternoon calls, because there were men present and Mara would amuse herself by wondering what each was like in bed, not that she had met any men she wanted to go to bed with.

Then there was bed, seldom after midnight. Sometimes she and Alexander made love and sometimes they didn't. It really didn't matter to Mara, but at least since they had been at the Park Alexander was less nervous and their love-making had improved. He touched her physically and she responded to him physically, as if he had a key which almost fitted, but she didn't think about it afterwards or want it beforehand. There was none of that aching lust which she'd known with Jamie, none of that half-guilty longing which would come over her when they were apart, no naughty thoughts which, when someone suddenly appeared, she had hidden behind a tell-tale smirk. No, there was none of that.

Despite the mindlessness of her existence, Mara was kept busy. She dressed for lunch, changed before calling or receiving, sometimes taking twenty minutes to adjust a hat while Rachel patiently held a hand-mirror. After tea she bathed and dressed for dinner, again with Rachel's help. And of course for all these changes she needed clothes. The rest of her dresses had arrived from Madame Cecile but more were needed. As a rich man's wife she was expected to look smart, and as an attractive young woman she wanted to look fashionable. Magazines provided ideas: she fell in love with a pair of black silk trousers and a Chinese embroidered jacket: she knew she'd look good in a slinky evening dress: she cut out the pictures and showed them to Alexander, and he told her

212

to order whatever she liked. Before she could ride she had to have jodhpurs, a jacket, boots and a hat. The Banbury hunt ball was in March and she couldn't wear something she'd already been seen in. It was a life of spending ridiculous sums of money on clothes which she wore only a few times, of never having a moment to spare, and yet of having nothing to do. Nothing worthwhile. But timeless time is still time, and time is meant to be a healer.

Slowly Mara's bitterness against Jamie was becoming less violent. She still resented him and hated him for the way he had used her, that hadn't changed, and when she thought of how he had been intending to leave her in August, she felt sick with fury. But while previously she had been convinced that during every moment they had spent together he had been secretly laughing at her, she could rationalize that he couldn't possibly have known at the beginning that he was going to leave in August. It was only the latter days which were so tainted and twisted, and what hurt her most was that it was during those latter days when they had seemed so close.

Sometimes she thought of Alexander in terms of herself and Jamie. Did he love her as desperately as she'd loved Jamie? Was that why he was so good to her, too good to her? Was that why he gave in to her in a hundred little ways? When she remembered how she'd felt when Jamie had called her a bore and a limpet, she felt terribly guilty about Alexander and resolved to love him more. He was so very, very good to her.

'I've bought you a present,' he told her one morning. 'It's arriving today.'

'Umm.' Mara was lying in bed half asleep.

'Alison's bringing it over.'

Mara thought, what a bore!

213

'Don't you want to know what it is?' he asked deject-edly. She rolled over and smiled at him. 'Tell me.'

'It's a jolly nice little hunter called Mahogany. Alison's found her. She's just the ticket.'

She sat up and kissed him on the cheek. 'How lovely. Am I going to ride her today?'

'I think you'd better start on Blackie, the twins' old pony. I'll tell the groom to have him ready. The twins are riding this morning so you can go with them.' He paused and looked embarrassed. 'I think I'd better warn you, darling, but it's nearly always . . . er . . . Bonner who takes them.'

'Bonner? Oh, yes.' Mara remembered the ruddy-faced young man who had refused to shake her hand. She was on the point of saying she wouldn't go, when she saw that not to do so would mean she would never get the better of it, she might have won over the maids, but they were impressionable girls: she still had a long way to go. 'I've never worn jodhpurs before,' she said, keeping her voice light and casual. 'They seemed very . . . tight when I tried them on.'

Alexander kissed her on the forehead. 'They'll suit you. Everything you wear suits you. Everyone says you dress marvellously.'

'Do they?' She smiled sleepily.

'Yes. The Old Man says you're our bird of paradise.' He kissed her again and left.

It was true what he said about Mara's dress sense. Everyone said, 'Mara's so lucky, she can wear absolutely anything,' because she had that type of looks which suit exotic clothes. It was almost as though she had no personality of her own but merely took that of her clothes: a temptress in a slinky evening dress; a Chinese bohemian in wide-legged silk trousers; a mysterious

214

French woman in a tight black dress and a beaded beret – just the piano tinkling in the background and the high stool were missing. But they were wrong about her being able to wear anything; in a plain conservative skirt and cardigan she looked just that, plain and conservative. So she steered clear of the skirt and cardigan, and because she could wear the exotic everyone presumed she could wear the plain.

An hour later Mara walked self-consciously downstairs in her squeaky new leather boots, her tight new jodhpurs and her brand-new riding jacket. She wasn't usually self-conscious about clothes, it was just that the tightness of the jodhpurs and the smartness of the whole outfit seemed so ostentatious for someone who had never sat on a horse.

She found the twins already mounted and waiting on the gravel between the front steps and the South Lawn opposite. Damon was on a brown pony and Atalanta on a white one. They both wore perfect little riding outfits, and they sat straight on their ponies' backs, their knees tucked in and their hands neat and together.

'Here comes Blackie,' said Atalanta, nodding towards a fat black pony which was being led by Bonner. He looked at Mara and muttered and she said, loudly and clearly, 'Good morning.'

Bonner handed her Blackie's reins and went to adjust the girths of the other ponies. Mara stood looking uncertainly at the black pony. She had a horrible feeling that amused eyes were watching her from the tall windows of the Park.

'Would you mount, madam,' said Bonner, without either looking at her or coming to help her.

Remembering how she had thought she'd seen other

215

people get on to a horse, Mara put her right foot in the right-hand stirrup.

'Not like that!' shouted Atalanta, bursting into fits of giggles. 'You'll be facing the wrong way.'

Blushing furiously, Mara took her foot out of the stirrup.

'It's your left foot and keep your back to Blackie's head,' said Damon, edging his pony over to her. 'Bonner, please help Mrs Rushton.' Bonner came over and gave Mara a sullen leg up.

Mara sat on Blackie's back as he ambled towards the parkland with Bonner walking behind her. Ahead, Damon and Atalanta urged their ponies into a trot but to Mara's relief Blackie had no more desire to hurry than she did. She tried to remember how the twins had held the reins, if they had held them between the thumb and the forefinger, and whilst she was trying out various ways she kept dropping them.

Whatever the strength of Bonner's feelings against Germans, his affection for horses was as powerful, and he couldn't bear to see one ridden incorrectly. He came up beside Mara and still without looking at her said, 'You hold the reins like this, madam.' He took them from her and showed her. 'And you keep your knees in and your heels down.' He patted Blackie fondly and with a certain commiseration. 'And keep your hands down. Don't pull on his mouth.'

Mara nodded. 'I've never ridden before.'

Bonner said nothing.

She rode Blackie slowly across the parkland. In the distance the twins were cantering up and down and calling to each other. Then she turned the pony round, trying to keep her hands down, and her heels down, and all the other things Bonner had told her to do.

After nearly an hour, when Mara was beginning to feel somewhat stiff, she guided Blackie back towards the house, to where Bonner was standing watching them. The twins passed her, galloping, but Blackie plodded on. As she drew near the house she saw Alexander and Herbert talking to Alison by the archway which led through to the stables.

'Ah, here she comes,' bellowed Herbert, walking over to meet her. 'How's she doing, Bonner? And how's old Blackie?' He raised his hand and slapped the black pony on the hindquarters.

The next thing Mara knew she was on the ground.

'Oh God, I am sorry,' said Herbert, laughing as Alexander rushed to his wife's side. 'I didn't mean to hit her so hard, are you all right?'

'Darling . . .' Alexander knelt down beside her.

Ignoring her bruised arm, Mara stood up and dusted herself down. 'I'm fine.' She took a deep breath. 'Perhaps I'd better get on again so I don't lose my nerve.'

This time Bonner didn't have to be asked to give her a leg up.

Lying in a hot bath, after first having had to spend what seemed like a lifetime admiring her new horse, Mara came to the conclusion that Herbert might have done her a favour. At first she'd been furious with him, as had been Alexander, but now she wasn't so sure. By bullying her, Herbert had also bullied poor old Blackie, and she'd sensed a sort of truce on Bonner's part when she'd finally handed Blackie back to him. She had also sensed sympathy from the other grooms and the stable lads: that although she might be a German she hadn't deserved to be knocked off her horse.

Herbert is a bully, she thought. Poor Sophia, no wonder

217

she's so downtrodden. Fancy having to go to bed with Herbert. The idea made her flesh crawl. No wonder she's so ill and miserable. I'd be suicidal if I were married to Herbert.

When Alexander came up to change for dinner Mara had a desperate urge to jolt him out of his complacency. 'Why is Herbert so hard on Sophia?' she asked.

He looked at her in amazement. 'Hard! What do you mean?'

'He's not very sympathetic to her and she's obviously not well.'

'It's only because he's disappointed.'

'In Sophia?'

'No. She had another . . . er . . . miscarriage at the beginning of December.'

'Poor Sophia!'

'Yes, it was her third.'

'Well, why don't they . . . umm . . . stop trying to have children? They could' – she blushed – 'do what we . . . umm . . . do. After all,' she went on quickly, 'they have the twins. It's not as if they haven't any, is it?'

'Herbert wants another son.'

'What's wrong with Damon?'

'Nothing's wrong with Damon. He just wants another one.' He looked at her and smiled. 'I wouldn't mind having a son too.'

Mara walked over to the window and looked down on the parkland. 'Not yet,' she said. 'Not for a year or two. I'm not even nineteen, I'm much too young.'

'Oh, don't worry I'm not going to . . . er . . . stop . . . er . . . you know.' He disappeared into his dressing-room, and Mara stood looking out of the window and wondering, as she had that first evening at the Ritz, if all married couples did these little dances around each other.

Two people who lived together, slept together, and made love together, and yet they avoided being seen naked by each other and couldn't discuss, without appalling embarrassment, the physical aspects of their union.

She thought of what Alexander had said about children and wondered if there could be something the matter with her because she felt no desire at all to have a baby. I'm too young, that's why, she told herself.

But it wasn't that. It was the permanency Mara was rejecting.

Chapter 13

On the fourteenth of February the Dower House became free.

'Can we go and see it today?' Mara asked Alexander. She longed to see the house, not because she cared about the actual building but because it was to be her escape from the tensions of the Park. She was fed up with watching Herbert belittle Alexander and bored with having to make an effort with Sophia, who clearly was not prepared to like her because Herbert didn't, and she was irritated beyond belief with Atalanta who purposely asked awkward questions about Germany. But most of all she was fed up with being an honorary but not entirely welcome guest.

'Well actually, darling, I was intending to go and see a new hunter today. Alison's found me one over near Bicester. But of course if you want to go I'll cancel my appointment.'

'Don't you want to see the house?'

'Of course I do, I love it, it's my favourite house. I'm longing for us to go and live there, but there's someone else interested in the hunter and I do miss not having a day out with the hounds.'

'We'll go tomorrow.' She knew how he liked routine, she'd learned that in Koblenz, and how it annoyed him when plans were changed.

Alexander kissed her on the cheek. 'We'll go after church. Thank you, darling. I'm feeling so much better since I've been home I'm sure a few good days' hunting will do me a lot of good.'

Guiltily Mara said, 'Yes, you look much better, that's why I haven't asked you how you are.' And she thought, what a liar I am, I'd forgotten all about it.

Alison came to collect Alexander. 'Not coming with us?' she asked Mara breezily, pushing back her fair hair.

Mara shook her head. She always had the feeling that Alison expected to come one day and find her gone, and wouldn't be remotely surprised. 'I'm having a riding lesson.'

'Oh, jolly good. How are you getting on?'

'All right.'

'Bonner says she's doing very well,' said Alexander, smiling proudly at his wife. 'He says she has a natural seat.'

Mara was left to wonder about Bonner. Their truce had continued and he now gave her the odd grudging compliment, but she was surprised to hear he'd been quite so complimentary.

Alexander and Alison still weren't back by the afternoon so Mara decided to go for a walk. She wanted to explore the park on the side where their bedroom window looked out, which she hadn't been able to do because the weather had been terrible. Today at least it wasn't raining even though it was cold and overcast.

She fetched her coat and put on some walking shoes and slipped out of the side door into the garden, avoiding Prince because although she liked him well enough she had discovered he never obeyed anyone except Alexander and the Old Man.

The garden like the house was laid out in lines of rigid formality: straight paths, square lawns, and the neatly clipped hedges of the Box Garden. Even the statue of

221

Old Father Time, in the middle of the Box Garden, was well-scrubbed and well-behaved. Mara walked right round the house until she came to the gate in the garden wall and the path across the parkland which had beckoned to her in the moonlight. She was surprised to find it well-trodden, as if it led to somewhere often visited, although she had never seen anyone using it.

It took Mara fifteen minutes of flat parkland and odd trees, the trees which had become men in the moonlight, before the path began its climb up to the wood. She stopped and looked back at the house. From this distance it looked small and perfect: too perfect. She watched a car come up the drive and stop by the front door. Two people got out. Alexander and Alison, she thought as they went into the house. But Mara didn't go back, she kept on walking and soon she was deep in the wood. Alone and surrounded by the tall trees it would have been all too easy to drift back into the past, but she forced herself to keep her mind on the pleasure of being out of the Park, on the damp air on her face and the wet grass beneath her feet. Deep thinking was something she'd been trying to avoid since she had been at the Park. It was dangerous. One thought led to another, one memory to another.

Eventually the path emerged from the trees and Mara found herself at the top of a big field. At the bottom was a house, not a very large one, more an overgrown cottage. It had a thatched roof and black beams criss-crossed on white plaster walls, and surrounding it was a garden with a hedge to mark the boundary; not a well-trimmed hedge like those at Rushton Park but a thick mass of uncontrolled bushes. Looking down at it Mara was reminded of Damon, for there was something about the house and its garden which made it seem isolated from its environment.

Thinking about Damon – God, I feel sorry for Damon with a father like Herbert, no wonder he says he hates him – Mara walked down the field to the hedge and peered through a gap. She was so busy looking at the house that she didn't hear the dog approach, she merely felt his cold nose on the back of her knee. And she screamed.

'It's only a dog,' shouted a woman's voice from behind her.

Mara spun round. Halfway up the field stood the dark angular woman she had seen in church on Christmas Day.

'You're Alexander Rushton's wife, aren't you?' said the woman, walking down towards Mara. She was tall and broad and yet, despite her size, she moved with incredible grace.

Mara nodded. 'Yes.'

'I thought so. Well, I'm Elenora Harris and I live in the house you've been spying on.' The brilliant green eyes were amused.

Mara blushed furiously. 'I'm awfully sorry. I didn't mean to pry.'

The woman laughed loudly, throwing back her big head so that her untidy grey-streaked hair was tossed about her shoulders. 'Don't worry,' she chortled. 'I'm fascinated by other people and they're fascinated by me. The world's divided into doers and watchers – voyeurs and exhibitionists. I'm a watcher and' – she gave Mara a conspiratorial wink – 'sometimes a doer.'

Mara frowned. With Jamie she had been a doer. With Alexander she was a watcher. Suddenly she longed to confide in someone, no, not just someone, in this woman who seemed to understand and who could put into words the vagaries of thought. 'I know what you mean,' she said quietly.

'Do you?' Elenora was very curious. 'You're a bit young to have worked all that out.'

What was she thinking of, wanting to tell her secrets to a stranger? She must be mad! Back-pedalling into a social smile, Mara laughed lightly and gave what she knew was not a proper answer. 'I like to look at people's clothes. I'm a bit of a clothes-addict.'

The woman nodded but did not look down at her own clothes as most would have done. She seemed oblivious to them and to fashion, but somehow this added to her fascination. The clothes she wore were ghastly, a bright green Edwardian hobble-skirt and a bright yellow blouse, at least they would have been ghastly on anyone else, but they weren't on her. It was obvious she wore them because she liked them and didn't care what others thought. This gave her appearance and her movements a certain freedom which, along with her hard dark glamour and her almost biblical scruffiness, gave her the air of an unrepentant Mary Magdalene. 'Well, as you're obviously curious about my house you'd better come in and have some tea.'

'Thank you, I'd . . .' Mara was about to accept, then she seemed to hear Alexander's voice saying, 'We say hello but we don't call,' and Sophia explaining to her, 'One never calls on people one doesn't want to invite back.'

Elenora appeared to read her thoughts. 'Don't worry, I won't tell that stuffy family of yours. Not that your father-in-law would mind. It's the others.' She started walking down the hill towards the house. The dog, a cross between a black spaniel and countless other breeds, followed her, swishing happily along through the damp green grass, beside the bright green skirt.

Mara hesitated, but only for a moment. Why shouldn't she go? She wasn't a prisoner.

The woman was waiting for her by the front door. 'I'm a painter,' she warned, ushering Mara into the hall. It was stark, black beams on white plaster. Nothing else. Not even a picture.

'What do you paint?'

'This.'

An inner door was flung open and Mara stepped into a kaleidoscope of canvases – blues, reds, greens and yellows in circles, lines and squares all bouncing down on her from every wall of the studio. She stood looking up at them, bemused and half afraid.

'Like them?'

'I don't know. I mean . . .'

'Don't worry, you're not the only one. They take a bit of getting used to.' Elenora walked to the back of the room where there was a sink and a small stove. 'Sarah doesn't like them either. She's more interested in Marx.'

Mara wondered who Sarah was but she didn't like to ask. Was it possible that Sarah was her . . . that Mrs Harris was one of those women who . . . ? She felt anxious and uncomfortable but hoped it didn't show. She walked over to the window and ran her fingers along the dusty sill. There was a lump of black rock on it, like a lump of coal only it wasn't coal, and its surface was irregular, its blackness pinpricked with silver. 'I like this,' she said.

'What? Oh, that. Yes.'

'Where does it come from?'

'France.' The tap was turned on and the water thudded on the kettle's bottom. Mara turned away from the window and picked up a book which was lying face down and open on a stool.

Elenora shouted, 'Not a Red, are you?'

'A what?'

The water stopped. 'You know, a Red. Karl Marx, Lenin' – she pointed a wet hand towards the book – 'John Reed.'

Mara looked at the title, *Ten Days that Shook the World*, and hurriedly put down the book. 'I don't know anything about it.' She felt inadequate and stupid and wished she hadn't come.

Elenora smiled at her. 'No, I don't suppose you do.' The thudding began again.

When the kettle had boiled and the tea was made they sat down at a rough pine table. One end was covered with magazines, not *The Tatler* and *Country Life* as they had at the Park but less glossy ones with names like *New Statesman* and *Egoist*.

Retreating to the safety of social chit-chat Mara said, 'This is kind of you, Mrs Harris.'

'For goodness' sake call me Elenora. Everyone does.'

'Oh . . . er . . . my name's Mara.' She waited for the usual comment on her unusual name. But there was none. Elenora Harris was used to the unusual.

'You're German, aren't you?' she said bluntly.

'Yes.'

'And your mother was English.'

'How do you know?'

'Local gossip.'

Mara tried to look nonchalant. 'There's a lot of bad feeling about my being German, isn't there?'

'Yes. Have you had any trouble?'

'Umm . . . yes.'

'Oh, what happened?'

Mara hesitated. But why shouldn't she tell someone? Why should she be made to feel that she had some frightful disease? She told Elenora about the woman at the Ritz and about Bonner, ending with, 'But he seems to like me now, in spite of my nationality. At least he would if he let himself.'

Elenora laughed and reappraised Mara. From what she had heard, Alexander Rushton's wife spent a fortune on clothes, didn't say much, but was nice, considering . . . Several people had gone further and said Mara Rushton probably hadn't much to say for herself, which was all to the good as they preferred to look at her rather than to hear her German accent.

Mara asked, 'Do you think the anti-German feeling will die down?'

'In all honesty not for some years, but if you're clever they'll get used to you long before that. Luckily you don't sound very German, just a bit teutonic. Start hunting and they'll soon forget. Horses are a great leveller.'

Mara laughed. 'So that's the answer. I couldn't ride at all when I came.'

'So the whipper-in said.'

Mara was a bit taken aback. She had expected them to discuss her but she hadn't realized they all knew her every word. 'He was shocked, wasn't he?'

'Yes, the idiot. What does it matter? Local gossip says you were stuck up on old Blackie within a fortnight. I gather Herbert did his bit.'

Mara felt awkward. She didn't like to say anything against her brother-in-law to a stranger, particularly when every word she said seemed to go straight round the neighbourhood.

'Oh, don't worry, I won't say anything,' said Elenora, reading Mara's mind. 'Everyone knows that Herbert's a

227

frightful bully. People try to feel sorry for him because he, unlike Alexander, was brought up as a coachman's son and only went to the village school. But it's difficult to sympathize when Samuel Rushton spent all of his life, up to the age of thirty, as a coachman or chauffeur and he's no ruffian.'

'A coachman?' said Mara, very puzzled.

'Don't you know?' It was Elenora's turn to look puzzled.

'Well, Alexander told me his father had looked after Sir Henry's cars.'

Elenora groaned. 'I don't mean to criticize your husband but he is a frightful snob. His father was Sir Henry's coachman, the Rushtons had been coachmen to the Gaunts for generations. It was only because his father was so clever and came up with an idea for a car, and dear old Sir Henry who hasn't any children, loved Samuel as though he were his own and believed in him, that the Rushtons aren't still living in the coachman's house and earning twenty-five shillings a week. Do you mean no one's told you?'

Mara remembered Alexander's resigned voice and the way he had clung to her hand in the car. 'He told me most of it,' she said loyally, trying not to show how shocked she was. Not because the Old Man had been a coachman, it made her admire him all the more, but because Alexander had not been able to tell her the plain facts of the situation. She was sure he believed he was honest, and that he was deluding himself just as much as he had deluded her. Looking down into her mug of tea, she recalled how she had been mildly dissatisfied with his explanation. So it's not only a little dance around each other's bodies, she thought, but also around everything he doesn't want to see. 'Everyone seems to know every-one else's business round here,' she said eventually, wondering how long it would be before Alexander heard she'd met Mrs Harris.

Elbows on the table, hair streaked and straggled, Elenora gave a knowing grin. 'Nothing else to do. Not that that makes much difference. People gossip just as much in London.'

'Don't you like London?' Mara wished she could go back there.

'I love London but I like change. A few weeks here. A few weeks in London. The odd month in Florence. I love them all.'

'Florence must be beautiful.'

'It is. There's something wonderfully decadent about Italy.'

Mara could think of no answer to that. She sipped her tea and wondered what had happened to Mr Harris. Had he been decadent – or perhaps not decadent enough?

The light was fading by the time Mara left the cottage clutching two *Egoist*s and one *New Statesman* under her arm. She had borrowed them partly out of curiosity and partly to show that she too could be interested and interesting, but her main reason for borrowing them was to have an excuse to return to the cottage. At the top of the field she stopped and looked back. The cottage had resumed its air of isolation, the trees inside the garden seemed different from those outside, their branches grew with less inhibition, just like their owner. She was reluctant to leave in the same way a traveller in the desert is reluctant to leave an oasis.

Eventually she dragged herself away and climbed the stile. Straddling it, one leg either side of the top plank, she took one last look back at the cottage. A car was travelling slowly along the lane at the bottom of the valley. With the distance and the fading light she couldn't see who was in it, but there was something about the long sleek body and the large headlamps on their tall stalks which made her think of the Old Man's Rushton-Gaunt saloon. She watched it draw level with the cottage and disappear behind the unclipped hedge, waited for it to come out on the lane beyond. But it didn't.

It could be anyone, she told herself firmly, the Old Man's not the only one with a car like that, and anyway why should he visit Elenora? She clambered down off the stile and hurried along the path through the woods. Elenora would have told me if she was expecting him. Surely? Of course she would have. She'd have got him to give me a lift back. She tripped over a gnarled root, stumbled, and carried on walking. Alexander would be furious if he knew I'd suspected his father of visiting Mrs Harris. Then, suddenly, she laughed out loud. Doers and watchers!

It was dark when Mara finally reached the Park. Praying she had not been missed and formulating excuses, she scuttled across the gravel and up the front steps.

But no one could get past Mortimer. He appeared as she crept through the door, took her coat and said reprovingly, 'Mr Alexander was looking for you, madam. He held tea but . . .'

'Yes, Aunt Mara.' Atalanta shouted down at her from the banisters on the first floor. 'Uncle Alexander is f u r i o u s.' She pronounced it as slowly and as loudly as possible. Then she rolled her eyes with glee and screamed, 'Uncle Alexander! Uncle Alexander! She's back,' dissolving into giggles and retreating from view, though not from earshot.

230

Alexander came out of the dining room. 'Mara, darling, where were you? Where have you been?'

'I went for a walk.'

'But Mara, you've been gone over three hours.'

She knew Atalanta was listening so she walked straight into the dining room, with Alexander following, and closed the door before demanding angrily, 'Aren't I allowed out?'

'Yes, if you say you're . . .'

'I can't sit in the house all day.' He had disappointed her and now he was trying to imprison her.

'But, Mara . . .'

'What's the matter, don't you trust me?'

Alexander's face crumpled. 'Of course I do, darling, and of course you can go out. But could you please tell someone if you're not coming back?'

'Not coming back! Of course I'm coming back. Did you think I'd run away?'

'No, no.' He patted her arm. 'I meant if you're not coming back for tea. Otherwise it's held for you . . . upsets the routine . . . the servants.'

The routine. She pictured Elenora and the cottage, and the tedium of her own life hit her. 'I'll tell Mortimer next time,' she snapped. And she pushed past Alexander, went out into the hall, up the stairs, and to her room. If he'd said anything more to her she knew she'd have slapped him.

Not even her bedroom was her own; she shared it with Alexander. There was nowhere in the house she could call hers, no place where she could shut the door and be sure of solitude. And she needed to be alone. Desperately. She needed to be able to talk to herself about her life in order to come to terms with it. The limitations of her freedom and her existence, which she had known were there but been too socially busy to see, had suddenly risen up in front of her wearing a 'No Entry Beyond This Point' sign.

I'm a prisoner, an imprisoned cog in a well-oiled wheel, she decided, and her thoughts turned to Jamie. What would he have said if someone had tried to rule his life with a tea tray? She could just imagine. What would he say if he knew she was ruled by a tea tray? He would laugh and say it served her right. And Elenora? Mara glanced at the *New Statesman* and the *Egoist*s tossed carelessly on her dressing table. She would laugh too. They would both laugh. For the first time since her marriage Mara was near to tears.

But she couldn't give way to tears because Rachel came bustling in to help her dress for dinner – and it all began again. Which dress? Which shoes? Which earrings? The well-oiled wheels went round and round. Mara stayed in her room for a week pretending to be ill. Sometimes she lay in bed staring up at the plaster mouldings and other times she sat by the window, gazing blankly out over the wet parkland. She puzzled and questioned. What's it all about? What am I doing here? What are any of us doing here? Did other people wonder about these things? Was that why they turned to religion? She remembered how Jamie had asked her if she believed in God, and then gone on to say that what had happened to her with her father and Herr Steiger had been inevitable, but perhaps some all-powerful being had had a hand in the timing of things. Gradually she had begun to see what he meant, although she still didn't agree that the timing could have been worse: if Herr Steiger had raped her and not tricked her, then perhaps she wouldn't have reacted so violently to Jamie: perhaps she wouldn't be here.

Had meeting Elenora anything to do with her dissatisfaction? Mara didn't know. Or was it the bitten-back tears? Or the recognition of the limits of her life-space and of her relationship with Alexander? Perhaps it was a conglomeration of all three. And Jamie. Jamie who had taught her how to love. Jamie who had tried to make her think. Jamie who'd shown her there was more to life than being decorative. Jamie who'd forced her to work and made her experience the tired satisfaction of a job well done – and subsequently ruined her. She knew that however contented she might manage to make herself with Alexander, there'd always be times when she'd question the mindless luxury of her existence. It's Jamie's fault, she told herself, if it wasn't for him I'd be quite happy.

On the Saturday morning Mara had to get up. The Old Man had arranged for her to visit the works and, as Alexander told her tentatively, everyone would be very disappointed if she didn't go. She rose early and dressed carefully in what she hoped was a boss's-daughter-in-law's outfit: a long cream jacket belted round the hips over a tubular cream skirt, with a matching hat which looked like the sort of helmet invading barbarians once wore, except it had no horns. Madame Cecile had written that it was the latest fashion.

'What do you think, Rachel?'

'You look lovely, madam. The 'at looks like the leather 'elmet old Mr Rushton used to wear when 'e was racing.'

Mara smiled. She did like Rachel. 'Well, so long as they don't think I'm going to race. I can't even drive yet.' She paused. 'My husband said I had to learn to ride first.'

'Oh, did he say you could learn to drive when you could ride, madam?'

'Well . . .' Mara grinned at the girl, 'not exactly.'

233

Feeling surprisingly happy Mara went downstairs. She was about to go into the drawing room when she heard Herbert's voice. 'I've had just about enough of you,' he was saying.

Mara stopped dead outside the door and hovered, wondering to whom he was talking and if she could creep away. Then she heard Sophia. 'Herbert, please, he's just going through a phase.'

'Phase! A permanent phase. I speak to him and he pretends he doesn't hear me. He looks at me with those cold eyes. And you know where he gets it from, don't you? *Her*. He's copying *her*. Ever since she came the twins have been impossible.'

'Not in front of the children, Herbert,' Sophia said timidly.

'Why not? Atalanta sulks because the Old Man and Alexander only have eyes for Mara. I'm fed up with it.'

Terrified someone might come out and find her in the hall, Mara tiptoed across to the front door and went out into the garden. She walked over to the fence which, on this side, separated the lawn from the parkland. So Herbert hated her. She'd suspected it and now she knew.

'You heard, didn't you?'

She turned to find Damon just behind her. 'Yes. How did you know?'

'I saw you walking across the lawn. You must have come out through the front door. Don't worry, no one else saw you.' He took a step forward. 'He's hateful, isn't he?'

'Yes, but he doesn't know it.'

They stood there, side by side, looking out over the parkland, Mara holding on to the top bar of the fence, and Damon holding the lower one because he was too small to reach the top one. They stayed there until

Mortimer came to say the Old Man and Alexander were waiting for Mara, but that Damon and Atalanta would not be going with them.

'I don't care,' Damon whispered. 'He thinks he can hurt me but he can't because I don't care.'

They walked back to the house together and separated only when they reached the front steps, Mara entering the car, Damon running up the steps into the hall then on up to his room.

Chapter 14

The Rushton-Gaunt motorworks were some three miles south-west of the Park, in the direction of Oxford. They had been built on the flat field which Sir Henry had given to Samuel Rushton at the beginning, at the edge of a plateau which had been the boundary between Sir Henry's estate and that of the old recluse. The buildings consisted of one large three-storey office building built like a horseshoe round gravel courtyard, with the workshops, the storerooms, the testing bays, the coachworks and a canteen fanning out behind it like the tail of a peacock. Running round it was a test-track, which gave it the appearance of a rather straggly castle surrounded by an oval moat.

'Of course we've had to expand,' the Old Man told Mara as they turned off the road and on to the concrete drive leading to the works. 'As soon as I bought the Park I added that field.' He pointed to the right.

'The Dower House is back there, darling.' Alexander, who was sitting next to Mara in the back of the car, twisted his head to look back. 'Down in the valley opposite where we turned in. We could go and look at it later,' he ventured. He was frightened of her just as he had been after the incident on the stairs at the Ritz, and he cursed himself for having been cross with her the previous Saturday when she'd gone out. But part of him kept saying he'd been within his rights to be cross.

The car drew to a halt by a short flight of steps which led up to the main door, positioned exactly at the top of the horseshoe. They went in, the Old Man leading the way.

Inside the main door was a large reception area which reminded Mara of an old-fashioned but extremely well-to-do dentist's waiting room. There was a beautiful Persian carpet laid on a polished wood floor and a number of large leather chairs placed around a long low table. In the middle of the table were three impressive silver cups: there were more cups in a cabinet on the far wall.

'The Old Man won them,' Alexander whispered to her.

The first person Mara was introduced to was the receptionist, Mrs Wright, an elderly bosomy blonde whose motherly concern oozed over everyone from the lowest apprentice mechanic to Samuel Rushton himself. She clasped Mara's hand. 'So nice to meet you, dear. I'll call the typists.' From a side room three girls trooped out and shook Mara's hand.

The Old Man said, 'Now we'd better go through the offices. Please tell Smithy we're here, Mrs Wright. Smithy,' he explained to Mara, 'has been with me from the beginning. He's as much Rushton-Gaunt as any of us.'

Mara nodded. She really didn't know what to say. She felt like one of the silver trophies on the table about to be examined by the whole workforce, who would then decide if she were tarnished. They looked into three very smart offices, each with its large desk and large chair. On the walls were pictures of cars. 'These are our offices,' said Alexander. 'This one's mine.' She noticed his was the smallest. The Old Man's was the largest. 'And this is where we have lunch.' There was a small dining room with a highly polished oval table.

'This is the accounts department.' The Old Man led the way up to the first floor and into a huge room. There he introduced her to Mr Griffin, the tiny bespectacled accountant, who in turn introduced her to rows and rows of clerks, all with ink-stained fingers. Then they went on up again, to the second and third floors, where there were secretaries and storerooms and more clerks. 'More than my life's worth to leave anyone out,' he said loudly, and they all laughed.

It was obvious they loved the Old Man. Mara saw this when he spoke to someone. Their face lit up and even after he'd moved on to talk to someone else, they still smiled. She thought of what Elenora had said about her father-in-law having been a coachman or chauffeur till he was thirty, and she wondered if his employees saw in him a hope for the future. Did they think, because he had succeeded, they might, or were they just pleased that one of them was successful? Whichever it was, they certainly didn't resent his success. And she was surprised they didn't resent her either. There were the occasional glances passed because of her accent, but that wasn't the sort of resentment she had expected. She'd expected some of them to have hoped that their daughter might marry the boss's son. But obviously not. As they went back downstairs, she came to the conclusion that they saw her as glamorous and elegant; the natural acquisition for a boss's son.

Smithy, the foreman, was waiting in the reception. He was a funny little man, a bit like a chipmunk, with a bright beady smile and almost no teeth. At first when he smiled his few teeth reminded Mara of stalactites hanging from the ceiling of a cave, but gradually she grew accustomed to them. There was something of the Old Man in Smithy: he marshalled them all out of the back of the building, saying, 'The lads 'ave all washed their 'ands, madam. They're all waiting to shake yours.'

'Oh, they shouldn't have bothered,' said the Old Man, taking Mara by the elbow, 'my daughter-in-law's not one of these girls who minds a bit of dirt.'

'No, I hope I'm not.' Mara gave her smart cream suit a doubtful look.

Smithy grinned at her. 'We'll soon have a pretty pattern of oil stains on that for you.'

She grinned back at him. 'Just what I need.'

They went into a long low building where rows of chassis were being welded. 'A bit noisy!' Smithy shouted at her.

'Yes.' She laughed and tossed back her head. The noise was deafening but to Mara's surprise she didn't mind it, or the smell of oil or the sweaty faces which smiled at her as the men lined up to be introduced.

'Seen enough, darling?' Alexander asked her as the men went back to their tasks.

'Of course she hasn't,' growled the Old Man.

'Well, I . . . er . . . might go outside, the dust makes me cough.'

The Old Man gave his son a long sad look, then he took Mara by the arm and steered her up and down the aisles, telling her what each man was doing. 'As you see, we build the whole car here,' he said proudly, 'not just the chassis and the engine but the bodywork too.'

Mara nodded. She had no idea that this was unusual. 'How many do you make?' she asked.

'We'll make over a thousand saloons this year and when we get the Roadster going, we'll make five or six hundred of those a year. Before the war we made half that, but now everyone wants to own a car.'

'How many cars do most . . . works make?' She hoped that was an intelligent question.

'Old Henry Ford makes over eight thousand a year, at

239

least he did three years ago, but his are cheaper. Much cheaper. We're nothing like that big but then ours aren't mass-produced. We're a bit bigger than Talbot and Riley, and a little more expensive. Ah, I see their names mean nothing to you.'

Mara longed to ask, 'How expensive?' but she didn't like to.

'And for your information,' he gave her a craggy grin, 'a saloon costs nine hundred pounds and the Roadster will be about seven hundred which, my dear young lady, is a lot of money when a workman is lucky to earn a pound a week and even a doctor or a solicitor sees little more than four pounds a week.'

Four pounds for a doctor, thought Mara. Her cream suit cost more than that.

The Old Man studied her face. 'You like it here, don't you?'

'Yes, I do.' She watched the men whose muscles rippled as they bent to weld or to hammer. 'I'd no idea it would be so full of . . . life.'

He smiled and took her through into another workshop.

Mara thought, I like it because there's life and movement, vitality and action, all the things that are missing from my life. One moment there's a rectangle of steel and the next there's a car, shining and ready for the road. She saw that these workshops, and not the pristine offices, were the true heart of all her father-in-law had done. From here the cars were pumped out to showrooms and distributors as the heart pumps life blood to every corner of the body. Now Mara began to understand how the Old Man had risen from his lowly origins and what it was in him that made people from all walks of life respect him. He had created this heart. He was Rushton-Gaunt. Watching and listening to him, she became convinced that whatever he owed to Sir Henry, and he did owe a lot, people were wrong in thinking that without Sir Henry, Samuel Rushton would have been no one. The Old Man would have risen somehow, she was sure of it.

'This is where they're given the final polish,' he told her as they went into another building. 'How are you, my beauties?' He stroked the gleaming bonnet of a finished car.

Two young lads were giving the cars their final rub and shine. Mara studied the double row of cars awaiting their turn. They reminded her of women waiting for their hairdresser, and it seemed to her that as each car received its rub and was rolled away, it purred with the confidence of a woman who knows she is looking her best. Just like women heading for an evening of excitement, the cars headed for their new owners; smart young men who would fall in love with them, and sign a cheque, and take them home where they would live in luxury, their bodies frequently polished.

'And this is the new Roadster.' The Old Man led her off to another workshop. 'Of course we're still working on her.' The chassis, the engine and the bodywork lay in different parts of the building. They were standing there looking at it, and Mara was beginning to feel she had seen enough, when a voice from the doorway said, 'Hello, sir, Alexander said you'd probably be in here.'

Mara looked round. A young man was walking towards them and she knew it had to be Mark Hatton. Alexander's description – Eton, Oxford, Royal Flying Corps, which at the time had seemed to her no description at all – now struck her as being appropriate. Mark had all the confidence of someone who in his schooldays had strolled across the playing fields of Eton, where his father and his father's father had strolled before him, and all the charm of a young man to whom doors, both social and bedroom, were seldom closed. On top of all that he was not only very good-looking in a fair-haired clean-cut acceptable English way, but his looks, his figure and his manner were boyish, which made him appear younger than his twenty-seven years. In fact when people discovered Mark had been in the Flying Corps they were horrified to think that a mere boy, and such a charming one at that, had risked his life daily. Somehow it mattered more. And somehow they were more grateful to him because it seemed he had so much more to lose.

Mark was smiling at Mara with frank admiration and holding out his right hand while smoothing down his fair hair with his left. 'You must be Mara,' he said.

The Old Man slapped Mark on the shoulder. 'Yes she is. Mara this is Mark. And what have you been up to, you young scoundrel?'

Mark grinned at Mara. 'Visiting elderly relations, what else?'

'I can believe it!' The Old Man turned to Mara. 'Breaking hearts, more likely.'

Mara laughed. She could see why Herbert was jealous of Mark; Herbert was like a cart-horse forced to drag a heavy roller up and down a race-track in order that a race-horse might gallop down it without catching its well-bred feet on any lumps of earth. She could see why the Old Man liked Mark, for in spite of the boyishness and the charm there was a certain toughness in him. She herself liked Mark, though she wasn't sure if she found him attractive or if it was simply that he was a breath of fresh and uncomplicated air.

They went out of the workshop and walked round to the front of the main building. Alexander was leaning against the car.

He nodded at Mark. 'You found them.'

'They were with the Roadster, as you said they would be. I must say, I'm itching to drive her. When do you think she'll be ready?'

The Old Man answered, 'Summer.'

'Not earlier? No chance of having a run at Brooklands? They're reopening this year.' Mark gave the Old Man a hopeful smile.

The Old Man shook his head very firmly, and Mara was pleased to see that however charming and persuasive Mark might be her father-in-law was unswayable. 'No chance at all. The first step is to run her on our own track.' He touched Mara's shoulder. 'You can see it over there, it laps the works but it's only a mile round. Used to practise on it myself, but of course we didn't go so fast then.'

'But you lapped Brooklands at over a hundred, sir,' said Mark respectfully. The boyish charmer had gone and in his place stood a young man speaking to his sage.

The Old Man smiled. 'So I did.'

Mara was impressed. The speed limit, Mark informed her, was twenty miles an hour, although everyone went at thirty. But a hundred! She looked at her father-in-law and wondered if he'd been frightened.

'And you could do it again, Papa,' said Alexander loyally.

'Oh no, I'm too old. But I'll always regret I couldn't beat Hornsted. He did a hundred and twenty-eight just before the war.'

Mark said, 'In a Benz.'

'Yes, good car. He broke the record four times in a Benz. Well, I'll see you young people later. You'll have lunch with us, won't you Mark? I suppose you're staying

243

with Sir Henry. Invite him too . . . Oh, he's gone up to London. Well, see you later.'

'I must say you Germans make jolly good cars,' Mark said to Mara.

She was incredibly aware of Alexander. Germans and Germany were subjects to be avoided. But here at last was somebody who didn't speak to her as though she were an escapee from a leper island. 'Yes, they are good. My father had one.'

'You should have brought it with you.'

'It was old and broken-down.'

'We'd have got it going.' He looked at Alexander. 'Shall we go?'

Alexander hesitated. They had planned to go straight to the Dower House, and Mara sensed his dilemma. He wanted to go there now because that was their plan, but he didn't want to take Mark, he wanted to take her on her own, to show her their new home by himself, perhaps even to carry her over the threshold. A week earlier Mara would have submitted to his silent wishes. But why should I now? she asked herself. I wanted to go last Saturday but he insisted on going to see a horse, which he didn't even buy after all, and when I went out on my own he was angry. She turned to Mark and, ignoring Alexander's look of anguish, said, 'We're going to the Dower House. Come with us.'

From the moment Mara saw the Dower House she liked it. It had an elegant yet well-worn simplicity, outside and inside, and none of the excessive opulence of the Park. Alexander had talked fondly about it and his enthusiasm had sometimes worried Mara; she knew how different their ideas were. But over the Dower House they were in complete agreement. 'It's beautiful,' she said, looking up at it. 'Much nicer than the Park. Don't you think so, Mark?'

'Of course it's nicer than the Park, but the Park will be all right in fifteen years' time when everything looks less bright.'

'It had to be completely redone.' Alexander was defensive.

Mara felt a twinge of conscience. She'd ruined Alexander's day by bringing Mark and now she and Mark were criticizing his home. 'I'm sure it did,' she smiled at him. Then she turned her attention back to the house.

It had been built at varying times, the original being a Tudor cottage not unlike Elenora's, with low black beams and white plaster. Attached to this cottage, like the long stroke of an L, was a new wing in a completely different style, three storeys high and very formal looking. It was an arrangement which could have been hideous, but instead gave the whole thing great character because it pushed up roofs of differing heights and made the creeper-covered cottage look like a little old man leaning on the arm of a tall young one.

The interior was interesting too, although it was badly in need of redecoration. There was a huge drawing room which, together with a dining room, occupied the entire ground floor of the new wing. Above them were three bedrooms, a small dressing room and a bathroom: the largest bedroom looked out over the garden, towards a big oak tree.

'Is that the oak tree you told me about?' Mara asked as they stood by the window.

Alexander smiled at her. 'Yes. You remember?'

'Of course I do.' She felt guilty at having made him unhappy.

They went on round the house. Above the bedrooms

were little bedrooms, the servants' quarters. In the old part was a study, another little sitting room, kitchens, and on the first floor – the only floor apart from the ground floor – a largish bedroom with a very decrepit bathroom, and two more little bedrooms.

'You'll have to do something about the bathrooms,' said Mark, touching the chipped enamel bath.

Mara looked from him to Alexander and wondered how she would feel if she were coming to live here with Mark instead of with Alexander. It would certainly be more exciting, she thought, but I wonder if I'd ever be sure of him. At least with Alexander I feel safe. She linked her arm through her husband's as they went out into the garden.

It was beautiful. Soft lawns dipped and rose with the natural flow of the earth, the grass giving way to the gnarled roots of the huge oak tree but coming into its own, long and luscious, between the flowering shrubs which mingled and twisted together. It was a garden designed by nature for nature. Nothing could have been more different from the rigid layout of the garden at the Park.

Things will be better when we're here, she told herself. Living at the Park, that's what it is. We'll be all right when we're on our own.

At lunch Mara's sympathy for Herbert and Alexander returned. The Old Man and Mark went on and on about the works. 'Once the war contracts were cancelled a lot of people were in trouble,' said the Old Man. 'I mean aviation people. Not us, of course, because the world and its dog wants to own a motorcar.'

'Aren't ours a bit expensive?' ventured Alexander.

Herbert cleared his throat. 'Yes, that's why I'm in favour of us getting into mass production.'

Here we go again, thought Mara.

The Old Man thumped the table, making the cutlery and the glasses dance. 'How many times do I have to say it? Rushton-Gaunt stands for quality! I'm not cutting corners. If people want a cheap car they can go to Henry Ford or William Morris, if they want something better then I hope they'll come to us, and if money's no object they'll go to Rolls-Royce. I know the sort of people my cars should go to.'

Mara looked down at her soup. What had Alexander told her in Koblenz? That a Rushton-Gaunt was a status symbol? Then why didn't he say so now! Why did he have to keep agreeing with Herbert who, when it suited him, did his best to make Alexander look a fool?

Mark was talking to the Old Man about some friend in the Flying Corps. 'He was shot down in the end by the Red Baron.'

'Was he killed?' asked Sophia.

'God, yes. But if one had to be shot down by anyone I'd have chosen the Red Baron any day. The man was a genius.'

'But he was shot down himself eventually,' said Herbert looking at Mara.

'Yes, but he was still a genius.' Mark seemed unaware that mention of the war had brought a certain awkwardness to the table. 'I suppose you didn't know him, did you? That would be too much to hope for.'

Mara knew Alexander was watching her but she couldn't ignore the question. 'You mean . . . umm . . . von Richthofen?'

Mark smiled at her. 'We called him the Red Baron. I'd have given anything to meet that man.'

247

Herbert said, 'Presumably to shoot him down?'

'Not if I'd met him in peacetime. Then I'd have been honoured to shake his hand, just as, had I confronted him in battle, I'd have been honoured to fight him.' Mark smiled at Mara and she smiled back. At the works he had made her feel that she wasn't an escapee from a leper island, now he made her feel that if she had escaped from any island at all it was from one just as honourable as the island in which she found herself. 'Flying transcends nationality,' he went on, 'and so does genius.'

'Well, I must say!' protested Herbert. 'And coming from you, Mark.'

'Yes,' said the Old Man, 'explain yourself, Mark. It's not that I disagree with you, it's that I want to hear why you think that.'

Alexander cleared his throat. 'Papa, couldn't we talk about something else?' He looked at Mara as if to say, 'I'm doing my best to protect you.'

But his father took no notice. 'Come on, Mark!'

'Well,' Mark looked round the table, 'as I see it, to exclude the talents of those who are born outside England is to limit the quantity of talent in the world. It's like . . .'

Mara thought of Elenora. 'Like denying the talents of women?'

'Yes. Exactly. Women make up fifty per cent of the population of this country.'

'More than that since the war,' said the Old Man. He looked from Mara to Alexander and added, 'You didn't tell us she was a suffragette, Alexander.'

They all laughed and went on to talk of other things. Mara listened to the conversation and thought, if it hadn't been for Mark the war would still be a dirty word but now, finally, it's out in the open. And she looked at Mark and smiled when he caught her eye, and in her

248

mind he grew to almost heroic proportions: a man who accepted people for what they were and didn't despise them for where they came from.

Mark went up to London the next day and Mara didn't see him before he left. She was disappointed, although she tried not to be, telling herself she was being silly. At least she had the Dower House. It was her saviour. She needed other saviours, for her spirit was being sapped by the tedium of life at Rushton Park, but at least she now had something to think about, even if it was only what colour the wallpaper in the drawing room should be; and more important than that, she had somewhere to go where she wasn't an unwelcome guest but the future mistress of the house. She went there nearly every morning, although that too began to pall, but it was better than hanging around the Park. If it was raining Owen drove her over but if it was only drizzling – it never seemed to be sunny – she rode, and the twins went with her if they could escape from Miss Pinner. Bonner always went with her because she didn't yet ride well enough to go out alone. He never spoke to Mara unless she spoke first, but she sensed he grudgingly liked her.

One day he brought Mahogany and not Blackie to the front door. 'She needs exercise,' he said by way of explanation. He wouldn't go so far as to tell Mara to her face that she was now good enough to ride the little bay hunter.

Mara hadn't been particularly interested in Mahogany when the horse first arrived, mainly because she'd never been interested in horses or in learning to ride and had only done so because it was expected of her, but now she found that she enjoyed it and she became very fond of Mahogany. She would ride along, holding imaginary conversations with her horse, and often had the feeling that Mahogany understood, for her ears would twitch backwards and forwards as if she were anxious to catch each word.

Mara usually took Prince as well, because if she didn't he subjected her to the most appalling moral blackmail; he would sit opposite her all evening, staring at her with accusing eyes, his ears flat down the sides of his black head. He's just like Alexander, Mara decided on one of their outings, only Prince is worse. They're both moral blackmailers but Prince is a tyrant as well. I'm sure he thinks I'm some slave Alexander's acquired for their mutual benefit. She looked down at Prince and he grinned up at her, then loped off into the undergrowth.

Once, because Alexander wanted her to, Mara asked Sophia to go to the Dower House with her, and Owen drove them over in the car. They got on much better without their husbands and Sophia was very helpful. We've nothing in common, Mara thought as they drove home, that's the problem, and we're very different, at least I hope we are. But what on earth would I be like if I'd married Herbert? Downtrodden like Sophia? No, because I'd never have married him. I still can't understand why she did.

Another day Mara and Sophia went down to Oxford to look for curtain materials. Mara hadn't been to Oxford before and she would have liked to explore the mellow stone courtyards with their velvet green lawns, glimpsed through black iron railings. But Sophia was tired so they went straight home.

One afternoon Mara walked over to the Dower House. She followed the same track they took when riding, going halfway down the drive then cutting across the parkland, heading south-west, through the edge of a wood and down a steep field to the house which stood at the entrance to the valley. But when Mara arrived she found the workmen were busy and it was obvious that she was in the way. Not wanting to go back to the Park yet – the dreaded tea tray was still two hours away – she made her way back up the field and started walking along the top of the hill, following a path through the woods. After an hour, just as she'd hoped, she came out above Elenora's cottage, and realized that the Dower House, the Park and the cottage formed the three points of an uneven triangle. The Park was the top point, the Dower House the middle point, and the cottage the right-hand point. What pleased her most was that the valley in which the cottage nestled was an extension of the Dower House valley; the two were joined not only by that valley but by the woods which ran along the top of it, their interconnecting path entirely hidden by trees.

When Elenora came to the door she said, 'There you are. I was just talking about you.'

It hadn't occurred to Mara that other people might be there and she wished she hadn't come, but she could hardly turn tail and run. So she followed Elenora through into the studio and was introduced to a rather plain girl with mousy hair and an anaemic face. Mara thought she looked as though she lived on carrots and celery and never touched meat. That was from her complexion, which was very white and rather greasy, but not from her body, which was buxom and motherly. 'This is Sarah Bucklethwaite,' said Elenora. 'And this,' she pointed to a young man who was lounging against the window, 'is Paul Lacy. Paul owns an art gallery in London. We're old friends.' She pushed Mara into the middle of the room. 'And this is Mara Rushton.'

Sarah looked Mara up and down, taking in Mara's

smart russet-coloured suit and new grey-and-russet-checked coat. 'Oh, to marry money!' she exclaimed.

Mara was furious. 'I didn't marry money.' She hadn't married Alexander för his money. How dare this plain, mousy girl, who would probably never marry anyone, rich or poor, suggest she had?

'Now then, stop that Sarah,' said Paul, producing a chair for Mara. 'Just because you've rejected your parents' wealth, there's no need to expect us all to do the same.' He said it firmly but there was a fondness in his eyes as he looked at Sarah. Mara was surprised by it. What on earth could this rather dapper young man see in a scruff like Sarah?

Elenora smoothed the ruffled feathers. 'Perhaps Mara hasn't had such an easy life as you, Sarah,' she said gently. 'It's all very well to give things up, but you've got to have them first.'

Mara said nothing. Is it so obvious, she wondered. Did she still have that haunted, hunted look about her? They went on to talk of other things, of books and paintings, and Mara was glad although she knew nothing of what they discussed. But at least they weren't talking about her. Nor did they talk to her, and as she had nothing to add to the conversation she sat in silence, wishing she hadn't come. Elenora sensed this and at the first break in the conversation said, 'Are Rushton-Gaunt racing this summer?'

This was home ground for Mara. Never had she thought all those endless discussions about cars she heard at the Park would stand her in good stead. By the time she stood up to leave she was feeling a little better. 'I didn't bring your magazines,' she told Elenora.

Elenora touched Mara's arm. 'Bring them next time.'

Mara smiled uncertainly. She wasn't sure she wanted

to come again. She remembered how, when Alexander had been angry with her, she'd thought of Elenora and how they would laugh. But laugh together, not that she would come here and other people would laugh at her.

'Don't let Sarah upset you,' said Elenora, 'she does that with everyone. Attack is her way of dealing with her lack of self-confidence.' She smiled. 'We all have our different ways of dealing with it, don't we?'

We certainly do, thought Mara as she walked up the steep field to the woods. I wonder what my way is? Hiding behind my barriers. Pretending I don't care. Being clumsy when I'm nervous. She was still disappointed that other people had been at the cottage, it was as if the water of the oasis were slightly brackish. But what did I expect? Someone like Elenora is bound to have friends more interesting and more clever than I am. She went on through the wood and it began to rain.

When Mara came out of the woods and saw the Park she felt even more depressed. 'Back to prison,' she muttered. 'And will it never stop raining?' She bent her head to protect her face, just as she had done when she'd gone into Koblenz each week to ask about her father.

Suddenly she heard the sound of a horn. She looked up. A car was going up the drive towards the house. It stopped and the driver hooted at her again. Thinking it must be Alexander and wondering what reason she could give for coming out of that part of the woods, Mara hurried over to it. But it wasn't Alexander, it was Mark Hatton. He was alone in the car and his arm was resting on the ledge of the open window as he turned his head to watch Mara approach. 'So that's where you disappear to,' he said.

'What do you mean?' Mara was rather embarrassed now that she had come face to face with him. Since the time when he had talked of von Richthofen, she had built him up into a white knight complete with sword and charger.

Mark said, 'Oh, to the woods, to the woods.'

For one awful moment Mara thought he knew about Elenora. 'I went to the Dower House,' she answered quickly. 'I had to walk because Owen and Bonner were both busy and I don't ride well enough to go out on my own.'

'You should learn to drive.' Mark said it casually and confidently as though all Mara had to do was to click her fingers and whatever she wished would be hers.

'I wish I could.'

'I could teach you.'

Mara hesitated. 'Alexander wanted me to learn to ride first. I'll probably learn to drive later.'

Mark laughed and his face became even more boyish. 'Don't tell me he doesn't believe in women driving?'

'I don't know, but I'm sure Herbert doesn't.'

Mark looked at her. 'My dear Mara, Herbert's an uneducated bore.'

He's right, thought Mara, but she felt guilty at having listened to him.

'Come on, get in,' he said. 'You're getting drenched standing there. I'm going to the Park anyhow, I'm dining "*en famille* Rushton" tonight.'

Mara climbed in beside him and he turned to smile at her before driving on. 'I'm sure if poor Sophia had known quite how bad he was going to turn out she'd never have married him,' he added. 'Of course it's too late now, she's terrified of him.'

Mara's curiosity got the better of her. 'Wasn't he always like this?'

'He was pretty bad but one hoped for improvement.

254

After all, when she married him the Rushtons had only just moved to the Park. Mind you, I do feel a bit sorry for Herbert. Alexander had a gentleman's education and looks like a gent, Herbert went to the village school and looks it.' They had reached the house and were parked in front of the steps.

Mara nodded. It was true. Benefits. 'Why . . . why did Sophia marry Herbert?' she asked tentatively.

'Because she wanted to marry someone else and he wouldn't marry her because she hadn't any money, so rather than be buffeted around from one relation to another she accepted Herbert who had money but wanted a well-bred wife. I, on the other hand, am well-bred but need a rich wife.'

Mara laughed. He said it so matter of factly that she couldn't believe it was true.

'You know you're a most attractive lady,' said Mark, studying her face. 'If you weren't married to Alexander I'd be most tempted to try to seduce you.'

Mara felt she should be cross with him for saying that, but he was so charming. When he opened the car door for her, and said with a naughty smile which reminded her of Jamie's wicked smile, 'You never know, I might try just the same,' she was still unable to be cross.

That night at dinner Mara felt Mark's eyes on her. He was sitting opposite her and every time she looked up he smiled and gave her a little half wink, and she blushed and hoped Alexander hadn't noticed. She still wasn't sure if she found Mark attractive or if it was simply the attention he was giving her that made her feel warm and alive, and a little bit excited, but in any case it made the endless talk of cars more interesting because she could listen to Mark and imagine him saying, 'I might try just the same.' Not that I would, she told herself firmly. Adultery! It had never occurred to Mara that she might be unfaithful to Alexander because she hadn't expected to meet anyone with whom she would want to do it. Jamie had said to her, 'One day you'll meet someone you love,' but she already had, and what good had it done her? That she made love with Alexander but was not in love with him was, to Mara, entirely different.

'The trouble with the aero-engine designs,' the Old Man was saying, 'was that they were foisted on me by those people from the war contracts. We made the engines and some other wretches made the airframe. That seems crazy to me.'

Mark said, 'You're right, sir.'

'And I'm sure they've got the whole thing wrong. Birds fly and they aren't biplanes. Have you ever seen a double-winged bird, Mara?'

'Er . . . umm . . . no.'

'The Vogels weren't double-winged then?'

'Er . . . umm . . . no, sadly not.' She answered as best she could and forced herself to pay attention; the Old Man had a disconcerting way of springing questions on people just to make sure they were listening.

Mark picked up his wine glass and smiled at Mara over the rim as he turned it slowly, making the deep red of the wine glow in the light from the candles. 'It's often occurred to me, sir, that wood isn't the right material. It makes the plane so clumsy. I'm sure I could come up with a better design for the airframe, but in aluminium.'

The Old Man put down his knife and fork. 'You're quite right.' He chuckled. 'I've already worked out a few modifications – twin engines, I can't help feeling that's the answer.'

Herbert interrupted. 'Papa, can I . . .'

But his father went on, his face alight with enthusiasm. 'Well, what do you say, Mark? Shall we have a crack at this aviation business?'

Mark raised his glass to the Old Man. 'If Sopwith can do it with his Camels . . .'

'Ah, but Sopwith's a genius.'

Herbert mouthed something at Alexander, then said, 'Papa, we . . .'

The Old Man ignored him. He turned to Mara: 'Tom Sopwith's the greatest aviator of our time – of any time.'

'Papa!'

'Well, what is it, Herbert?'

'We've got the Roadster to produce and we're still behind with the orders we took for the saloon at the Motor Show last November.'

'So?'

'Alexander and I agree that . . .'

'Agree what? You haven't had time to agree anything. Alexander!'

Alexander looked nervously from Herbert to his father. It was obvious to Mara that he didn't want to say anything but that if he didn't Herbert would later accuse him of being weak. 'Herbert has a point,' he said. 'We are very behind and a . . . er . . . areoplanes is a new venture.' He looked wildly round the table, hoping someone else would speak up and support him, but no one did, so he went on, even more nervously, 'Perhaps we could do it in a year or two.'

'And let someone else do it first? My God, if technology were left up to you two we wouldn't have discovered the wheel yet.'

Chapter 15

What a difference the spring made! It crept up slowly through the mist and cold of early March and then suddenly it was there, in the house, in the garden, in the woods and the park but most of all in Mara, for spring was Mara's time of year.

She came alive in the spring, throwing off her bout of questioning depression as she put away her winter clothes. She came alive in the house, laughing and joking to the amazement of all who had thought her reserved and rather cold. She came alive in the park where she rode each morning, her hair shining in the wind and her laughter echoing across the grass as she urged Mahogany into a gallop. She came alive in the woods through which she slipped unnoticed to visit Elenora, and alive again in the cottage where not even Sarah Bucklethwaite could deflate her. But most of all she came alive because she was young and so was spring, and like the spring she pushed the dark deep winter behind her.

She still thought about Jamie, but it was now nearly four months since she had seen him and, although she remembered very clearly each separate feature of his face, the bitterness she felt towards him blocked its entirety. It was easier for her to remember Koblenz and the house, inanimate objects whose corners and edges did not change and would not change. Jamie was in her emotions and in her mind, he inhabited the vast brooding jungle of her thoughts: that part, hidden by the door behind the eyes and the mouth which separates the person-real from the person-exposed, which somehow physically manages to fit the small space inside the skull although its boundaries are limitless, reaching to the edge of experience and beyond. That was where Jamie now lived, along with her father, her mother, her brother. All vague shadows and impressions, half-remembered faces and expressions: a raised eyebrow, a peculiar smile, a lock of hair falling forward, or whatever of them clung to her memory as their faces blurred with time. Never to be forgotten, just less well defined.

And another thing had happened with time, something which seemed almost a betrayal of herself: she was beginning to understand why Jamie had pressed her to do something with her life. In Koblenz she had been convinced he was adding insult to injury by trying to condemn her to a drab existence as a shopgirl or a governess but now she wasn't so sure. She despised herself for giving Jamie even the smallest benefit of doubt, but meeting Elenora had opened her eyes. For if a girl like Sarah Bucklethwaite had an interesting job – she was a social worker in the East End of London, not that that appealed to Mara – then surely she herself could have done something. And what about all those articles in Elenora's magazines? Articles about women and by women who ignored the 'women-aren't-capable-of-doing-that' and projected themselves into whatever sphere they chose. But it's all very well for them, Mara told herself, they're clever and talented, I'm not. I'm not stupid. But I'm not good at anything. And she would send Rachel to ask Bonner to get Mahogany ready and then she would ride out in the spring, and forget about it.

She would forget about Alexander as well, and try not to think about Mark. Between herself and Alexander things had reached a point of contented coexistence; they

259

didn't argue, he no longer asked her where she went if she was late back, they talked mainly about the Dower House and how pleased they were with its progress, but she felt none of the excitement with him that she felt when she was with Mark. Sometimes this worried her, but most of the time she ignored the danger signals, telling herself it was Alexander's fault for not being more fun. Mark was fun. He came and went as he pleased, disappearing off to London for days on end then reappearing suddenly.

One day Mara met him in the village. 'So when am I going to teach you to drive?' he asked.

'I don't know. Later.'

'Coward!'

They were standing on the village green outside the pub and Mara was very aware that Owen was sitting in the car waiting for her. 'I must go.'

He nodded towards the pub. 'Come and have a drink.'

'Oh, no.' Mara had never been in a pub and as far as she knew ladies didn't.'

'Coward.'

She laughed, then remembered their previous conversation. 'You'll never find a rich wife in there, you know.'

'I'm drowning my sorrows because you won't let me make passionate love to you.'

'In the middle of the village green!' She turned and walked back to Owen, calling over her shoulder, 'Lady Henrietta's coming to stay tomorrow. Try your charm on her.'

'No,' he shouted, 'I'll try it on you at the hunt ball.'

The hunt ball was something Mara was looking forward to with a mixture of excitement and dread. She was longing to wear her beautiful new dress, a mermaid's dress was how Madame Cecile had described it – the finest silk chiffon, neither blue nor green but halfway between, and very pale, like an exquisite aquamarine lying on the bottom of a clear sea. When Mara tried on the dress, as she had done several times, and twisted and turned in front of the mirror, it became just like the sea rippled by the graceful dive of a mermaid. But the trouble was in the mermaid. Mara hardly knew how to dance.

The next afternoon Mara and Alexander were sitting on the drawing-room sofa – he had come home early from work so as to be there for Lady Henrietta's arrival, Herbert and his father being tied up at work. Mark was lounging in an armchair reading the newspaper and Atalanta was brushing Prince's tail with a feather. 'I have a problem,' she said to Alexander in a low voice.

'What, darling?' He looked concerned.

She pulled a face. 'I can't dance.'

His look of concern changed to a smile. 'Can't dance?' he said loudly. 'But everyone can dance.'

Atalanta sat up straight. 'Why can't you dance?'

Mark yawned and put away the paper. 'You must be able to dance. Didn't you have lessons when you were a child?'

Mara was furious with Alexander for having spoken so loudly, now she not only couldn't dance but everyone knew she couldn't. Atalanta came over and wheedled her arms round Alexander's neck, pushing her face up against his so that her long dark curls tickled his chin. 'Why can't you dance?' she asked again. 'All girls can dance. Even I can dance. Miss Pinner teaches us.'

Mara said, 'I can't dance because I haven't had a dancing lesson since I was twelve, and then it was only the basic steps.'

'But why?' Atalanta persisted.

'Because the war came and the lessons ended.'

Atalanta looked at Mara and whispered loudly to Alexander, 'If Aunt Mara can't dance and I can, am I prettier than she is?'

Alexander laughed and hugged his niece. 'Oh, you'll be just as pretty when you're grown up.'

Atalanta thought for a moment. 'When I'm grown up, Aunt Mara will be very old, won't she?' She watched Mara with glee.

Mark came over to them. 'She may be very old, Atalanta,' he ruffled her hair, 'and you may be much prettier than she is, but you'll never be as beautiful, because to be beautiful a woman must have both aggression and vulnerability and to have that' – he looked at Mara – 'she must have suffered.'

For once Mara was glad of Atalanta's presence, for her chatter covered what could have been an embarrassing moment. 'Mrs Taylor doesn't think Aunt Mara's beautiful,' Atalanta said, trying to regain her dancing superiority. 'In fact, I heard her telling Mummy that she didn't know what all the fuss was about. She even said' – Atalanta gave Mara a triumphant smile – 'that she thought Aunt Mara was on the plain side.'

The old cow, thought Mara, but she had to laugh because Mark was roaring with laughter and Alexander, who had been cross at first, was also beginning to smile. 'She's probably disappointed,' said Mark, glancing at Alexander.

'What do you mean?' demanded Atalanta.

'Never you mind. Now, how are we going to teach your wife to dance, Alexander? I know what' – he clapped his hands – 'we'll ask Sophia to play the piano and we'll have a lesson. Come on! Atalanta, go and fetch your mother. Hurry!' He swept them all up with his enthusiasm

262

and they rushed along to the music room where they rolled up the carpet and cleared away the chairs.

'Atalanta said you wanted me to play the piano,' said Sophia, coming into the room. 'She said Mara's having a dancing lesson.'

'Yes.' Mark put an arm around her thin shoulders and led her to the piano. 'A waltz first if you please, maestro.' He executed a low bow before her. 'And nothing too difficult. Something like "The Blue Danube", oh nimble-fingered one.'

Laughing, Sophia shuffled through her music sheets. 'Can't you dance at all, Mara?' she asked, smiling sympathetically, her cheeks flushed and her eyes full of pleasure at being included in their games.

'No, I can't. Only a few basic steps.'

'Well, you'll soon learn, darling.' Alexander slid his right arm round her waist and took her right hand in his left. 'You go like this. One-two-three, one-two-three. Hurry up with the music, Sophia!'

'I'm ready, I'm ready.' She played the first few bars of 'The Blue Danube'.

'What's going on?' asked Damon, running into the room.

'Mara's having a dancing lesson,' replied his mother.

'And you're going to dance with me,' cried Atalanta, grabbing him round the waist and dragging him into the middle of the room.

Miss Pinner put her head round the door. 'I was looking for the twins, Mrs Rushton.'

'They're dancing, Miss Pinner,' said Mark. 'And you' – he went up to her and took her by the hand – 'are going to dance with me,' and before the startled woman could object, he'd whisked her round the room, shouting, 'One-two-three, one-two-three, come on, Mara, stop pulverizing poor Alexander's feet.'

They were all laughing and shouting at each other and humming in time to the music. 'And now the foxtrot,' called Sophia, changing to another tune. They changed partners, Damon with Miss Pinner, Alexander with Atalanta, Mark with Mara.

He's like a master of ceremonies, Mara thought as he whisked her round a corner. Look at us all, we're happy. We just need someone to make us all happy. We need Mark.

'Good heavens!' exclaimed a woman's voice from the doorway. 'My dear Samuel, I'd no idea such things went on at Rushton Park.' The music stopped and they stopped dancing. Standing in the doorway, with the Old Man beside her and Herbert just behind them, was Lady Henrietta. 'What is going on?' she asked, smiling at Sophia.

'Mara's having a dancing lesson. She felt she needed a bit of practice.'

Lady Henrietta looked at Mara and then at Mark, whose arm was still round Mara's waist. 'What a good idea. So nice to see you all having fun. Hello everyone.' She smiled at Alexander, and Mara, and at each of the twins, wished Miss Pinner a good evening, then said to Mark, 'Ah, Mr Hatton, I think we've met before.' She held out her hand so Mark was forced to release Mara and go over to her.

Mara took two hours to get ready for the ball. First she had a long hot scented bath, then she washed her hair and sat in front of the fire to half dry it; after that Rachel twisted the ends round some of Sophia's curlers – Mara didn't normally use them – to make sure it would turn under in a soft roll. Whilst waiting for her hair to dry, Mara fiddled around at her dressing table, painting her nails and chatting to Rachel. 'I do hope my dress is going to be all right,' she said. 'It's a bit transparent. You can see my legs when I walk.'

'It'll look lovely, madam,' Rachel reassured her.

'Can I interrupt?' Alexander came in, doing up his bow tie.

Rachel gave a little bob. 'Call me when you need me, madam. I'll wait outside.'

Alexander said, 'Oh, don't leave, Rachel. I want to see if you approve of the present I've bought my wife.' He held his big hands, which were clenched together, in front of Mara. 'Close your eyes,' he said, She closed them. 'All right. Open them!'

Mara looked down. Lying in the large flat palms of his hands was a long string of pearls. They were just what she wanted but had not liked to buy because they were so expensive. 'They're beautiful! They're just what I wanted. How did you know?'

He laughed and slipped them over her head, then wound them twice round her neck so that they formed a pearl choker but with plenty to spare, to hang down almost to her waist. 'I saw you admiring some in a magazine. Well, Rachel, what do you think?'

The maid nodded her head vigorously and after Alexander had left the room, she said to Mara, 'You're so lucky to have a husband like Mr Rushton, madam.'

Mara reached up her hand to touch the pearls. I suppose I am, she thought, and she stood up and took out the rollers and waited for Rachel to hand her the dress.

Samuel Rushton's party consisted of sixteen people. Apart from his family and Mark and Lady Henrietta, there were the Taylors and Alison, Sir Henry Gaunt, a couple in their mid-thirties called Geoffrey and Caroline

Plumstead, who had a large farm near Banbury, Caroline's pretty debutante sister Judith, Geoffrey's gangling cousin Paul, who like Alexander had just left the Army and was about to go into the diplomatic service, and a middle-aged widow called Mrs Hartlett who lived the other side of Gaunt and was a great friend of Mrs Taylor's.

By the time Mara came downstairs they had all arrived and were being ushered into the drawing room. 'Ah, there you are,' said Alexander, smiling with relief. It was desperately important to him that Mara's first social event of any magnitude should be an unqualified success, both from her point of view and from his. He was aware that she was different from the other girls he knew, it was her difference which had attracted him in the first place, but now she was his wife he wanted her to keep that difference but also to conform. She was a strange and exotic creature he had brought home to keep in a glass cabinet, only she'd refused to stay inside it, but that didn't mean she could be late. She had to follow the rules. This time she'd just managed not to break them, and he smiled proudly at her for what he was convinced was her good timing and because she looked so beautiful, in her blue-green dress with his pearls around her neck.

He led her across to Mrs Hartlett. 'I don't think you've met my wife.'

'But I've heard all about her,' said Mrs Hartlett, giving Mara a surprised smile, 'though I hadn't realized she was so beautiful.' Her eyes drifted across the room to Mrs Taylor's ample back, encased in red moiré, then to Alison looking uncomfortable in pale lemon, and her mouth puckered with wry amusement.

Mara was about to extricate herself in order to find Mark, when Sir Henry came up. 'You're looking very lovely, my dear. Now,' he patted her hand and winked at Mrs Hartlett, 'don't be offended if I don't ask you to dance. I'm too stiff for that sort of thing now, and I never really enjoyed it, all that twiddling around always made me feel a bit of a fool. My dear wife used to enjoy it so I danced to please her, but after she died I thought, why should I do it any more? But I'll ask you to sit out one with me so we can get to know each other better.'

Mara smiled at him. 'I'd love to sit out a dance with you, I'm not much good at dancing myself. In fact,' she confided, 'this is my first ball.'

Sir Henry patted her bare arm. 'An attractive woman can get away with being a bad dancer. I'm always very suspicious when I hear of girls who are good at everything, it usually means they're ugly.'

Mara was longing to find Mark, she wanted to see the admiration in his eyes when he saw her in her beautiful dress. Murmuring an excuse to Sir Henry she made her way across the room, to where Mark was partially hidden by Herbert's massive form. But as she drew near she saw that Mark was in animated conversation with Judith, who had been hidden from Mara's view by Herbert's wide back. Judith was smiling up at Mark and twisting her russet curls around the fingers of her left hand, then drawing them across her face so that her lips were smiling and shiny through her hair. It was a movement of conscious sensuality and Mark was responding to her with his eyes and his words. Watching them Mara felt an appalling pang of jealousy. Mark was hers. She might not want him. But he was hers. Quickly she turned away to talk to Alexander and Caroline, pretending that it was them she'd been intending to join all along. But as she did so, she caught Lady Henrietta's eyes and had an unpleasant feeling that her true intention had been obvious. Mark means nothing to me, Mara told herself, smiling at Caroline and saying, 'Yes, I'd love to come and spend the day with you. I haven't been to Banbury yet but I want to go, I want to see the cross.'

Alexander said fondly, 'Mara used to think it was the white lady on the cockhorse,' and they both laughed.

But Mara's mind was on Mark. She remembered how she'd once thought of him as her white knight complete with sword and charger, and she came to the conclusion that she read far too much into what people said. With a couple of sentences Mark had made her feel she wasn't a leper and, although she would always be grateful to him, she saw that from his one opinion on one subject she had created of him a far superior being. It was as if someone, seeing her with Elenora's *New Statesman* and *Egoist*s under her arm, had concluded that she, Mara, was an intellectual, and upon discovering that she spent her mornings reading fashion magazines they had felt wildly let down by her. It wasn't Mark's fault that he was just a quick-witted charmer, it was her fault for expecting too much of him.

They had dinner at the Park before going to the ball. The dining room and the room next to it had been opened up to make one large room. Mara sat between Geoffrey who talked to her about cows and Sir Henry who said very little. Opposite her sat Mark; she took no notice of him and even when she looked up she didn't look directly at him, but to one side or the other. Two can play at this game, she thought and she smiled at Geoffrey, and said, 'How fascinating.'

The ball was held at Kentington Park where, so Alexander told Mara, The Banbury hunt ball was always held. By the time Samuel Rushton's party arrived it was about to begin and the band was playing a waltz to get people in the dancing mood, while car after car crunched up the gravel drive to deposit its eager passengers in front of the great house. There were shouts of delight as friends greeted friends, the men slapping each other on the back, the women paying compliments on each other's dresses and mentally valuing each other's jewellery.

'I could buy six decent hunters with one of her earrings,' Mara heard one woman remark about another.

'You look better than any of them,' Alexander told Mara as he helped her out of the car. He smiled proudly down at his wife, wrapped in the sable he had given her at Christmas, wearing the pearls he had just given her.

She smiled up at him, drew the sable around her, and thought, he's just as good-looking as Mark and much nicer. 'The pearls are beautiful,' she said. She touched them, then stretched out her hand and touched his jacket where it met across his stomach. It was a gesture of affection and intimacy, and when she turned to walk towards the imposing double staircase which led up to the first-floor entrance and hall, she had the satisfaction of knowing that Mark had seen her. But I didn't only do it for that reason, she thought, I did it because I wanted to.

They joined the throng of laughing, chattering people in the main ballroom and soon they were engulfed by them, finding themselves chattering and laughing too although it was impossible to hear a word. Mara noticed that all the women were busy with their cards, pencilling in the name of their partner beside each dance.

'Alexander, you must look after Mara,' said Lady Henrietta, handing her a card and a pencil.

He blushed. 'Oh, yes, of course. I'll have the first,

darling, and the supper dance and the last. You write my name down next to it.' He showed her how.

'And I'll have the third with my new daughter-in-law,' said the Old Man pointing at the third space on her card.

Herbert asked her stiffly, 'May I have the fourth, Mara?' Mara knew he'd only asked her because he had to, just as Alexander would have to dance with all the ladies in their party, but she couldn't help feeling a bit sorry for Herbert, not only because he had to dance with her when he didn't want to, but because he'd had to come to the ball where he looked so hopelessly out of place. Not even his well-cut tails and his snow-white shirt could hide the fact that he would have been more at home at the back, with the chauffeurs, than inside with the so-called gentry. And she noticed that Sophia, despite being afraid of her husband, was slightly embarrassed by him. This was Sophia's home ground and there was a look about her which seemed to be saying, 'I'm sorry I brought a cart-horse to the meet.'

Mara watched her card fill up: Geoffrey took two waltzes, Mr Taylor took a foxtrot, Paul booked the polka, and Sir Henry asked her to sit out one with him. But Mark hadn't asked her for one dance, he hadn't even spoken to her. As the minutes ticked by Mara became angry. How dare he humiliate her in this way! She looked down at the three blank spaces on her card and hoped someone else would book them, so that if and when Mark came she would have the pleasure of turning him down. But he's not really humiliating me, she thought, it's only because he's spent the past month doing all he could to get me alone and now he's found someone he can not only get on her own but who isn't married, he's not interested in me any more. It's quite understandable. She was thinking all these things when a hand came over

270

her shoulder and took her card. 'Just in time,' said Mark grinning at her, and he squiggled 'M.H.' next to the second, the fifth and the seventh. 'Three. Mustn't take more than the husband or people might start talking,' he murmured in her ear. And then he was gone and the band sounded the opening bar of the first waltz.

Alexander steered Mara on to the floor, slipping his right hand around her waist and linking his fingers into the soft chiffon of her dress. 'I'm so proud of you, darling,' he said, looking down at Mara's glowing face. 'Everyone keeps saying how beautiful you are.' He glanced over her shoulder at the other women as if he were pitying them because they were not like Mara.

Dancing wasn't so difficult after all, Mara soon discovered. The floor was sufficiently full that those twists and turns she had been afraid of were practically impossible.

'You're doing very well, Mara,' Alexander told her as they successfully turned the corner and started back down the length of the room. 'Very well.'

But at that moment she trod on his foot. 'Sorry.' She pulled a face.

'Don't worry.' He held her closer. He danced well, nothing fancy but competently, and by the time their waltz ended Mara was feeling much more confident.

'I'm glad my first dance was with you,' she told him as he led her off the floor. 'Anyone else wouldn't have been nearly so patient.'

Alexander squeezed her hand, and Mara was reminded of how it had been at the Ritz: he had wanted her to look elegant but he'd liked it best when she was a little unsure of herself.

Mark was standing in front of them. 'I think it's my dance next,' he said, taking Mara's hand. It was the first time they had touched since they had first been introduced and he led her towards the dance floor, his hand locked in hers, as if she were his, not Alexander's, wife. In the middle of the dance floor he stopped and slipped his arm around her waist. 'I suppose this is the nearest I'm going to get to you?'

Whether Mara found him physically attractive or not she still wasn't sure, but he certainly made her feel something. Despite his boyish figure his arm was strong – she could feel that as she tried to pull away from him.

'What's the matter, Mrs Rushton?' He gave her the benefit of his most charming smile. 'Don't you like dancing with me, or are you afraid we'll cause a scandal?' He moved his fingers very slightly against her back as he said the word 'scandal'.

Mara had no intention of succumbing to his charm, she wasn't some impressionable girl even if she was at her first dance. 'Not at all, it's simply that you're crushing my dress.'

'I'm not crushing it, I'm ironing it for you. And while we're on the subject of your dress, what do you expect if you wear something that looks like a sea anemone, floating and semi-transparent and with a soft' – he looked down at her lips – 'centre.'

Mara frowned. 'Stop it, Mark!'

He steered her to the far corner of the floor, away from Alexander who was dancing with Sophia. 'I watched you when we went in to dinner. I loved the way the skirt of your dress caught on the silk of your stockings as you walked. It made your legs look as if they were encased in this delicious nothing.' He stroked the material at her waist, letting the tips of his fingers linger against her back. They danced on in silence, she with her eyes on his

272

shoulder, he with his eyes on her mouth. 'I want to see you alone,' he said.

Mara shook her head. She admitted now that she wanted him, that her body wanted his, and that she craved the excitement he offered her. But the word 'adultery' rose up before her and she shook her head again more firmly.

She danced with the Old Man who was a wonderful dancer, then with Herbert who danced surprisingly well. Only Mara was uncomfortable with him, she was sure he had no more desire to dance with her than she had to dance with him, and yet, once when she looked up at his face she found that he was watching her mouth in the same way Mark had. I'm imagining it, she thought, but she was glad when Mark came to claim her. This time they danced in silence, and in silence he handed her over to Alexander for the supper dance.

At supper Mara was entirely occupied by Alexander who kept introducing her to people whose names she couldn't catch but whose hostility, though carefully veiled, was there. Once when they turned away from one group Mara heard a man say, 'She's certainly very attractive,' and a woman answered him, 'But why couldn't he marry an English girl? There are plenty around, and much prettier,' and a younger man's voice said, 'Prettier maybe, but she's got something and I wouldn't mind knowing her better.' There was a shocked gasp from the woman but the men murmured in agreement.

After supper Mr Taylor came for his foxtrot. 'I'm afraid I'm not very good,' Mara apologized after kicking him on the ankle.

'Not to worry.' He swung her round a corner and she nearly fell over. Regaining her balance Mara caught Alexander's eye. He was dancing with Judith and he gave

Mara a sympathetic smile. She smiled back at him and raised her eyebrows as if to say, 'I'm doing my best in the circumstances.'

After the foxtrot Mara sat out a dance with Sir Henry. She found him with Lady Henrietta, sitting on a sofa in a small drawing room away from the noise and the bustle of the ball. 'There you are, my dear,' he said. 'Come and sit down. I hope you don't mind missing the fun to keep an old man company.'

Mara laughed and sank thankfully into an armchair. 'I'm delighted. My feet are beginning to ache, but not I'm afraid as much as those of my partners. Poor Alexander, I trod on his. And, oh dear, poor Mr Taylor, I kicked him.'

'Do him a power of good,' growled Sir Henry. 'The man needs a good kick. He keeps complaining about the villagers grazing their cattle on the green. Why shouldn't they, I say.' He got up stiffly. 'I could do with a glass of something and I expect you could, Mara. And you, Henrietta? No good asking the footmen, they're run off their feet. I'll be back in a minute.' He marched off towards the bar.

'You're shaping up very well, Mara,' said Lady Henrietta once they were alone, 'I was sure you would.' She gave Mara a wry smile. 'I gather you haven't forgotten Madame Cecile.'

Mara blushed. 'I've been rather extravagant.'

'Ummm . . . the Rushtons can afford it. Why shouldn't you have pretty clothes? That dress is quite lovely. A girl needs clothes, just so long as they're not the only thing she thinks about.'

'They're not,' said Mara, thinking, I think of Mark . . . and Jamie. And she wondered what Jamie would say if he could see her now.

'How are you getting on?' Lady Henrietta asked bluntly.

'Fine.' Mara put on a bright smile.

'Samuel tells me there was a bit of trouble with one of the grooms but he seems to think you coped pretty well.'

'Yes. Bonner. We've established a sort of truce.' Mara looked towards the exuberant crowd beyond the door. 'But I still have a long way to go.'

'How do you get on with Herbert?'

Mara shrugged her shoulders.

Lady Henrietta looked purposefully at a picture on the wall opposite. 'Young Mark Hatton seems very at home at the Park.'

'Yes.' Mara prayed she wouldn't blush.

'Not succumbed to his charm, have you?'

She turned to face Mara, who forced herself to look the older woman straight in the eyes and say, 'Oh, no, I think he's great fun, that's all.'

'Because it wouldn't do,' said Lady Henrietta. 'The discreet affair of an older woman is one thing, for a newly married girl in your precarious position to have even the mildest of flirtations is asking for trouble.'

Mara was shocked. A discreet affair sounded so calculating. 'I can assure you there's nothing between Mark and myself.'

Sir Henry came back. 'I thought orange juice would be the most cooling drink,' he said, handing them each a glass. 'Now, what are you girls talking about?'

'We were talking about Mark,' replied Lady Henrietta. 'Poor Mark! I gather old man Hatton's as mean as sin and tedious with it. Mark must find himself a rich wife.'

Sir Henry laughed. 'So he keeps telling me.'

Mara didn't hear the rest of the conversation because Paul came to claim her for the polka, one of the few dances Mara could do. But sadly Paul couldn't. It was like dancing with a daddy-longlegs. After that she danced with Mark again, and with Lady Henrietta's words still ringing in her ears she kept her arms rigid, forcing him to keep his distance.

'I saw you talking to Lady Henrietta,' he said.

'Yes.'

'Was it about me?'

Mara didn't answer him. In a paradoxical way, now he was a forbidden fruit she found him more attractive. She wondered if she'd not been married and had met him if she'd still have wanted him. It was impossible to say.

Mark steered her to the far corner of the room, just as he had during their first dance. 'So when are we going to meet?' he asked. 'Can you get up to London?'

Mara shook her head.

'Why not?'

'Because I don't want to.'

'I don't believe you.' He dug his fingers into her back.

'Believe what you like.'

They danced on in silence. 'If you won't meet me I shall' – he looked over her shoulder and his eye fell on Alison Taylor dancing with Herbert – 'go and seduce that horsy girl in the yellow dress.'

Mara turned her head to see who he was talking about. Then she laughed. 'Alison! You wouldn't stand a chance.'

'Wouldn't I?' He pulled her closer. 'Do you want to bet?'

At that moment the music stopped and Alexander came to claim Mara for the last dance. And when the last dance ended, the huntsman suddenly leaped up on to the rostrum with the band and blew the hunting horn, and Mara found herself pushed into a human chain which proceeded to gallop round the ballroom, the men shouting and hallooing, the women giggling and shrieking. 'The post-horn gallop,' Alexander shouted down Mara's ear, taking a firmer hold on her waist as the human chain went round faster and faster beneath the watching portraits whose subjects had done just the same many years before.

When Mara had collected her coat and they were all standing in the hall, everyone saying goodbye to everyone, everyone saying what a good ball it had been, she looked for Mark and to her surprise saw him standing near the bottom of the stairs engrossed in conversation with Alison. I don't believe it, she thought, watching them. Mark was being his most charming and whatever he was saying was having its effect on Alison, who was gazing rapturously up at him, her unmade-up face glistening in the light from a huge chandelier. He wouldn't. He couldn't. She wouldn't. Mara drew her sable around herself and rolled the pearls between the fingers of her right hand. Mark looked over at her and his eyes took in not only Mara's face but the richness of her coat and pearls, and suddenly it occurred to Mara that part of her attraction for him was that she'd done what he wanted to do: she had married money. In his eyes she saw admiration for what she was and for what she had done, the same admiration she had felt for the pearls when she'd seen them in a magazine. They'd been too expensive for her to buy and that had given them an allure which had made her want them all the more. That was what she was for Mark, too expensive. Her unattainability was her great allure.

She smiled across the room at him and ran her hand over the shivering tips of her sable, then she linked her arm through Alexander's and they went out into the night, to the chauffeur and the smart car, to the enormous house with its many servants. And Mara smiled to herself. It was a game that two could play.

277

Chapter 16

Mark went away three days after the ball. Mara didn't see him before he left and she only knew he'd gone because she overheard Herbert saying to Alexander, 'This business of the aeroplane has to be stopped. Did you know Mark was going to America to look at what their aviation industry's up to? No, I didn't either. I'm going to say something to the Old Man as soon as Lady Henrietta goes home and we're on our own. And I jolly well hope you'll support me. Mark's away for two months so we've plenty of time. Good. That's settled. The whole thing's a bloody farce. The Old Man must be losing his marbles.'

Mara was irritated too. Mark could have told her he was going away.

Having Lady Henrietta at the Park made a pleasant change. No longer was the conversation at meals about the works, for Lady Henrietta didn't approve of men talking business in front of women. 'That's quite enough,' she told the Old Man one evening. 'I'm not training to be a mechanic.'

'Yes, teacher,' said the Old Man, and they all laughed. 'Thank you, teacher.' He gave Lady Henrietta a craggy smile to which she inclined her head, and Mara saw that they were alike in their way and that they were very fond of each other.

During Lady Henrietta's visit she and Sophia and Mara went over to the Dower House. They took the twins with them and had a rather cold picnic on the terrace outside the drawing room. 'You've been very clever to choose that pale sage green for the drawing room,' Lady Henrietta told Mara. 'Such a smart colour.'

Mara admitted, 'Actually it was Sophia's idea.'

'Then, clever to have taken good advice.'

Damon and Atalanta were wandering round the garden. They stopped under the big oak tree and looked up at its massive branches. Watching them Mara remembered how Alexander had looked up at the tree and she suddenly felt very fond of her husband for that simple confession of childhood. If only we could have more of that, she thought, more of telling each other the things which are important. We never say what we feel. She pictured them sitting alone in the long dining room and wondered what on earth they would find to talk about once they moved to the Dower House.

Damon was retying the ribbons in Atalanta's hair. He was doing it very gently, stroking the long dark curls up into his hand before tying each ribbon. Mara heard Atalanta say, 'Don't hurt me, will you?' and Damon reply, 'Do I ever hurt you?' and Atalanta, 'No, never, not like Miss Pinner. She's so rough.' They looked so sweet together, Damon with his beautiful face set solemn to his task, Atalanta with her head slightly bowed and her curls waiting to be tamed. Whenever Mara saw the twins together like this she was shocked to feel twinges of jealousy. Damon was hers. Atalanta was Alexander's. Atalanta disliked Mara and she herself had little time for the girl whom she saw as growing up into a real bitch. But although the feeling between herself and Damon was strong, seeing them together forced her to accept that between Damon and Atalanta there was also great feeling.

Mara turned to Sophia and began to talk about the

279

wallpaper for the dining room, telling herself that she was silly to be jealous and that she was becoming as bad as all the rest of the family.

Another day they all went over to see Geoffrey and Caroline Plumstead and on the way back they did a detour through Banbury so Mara could see the cross. Owen stopped the car, and Sophia said, 'It's there.'

Mara would have liked to leave the car and look closely at the carved figures at the base of the cross, perhaps even to run her fingers down their grey stone curves, but they were in a hurry to get home for tea so they drove on. Home for tea, she thought closing her eyes as they went up the steep hill on their way out of Banbury. Ruled by the tea tray! A wave of depression rolled over her.

Lady Henrietta left next morning and Mara went straight over to Elenora's cottage. The depression which had come over her as they left Banbury was still in its embryo form, like a huge black cloud which at any moment could come down and squash her in its blackness. I can't afford to let it happen, she told herself as she hurried through the sunlit woods. If it can happen now, in the spring, when the sun's shining and there's hope in the air, then I'll never get rid of it. As she came out of the woods above the cottage and began to run down the field Prince caught her up, his tongue lolling out of his black jaws and his sleek sides heaving with exertion. 'Oh, Prince!' She looked down at him and he wagged his tail. She'd never taken him to the cottage before because of Elenora's dog, but now she couldn't go back, not just for Prince.

Elenora was in the garden. 'Hello.' She looked at Prince. 'And hello Prince.'

Mara said, 'You don't mind? He followed me.'

'Not at all. He and Percy are great friends.' The black sort-of-spaniel came haring out of the house and bounded up to Prince. Mara watched the dogs roll each other over. She wondered how and when Prince had become great friends with Percy, then decided it must have been when Alexander was in the Army and the labrador had roamed over here in search of company, rather as she had.

Mara was relieved to find Elenora was alone. They sat outside the cottage on a rough wooden bench, their elbows leaning on a rough wooden table, mugs of tea in their hands.

'So, did you enjoy the ball?' Elenora asked.

'Umm . . . yes.' To Mara her two worlds, the one at Rushton Park and the one at the cottage, were so separate in her mind that it astounded her to find they had any connection or, as with Prince, that one world knew about the other.

'I used to go,' said Elenora, 'but I don't any more.'

Mara wondered whether Elenora used to go with Mr Harris and if he had been an avid post-horn galloper. She said, 'I've never been to a ball before and I'm not a very good dancer. I kept treading on people's toes.'

Elenora laughed. 'I'm sure it did them a lot of good. They need it. Sarah went to a ball in London a couple of years ago, her first and last, and she nearly broke some man's ankle.'

'I can't imagine Sarah going to a ball.'

'She looked very good. She brought her dress here and tried it on to see what I thought.'

Tentatively Mara said, 'Yes, I suppose she could be quite attractive . . .'

'She is already.' Elenora lit a cigarette and pushed back her straggly hair. 'She's one of those girls whom a number of men find attractive for reasons inexplicable to women. I think men feel she's inherently good, like their mothers were – or should have been.'

Mara remembered the fondness in Paul's eyes when he had looked at Sarah. 'Paul seems to think so.'

'Yes, he's mad about her,' Elenora laughed, 'and she's not remotely interested in him. He's too money-minded for Sarah. She needs someone who intends to dedicate his life to the good of others. Anything less than that would be hopeless, she'd be unbearably sanctimonious and the man would feel a continual heel.'

Mara smiled. She thought of Jamie. Was he someone who intended to dedicate his life to the good of others? She wasn't sure. 'To dedicate one's life' sounded desiccated and saintly and Jamie was neither of those.

When Mara returned to the Park she was feeling much better. Being with Elenora had lifted her depression, the black cloud had gone up into the sky.

Sir Henry came to dinner that evening so Herbert and Alexander had to wait till lunch the next day, Sunday, before tackling the Old Man about the aeroplane. Mara could feel the tension brewing up as the Old Man carved the roast beef.

When he had sat, the vegetables had been handed round and the servants had withdrawn, Herbert began. 'I gather Mark's gone to America to look at airframes, Papa.'

The Old Man tucked his napkin under his chin. 'He has. And we're going to call ours the Gemelli because she'll have twin engines and Gemelli, for the uneducated, means twins.'

Damon said, 'We're twins, will we be able to fly in . . .'

His father cut him short. 'Be quiet, Damon!' He drew

a deep breath. 'Papa, Alexander and I feel this aeroplane idea is getting out of hand. We simply can't afford it. I've looked at the books and . . .'

'Rubbish!'

'It'll cost a fortune.'

'We can afford it.'

'Only if the men forgo their rise in August.'

Alexander looked appalled. 'But they always get a rise then. It's only an extra shilling per week.'

'They'll have to do without.'

Alexander gave his father an anguished glance. 'Herbert, we can't do that!'

'Oh, do shut up! You don't understand a thing about the works so stop pretending you do.'

'That's quite enough,' shouted the Old Man, banging on the table. An empty wine glass fell over and snapped at the stem but no one made a move towards it.

Mara felt horribly embarrassed for Alexander. Herbert had humiliated him, not only in front of her but in front of Sophia and the twins. She longed to scream at him to defend himself, to stand up to Herbert and not to let himself be trodden underfoot or manipulated into looking a fool. She turned to her father-in-law and found him watching her.

'We'll talk about it in the study after lunch,' he said, looking at his sons, but Mara had the feeling he was trying to tell her not to say anything, that he would deal with it later.

'Papa . . .' Herbert's heavy jaw protruded obstinately.

The Old Man cut him short. 'I said we'd talk about it later, now let me eat my lunch in peace.'

Mara could not honestly say it was by chance she went into the garden after lunch and settled herself, ostensibly with a magazine, on a bench near the study window. But she would have been furious if anyone had suggested she went there for the sole purpose of eavesdropping.

The first she heard was her father-in-law: 'I'm not going to discuss the question of the men's rise. I was sickened by what you said, Herbert. Do you realize what an extra shilling means to a man who only gets twenty a week?'

'All right, all right, let's talk about the aeroplane. That's the real problem. As I say, it's simply economics . . .'

'The sort of economics you employed over the war contracts?' There was an edge to the Old Man's voice.

'What about the war contracts?' Alexander sounded puzzled.

Herbert answered, 'Oh, just the spares for the trucks and planes, that's all.'

'What about them?'

'Your brother,' said the Old Man, 'parcelled up the reject stock, which was meant to go back to the foundry, and sent it out with the rest, thus making a tidy little profit for himself. Or rather, he would have done had I not caught him.'

Alexander's voice rose with indignation. 'You mean, you . . . we . . . but I saw men die because their trucks broke down. I saw men blown to pieces as they tried to get them going.' He started to cough, on and on and on, as if the memory of the war had brought the mustard gas back into his lungs.

Mara sensed the Old Man was standing back to watch his sons battle it out. She knew, without seeing him, that he was hoping Alexander would finally rise up and attack. But Alexander said nothing, though he had stopped coughing, and eventually Samuel said, 'I'm glad to say that was only in the first consignment and I immediately

sent out a whole new consignment, free of charge. I t[
the War Office that the two loads had been inadvertently
confused, because I was unable to tell them what my son
had done.' He paused. 'Do you still have the nerve to tell
me how to run my business, Herbert?'

Herbert said nothing.

The Old Man went on, 'And you, Alexander, it's time
you stopped to think before you let your brother speak
for you. You can't run with the herd all your life.'

'Yes, Papa.'

'Now, clear out of my study and leave me in peace,
and let's have no more arguments, particularly in front of
the ladies.'

At that point Mara decided she'd better move quickly
before someone saw her. She went up to their bedroom
and waited for Alexander, convinced he would come to
her for sympathy. She prepared her words of comfort,
deciding that she wouldn't be too vehement in her dislike
of Herbert. Perhaps this was just what they needed. They
would live elsewhere, even the Dower House was too
close. Alexander would be less involved with his family.
Together they would be a unit, a couple, instead of two
members of a group who happened to share the same
bedroom. For the first time she thought seriously about
making her marriage work. Not just about existing
together but about building a foundation from which it
could thrive.

But Alexander didn't come up until the usual time he
changed for dinner. 'Oh, there you are.' He looked
subdued but forced a smile. 'Wondered where you were.'
He walked over to the window and gazed out at the
parkland.

Sitting at her dressing table, Mara watched him and

285

occurred to her he might be saying goodbye to
and she didn't want to interrupt.

building the Gemelli after all,' he said
eventually.

'Did Herbert agree in the end?'

'Oh, yes. We Rushtons never disagree for long.' That
was all he said. But was it what he wanted to believe or
what he wanted her to believe? Mara only knew that so
long as this barrier of self-deception or pretence, whichever it was, existed there was no solid rock on which to
build the foundations of their marriage. They would never
grow beyond what they were now, never deepen their
understanding, never communicate without words. To
cover her disappointment she opened her jewel case and
took out the pearls he had given her.

The sight of the pearls reassured Alexander. Other
people might not play the roles they were meant to, but
his wife, sitting at her dressing table holding her present,
was playing hers. He walked over to her. 'Still happy
with your pearls, darling?'

'Of course.' She slipped them over her head and smiled
up at his reflection in the mirror. He smiled back and his
brown eyes, soft like a labrador's, were simple and happy.
Then she looked down at the pearls. Beautiful, decorative
and entirely useless.

'Pearls suit you,' he said, stroking her neck with his big
flat fingers.

'Yes.' Decorative and entirely useless.

'I must buy you some more jewellery.' He pulled her
back gently so that her head rested against his stomach.

'I have plenty.' Automatically she pressed against him,
her shoulder blades moving into his body, the folds of
her red velvet gown falling open to his hand as it slid
down into the valley of her breasts.

He kissed her, his mouth nuzzling the hair above her ear, and whispered, 'Let's go to bed.'

She tried not to feel deflated as he pulled her to her feet. For one wild moment she had thought – hoped – he would take her where she was, on the chair. Or even over the dressing table. Or on the floor. Or drag her into the bathroom and make love to her in the bath. To take her unconventionally, brutally, perhaps even hurt her. But not always, always, with tender respect to which she responded with affection and muted desire, never with a pure savage lust so all-engrossing as to drive away the pity she felt for him so that she wouldn't notice, because she'd be beyond noticing such things, that she was still wearing her pearls when he made love to her. They lay across her bare stomach between them, so beautiful but so entirely useless.

Chapter 17

At the beginning of June Alexander and Mara moved to the Dower House. They had meant to move a month earlier but Alexander had been intermittently unwell ever since the arguments in the study, and Doctor Phillips advised that they should wait till the dust from the building-work had well and truly settled as it might exacerbate his cough. This period of waiting had driven Mara nearly mad; her escape was ready but she had to put up with another twenty-eight days at the Park.

But finally they did move, and Mara discovered one of the advantages of wealth: she wasn't expected to involve herself in any of the hard work. Rachel packed up her clothes and unpacked them the other end, Alexander's valet, a new addition with the unfortunate name of Fowler, did the same for Alexander, and strong men heaved in the furniture. Most of the domestic staff had previously been employed by the tenants, so they knew the house well. Jenkins, the butler, organized the footman and the three housemaids, while Mrs Kent, the cook, was in charge of the kitchenmaid and the tweeny. And when everything was ready, Lord, the head groom, and his assistant brought Mahogany and Alexander's three recently-acquired hunters to the stables in which the two stable boys had laid fresh straw. All Mara had to do was to stand in the hall and say, 'I'd like that over there, please. No, not there, on the other side. No, back where it was before.'

On their first evening they dined alone, sitting at their

own polished mahogany table, waited on by their butler and their footman, and afterwards they went into the study, where the smell of old leather from the chairs which Alexander had found in the attic at the Park mingled with the scent of honeysuckle coming from the garden. I knew it would be better once we were here, thought Mara, perching on the window-sill and smiling down at Alexander who sat at the desk. For a moment she was reminded of Jamie, sitting at another desk, also with the smell of flowers and leather. Then she thought of her father. 'I'd like to plant some roses,' she said, 'not a formal rose garden, but a clump of red ones out here.' She glanced over her shoulder at the terrace whose flagstones gleamed in the light from the study.

'I didn't know you knew anything about gardening.'

'I don't.'

'Then perhaps you'd better tell the gardener what you want and leave it for him to do.'

'Oh, no, I want to do this myself.'

He smiled at her and patted her knee. 'I've been meaning to ask if you'd like me to see if the Old Man would let us have Bonner. I'm sure he would. Our groom . . . what's his name . . . Lord . . . could go to the Park instead.'

Mara thought of Bonner. To ask him to work for her would be to impose on their truce.

'No, thank you,' she replied.

'I thought you liked him.'

'I do but I'm quite happy with Lord.'

'Very well, darling, so long as you're happy.' He took her hand in his, turning it over so that the soft palm faced upward. Then he lifted it to his lips and kissed it. 'Let's go to bed.'

They went upstairs to their new bedroom and Alexander went into his dressing room. When he came out wearing his dressing-gown over his pyjamas, Mara was sitting on the end of the bed, still dressed. 'Isn't Rachel helping you?' he asked.

'I told her not to bother to wait up.'

He sat down beside her and picked up her left foot and took off her shoe. Then he did the same with her right. 'I've always hoped I'd come and live here when I was married,' he said. 'My father had this room when we lived here.'

'Where did you sleep?'

'In the third room on this floor,' he laughed, 'the smallest one.'

'Oh, that one.' Mara stood up. 'Let's go and have a look at it now. Come on!' She went out of the door, padding along the corridor in her stockinged feet, and Alexander followed her, saying, 'Really, darling, we could look at it in the morning.' But Mara carried on until she came to the room. She had the sudden conviction that if she could get Alexander to make love to her the first time at the Dower House other than in their new double bed, then his break from tradition would set a precedent not just in their sexual life but in all things.

When Alexander reached the bedroom he peered in over her shoulder and said, 'You see. Just another room.' And he turned away and started back to their bedroom, calling softly, 'Mara, let's go to bed.'

The most important thing for Mara about the move was that she was now mistress of her own house. Jenkins was *her* butler, motherly Mrs Kent was *her* cook, the maids were *her* maids, the footman whose name she could never remember was *hers*. Rachel of course had been hers anyway. And the house was hers: ten bedrooms, four of which were small and occupied by the servants, Alexander's dressing room, two bathrooms, a dining room, two drawing rooms, a large hall and a study. It was hers to do with what she liked. Not that in all honesty Mara could be described as home-loving, she wasn't, but it was nice to be able to place the furniture as she wished, to order new curtains in the colour she liked, to move an ornament and not find it moved back to its original place next time she looked. And it was lovely to be able to go into the garden and, under the watchful eyes of the two gardeners, pick the flowers she wanted or to go round to the stables and not to find Mahogany shunted into the furthest box. All these petty things which, when added to the constant tension at the Park, had made her want to scream, suddenly no longer existed.

On the face of it Mara's days were not much altered. She still called and was called on, but not nearly as much as before. For one thing, unless Mara knew and liked the people she was meant to call on or unless Sophia made her feel she ought to go, and went with her, Mara couldn't be bothered. Why should she be bored to death in some stranger's drawing room when she could enjoy herself in Elenora's studio? And as for being called on, Mara was well aware that many people were still antagonistic towards her and that she wouldn't have many callers, so she saw little point in giving up an afternoon every week to sit religiously in her drawing room when no one but Sophia and perhaps Caroline and the Taylors would come. In the face of Sophia's disapproval, she announced that she would only be 'at home' on the second Tuesday of each month.

On the first occasion Mara sat herself down in her drawing room, thinking what a waste of time, no one's going to come. But to her surprise not only did Sophia, Caroline, Mrs Taylor and Alison arrive but also two women whose names Mara could never remember, an elderly female relation of Sir Henry's who was staying at Gaunt Hall, and Mrs Hartlett who remarked, 'One Tuesday a month! Very sensible. Quite sufficient.'

One big difference about being mistress of her own house was that when they entertained it was up to Mara to make the occasion a success. For their first dinner party they played safe – or safe according to Alexander – and invited the rest of the family, the Taylors, Sir Henry and Mrs Hartlett. Mara and Mrs Kent spent a whole day deciding on the menu, finally settling for Mint and Lamb Consommé, Dover Sole, Pork Cutlets.

'Do you think that'll be all right?' Mara asked anxiously. 'Aren't pork cutlets a bit . . . ordinary?'

Mrs Kent folded her arms across her ample bosom. 'Gentlemen like their food simple, madam. Good, plain cooking, none of the fancy stuff you get in restaurants. Now, what about the pudding?'

Mara remembered the chocolate gâteau at the Ritz. 'Let's have a chocolate pudding, a sort of cake. I had one . . . actually two helpings . . . at the Ritz when we were on our honeymoon.' She blushed as she remembered what a pig she'd made of herself, and Mrs Kent smiled fondly, imagining that Mara was recalling something quite different.

The dinner party was a great success, the guests stayed long after midnight, and when they left, they went out into the night still laughing and joking. Alexander closed the door on them. 'Well done, darling.' He hugged her but released her quickly when Jenkins appeared.

* * *

One sad thing about the move to the Dower House was that Mara hardly ever saw Damon. He wasn't allowed to wander that far and whenever Sophia came it was always for some formal reason, to call or for dinner, and he was either having lessons with Miss Pinner or was in bed. Mara would have liked to ask him over for the day but she was pretty sure Herbert wouldn't allow it, and in any case, much as Atalanta irritated her, it seemed cruel to invite one without the other. But the Old Man came to the Dower House more than Mara had expected. He often came back with Alexander after work, sometimes just for a drink, but other times he stayed on for dinner and Mara became convinced that he much preferred the Dower House to the Park. What was not altered in any way by the move was the endless dressing and undressing. Even when they were alone they dressed for dinner: Alexander mistrusted informality.

But there was an enormous difference beneath the façade of Mara's life: she was free – or relatively so. A prisoner suddenly allowed out for four hours each day kicks up his heels with excitement, although to those who are not in prison his four hours seem little cause for excitement. And so it was with Mara, she kicked up her heels. Not that she got up to very much, it was more a question of going where she wanted and when. And there was no one to tell her she had to be home for tea.

Only once did Alexander say, 'You seem to go out a lot in the afternoon.'

And Mara answered, 'Yes, I take Prince for a walk. He needs the exercise.'

The one other person Mara did miss, although she pretended to herself she didn't, was Mark. She hadn't seen him since the night of the ball. Since then he'd been staying at Gaunt Hall and the only time he had been to the Park was for lunch on a day when Mara and Sophia were visiting Caroline. What Mara didn't know was whether he'd kept away from the Park because of her or because of the tension over the building of the Gemelli. In a way she hoped it was because of her; because he wanted her and couldn't have her.

But perhaps it's better this way, Mara told herself. Safer this way. If he came to the Dower House and I was alone . . . The idea was exciting but dangerous.

At least she had Elenora. Sometimes Mara would go to the cottage and find it locked and deserted, and she would trail home disconsolately, dragging her feet through the dappled woodland grass. Sometimes it was deserted but not locked, and Mara would hang around outside, not liking to go in, waiting and hoping. But mostly during that summer she would find Elenora, either alone and painting, which Mara preferred, whistling through her teeth like a groom brushing a horse as she slapped on the colours, or sitting with friends. Amongst these friends were Paul, the gallery owner, and Sarah, whom Mara still disliked, and from time to time a Hungarian poet whom they all called Zak because no one could pronounce his real name. Zak was pale and gentle and he floated between them like a ghost, occasionally dropping into the conversation some remark so obscure that no one, least of all Mara, had a clue what he was talking about. But she liked Zak and Zak liked her. They were foreigners together and frequently their eyes would meet and they would laugh at the same thing. One of these things was that Zak, when he wasn't being floaty, liked to annoy Sarah by calling her 'the great white hope of the working classes'.

Elenora's friends were of all ages and backgrounds but they had one thing in common, or so it appeared to

Mara: they were clever. Literature, politics, sex, they argued frankly and eloquently. It was a fascinating world but one about which she had mixed feelings. On the one hand she was never bored, on the other she often felt inadequate and stupid. After such occasions she would wonder why she bothered to go and why, when she found other people there, she stayed. But perhaps it was because of Elenora: to run would have made her appear an unworthy friend. Or was it a matter of pride: to run would have been to give in to inadequacy. Or perhaps she too was beginning to question. But whatever, the cottage was a magnet and Mara would set off to it with a certain springiness in her step.

Once Elenora's friends got to know Mara, she came in for a good deal of teasing: about her clothes, her lifestyle, and her powerful family. Teasing was something the Rushtons, except for the Old Man, didn't go in for. But Hans had. So had Mara's father. So had Jamie and the Americans. And Mara knew Elenora's friends wouldn't tease her if they didn't like her. There was one exception to this: Sarah.

'You should give away your clothes to the poor,' she told Mara one day. 'Give away your money. Find a vocation and follow it. Do it now! Fight like the rest of us.'

Mara tried not to rise to the bait. 'I don't have any money,' she replied, 'not of my own. I don't have a vocation either. And I'm not talented like Elenora.'

'Exactly!' The mousy face lit up in triumph. 'You're the typical woman who thinks she can't do anything so she sells herself into marriage. It's because of people like you that we feminists have such a struggle. People like you who won't fight.'

Mara looked at the plain face before her, noting with

distaste the gleam of sweat on the indignant nostrils. How could men find Sarah attractive! She looked at Elenora and Paul, who were waiting like a jury for her defence. 'I lived in Germany during and after the war,' she said, 'and I can assure you, Sarah, I know what it means to fight for survival.'

'No, you don't. You've never faced starv . . .'

'Have you ever lived in an occupied country?'

'No, but . . .'

'When you have we'll compare notes.'

The others laughed and the poet clapped Mara on the back. 'Well done! You stand exonerated of your crimes. Mitigating circumstances for the defendant.'

'That's all very well,' said Sarah, accepting defeat with bad grace, 'but we all know there's never going to be another war.'

On the first occasion when Sarah attacked, Mara was disappointed that although Elenora might put in the odd word to even out the argument, she didn't actually defend her. But gradually Mara saw the logic in this: for Elenora to have defended her would mean that she, unlike everyone else at the cottage, was incapable of defending herself. And as she became more used to defending not only herself but the logic of any chance comment she made – no comment was allowed to pass without its maker being able to explain it – she gained confidence and even began to enjoy some of the heated discussions.

Elenora was a hard taskmaster as far as explaining yourself was concerned. When Mara finally remembered to take back the magazines, she asked, 'What did you make of them?'

Mara shrugged. 'I don't know.'

Elenora laughed. 'You must know what you think, Mara.'

'I suppose I do.'

'Well?'

'I think it's all very well for people who are good at something to be different . . .'

'But one doesn't have to make oneself different to be fulfilled. Everyone's good at something. The main thing is to find out what you're good at. Not everyone can paint or write poetry, we don't want a world full of artists and poets. Some people are good at just being, some are good with their families, some women are good at being mothers, though judging by the number of unpleasant children there are in the world I think a lot of women delude themselves on that score.'

'Can't I be good at just being?'

Elenora smiled. 'No, because you're not satisfied. You want more.'

One evening in August they were dining alone, and Mara was pushing a pea around her plate and thinking about Mark. He'd been back over a month but she'd seen nothing of him, and she was wondering if it was because he'd lost interest or if he merely thought it prudent not to call on her, when Alexander said, 'I had a letter today from the American authorities in Koblenz. They need to know what you want done with the house.'

Mara looked up sharply. 'Why did they write to you?'

'Because I told them to when we were married.'

'Why?' She stared at him down the length of the table and in the light of the flickering candles his face became distorted, making him appear older and jowly. 'Why didn't you tell me?'

'Mara, darling, what was the point?'

'Because it's my house.'

He sighed. 'I didn't want to bother you about it, so I

simply told the Americans to write to me when they decided they didn't need it any more, and today I heard that they won't be needing it after the end of August.'

Mara said nothing. She was thinking of Jamie. August! He would be going back to America. August! If she hadn't married Alexander she'd be there in Koblenz, standing on the doorstep watching him drive off, hearing him call, 'I'll write.' And then what? Day after day of nothing. Day after day of waiting for a letter that wouldn't arrive. And Jamie? She twisted her hands in the napkin on her lap. Jamie in America, laughing as he told his friends how the war hadn't been so bad after all because he'd found a little German girl who'd let him share her bed.

'Mara, have you gone to sleep?'

'No. Why?'

'I asked you what you want to do about the house.'

'Sell it.'

'Very well. I think that's wise. They say in their letter that they could sell it for you. I'd explained to them in mine that you'd be living in England, but I'm afraid they do say you won't get a lot for it. Apparently Germany's in a terrible economic depression' – he looked pleased as he said this – 'far worse than any of the little troubles we have in England.'

Mara thought of the house in Koblenz. She thought of the rose garden, her father's rose garden. It had been his house and he'd loved it. 'I want it sold to a German,' she said. She thought of Jamie. She couldn't bear the thought of him or anyone like him owning her father's house. 'I refuse to sell it to an American.'

'But darling, that's rather awkward for me to have to write.'

'If you don't want to, I will.'

'No, I'll do it, I'll do it. But what about the furniture?' He looked round the dining room. 'We could do with some of it here.'

'No. The furniture is to be sold with the house.' She couldn't bear the idea that she would look at a desk or a chair, inanimate objects, and know that they had seen Jamie more recently than she had. 'Sell everything,' she said. 'Everything.'

The talk of the house brought the past back to Mara and for several days she kept away from Elenora because she knew that if she went to the cottage it might all come pouring out and then she would have tainted that oasis with the bitterness of her past. Instead she stayed in the garden, which was looking beautiful for the weather had turned quite hot after a long wet spell. But Mara didn't notice the flowers, she wandered barefoot round the lawn and felt the warm, damp grass give beneath her feet, as she sat in a deckchair under the oak tree and looked up into its massive branches. On the third day she went for a short walk – not to Elenora's, towards Gaunt – and as she was making her way home, walking on the grass verge of the narrow road, she met Mark.

He came up behind her, driving one of the works cars. 'I was just thinking about you,' he said, stopping beside Mara.

Mara looked down at him. His face was on a level with her knees, for she was up on the verge and he was sitting in the car. 'How are you?' she asked lamely.

He squinted at her. 'Fifty per cent better for seeing you.'

'What about the other fifty?'

'Ah' – he gave her his naughty smile – 'now we're talking.'

He made Mara laugh, which was what he always did,

and that was one of his great attractions. 'Come back and have some tea,' she said.

'Do you think I should?'

'Why not?'

'Unmarried men aren't meant to call on unaccompanied ladies. Didn't you know? Why do you think I haven't been?'

'You're talking rubbish as usual.' It didn't matter that she only half believed him, the fact that she no longer expected great deeds of him allowed her to see the good in him.

Mark opened the far door of the car. 'Come along, let's shock the vicar's wife. She's coming now. I suppose she's been teaching the twins how not to play the piano.' As they drove off he asked, 'Have you learned to drive yet?'

'No. I must ask Alexander to teach me.'

'He'll say, "I don't think you ought to, darling."' It was a perfect imitation of Alexander's rather ponderous voice, and Mara giggled.

'But I can't learn to drive if he won't teach me.'

'I told you before I'd teach you. Look,' he stopped the car halfway up the long drive to the Dower House. 'The best thing would be if I gave you a few lessons and then you ask Alexander. If not, the first time you do something wrong he'll say, "I think you'd better stick to horses, darling."'

Mara hesitated. She didn't like to learn without telling Alexander but Mark was right, he'd try to put her off. Anyhow, hadn't he taken charge of the house in Koblenz without telling her? And what was more, she wasn't a chattel. 'All right,' she said, 'you teach me.'

'That's my girl! We'll go over towards Banbury. If

anyone sees us, we can pretend you wanted to go and do some shopping there and you asked me to take you.'

They drove on up to the house. He only stayed for half an hour; when he left they agreed he would pick her up at the end of the drive on the following morning.

'The first thing is to learn how to start the car,' said Mark. They were parked on a lonely stretch of road some five miles from Gaunt. 'And to save the battery you crank the engine.' He put the crank-handle into the slot in the front of the car then took Mara's right hand and put it under his. 'Keep your thumb on the same side as your fingers or you'll break it when the handle turns against you. Now, do it!' After three tries the engine burst into life.

They got into the car, Mara in the driving seat. Casually he took hold of her left leg. 'That's the clutch.' He pushed her foot down against a pedal. He took her right leg. 'Brake. Accelerator. Now, foot on clutch, accelerate, lift clutch. Slowly! Slowly! Wait till she engages. Oh, God!' The engine stalled.

By the end of an hour Mara began to wish she'd never begun. 'I'll never get it,' she said.

Mark laughed. 'Everyone drives like a rabbit at first.'

She pulled a face. 'Thanks.'

'There's nothing wrong with being a rabbit.' He gave her a naughty smile. 'They have a lot more fun than we do.'

After that, Mara drove whenever Mark could get hold of the car and away from the works, and gradually she began to get the hang of the clutch and to enjoy her lessons. At first she was terrified someone might see them and tell Alexander but after a couple of weeks, when they met no one they knew, that fear went by the by.

The weather was beautiful and they would drive along through country lanes, sometimes going nearly as far as Stratford, Mara in the driving seat, clutching the wheel, Mark sitting beside her, his arm resting across the back of her seat. Once they had a puncture and didn't return till after lunch but Mara simply told Jenkins that she'd been to visit friends.

Another time the car overheated and they had to stop on the edge of a wood to let it cool down. 'Now if I wasn't a gentleman . . .' said Mark, grinning at her.

'Oh, yes.' Now Mara had the measure of him she could laugh with him and at him.

He climbed out of the car and, taking a rug from the back seat, spread it on the grass. 'Come and sit down.' Mara sat down next to him. 'That's better.' He lay back and closed his eyes. Mara glanced across at him. He was wearing grey flannel trousers which were wide at the bottom as was the new fashion, a white shirt and a blue and red sleeveless Fair Isle sweater; Fair Isle was all the fashion for men though Mara couldn't understand why. It reminded her of the smocked dresses she'd worn as a child and which she'd hated because the smocking was stiff and prickly, and grown-ups kept telling her how some kind elderly relative had spent hours doing it. She'd always wondered why they bothered and why, if grown-ups liked smocking so much, they didn't wear it themselves.

Mark was watching her through half-closed eyes. 'You're still one of the most attractive women I know. I kept thinking about you when I was in America. I kept wishing you were with me. We'd have had such fun. Don't you wish you'd been there, Mara?'

Mara thought, America! 'Not particularly. I don't want to go to America.'

He rolled over on his side to face her and bent his arm at the elbow so as to prop his head up. 'I didn't mean America, Mara, I meant with me.' Very slowly he stretched out his free hand and took her arm, and then suddenly he yanked her down beside him. For a moment Mara lay looking up at him, wanting him to kiss her and to hold her, to take her there on the rug in the sunlight dappled by the trees. She didn't care who knew or what anyone had said or might say, she wanted Mark. He touched her cheek. 'Mara.' He bent to kiss her.

'A car!' Mara pushed him out of the way, banging his nose, and shot to the other end of the rug. 'Oh, my God,' she muttered, arranging her legs primly as the Taylors' car appeared over the hill. In the back seat was Alison.

The car slowed down. 'Hello,' called Alison. 'What are you two doing here? Broken down?'

Mark walked over to the car and rested his arm on the roof as he spoke to Alison. He was so casual Mara couldn't help but admire him. 'I took Mara in to Banbury to do some shopping,' he said calmly, 'and we overheated.' Mara thought, overheated's the right word for it. 'I should think we're all right now, Mara.' He turned back to Alison. 'I'll see you soon.'

As soon as the Taylors' car had disappeared they got into theirs; this time Mark drove. Mara was still shaken. Supposing Alison had come five minutes later, she thought. 'You don't think she'll say anything, do you?'

'There's nothing for her to say . . . sadly.' He put his hand on Mara's knee but she pushed it away. 'Don't worry! If Alison says anything about it I'll deal with her.'

Mara looked puzzled. 'Do you know her well?'

He laughed.

'Do you?'

'Don't you remember our conversation at the ball?'

'About Alison? Oh, yes.' She remembered how she'd said he wouldn't stand a chance and afterwards, at the end, how she'd seen him talking to Alison.

'I never can resist a dare,' he said, stopping at the bottom of the Dower House drive.

Mara couldn't believe it. 'You mean . . . ?'

Mark laughed. 'I wouldn't be a gentleman if I told you, would I?'

Mara thought of Alison. She was a nice, unsophisticated girl. 'You haven't?' She was horrified that he might have seduced poor Alison simply because she'd said he wouldn't stand a chance.

Mark gave her a look of disbelief. 'Why should you be so shocked?'

'You mean you have?'

He sighed. 'Look, Mara, I wasn't the first if you must know, so stop trying to make me out to be some seducer of innocent virgins.'

It hadn't occurred to Mara that Alison had lovers, just as, although they never talked of it, she was sure Alexander had never been with anyone but herself. Now she wondered. If Alison did, then perhaps he had . . . or still did. The idea didn't make her jealous, as she would have been with Jamie, but it gave her an unpleasant feeling of insecurity. Alexander was her husband and the fact that she had, half an hour earlier, almost been unfaithful to him didn't cross her mind.

'Don't worry, Alexander's not one of them,' said Mark.

'I never thought he was.'

He chuckled. 'Ooooo you are a liar! I could see your little mind going tick-tick-tick . . . they both like horses . . . they get on well . . . Mrs Taylor would have approved.' He laughed when she blushed. 'No, Alexander was not one of them. In fact, I imagine you're . . .'

Mara opened the door.

'Oh, don't get in a huff,' said Mark. 'I should never have told you about Alison but I thought you'd see it as I do?'

'How is that?'

Mark shrugged his shoulders and gave her his most boyish and frank smile. 'As a bit of a joke.'

That evening when Alexander came home, bringing the Old Man with him, Mara was very pleased to see him. He was good and pure. He didn't use people.

The Old Man stayed to dinner and they talked about the Roadster. 'Mark and I are taking her down to Brooklands next week,' he told Mara, 'and if all goes well in the tests she'll be at the Shelsley Walsh hill-climb in three weeks. You'll see her there.'

'Do you think you'll win?'

The Old Man gave her one of his craggy smiles. 'I wouldn't let her enter if I didn't think we stood a chance.'

'And what about the Gemelli?'

The Old Man winked at her. 'Oh, she's coming on fine. We'll start testing her in the new year if we have some decent weather.'

After a few minutes Alexander said, 'Herbert says there's going to be a rail strike. And a strike in the ironworks. Honestly, one would have thought they'd be glad to get home.'

The Old Man frowned. 'Perhaps home isn't quite what they expected. A man risks his life for his country then comes home to find he can't afford to live in it.'

When he left it was still early and not yet completely dark. 'Lend me a torch and I'll walk back,' he said, brushing aside Alexander's protests. 'Tell Owen to go home. I need some exercise.' He set off across the garden, calling, 'I'll cut up through the woods.'

Mara linked her arm through Alexander's as they stood and watched the Old Man until he disappeared into the dusk. She glanced up at her husband and thought again how good and pure he was. It's not his fault he can't give me what I want, because he can't see I want anything, she told herself. And I can't tell him what I want because I don't know.

Chapter 18

Mara missed the Shelsley Walsh hill-climb because she had flu. She spent the day in bed, with Rachel looking after her, and in the evening Alexander came back.

'What happened?' she asked as soon as she saw his glum face.

He pulled a chair up to the side of the bed. 'Tell me how you are first.'

Mara pushed back her hair and gave him a weak smile. 'Hot and sticky and yucky. But a bit better. Now, tell me what happened. And you'd better explain to me again what actually happens at a hill-climb.'

'It's like this' – he plumped up the bed covers into a little mound – 'this is the hill. And here' – he squiggled his finger down the mound – 'is the road. The cars meet at the bottom in a field called the paddock. That's sort of here.' He prodded the bedclothes. 'Each one takes it in turn to go up the hill' – he ran his finger up the first squiggle – 'which takes them round to the left, then back to the right for the Kennel Bend, and then left again for the Crossing Bend and on up to the finishing line. The one who does it in the shortest time is the winner, but it's not just winning that everyone's after, they want to break the previous record. A man called Higginson did it in about fifty-four seconds in nineteen thirteen with a Vauxhall, and no one's managed to beat that.'

'And how did we do?' Mara asked impatiently. She really wasn't interested in a man called Higginson, she wanted to know how Mark had done.

Alexander sighed. 'Not well.' He started to cough. 'Sorry, the dust was terrible.'

'Not an accident?' She'd not thought of Mark being in danger.

'Oh, no.' He coughed again. 'The car kept misfiring and losing power.'

'Why?'

'Well, we eventually discovered there was dirt in the petrol but by that time Mark had made both his runs.'

'Was your father very upset?'

'We all were.' He patted her hand. 'You were better off here, darling. Mark was very disappointed, his first drive since the war, and Herbert was extremely annoyed. He wasn't very pleasant.' It was the nearest he'd come to criticizing his brother.

By the time Mara was over her flu the summer had gone. The evening shadows stretching across the lawn were no longer summer shadows, their edges had a fuzzy autumnal quality. Elenora had gone to Florence for the winter, Mara had had a brief note from her during her illness with no indication when she would return. She missed Elenora more than she would have thought possible and often she would take Prince for a walk and wander through the woods to the stile in the fence. There she would sit and look down on the deserted cottage.

Alexander caught Mara's flu and he was much worse than she had been; it went to his lungs and for days he lay in bed, coughing and choking. During this time they became friends in a way they hadn't been before. Mara would sit beside the bed and read to him or, when he was better, they played 'Racing Demons'. Most evenings the Old Man dropped in to see Alexander and often the three of them would play cards: Mara nearly always beat

Alexander but the Old Man won every time. Sophia came too. She made Mara feel guilty for she was much more patient with Alexander and would read to him for hours without tiring, unlike Mara who tended to become restless, particularly if the sun was shining.

When Alexander went back to work Mara had even less to do. It was often too wet for her to ride and she spent a lot of time mooching around the house. Because Alexander tired easily, they entertained little, and then always the same people: the rest of the family, the Taylors, Sir Henry, Mrs Hartlett, Caroline and Geoffrey Plumstead, and on one occasion Mark. It was the only time Mara had seen him since that afternoon when Alison had nearly caught them. Mark was too busy with the Roadster and the Gemelli to give her driving lessons.

In November they all went up to London for the Motor Show. It was Mara's first visit to London since their honeymoon at the Ritz and to her relief they all stayed with Lady Henrietta: the Ritz would have brought back the incident on the stairs.

As they went through the main door at Olympia, the Old Man said, 'Last year we had all the eccentrics but they've fallen by the wayside. People have learned a hard lesson. The price of steel's pushed up the car prices, so unless you have a reliable product you'll never sell it.'

Mara nodded and looked around her. The great exhibition hall was divided into stands and upon each were cars of all different shapes and sizes: but with one thing in common. They all sparkled for the customer.

'We're over here.' He waved his hand towards the Rushton-Gaunt stand. 'Ah, there's Alexander.' Alexander stood beside the new Roadster, low, sleek and bright red, talking to a smart young couple.

Herbert, who had come up beside the Old Man, said, 'I'll go and help him.'

'No! Leave him to it. Come on, we three will have a look round.' He steered them down one of the wide aisles which separated the stands. 'See that big white car over to your left,' he nudged Mara, 'that's a Hispano-Suiza. They always remind me of matinée idols. Smooth, glamorous and encased in white.'

Herbert said, 'I don't know why everyone's so gloomy about the industry, there are even more exhibitors than last year. A hundred and forty-nine British makes alone.'

The Old Man went, 'Ummmph. But I wonder how many there'll be in ten years' time. Sixty?'

They had come to a halt beside a very small car, and Herbert remarked very casually, 'It depends whether one produces what the public wants, I suppose. I mean, look at this! The Monocar. Only a hundred and seventy-nine pounds.'

'And it looks like a toy,' said the Old Man, not caring if anyone overheard him. 'Our customers wouldn't be seen dead in it.' He walked on. 'Now let's have a look at something interesting, I want to see this thing Leyland have produced. Parry Thomas designed it. The chassis alone costs two and a half thousand, that's four hundred more than a Rolls-Royce. Poor old Charlie Rolls must be turning in his grave. I think Leyland want to beat Rolls-Royce at their own game.'

Herbert said, 'And I hope they do. Rolls have sat at the top for too long.'

They came to an enormous black car, with wide running-boards and huge wheels, which was attracting a good deal of attention. The Old Man turned to Mara. 'Well, young lady, do you think the Leyland Eight is going to beat the Rolls-Royce?'

Mara had only seen one Rolls-Royce and then only from a distance. She looked at the black car. 'I think the name Rolls-Royce sounds . . . smarter.'

He laughed. 'Yes, yes, perhaps they should have stuck to trucks. But I don't think we can discount Leyland. This is their first car but something makes me think it won't be their last.'

By the time they returned to the Rushton-Gaunt stand, Lady Henrietta had arrived and was talking to the smart young couple. She introduced them to Mara as Charles and Cynthia Barrie-Leith, brother and sister. Charles was tall, graceful, fair and aquiline, and he reminded Mara of a bored greyhound. To see him standing beside Herbert was incredibly cruel to Herbert. Cynthia was small, fair, pretty and fluffy, with a mass of short curly hair, which Mara later discovered was permed. She was talking to Alexander and was lisping up at him in a little-girl voice, speaking so quietly that he was obliged to bend his head down near her well-exposed bosom. 'This is my wife, Mara,' said Alexander, looking relieved as Mara approached.

'Umm, darling,' Cynthia kissed a startled Mara on the cheek, 'how lovely to meet you. I'm just trying to persuade your husband to meet us at the Embassy tonight. You will come, won't you? Charles come and meet Mara Rushton. They're coming to the Embassy tonight. Ummm, what fun!' She was irrepressible and Mara couldn't help liking her. At that moment she noticed Cynthia's blue eyes light up and her rosebud mouth compress into a small bud, and Mara turned to find Mark standing behind her.

'Hello, Mara.' He kept his charm light.

'Oh . . . er . . . hello, Mark.' Hurriedly Mara introduced him to Cynthia.

311

Charles came over and clapped Mark on the back. 'Hello, Hatton. We were at school together,' he explained to Mara. 'I'd never have dared clap him on the back then. He was two years above me which makes an enormous difference at school. And he was our hero. Smoking in the dormitories. A girl who "would" in London.' They all laughed. Charles turned to Alexander. 'I've just ordered a Roadster.'

'I thought you drove a Bugatti,' said Mark.

'I did, my dear chap, I did, but I had an unfortunate meeting with a tree in Monte Carlo and now the pater's tightened the purse strings and said I'm not to spend my miserly allowance on any continental rubbish. So it's a Roadster for me.' He looked at Mara. 'I suppose you don't come with it. No? What a pity.'

The Old Man had gone back to the Leyland stand and was talking to a big man in a Fair Isle sweater. 'That's Parry Thomas,' said Mark, 'one of the best.' At that moment the Old Man beckoned to him and he went, his face flushed with the honour of meeting the great racing-driver.

When he had gone Cynthia lisped up to Mara. 'Isn't he divine?' She winked at Mara. 'I'm not poaching, am I? He's not one of yours?'

Mara laughed. 'Oh no.' She was sure Cynthia Barrie-Leith was well able to take care of herself.

After dinner that evening Mara, Alexander and Mark went to meet Charles and Cynthia at the Embassy; Herbert and Sophia stayed behind, Herbert because he didn't like the Barrie-Leiths, Sophia because she was tired.

'Do I look all right?' Mara asked Alexander as they went into the famous nightclub. She'd spent all afternoon

312

wondering what to wear and in the end had settled for a black dress of silk chiffon with gold overtones which swivelled around her hips as she walked, its very low waist catching on the tops of her thighs. The thin gold headband which smoothed down the hair on the top of her head gave her a Red Indian look.

'You look fine, darling. Don't worry. If we don't like it we can always leave early.' He said this hopefully.

But Mara did like it. She liked the smart people lounging at their tables, the sophisticated chatter of well-bred voices, the music from the band that made her want to dance, but most of all she liked the excitement of night life. They found the Barrie-Leiths at a table with four other people; they'd all had dinner there. Mark took Cynthia off to dance and Mara and Alexander sat down. Then Charles took her off to dance, and, like everyone else, they danced cheek-to-cheek. Every so often someone would tap Charles on the shoulder and speak to him: he seemed to know everyone. 'Do you come to London often?' he murmured in Mara's ear.

She shook her head. 'No, we don't.'

'Not we,' he said, 'you.'

Mara didn't know what to say. For Mark to think her shockable was one thing, for this elegant and worldly creature to think her so was another. So she gave Charles a cool smile and said, 'I only go where I know I'll be amused.' Of course it was rubbish, she spent her life doing things that didn't amuse her.

But it was the right answer for Charles. He held her closer and Mara noticed a number of other women watching her with admiration.

At one point Mara and Cynthia went to the Ladies'. 'Charles is terribly taken with you,' confided Cynthia. 'We ought to make up a foursome with Mark.'

Mara laughed. 'I don't think Alexander would like that.'

'Oh, is he one of those?' Cynthia applied bright red lipstick to her rosebud mouth. 'Mind you, he's very good-looking. I can quite understand why you married him.'

Mara was puzzled. 'What do you mean?'

'Well, darling,' Cynthia pursed her lips at her reflection in the mirror, 'after all, the Rushtons aren't "quite". Filthy rich of course but not "quite". Just look at Herbert! Marrying Sophia has done wonders for him socially but he'll always look . . . well. Your father-in-law's different. He's divine. And having Lady Henrietta's patronage means they go everywhere because she's absolutely "it" socially.' She ended by saying, 'Not that all this matters since the war. Let's go back to the men, darling, I'm dying to dance with Mark again. If I don't seduce him within a week then I must be slipping.'

This time Mark asked Mara to dance, but she declined, and he danced with Cynthia instead.

Mara sat down next to Alexander. She suddenly felt very protective towards him, he was also subjected to prejudice. For once she was glad he saw only what he wanted to see.

Alexander went back to the Dower House on the following morning but Mara stayed on in London for a further three days. She went to Madame Cecile's and ordered more clothes, noting that while the manageress had been kind to her before, her attitude now was one of deference; the new Mrs Rushton had become one of her best clients.

On her last day in London Mara did what she had been secretly planning to do ever since she'd come to England: she went down to Tunbridge Wells.

Luckily Lady Henrietta was busy that day so she had

no need to make an excuse for her absence. It was all very easy. She took a taxi to Victoria Station and then a train to Tunbridge Wells. During the journey she thought of her mother and wondered if she too had made this journey. Or had she been born in Tunbridge Wells and never left the area except to go to Germany? Mara had no idea.

At Tunbridge Wells she asked for directions to the town hall, and there she found an elderly clerk who had lived and worked in the town all his life. 'Yes,' he said, 'I did know the orphanage. It no longer exists, madam . . . No, there are no records. Can I ask why you wish to know about it?'

Something in his question made Mara tell a lie. 'I'm just curious. My old nanny, of whom I was very fond, came from the orphanage.'

'Is she still alive?'

'Oh, no.'

The old clerk had nodded and thought for a bit, then asked, 'No children, the old lady?'

'Oh, no.'

'Well, the truth is, madam, it was a private orphanage. It was run by a most respectable gentleman, the brother of a Member of Parliament, and his lady wife. They only had about fifteen girls, and they paid for everything themselves, the gentleman and his wife, I mean, not the girls. Pretty girls, they were, I remember that. But then they would have been, wouldn't they? You see, madam, they were girls who'd . . . well . . . fallen into difficulties, or so rumour had it. It may not have been true, but the gentleman was a friend of Mr Gladstone.'

Mara had stood in front of him and thought of her mother. Had there been a secret behind those grey expressive eyes? Was it possible that her mother . . . ?

315

'That's why there were no records,' the old clerk continued, 'being as it was a private concern. Also the old gentleman wanted to give the girls a chance. A fresh start in life. Didn't want their pasts catching up on them. You see, madam, his wife used to teach them pretty manners and how to read and write, then the gentleman used to find them a position. And do you know what, madam? They say he never had a failure.'

Mara thanked him and left. She wandered round the town, through the narrow cobbled streets of the Pantiles, thinking of her mother. Was this something else that her mother had spared her from? Was it because her mother had been so 'unspared' in her early life that she had tried to spare Mara, from this truth, and from those other truths?

A few days after Mara returned to the Dower House, Alexander asked her, 'What would you like for Christmas, darling?'

'I know what I'd really like and that's a gramophone.'

'Very well. Do you want me to buy a selection of records or would you rather choose your own?'

Mara kissed him on the cheek. 'Don't worry, I'll choose my own.'

Christmas came and went. There were parties and dances and Mara enjoyed most of them. She got her gramophone and when Cynthia came to stay, ostensibly for a dance but in reality to see Mark, the two girls spent a whole afternoon jigging around the drawing room to 'Ain't We Got Fun'. They were still singing it in the car on the way to the dance, Alexander and Mark joining in on 'The rich get richer and the poor get poorer.'

* * *

316

In January Mara went hunting for the first time and Alison came to stay the night before. 'I've brought a couple of spare veils for you,' she told Mara as they were getting ready. 'When you want some more they cost six pence from the hairdresser.'

'I hardly ever go to a hairdresser,' said Mara, touching the ends of her tawny mane. She looked at Alison who was putting on her veil and wondered if she missed Mark; Mark, she gathered, was seeing a lot of Cynthia Barrie-Leith.

Mara enjoyed the hunt although it wasn't a very exciting day. They spent most of their time beside a dripping wood waiting for the hounds to find a fox, which they did, but then they lost it again. But at least I didn't fall off, thought Mara as they rode home in the gathering dusk. After that she hunted most weeks; sometimes Alexander went too but usually it was just herself and Alison, with whom she developed the kind of friendship people have when they have only one thing in common.

In February they began testing the Gemelli and Mara went to watch the great aluminium bird take off for the first time. She stood with Alexander, the Old Man and Herbert as the Gemelli, piloted by Mark, taxied slowly to the far end of a nearby field, then turned and roared back across the grass. For a moment it looked to Mara as if she would never get airborne but suddenly she was up, her silvery wings glinting as they caught the sun.

'Thank God for that!' exclaimed Herbert.

Alexander wiped his brow. 'Yes. What a relief. Well done, Papa!'

They watched the plane circle and Mara wondered if she would ever be allowed to go in her. She'd never flown. Very few people had. She wondered if she would be frightened – she was sure she would be, but it would be worth it.

A couple of Sundays later they all had lunch at the Park and Herbert made what Mara considered his first sensible suggestion: 'I think we should have a public launching for the Gemelli. We should invite the press down, open the park to the village, give a garden party for our friends. Make an occasion of it. And Mark could fly over in the middle of it. He could do a display, the sort of thing he says they do in America. Right, Mark?'

Mark nodded. 'I'm on.'

Sophia brightened. 'A garden party. We haven't given a party for ages.'

Herbert rewarded his wife with a genuine smile. 'Yes. You're so clever at entertaining. A garden party.'

Mara, who had been calculating the chances of Elenora being back from Italy, sat up eagerly. 'Oh, yes, Sophia. I'll help you. What fun!'

'What about it, Papa?' Herbert beamed down the table at his father.

Samuel Rushton laid down his knife and fork and looked at his sons and their wives. 'I see. Want to turn the thing into a circus, do you?' He spoke with gruff amusement.

Herbert missed the humour in his father's voice and saw only that once again his ideas were being opposed. 'We're in a competitive market,' he said crossly, 'and a great deal of money's been spent on this machine and . . .'

The Old Man cut across him. 'Have I said no? Personally I think if a product's good it will find a market without the help of a whole lot of important journalists and gawping strangers, but . . .'

'Exactly, Papa, I think . . .'

318

'And what does Alexander think?'

'Alexander knows nothing about publicity.'

The Old Man frowned. 'Alexander's a Rushton and he's a right to his say. Well, Alexander?'

Mara pleaded silently to her husband, Come on! Say yes! Let's have some fun. Come on!

Shrugging, Alexander smiled benignly. 'As Herbert says, Papa, I've no experience.'

'Doesn't stop you having an opinion, my boy.'

'No, well then . . . er . . . yes, I'm in favour.'

The Old Man raised his hands in mock horror. 'Outnumbered, am I? Then I suppose I'll have to think about it. Yes, I suppose I'll have to think about it.' He put some roast beef into his mouth and chewed it calmly and slowly. They sat in expectant silence and watched him. When he had swallowed it, he spoke again. 'A public launching for my Gemelli. A garden party. But supposing something goes wrong. Do you want a public failure?'

Herbert smiled reassuringly. 'You said yourself the tests were going better than you hoped.' He seemed to have forgotten his months of grumbling about the Gemelli.

But the Old Man hadn't and although he didn't remind Herbert, it was in his smile and Mara saw it. She sensed that he was going to give Herbert and Alexander a run for their money but that in the end he would make up his own mind, and nothing they could say would alter whatever decision he made. In the meantime he was having fun with them. 'Things can go wrong even in the best-tested projects,' he said gloomily.

Herbert said, 'What?'

'I don't know. But they can. They do. I remember the first car I built. Sir Henry and I tried it out very early one morning. Damned thing wouldn't start.' He looked at

Mara and Sophia. 'Don't mean to swear, my dears, but damned it was. At least we thought so. Took us a week to work out what was wrong with it.'

'And it went perfectly,' said Herbert impatiently. 'Just teething problems. Not surprising, Papa, because you didn't have all our modern machinery. You know the Gemelli'll go like a dream.'

None of them had noticed Atalanta had sidled in through the dining room door. 'I want a party,' she squeaked. 'I want to wear my new dress.'

Herbert frowned. 'That child's always eavesdropping.'

'I'm the Gemelli,' Atalanta ran to her grandfather and hugged his arm. 'Aren't I, Grandpapa? Gemelli means twins. I want to wear my new dress for the party.'

'I'm the Gemelli, too,' said Damon. He was standing by the door watching them thoughtfully.

Atalanta giggled. 'But you don't have a new dress.'

Samuel Rushton smiled down at his granddaughter, then looked over at Mara. 'And you, Mara? What do you think?'

They were all waiting for her to answer. Of course she wanted a party. Parties, hunting, and clothes filled her life. What else did she have when Elenora was away? 'I think it's a good idea,' she said, 'but we should choose a day that's easy to remember and have a . . . a slogan.'

Alexander nodded. 'Good idea. But what?'

'Yes, what?' The Old Man studied Mara curiously. He hadn't expected her to make a suggestion, just to say yes or no and plan her new dress. Clothes were all she seemed to think about now. He'd thought better of her when she first came, the way she had coped with Bonner and won him over but not insisted that he go and work for her. He'd heard what had happened with Blackie when Herbert thumped the pony on the rump, and respected Mara for climbing straight back on the pony after her fall. He'd been pleased at the way she was interested in the works; Smithy had liked her and Smithy was a good judge. He'd admired her at the ball and, unlike Lady Henrietta, been convinced Mara would have the sense not to succumb to Mark. But recently he hadn't been so sure; she was good company, better company than before now that she had more confidence, and she and Alexander seemed quite happy together. Alexander was obviously besotted by her. But he sensed that Mara was looking for something in life and that she was misguidedly trying to occupy herself in a social whirl so that she didn't have time to think.

'I don't know.' Mara frowned and thought. 'Yes, I do. How about, "The first of May is Gemelli Day"?'

She looked at them, and they looked back at her. Silence. It was as though she had told a supposedly funny story and not one of them had got it. Failed again, she thought ruefully. Should have shut up. Can't think why I didn't.

But suddenly they all began to shout, 'Well done! Brilliant! How did you do it? What a good idea!'

It was funny how praise affected her. Even Herbert didn't seem so bad.

After lunch the Old Man disappeared into his study and the others hung around in the drawing room wondering what he would decide. This gave them a certain unity, like children waiting to hear if they were going to be given a treat. Even Herbert was affable. 'That was a jolly good idea of yours, Mara.'

Damon came and stood beside Mara. 'You could always get a job at making up slogans,' he told her, 'and I could write the music to them.'

'And I could wear my party frock and dance to them,' added Atalanta, twirling in the middle of the floor.

'You could make a lot of money,' said Alexander, 'and then you, instead of I, could keep Madame Cecile's establishment in business.'

They all laughed. It was the first time he'd even hinted to Mara that she was extravagant.

At tea the Old Man came to join them. They all looked expectantly at him. 'Well,' he said, sitting on the sofa beside Sophia, 'I have thought about it and, although I'm against public displays because I think they're vulgar, I'm prepared to agree if it will help to sell the Gemelli. And before you all interrupt me, I'd like to add that one of the deciding factors is that the aviation industry is in a bad way. I've been studying various reports this afternoon and we've a lot of competition and not many buyers. The public seems to have forgotten the part the aeroplane played during the war and relegated it to a sort of flying postman. The future of the aeroplane will be to carry passengers.' He raised his hand to silence Herbert. 'And I also intend to start modifying the Roadster for racing once the Gemelli is sorted out.'

Herbert had been dying to speak. 'That's wonderful about the Gemelli but why must we do more work on the Roadster? Can't she race as she is?'

'No, she won't be fast enough. She needs to be light if we're to get anywhere. We need more power, but only on the one we're going to race. Can't have our customers killing themselves, it's bad for business.' He gave a craggy grin. 'But we must get back into racing, eh, Mark? We need a few good wins. Keep us in the public eye.'

Herbert was both frowning and smiling. More time on racing, on Mark, didn't please him. But the Gemelli launching did, although that too involved Mark. Only this might mean money; in Herbert's opinion racing was a continual diversion for Mark and a lot of hard work for everyone else. Watching him, Mara saw to her annoyance that he was convinced his own efforts had persuaded the Old Man. He remarked, 'I find it odd that you dislike the idea of publicity for the Gemelli but you're happy enough to get it racing?'

'It's quite simple,' replied the Old Man. 'In racing you risk your life and you earn your publicity, having a garden party you do neither.'

The organization of the garden party was left to Sophia and Mara, or rather to Sophia. In such matters as entertaining she came into her own; she had no flair for amusing guests once they arrived, her conversation relied entirely on small-talk, but she knew exactly what was right and what was wrong and no one ever left the Park complaining that all had not been done in the very best taste, however bored they might have been. Mara, on the other hand, sometimes did things wrong but even then it merely added a certain amiable chaos, and her guests always stayed late. But the garden party was at the Park and Sophia was mistress of the Park; Mara found herself addressing endless invitations.

'We need more cups,' Sophia told her one afternoon. 'We have a hundred but we ought to have two dozen in reserve.'

'I'll go and buy some,' Mara offered. She was longing for an excuse to get out of the house. 'I'll phone the works and see if Owen can take me into Banbury.'

She telephoned and was put through to Herbert, who said, 'Owen's busy but I'll send Mark.'

It was the first time Mara and Mark had been alone together since the afternoon when Alison had found them

323

beside the road and as soon as they drew away from the Park, he said, 'So how's my favourite married lady?'

'Not too bad.'

He glanced at her. 'Looking a bit bored with life by the look of things. Ah, Mara, if only you had the courage of your appearance.'

'What do you mean?'

'Simply that beneath that exotic stylish exterior there beats the heart of a true suburbanite.'

Mara knew he was trying to rile her, and he was succeeding. 'Just because I didn't succumb to your charms . . .'

'But you would have.' He said this with a certain triumph which annoyed her all the more.

'How do you know I'd have succumbed?'

He laughed. 'Want to drive or are you now too conventional to disobey the beloved spouse?'

'Of course I'm not,' Mara answered crossly. They stopped and switched places, and she drove on. Mara wondered how she could ever have found Mark attractive. He's just a spoiled boy who's used to having his own way, she concluded.

'At least you haven't forgotten how to drive,' he said after a while.

'Thanks.'

As they came into Banbury Mark said, 'You'd better stop soon. We wouldn't want the beloved spouse to hear you'd been driving, would we?'

'Do stop calling him that!' she snapped.

'Well, he might stop your clothes allowance, mightn't he? And we couldn't have the exotic but secretly suburban Mrs Rushton going around in last year's clothes.'

Mara was furious. 'You're just jealous!'

'And what if I am? I'm fed up with having my face rubbed in Rushton money.'

'Well, why take it out on me?'

'Because you don't only flaunt Rushton money in my face you flaunt yourself. Now stop the car, Mrs Rushton!'

But Mara didn't stop the car, she went on down the hill towards the town.

'Stop!' he yelled. 'Mara, stop!'

'What's the matter,' she yelled back, 'frightened by a suburbanite?'

'Mara!' He tried to grab the wheel.

'Stop it!' She pushed him away. They were coming down the hill fast now. She swung out to avoid a slower car, now they were on the wide part of the street with the cross straight ahead of them. She put her foot on the brake and the car juddered, she pumped the brake and it began to slow down.

'Watch that car! No!' He grabbed the wheel.

Mara had intended to swing round to the left, the car was going too fast to stop before the cross, but with Mark grabbing the wheel and her grabbing it back, they hit the bottom of the cross, the right-hand mudguard ramming into it with a sickening crunch.

'You bloody fool!' shouted Mark. 'Look what you've done!' He climbed out of the car and inspected the damage. 'Just look at it!'

Mara climbed out too. She was very shaken but had no intention of saying so. 'If you hadn't grabbed the wheel . . .' she retorted. She marched round to the front of the car and looked in horror at the bent mudguard. There was no way they could hide this from the Old Man and – she turned to look at the gathering crowd – there was no way he wasn't going to hear about it.

Luckily Mark managed to start the car and they drove

slowly back up the hill in frigid silence. Mara's anger had long since disappeared. The Old Man would be furious and it was her fault, she should have stopped when Mark told her to. 'Mark,' she said in a small voice.

He pulled the car over to the side of the road, keeping the engine running, and took her hand in his. 'Mara.'

'I'm sorry,' she said.

He pulled a face. 'It was my fault, I shouldn't have said what I did.'

She shook her head. 'No, it was mine. I should have stopped.'

They sat there looking at each other, two children who know they've been very naughty, and slowly he put his arms around her and drew her to him and kissed her on the forehead. 'You're still my favourite married lady,' he whispered, and Mara burst into tears.

They drove straight to the works and drew up outside the office building as the sun was setting. 'Don't worry,' said Mark, 'they only shoot people at dawn.'

'Oh, don't.' Mara felt sick with nerves. What would her father-in-law say? She looked at Mark and saw he was just as nervous as she was; joking was his way of dealing with it.

'He'll be in the hangar,' said Mark, leading the way round the back of the offices to the newly built hangar. Mara followed, praying that the Old Man would be alone.

But he was standing underneath the wing of the Gemelli, pointing up at something, and beside him were Alexander and Herbert. 'Ah, Mark,' he said, 'back already.' Then he saw Mara. 'And you too!'

They stopped just inside the big doors and Mara took a deep breath and cleared her throat. 'I'm afraid I've . . . umm . . .'

'We've had an accident,' said Mark. 'No one's hurt but the car's badly dented.'

'Oh, God!' exclaimed Herbert.

'What happened?' asked the Old Man. Instinctively he seemed to know there was more to the story than a dented car.

He was overtaken by Alexander who rushed to Mara's side. 'Darling, are you all right? You look very pale. Are you hurt?'

'I'm perfectly all right,' she replied, looking not at him but at her father-in-law. 'It was my fault. I was driving. I drove into the cross in Banbury.'

They all seemed to start talking at once. Mark said, 'No, it was my fault, I shouldn't have let her drive,' and Alexander said, 'But, darling, why were you driving?' and Herbert cursed and muttered about the expense.

'Be quiet!' roared the Old Man. 'Mark, you were responsible for the car. What happened?'

'I let Mara drive and . . . er . . .'

Mara interrupted. 'He told me to stop before we went into Banbury and I didn't.'

'And you didn't brake in time?'

'Yes.'

'But why were you driving?'

'Because I asked Mark to let me.'

'And you let her?' He turned to Mark.

'Yes, sir.'

'Not for the first time?'

'No, sir.'

He looked from Mark to Mara. 'Do you realize you could have killed someone?'

They both stared at the ground and said nothing.

There was silence for a moment and then the Old Man shouted, 'Get out of my sight the pair of you!'

Chapter 19

The Rushtons could not have asked for a more perfect day than that first of May. The sun shone. The wind dropped. The garden looked beautiful. And the people came. They arrived in their hundreds: friends, neighbours, villagers, total strangers and of course the inevitable journalists. All morning Mara watched them from the drawing-room window, a swarm of dark-suited men and colourfully dressed women spreading out over the green grass like the ripples of a multi-coloured sea. At midday the band, on loan from Alexander's old regiment, assembled on the front lawn and shortly afterwards they began to play, marching up and down, twisting in and out of each other as they turned, their gold braid and brass instruments glittering in the sun. The music and the laughter and the voices wafted in through the open window and it seemed to Mara that they were mocking her.

Over a month had passed since the afternoon of the accident and Mara was still mortified by what she had done. The Old Man had been quite right, she could easily have killed someone, and the worst part of it was, she hadn't even thought of that until he'd told her so. Alexander had been miserable about the incident, he had kept asking, 'Why did you do it?' and his misery had made Mara feel worse: she would have preferred him to be angry. Herbert, she suspected, had been pleased; she'd played right into his hand, she'd proved herself irresponsible. And she'd made Mark appear irresponsible too. Luckily the Old Man seemed to have forgiven Mark, or at least it had not made any difference to his position with Rushton-Gaunt: he was still to fly the Gemelli and still to race the Roadster. Mark had telephoned Mara one morning when Alexander was at the works and told her so with great relief in his voice. That was another thing which made Mara feel guilty: it hadn't occurred to her how precarious she had made Mark's situation.

The Old Man's attitude towards her was the one she found the most upsetting. The little understanding smiles he used to give her had all gone. She had disappointed him. She was no better than the wealthy and irresponsible young drivers who instead of slowing down as they went through Gaunt, speeded up and laughed at the old people and children forced to run for their lives. She had disappointed him, and he treated her with the polite detachment he applied to dinner guests with whom he had nothing in common but to whom he was obliged to be civil.

I'm not just the unwelcome guest, thought Mara, I'm the guest who has made herself unwelcome. To have been blamed for being born on leper island, a quirk of fate, had been unjust and she had inwardly protested against the injustice of it. But because it was unjust, a small self-righteous voice had comforted her; that voice couldn't comfort her now. This was no quirk of fate. It was her own fault. She had sailed over to leper island, stupidly thinking she was above contamination. And with her she had taken the one person who had never made her feel she was a leper. If Mark tried to make love to her again, Mara knew she would let him simply because she owed it to him.

Mara studied her reflection in the big oval mirror above the mantelpiece. Her outfit, the dress, a willowy reed of emerald silk, complete with matching headband and big round gold gypsyish earrings, had looked wonderful in *The Tatler*, and it looked wonderful on Mara, but she didn't feel wonderful in it. She wished she had put on something inconspicuous so that she could blend unnoticed into the background, but she didn't have anything like that, she didn't have clothes for disgrace.

'Mara.' Alexander put his head round the door. 'Come outside.'

Mara had to go to him, the least she could do was to make him happy in the little things of life.

'You look lovely.' He kissed her on the cheek. 'More beautiful than ever.' He gave her a proud smile. 'Chin up, darling!'

With a sudden rush of affection Mara slipped her hand through his arm and squeezed it fondly. She didn't deserve him. He was too good to her. They walked across the hall and out into the garden, and it was thus that the journalists and photographers first saw them, and thus they appeared in newspapers and magazines around the world. Arm in arm, smiling into each other's eyes, the dashing war hero and his exotic young wife.

And it was thus that Jamie saw her, months later when he was idly flicking through one of his mother's magazines. Mrs Turner never noticed that one went missing. Jamie had burnt it. He wanted no reminders of the girl who had chosen to become a rich man's wife and was so obviously enjoying it.

Punctually at three o'clock Samuel Rushton, flanked by his two sons, his daughters-in-law and his grandchildren, walked out of the front door and across the gravel drive to the South Lawn, where uniformed maids stood behind tables covered with plates of dainty cakes and thinly cut sandwiches.

Mortimer was just putting the finishing touches to the last table. The Old Man looked beyond the garden to the park, where those who had not been invited to the garden party picnicked in little groups, and there was something in his expression which made Mara think he would have much preferred to be there than here.

'Ah, here come the Taylors,' said Alexander as the first car crunched up the drive.

The Old Man nodded and muttered, 'The circus begins.'

By four o'clock the lawn was packed with guests and they were starting to look upwards, at the clear blue sky, and whisper to each other, 'Where is this aeroplane, I thought it was meant to be here by four?'

Mara was talking to Caroline when Alexander beckoned to her. She went over to him. 'He's late,' he said quietly. 'Herbert's going mad. The men from the press keep asking if there's been a crash.'

Mara was about to reassure him when she heard a distant humming. 'Listen!' She touched his arm. 'Listen!'

Everyone seemed to hear it at the same time. Conversations were stopped in mid sentence, hands stretching out towards cakes and sandwiches froze in mid air, and cups being lifted to the lips hovered somewhere near the chest, as every head tipped back and every pair of eyes searched the sky.

'Come and stand on the steps,' said Alexander. 'The others are there. We'll have a better view.' He dragged Mara across the gravel to the steps. She didn't want to go, her father-in-law was there, but she could hardly refuse. No sooner was she installed between Alexander and Damon, who like Atalanta was standing on a chair, than Damon shouted, 'Look! Look!'

At the same time hundreds of others shouted, 'Look! Look!' and pointed to the west, from where the Gemelli, like a great silver bird, was swooping down from the sky. Nearer and nearer she came, the roar of her engines now obliterating the chatter of the crowd, over the South Lawn, and when it seemed as though she were bound to hit the trees beside the stables, she lifted herself up with the grace of the bird she was, skimmed their shivering leaves and vanished as quickly as she had come.

A great cheer rose from the crowd. Mara felt weak with fright but at the same time she was exhilarated, wishing she too could have been going up into the blue sky. Alexander gripped his father by the arm. 'Well done, Papa, well done!'

The Old Man's eyes filled with tears. He brushed them aside and nodded. His Gemelli! He had dreamed her, built her, nurtured her and loved her: his first aeroplane.

The Gemelli had turned beyond the trees and now she came back again, over their heads, swooping over the lawn and the parkland, then rising up, higher and higher towards the sun, as though her silvery body were attracted to it like a magnet. Then she turned and twisted and rolled and straightened out again, and another great cheer rose from the spectators. They had come to be impressed and they were.

'You are clever, Grandpa,' said Atalanta, climbing down from her chair and pushing her fluffy yellow muslin self between Alexander and his father. 'Very clever.' She said it as though she expected no less and with almost regal aplomb, as if she were Queen Anne commending the first Duke of Marlborough for winning the battle of Blenheim. She'd known he could do it, and he'd done it.

The Old Man laughed at his granddaughter. 'At least you never doubted me, Atalanta.'

'Of course I didn't, Grandpa.'

'And what did you think, Damon?' Mara touched his arm.

He smiled quietly to himself. 'I think she's too beautiful.'

After circling again, Mark brought the plane down to the east of the house, then he taxied slowly across the grass, coming to a halt right in front of the South Lawn. As he climbed out of the cockpit everyone cheered.

'Hold it right there, sir!' shouted a photographer. 'Just hold it, sir!' shouted another. 'One more moment!'

The Old Man pushed his way through them. 'Well done, Mark,' he shouted, holding up his hand for the pilot to shake.

'Nice one!' shouted a photographer.

Mark climbed down from the aeroplane.

'And one against the plane, please.' They snapped away as Mark and the Old Man stood in front of the Gemelli.

Eventually the Old Man said, 'This young man needs something to drink, gentlemen, and so do all of you. You'll find what you need at the house.'

Together, the Old Man and Mark walked towards the South Lawn, the crowd parting to let them pass, everyone smiling proudly as if merely by their presence they had helped the Gemelli to fly. On the lawn the two men were besieged by friends, all wanting to shake their hands. Mara watched Mark: he was dusty and sweaty but that didn't prevent people wanting to be near him. He was a hero. This, Mara saw, was what Mark needed: adulation. Eventually he made his way over to her and said, 'Well?'

She smiled at him. 'You were wonderful, Mark, but

333

you frightened me. When you came towards the house that first time . . .'

He threw back his head and laughed his boyish laugh.

Someone was shouting, 'Speech! Speech! Come on, Samuel!' And several other people added, 'Aren't we going to see her go up?'

The Old Man stood on the steps. He cleared his throat and looked around at the waiting crowd. 'Ladies and gentlemen, you have done me and my aeroplane a great honour by coming here today. I trust you have enjoyed yourselves.' He waited whilst they all shouted, 'Yes', then went on, 'But I am not the only person who has had a hand in the Gemelli. Apart from my employees at Rushton-Gaunt who've worked so hard, much of the detail in the design of the airframe came from Mr Mark Hatton, whom you saw flying her today.' There was a round of applause and heads turned to look at Mark. 'Now, as to your seeing the aeroplane fly again, she will take off in a few moments and I myself was intending to be her first passenger. But I should like to offer that opportunity to another man. To Sir Henry Gaunt,' he looked across the lawn to Sir Henry, 'without whose help Rushton-Gaunt would not exist. He supported me when I had nothing but a dream and over the years he has never failed in his friendship towards me.'

There was a roar of approval from the crowd, followed by satisfied nods and exclamations of 'Well done! Wonderful old boy! One of nature's gentlemen!'

Sir Henry stepped forward eagerly, his stiffness forgotten, his ancient face alive. 'I . . . I can't thank you enough. Why, it's . . .' Then the eagerness died and he seemed to shrivel. 'But of course I can't accept. I know what the Gemelli means to you.'

The Old Man marched down the steps, the crowd

separating before him as the waters of the Red Sea before Moses. In fact, given a set of biblical clothes he'd have made a very good Moses. 'Please accept.' He touched Sir Henry's shoulder.

'Well, I think we've exonerated ourselves,' Mark told Mara. 'You in your amazing dress and me with the Gemelli.'

'I hope so Mark, I felt awful for you.'

He looked at her and then he smiled his naughty smile and lowered his voice. 'Damn Alison for turning up when she did.' Before Mara could reply he walked off towards the Old Man and Sir Henry, calling over his shoulder, 'See you later.'

Mara followed him at a distance. She was just in time to hear the Old Man say, 'Just do a couple of gentle circuits and bring her down, Mark. Sir Henry's not a young man any more.'

Sir Henry had overheard too and he was incensed. 'I may be getting on but there's life in me yet. You give her stick, my boy, show me what she'll do!'

Mara joined Alexander on the steps with Herbert and Sophia. She felt immensely proud of her father-in-law for giving up his place to Sir Henry, she knew how he had been looking forward to the flight, and for the first time she felt proud to be a Rushton, to be a member of a family which included such a man. 'It was very good of your father,' she told Alexander.

'The Old Man's a better man than I am.'

'Oh, rubbish!' Herbert butted in. 'The Old Man's a fool. We don't owe Sir Henry anything, not any more, he's been well repaid. I'm fed up with all this bowing and scraping.'

In the silence that followed, Mara went into the house

335

to look for Damon. She found him in the drawing room, gazing into space. 'Don't you want to watch?' she asked.

'So long as I don't have to listen to my father running down Mark. I like Mark, don't you?'

Mara nodded. 'Yes.' By the time they returned to the steps the engines had been started. The Gemelli taxied slowly across the front of the house, turned and headed across the park, gathering speed as she went. Wheels turning faster and faster, engines roaring louder and louder. Then she was up and a cheer from the crowd went with her.

This time, although people watched the aeroplane, there was not that initial fascination: they'd seen her fly already; they'd seen her sitting on the ground and, despite not being allowed to touch her, they knew she was obedient to man. Mara found herself drawn into conversations, expected to laugh and smile, when she would have preferred to watch the Gemelli. Mark was taking the Gemelli even higher than he had gone before. The nose of the plane rose up as if on a switchback, then suddenly the hum of the engines stopped and the plane tipped back and began to fall out of the sky, rocking backwards and forwards as an autumn leaf drops to the ground. The crowd, suddenly aware, stood in shocked silence waiting for the inevitable crash. Then just as it seemed that the beautiful bird would dive into the ground, her nose dropped, the engines roared into life, and the Gemelli arced round in a graceful turn to fly low over the cheering people with Mark grinning and waving to their adulation.

White-faced, Alexander turned to his father. 'What went wrong?'

'Nothing went wrong. The bloody fool's just treated us to a trick he learned in the war. It's called the "falling leaf", the most dangerous manoeuvre in flying. It's a way of shaking off the enemy by pretending you've been hit. By God, I'll give him a roasting when he gets back down!'

Why did Mark do it, thought Mara, he must have known the Old Man would be furious. The plane went down into a dive. He's played right into Herbert's hand. We'll never hear the end of it. She watched as the Gemelli twisted and turned before straightening out. At least he wasn't trying to do that leaf thing again. But suddenly it seemed to her that the nearest wing was no longer straight to the body of the plane but bent backwards. 'Alexander! Alexander!' she cried – at the moment the wing broke away. It all happened so quickly and yet it was all in slow motion. Hours seemed to pass between the time when the wing began its descent and the plane spun out of control, and in those hours, which were merely seconds, the drama in the sky communicated itself to the people on the ground.

There was a cry of horror from the crowd. People gaped upwards, pointing, their mouths opened for screams which came out as stifled gasps. Mara stood watching, her eyes fixed on the plane, her arms hanging helplessly by her sides. She could not believe what she saw, none of them could. Samuel Rushton, his face drained of colour, his eyes unblinking and unbelieving, stared upwards as they all did. Then everything speeded up. The Gemelli was spiralling down and down. Mara could feel Mark fighting for control, but there was nothing he could do, she thought of his charm and his smile and the way he had waved to the crowd just moments before.

With a deafening explosion the Gemelli hit the ground to the west of the house, behind the trees. Seconds later another explosion. And then silence. A black cloud lifted up and even as they watched, frozen in their places, the blackness drifted off to mingle with the blueness of the sky.

The silence was broken by the Old Man's choking voice. 'I shouldn't have let him do those aerobatics. The forces were too high, put too much strain on the airframe.' He looked down at his feet and shook his great white head. 'It's my fault.'

Mara longed to go to him and comfort him, to tell him . . . what? . . . that it didn't matter? . . . no, not that. Simply that she understood, but Alexander grabbed her by the arm and pushed her towards the front door, saying, 'Take the children! Go inside. And you, Sophia. Quick! The crowd may . . . Mortimer! Take them into the drawing room. And you, Papa, go with them.'

The Old Man turned his harrowed eyes on his son. 'What! Not go and see? Oh, I know there's no chance they're alive, I've seen too many accidents to have false hopes, but the Gemelli was mine and her disaster is mine, and I'll not go hiding myself in the drawing room with the ladies. I may have lost two dear friends but I haven't lost my sense of honour.' And with that he pushed his way through the gathering journalists, shouting, 'Out of my way! Out of my way!' and ignoring their questions of, 'What went wrong, sir? What have you to say, sir?'

It seemed to Mara that she and Sophia waited for hours in the drawing room. Miss Pinner had immediately been summoned to take the twins upstairs, Atalanta loudly tearful, Damon rigidly silent. Then Mortimer came in and said, 'I'll make some tea, madam,' and Mara thought, even death can't displace the tea tray. She tried not to think about Mark now because she didn't want to cry, not in front of Sophia, not at the Park. He deserved better than that. She would think about him when she was alone, taking him up with her to the woods, mourning

338

him as she walked along the grassy path. And she would think about him when she was driven through the lanes where he had taught her to drive, but most of all she would think about him each time she went into Banbury and saw the cross.

Suddenly Sophia, who had been gazing silently at the floor, said, 'Such a horrible day for everyone.'

Mara stared at her sister-in-law. She was about to say, 'How could you think of anyone else but Mark and Sir Henry? What does it matter if other people have had a horrible day? Those two are dead.' But then she realized that Sophia, unlike herself, had probably never seen death before. The enormity of the disaster was too much for her. It was easier to lament a horrible day because she herself had had horrible days, many of them, just as it is easier for people, on hearing that a ship has sunk with all hands, to lament the death of the ship's cat. The idea of hundreds of floating bodies is unimaginable. Most people have seen a dead cat.

Later, Herbert appeared and insisted they each had a glass of brandy. He had three. 'Now, go up to bed, my dear,' he told Sophia, shooing his wife out of the room. 'I'll come up later to see how you are.' His wife departed, he hesitated on the threshold. Mara knew he was looking at her, she could sense it, but she kept her eyes down until she heard him move off.

Alone, she went over to the window. In the west the sun was dipping and the rose bushes on that side of the garden threw long shadows across the velvety lawn. On any other day it would have been a beautiful evening: it was still a beautiful evening. Too beautiful.

Slipping out through the French windows, she made her way across the lawn to where the park began and the grass grew long. Her husband and her father-in-law were standing side by side under a tree. Both were looking to where lumps of twisted metal caught the evening sun. Mara approached them tentatively and they turned to look at her with blank expressions, waiting politely for her to speak, just as if she were a stranger intent on asking the way.

'I'm so sorry, so . . . sorry,' she said, her voice breaking with emotion.

'Yes, I believe you are. I really believe you are,' replied the Old Man.

They walked back towards the house, the Old Man in the middle. Ahead of them went their shadows, forging through the grass. The few people still around looked at the trio, but not at their eyes – they were unable to meet their eyes. It was as if they had gathered to gloat at a public execution and now, faced with the relatives of the condemned, they were suddenly reminded of their consciences, and they were ashamed. Guiltily they slunk away, and by the time Mara, Alexander and the Old Man reached the front steps all that was left of the vast crowd was a number of dark dots scurrying off into the distance.

And as they went up the steps Mara remembered how Mark had told her, 'I never could resist a dare.'

Chapter 20

Tragedy unites! Whoever thinks that has never met the Rushtons, Mara decided. They had just arrived back from Sir Henry's funeral, an hour of dusty sunlight in the village church unaffected by the ripples of tension at the Park. Now they were all in the drawing room sipping their pre-lunch sherry; that is, all except for her father-in-law who had disappeared after the service.

'Where did the Old Man go?' asked Herbert, helping himself to some more sherry.

Alexander was standing by the window staring gloomily out at the trees beyond which the twisted metal had lain. He shrugged his shoulders and muttered, 'No idea.'

'Either of you know?' Herbert turned to Sophia and Mara who were sitting side by side on the sofa, the skirts of their black dresses well pulled down over their black-stockinged knees. They shook their heads.

Mara thought of Sir Henry and of how his funeral had been attended by people who had known and loved him for the old warhorse he was, and of how his remains would lie in his family vault in the church at Gaunt. Then she thought of Mark. Two days earlier they had attended his funeral in another church, in a village south of Oxford, where neither the church nor the village and most of all the people bore any relation to the Mark she had known. His father, the dour owner of a small estate, his relations, elderly women in conventional hats, the local people, solid and worthy. Mara found it extraordinary that Mark had been the person he was, coming from such a place.

Only Mark's friends from the Flying Corps, from Brooklands and from London who, compared to the rest of the congregation seemed like creatures from another planet, had any connection with him, and even they were a little too sophisticated.

And when the creatures from the other planet went home, Mark stayed behind in the churchyard which had nothing to do with him. It was as if, having spent his life in luscious valleys, he had been left on a bare mountain.

What Mara found most difficult to accept in Mark's death was that, whereas Sir Henry had been older than all of them and therefore it seemed right he should die first, Mark had been young. He had lived and died within other people's lifespan, and so had been cheated of his rightful allocation. For some reason Jamie came into her thoughts. The idea that he might die without her knowing appalled her. She analysèd what it was she found so appalling and was forced to admit that so long as they were both in the same team, the earthly one, there was always the possibility they might see each other again.

Her thoughts were interrupted by the return of her father-in-law.

'Where have you been, Papa?' demanded Herbert. He was agitated and more than a little drunk.

The Old Man checked to see if anyone else wanted some more sherry before helping himself. 'I went to Gaunt Hall to see if there was anything I could do, but Lewis seems to have everything under control, he's Sir Henry's solicitor as well as ours, and he's a good man. After that I went to the works.'

'Why Gaunt Hall if Lewis . . .'

'I just wanted to offer my help.' He smiled sadly but proudly. 'Lewis tells me that Sir Henry's will provides for a silver trophy to be won at Brooklands each year. The details of the race have been left up to Lewis and me.'

'The Gaunt Cup?' said Alexander.

'No, we've decided to make it the Hatton-Gaunt Cup. I know Sir Henry would approve. Of course it should be the Gaunt-Hatton Cup, but the other way sounds better and Sir Henry wouldn't object to being placed second.'

Herbert sighed. After a short while he asked, 'Are they going to sell Gaunt Hall?'

The Old Man shrugged. 'I don't know. It's been left to a cousin but he's out in India so he may not want it.'

'So we have to look after it until this cousin decides if he prefers to lord it over Gaunt or kick natives around in India.' Herbert helped himself to more sherry, banging the decanter down on the table. 'And I suppose if he chooses to honour the neighbourhood with his presence, we'll have to make him feel welcome because, of course, we now owe Sir Henry his life along with everything else.'

'I owe him my life,' his father answered. Though his voice was quiet it was also icy, and his words vibrated on the tension in the room so that Mara and Sophia, sitting at their opposite corners of the sofa, stiffened and avoided looking at each other because they knew that if the volcano erupted they would find themselves on opposite sides of it.

'But I don't owe him mine' – Herbert moved up behind his father – 'and I've no intention of spending the rest of my life pretending I do.'

'Herbert, please, you're upsetting Papa.' Alexander laid a consoling hand on his father's arm, adding, 'He doesn't mean it, Papa, he's upset. We all are.'

'Oh, for God's sake!' Herbert downed the contents of his glass and took a deep breath during which they waited for him to explode. But then, as if he knew, and it were just another of his cat and mouse games, he began to talk about the Gemelli in a forcedly cheerful tone. 'It's a set-back, Papa, but not the end. We'll soon build another. Six months at the most. She's a good plane. It was just an accident. A set-back.'

'A set-back.' The Old Man choked on the words. 'You call the death of a brilliant young pilot and a wonderful old man a set-back?'

'A misfortune then. But an accident.'

'There's no such thing as an accident, an accident is a miscalculation. The aerobatics strained the airframe. It wasn't strong enough.'

'So it was Mark's fault.' Herbert gave his father a triumphant smile. 'You told him to take it easy, and just look at that fool thing he did.'

The Old Man studied his elder son as if, thought Mara, he'd never seen him before. He turned his glass slowly in his hand and when he spoke it was as though he were speaking to the amber-coloured liquid in it. 'First of all, how dare you criticize a brave young man who is no longer here to defend himself? The falling leaf is dangerous because it allows for no margin of error, that's all. And secondly, I told Mark to take it easy because of Sir Henry's age, not because I thought there was anything wrong with the plane. Had I for one moment suspected that, I should never have allowed it to fly.'

Herbert sighed. 'All right, all right, I'm sorry. I didn't mean to knock Mark or anyone else. But let's face it, Papa, you can cure the problem.'

'Can I?'

'Of course you can.'

'Perhaps. But I won't. The Gemelli will never fly again. Not this Gemelli or any other.'

344

'But Papa . . .' Herbert moved nearer to his father, looming over the older man, large and menacing. More than at any time since Mara had met him, he was Herr Steiger.

Alexander tried to push between them. 'Do leave Papa alone. Can't you see he's . . .'

Mara held her breath as Herbert swung round angrily. 'You keep out of this!' he shouted, pushing his brother away and grabbing hold of the Old Man's arm. 'Listen, Papa, you can't stop now. The Gemelli has to fly again. We've invested too much to pull out.'

'Money!' The Old Man tried to free himself from his son's grasp. 'Money! I knew you'd think of that. Yes, I knew. But the Gemelli was mine. Mine to build and mine to end. That's why I went to the works today. I went to burn the designs. Now, will you let me go?'

Too incensed to remember he was dealing with a much older man – or had he forgotten? – Herbert gave his father a violent push across the room. It was all too much for Samuel Rushton. His beloved Gemelli had blown apart, his lifelong friend had been killed, his son was the bully he had always feared. With a cry of intense pain he gripped his chest and staggered into a table and, before anyone could move, he crashed to the ground, his right leg twisting under him and his head hitting the carved wooden claw which formed the foot of the table leg. In the long horrified silence which followed Mara was aware of a bird singing and the click of a gardener's shears as he trimmed a hedge. Herbert and Alexander had frozen into statues and Sophia was biting her colourless lips. No one moved. Nothing moved, except a thin line of blood which trickled down from the Old Man's forehead, across his cheek, to the floor.

'Is he dead?' whispered Sophia.

Her words brought them back to life. Alexander pushed past Herbert and knelt down beside his father. Remembering her days at the hospital, Mara darted forward, crying, 'Don't move him. You mustn't move him.' She felt for his pulse as she had seen Jamie do. It was faint but there. 'He's alive. Fetch a doctor!'

Alexander shouted for Mortimer. The old butler appeared. He looked down at his employer, the shock registering in every crease of his face. 'I'll telephone for Doctor Phillips.'

'Yes. And bring a blanket.'

Feet rushed across the hall, feet ran up the stairs, feet sped along the corridor above. The doctor was telephoned. A blanket was brought. Sympathy. Questions. How did it happen? Evasive answers. He fell. He tripped.

Through it all Herbert had not said a word. He stood looking down at the crumpled form whilst Mara and Alexander scuttled round him, careful not to touch him just as though he were a leper – or a murderer. As soon as the servants retired and the family was alone, he cleared his throat and said, 'It wasn't my fault. I didn't push him. Not hard.'

No one answered him.

'You saw what happened. He fell. I'm not to blame.'

Kneeling beside her father-in-law, Mara sensed Herbert was searching for eyes to meet his own so he could bully their owner into agreeing his innocence, and she kept hers firmly on the ground.

'No one's blaming you,' Sophia assured him nervously. She was still by the sofa, only now she was standing, the backs of her legs pressed hard against it.

But it was not his wife's reassurance Herbert wanted. 'Alexander, you saw what happened.'

346

'Yes, I saw.'

'Well then?'

'I told you to leave him alone.'

'For God's sake, I hardly touched him.'

Mara didn't dare look up, she didn't want to do anything which might distract Alexander from speaking his mind.

'I told you to leave him alone,' Alexander repeated, 'but all you could think about was money. It's all you ever think about. If Papa dies, you . . . YOU . . . will have killed him. You'll have killed your own father. Do you understand? You . . . you murderer.' Anger, made all the more savage by the fact that he was unaware of having hidden it and therefore had no practice in controlling it, erupted from Alexander's subconscious. He took a step towards Herbert and for a moment Mara thought he would hit him, then he turned away and slumped into a chair. 'And you know what,' he gave a dry, hollow laugh. 'No one will ever know because we Rushtons keep our scandals to ourselves.'

Samuel Rushton was taken to hospital. His sons followed in another car; they did not speak during the journey. Mara and Sophia remained at the Park.

'I think I'll go to bed,' said Sophia. 'If you want to lie down or go to bed, you can use your old room.' She hurried off and Mara heard her feet running up the stairs. It was obvious that Sophia had been terrified the argument might continue between them.

But although Mara felt exhausted and drained, she stayed in the drawing room. She didn't want to go and lie down on a comfortable bed and for her thoughts to drift off into that dozy land where fantasy impinges on reality, she wanted to think her thoughts with clear-cut precision.

Thoughts of her father-in-law, the pivot of Rushton life, the sinew of moral fibre which held them all together. If he died, what would happen? Would the whole thing fall apart? Would she and Alexander drift aimlessly through the rest of their lives like a boat without a captain, whilst Herbert, a relentless gale, buffeted them to and fro until they sank in whispers beneath him? Thoughts of Alexander: he'd shown his claws at last. But would he keep them out, relishing in his new-found strength, or would he draw them back into the softness of his paws and pad on, even more gently than before because he was now aware that even gentle moggies must be careful not to hurt people? Of course he won't, Mara told herself firmly. Apart from anything else, I won't let him. I'll make him see the only way is to fight back.

She pondered her relationship with Alexander. She knew what was wrong with Alexander for her: he was too slow and too weak. And she knew there were things wrong with her for Alexander: she was too strong and too independent. But she hadn't always been independent, she hadn't been with Jamie, she'd been a limpet to Jamie. Now Alexander was being a limpet to her. Did Alexander force himself not to cling? Did he tread nervously along the path of controlled affection, that advanced stage of playing-hard-to-get? As one who had been that way, she felt desperately sorry for him if he did. If the Old Man dies, she thought, I must not let it be for nothing. In an optimistic frame of mind Mara told herself that this tragedy could be their turning point. With her help the unequal balance of power between Herbert and Alexander could be equalized, and with that the power-play between herself and Alexander would also be equalized. She would admire him for having had the strength to stand up to Herbert and he would respect her opinions because she had helped him to have that strength. He would no longer say, 'Women aren't good at . . .' and she would no longer think, Alexander can't do . . .

In this positive mood Mara waited for her husband. It was nearly midnight when she heard the car crunching over the gravel, the slam of car doors, footsteps in the hall. Then Herbert came in, his face flushed with petty triumph. Alexander followed.

Herbert looked at Mara who was sitting in an armchair by the fireplace. 'Ah, the devoted wife, waiting for news of her beloved father-in-law. Well, my dear sister-in-law, shall I tell you?'

Mara glanced anxiously at Alexander but he was staring at the floor. 'Tell me!' she said.

'The news is that the Old Man had a stroke.' He laughed. 'Old men do have strokes. Young men have them too. And I shall have a brandy.'

Mara felt sick with . . . what? Disappointment. So Alexander's victory was to disappear in the brevity of a medical term. She sat perfectly still, her grey eyes fixed on her brother-in-law because she couldn't bear to watch her husband who wavered by the door, his arms hanging dejectedly.

'So, there we are.' Brandy glass in hand, Herbert crossed to the fireplace and leaned against it, his arm lying along the marble mantelpiece. He looked down at Mara and smirked, then he looked over at Alexander. 'Yes, there we are. And here I am, knowing exactly what you think of me, brother dear.' He laughed, and his piggy eyes disappeared into his cheeks. 'It was amusing. Most informative. And all . . . all for nothing.'

'The fact remains,' said Alexander a little unsurely, 'I mean, the fact is . . .'

349

Silently Mara begged him, 'Don't give up! Don't back down!' She wished she could answer for him but that would have defeated the object, it would have made him appear weaker.

'What fact?' demanded Herbert.

'That the Old Man probably wouldn't have had a stroke if you hadn't pushed him.'

'Probably. But not definitely, my dear chap.' He drawled the 'my dear chap' in an exaggerated imitation of Alexander's accent. Though he hated to admit it, Herbert had been badly frightened when his father had fallen. He'd been terrified up till the moment the doctor had said, 'a stroke'. But now . . . well . . . he could laugh. He could laugh with relief – and with satisfaction. What chance did his slow-witted but worthy brother stand against himself? He poured himself another brandy. 'Brandy, Alexander? I think you need one. No? What about you?' He waved the decanter at Mara who shook her head.

Unable to stand Alexander's humiliation any longer, Mara stood up and said, 'I'll wait in the car.' She walked across the room towards the door, keeping her eyes firmly ahead and refusing to look at Herbert, until suddenly he lurched in front of her and she was forced to.

'Not going to share a nightcap with your dear brother-in-law, eh?' He was drunk, wonderfully drunk, and there was something about Mara which, although she wasn't his type – he liked his women blonde and buxom – provoked the anger in him. He'd felt it the first time he'd seen her, a savage desire to break her pride. He'd fantasized about her, imagined her struggling as he took her. But every fantasy had the same ending: he, the master, brutalizing her: Mara, the slave, begging for more.

'Leave Mara alone!' Alexander said sharply.

Herbert sneered. 'Don't worry, I'm not going to touch her.'

Mara tried to walk round him. Her palm was itching to slap his face.

But Herbert hadn't finished. Stuck up little bitch, he'd show her! 'No,' he said, 'I think I'm just a little bit too patriotic.'

Mara stopped dead. She could feel the angry flush creeping up her neck.

'What do you mean?' demanded Alexander.

'Nothing, absolutely nothing. I find your wife charming and I quite understand why you married her, but . . .'

'But what?'

'But I, myself, would not have married my enemy.'

There was silence, then a thud, and Mara turned just in time to see Alexander's outstretched fist, and Herbert staggering backwards into the sofa. As he sat down his hand loosened on the decanter and it smashed to his feet, the brandy running between the roses and the leaves of the Aubusson carpet. There he sat, gazing up at Alexander with a look of sheer incredulity.

Without saying another word Alexander put his arm around Mara's shoulders and ushered her out of the room.

'What will the servants think when they find the mess?' As Mara said this she realized with horror how Rushton-ized she had become.

'Damn the servants! And damn Herbert!' Alexander led her across the hall and out into the night, to the waiting car, and back to the Dower House. He took her straight upstairs to the bedroom and made love to her, and for once there was no hint of duty in Mara's response to him nor any respectful inhibitions in him to her.

Tragedy had not united them. Perhaps a common enemy would.

Chapter 21

On the following morning Alexander's lung complaint chose to manifest itself and to Mara it seemed a catastrophe. He should have been up and about cementing his position and showing Herbert that he now had a brother to contend with, not lying in bed, coughing and choking and running a high temperature. Mara was so disappointed she could scarcely find it in herself to be sympathetic. She wandered around the house, muttering curses under her breath and railing against whatever god it was who had done this to them.

The Old Man, so the hospital told Mara when she telephoned, was stable but very ill, far too ill to see anyone but immediate family. 'No, only his sons.' A daughter-in-law didn't count. In this too Mara saw catastrophe. Herbert would be ingratiating himself with the hospital, and in their eyes he would appear to be the only one who cared.

As to the story being put out by the Park, Mara heard it from Jenkins. 'We're all so sorry to hear Mr Rushton has had a stroke, madam,' he said to her on that first morning. 'Such a strong man! But they say it can happen at any time.'

From Rachel, Mara heard, 'Bonner tells me Mr 'erbert 'ad a bad fall the other night, madam. 'E slipped on the stairs and 'it 'is eye on the banister.'

They were in the second bedroom, where Mara was sleeping while Alexander was ill. 'Yes, I believe he did,' said Mara casually, 'I've been so worried about my husband I'd forgotten all about it.'

'Of course, madam.' Rachel gave her an understanding smile. 'Mind you, Bonner says Mr 'erbert's got a real shiner.'

It was Herbert's black eye which made Mara decide that perhaps after all Alexander's illness was a blessing in disguise. Although she was convinced Alexander would hold his own, she had an uneasy feeling that, had he seen Herbert's black eye, he would have been unable to stop himself from apologizing. And had he apologized, Herbert would have pounced on him and fed off his guilt, making Alexander feel he had committed some frightful crime which could only be exonerated by submission. To lose what they had gained would be worse than if they had never gained anything. By the time Alexander was well enough to go back to work, three weeks later, it was too late for apologies: the angry fires had dulled to frigid embers: the black eye was barely visible: the story of the Old Man's stroke and Herbert's fall was accepted by everyone. The Rushtons kept their scandal to themselves.

The first evening when Alexander came home from work Mara was in the drawing room, dressed for dinner. She kissed him on the cheek. 'Had a good day?'

'Not bad. I went to see the Old Man. He's a bit better but the leg's still bad. They think he may never walk again. It's not set very well.'

'Can I go and see him?'

'Not yet, darling.'

After a few minutes Mara said, 'Tell me what you did today?'

He yawned. 'The usual. What about you?'

Every evening was the same. She questioned. He was evasive.

A fortnight later Mara had a card from Elenora saying she was back, and she immediately sent for Mahogany and rode over to the cottage. She hadn't even tied the horse to the garden gate before the front door flew open and Elenora ran down the path, her arms open wide.

'Oh, how I've missed you,' said Mara as they hugged. 'I've longed for someone to talk to. We've had a terrible time. The plane crashed, and Sir Henry and Mark Hatton were killed . . . the Old Man had . . . a stroke, Alexander's ill . . .' It came gabbling out.

'I heard,' said Elenora. 'How is your father-in-law?' She turned away and patted Percy, the sort-of-spaniel, who had followed her out of the house.

'Better, I think. Actually I'm not allowed to visit him.' Mara pulled a face.

'Herbert?'

'Yes.' She hesitated, wanting to tell Elenora the truth but afraid that once she began she might not be able to stop with the Rushtons, and would go on – to her father, her mother, Herr Steiger and to Jamie, and she didn't want to think about the past when she was trying to make her marriage work.

Mara went to the cottage every couple of days. It was her oasis although she hated to think of it as such because that meant to admit her hopes for herself and Alexander were foundering. I mustn't give up, she told herself, it takes time. And every evening she would be waiting for him in the drawing room, dressed for dinner so as not to waste a single moment of their evening together.

Several times she asked if she could visit the Old Man but the answer was always no, the sons-only rule stood.

'Anyway, darling,' he told her one day, 'he's been moved to a nursing home.'

'I thought they were going to do something about his leg when he was better.'

Alexander sighed. 'Herbert doesn't think there's much point. Just put him through a lot more pain. It's not as if he's going to . . .' He fell silent.

'To what?'

'Get out and about.'

'Why not?'

It was then that he told her the Old Man was reckoned to be slightly confused, adding, 'It often happens after a stroke.'

Mara asked, 'Who says he's . . . confused?'

'Various people.'

'Herbert?'

'Yes.'

Mara groaned inwardly. 'How's the Racing Roadster coming on?' she asked him.

'Well, we've . . . er . . . stopped work on it for the moment. After all, without Mark to race her we'll have to find someone else and that sort of thing has always been left to the Old Man. But we're getting on fine with the back-orders,' he went on quickly, 'we've almost caught up. And we're selling well on the Roadsters too.'

His answers were logical, but as the summer progressed Mara began to suspect all was not going well for Alexander. At first it was just a suspicion, then she was sure. Day after day Alexander would slink home, his face grey with worry and exhaustion, and he would go straight into the study to sit at his desk, staring despondently at the wall. The most frustrating thing for Mara was that when she asked him what was the matter, he pretended that nothing was wrong.

One evening she said, 'Look, I know something's wrong. What is it? Is it Herbert? Is it your father? If you won't tell me how can I help?'

'I'm only tired, darling, that's all. Nothing's the matter. We're just very busy at the works.'

'Can't I help?'

He got up from his desk and took her in his arms and kissed her on the cheek. 'Of course you can't help, Mara.' He kissed her again. 'I'm sorry I'm not very good company at the moment. Why don't you go and stay with Caroline for a few days? You'd enjoy that.'

Mara stood there, with Alexander's arms around her, and she nearly screamed with frustration.

But Mara didn't go to stay with Caroline, she went to Lady Henrietta who told Mara on her arrival in London, 'It's too late in the season to arrange for you to be presented, my dear, but doubtless you'll be able to amuse yourself.' Mara did. She telephoned Charles and Cynthia Barrie-Leith and immediately she was swept into a social whirl of bright young things who danced till dawn and only read the gossip columns, never the tedious outpourings of trade unionists or the endless gloomy articles about the starving unemployed. Who cared about these things? Not Mara's new friends.'

The Barrie-Leiths, so Mara discovered from a girl called Sybil whose oddly strait-laced brother Jeremy was pursuing Cynthia, were the children of a dissolute baronet and his domineering wife: the parents had separated in mutual enmity, he to his mistress, she to her good works. Charles was at Oxford, although by the amount of time he spent in London no one would have known. Cynthia did nothing except spend money. They were considered fast even by London standards.

356

One day Mara and Cynthia went to Madame Cecile's and spent a fortune on low-waisted satin flapper dresses. At Wimbledon they saw an enormous American nick-named 'Big Bill' win the men's singles, and Mara giggled when Cynthia whispered, 'I do like a big man.' At the '43', run by the renowned 'Ma' Merrick, they drank long after licensing hours and if they weren't at the '43' they were at the Embassy, Charles and Mara dancing cheek-to-cheek, Jeremy trying to keep Cynthia away from other men.

Charles was pursuing Mara, although not in quite such an obvious way as Jeremy was pursuing Cynthia. It was simply that he made a point of dancing with her or sitting next to her. One afternoon they went to watch him play cricket. 'It's the men I watch, not the cricket,' lisped Cynthia as they settled to their Pimms. Charles came to join them when he wasn't batting. He lounged in a deckchair beside Mara, his ankles crossed and his whites touching the grass, as he gave her his elegant smile and treated her to salacious gossip about the other players.

Another afternoon Cynthia and Mara and the slightly prim Sybil sat through two performances of *The Sheik*, and as they came out of the cinema Cynthia said, 'You wouldn't catch me struggling if Rudolph Valentino wanted me in his tent. There's no need to look so shocked, Sybil, you enjoyed it too.'

Sybil gave a sweet smile. 'I liked the bit where she nursed him the best.'

The others laughed and Mara said, 'I liked the bit where she struggled.'

Cynthia nudged her. 'I'll tell that to Charles.' It meant nothing to her that Mara was married, and she regarded Alexander as a sort of bank manager who had to be placated from time to time. Occasionally Mara would

357

wonder what she had done to deserve the attention of the Barrie-Leiths and their set. Of course Charles wanted to get her into bed, but that alone would not have been a passport to his circle.

Whatever it was, Mara had fun with them, so much so that having arrived in London at the end of June intending to stay a week she was still there at the end of July, despite Alexander's 'I miss you' down the telephone. Lady Henrietta had encouraged her to stay on, telling Alexander, 'Let the poor girl enjoy herself. Heavens above, we're not living in Victorian times.'

But eventually Mara said, 'I think I'll have to go, Alexander needs me.'

Lady Henrietta replied, 'Yes, duty calls. But next summer you must have a proper London season. Sophia must come up too.' Mara nodded. She hadn't told Lady Henrietta anything other than the accepted story of the Old Man's stroke.

On her last night in London Mara got drunk. Drunker than she had ever been before. Drifting on a cloud of cocktails, she somehow found herself back at Charles's flat. And somehow she was lying on a chaise-longue and her white satin dress was slipping down beneath Charles's sophisticated fingers. 'I wanted you the first time I saw you,' he was saying against her lips, 'and I know you felt the same, I could feel it.' His hand sought her right breast. Deftly he massaged her nipple, never for a moment losing his greyhound grace.

Mara was tempted. Very tempted. She was drunk and the thought of getting up made her head spin. But something made her stop him.

'Why, Mara? You know you want to?'

I don't, she thought. Not really. And she said, 'Of course I do, Charles, but I am married, you know.'

He ran his hand up her thigh. 'Fidelity's awfully old-fashioned, darling, surely you don't believe in all that?'

Having set herself on a course of redemption, Mara pushed his hand away and stood up. She had a wild desire to say, 'I don't fancy you, that's why,' but Charles and his kind didn't talk like that, so she smoothed his ego by telling him she must stick by her principles but he was the only man to have tempted her since her marriage which was of course a lie. She had been far more tempted by Mark than she was by Charles.

When Mara returned to the Dower House she found Alexander even more miserable, and felt guilty to think she had been enjoying herself while he suffered alone. But she didn't feel guilty about Charles. He amused and attracted her but he was too graceful to care for, except as she might have cared for an exquisite piece of porcelain. And like a piece of porcelain, Mara suspected he had no soul.

The break from Alexander and the confidence of finding herself socially popular had done Mara good. She was more determined to help him, even if he resisted her attempts. After the excitements of London she was not prepared to go back to their dull routine.

On her first night home they dined alone, Alexander bowed and silent over his plate. Halfway through dinner Mara stood up and walked round to him, pulled up a spare chair, and sat down with her arm around his shoulders. 'Alexander,' she said gently, 'what's wrong?'

He looked up at her and smiled, and Mara was struck by how ill and old he looked. Almost broken. 'Aren't you well?' she asked. 'Is it your lungs again?'

He touched her cheek with the side of his hand. 'No, I'm fine. I was just thinking how much I love you. When I came home tonight and saw you, I thought just that . . .

that I love you. I missed you so much while you were away, I was lost without you.'

Mara kissed his hand. 'If you love me then you have to tell me what's the matter.'

'It's nothing.' He looked anxiously at the closed door. 'You'd better go back to your place or . . . er . . . what's his name, Jenkins, will be shocked.'

She stood up. 'Very well. But after dinner we must talk.'

Later, in the low-beamed study where the smell of old leather mingled with the scent of the honeysuckle outside, Alexander finally told her. He was sitting at his desk, staring at the wall ahead; Mara perched on the window-sill beside him. 'It's about the wages. The men get a rise on the first of January, like most factories, but the Old Man always gives them an extra shilling from the beginning of August.'

Mara nodded, remembering the row about it the previous year.

Alexander continued, 'Yesterday the accountant, Mr Griffin, asked me if this still stood. I said of course it did. It never occurred to me that . . . that . . .'

'What?'

'That Herbert was planning to do away with it. He was furious, Mara. I've never seen him like that, not even on the day when . . . when the Old Man fell. He said I'd no right to agree and we couldn't afford it since the Gemelli disaster, that he was planning to get rid of some of the men anyway. He said some of them were too old. Like Smithy, the foreman, who's been with Rushton-Gaunt since the beginning. I . . . I couldn't believe it. Smithy's not yet fifty.'

I can believe it, thought Mara, and surely you could have seen it coming. 'Can you afford the rise?'

'Of course we can, it's only twelve pence per man each week.'

'How many are there?'

'Well, including the office staff, about a thousand now. An extra shilling all round would cost us . . . fifty pounds a week.'

Mara laid a hand on his shoulder. 'But surely your father is still in charge – officially – and if he gave the order . . .'

'That's what I told Herbert.'

'And?'

'He said he'd sort it out with the Old Man tomorrow.'

'I see.' Mara frowned. 'Well, I could always go and see your father too.' She waited for him to say she wasn't allowed to, but he didn't, so she went on, 'I know you say Herbert thinks he's confused but I'm sure he'll be all right with me.'

'Could you, darling?' The lines of his face softened with relief. 'He may not realize what's going on but if you can get through to him . . . I'm so afraid Herbert will bully him. But if you got there first . . .' He stood up and hugged her, and together they went upstairs to bed.

As they walked along the corridor to their bedroom it occurred to Mara that Alexander was not only afraid that Herbert would bully the Old Man, but he was also too afraid of Herbert to go to the nursing home himself, in case his brother caught him there. But he's not afraid for me, thought Mara, even though he loves me.

Early next morning Owen drove Mara to the nursing home, and it was down the corridors of this politely named asylum that Mara walked, her yellow silk dress shimmering against the bright hygienic walls. And the smell of the place – chloroform, carbolic and ether – took

361

Mara straight back to Jamie. She remembered the missing button on his coat and wondered who sewed on his buttons now.

At the reception desk a nurse gave Mara an officious smile and told her, 'Mr Rushton is only allowed to see his sons and we've already had one upset this morning.'

'Oh?'

'Mr Herbert Rushton came half an hour ago. There was a terrible argument. I had to ask him to leave.' She gave Mara a disapproving look as if she were to blame.

Mara said, 'My husband wants me to see his father and I know my father-in-law would like to see me.' Of course she knew no such thing – the Old Man might really be raving and might throw a fit at the sound of her name.

The nurse called the doctor and Mara explained again. He looked worried, then said, 'Your father-in-law has asked for you several times so I'll allow you five minutes, but no more.' He escorted Mara down the corridor and as he put out his hand to open a door, she whispered, 'He's not really . . . I mean, he won't be certified, will he?'

'Not by me, he won't,' the doctor assured her.

The room was stark and bright, with a washstand, two wooden chairs, and an iron bed on which her father-in-law lay with his eyes shut and his right leg propped up. His face was thinner, he looked older.

Mara pulled up a chair and sat down, taking his hand in hers. 'It's only me,' she said softly, 'me, Mara.'

He opened his eyes and said, 'How is it possible that I could have bred a son like Herbert? How is it possible that he can forget what a shilling would have meant to him, had it not been for Sir Henry?' He paused. 'But you know what a shilling's worth, don't you, even if you do fritter them away?'

362

'Yes, I do.'

'How did you manage to persuade them to let you in?'

'The doctor.'

'Ah, the doctor. I've much to thank him for, he's all that stands between me and Herbert having me certified.'

'But he can't do that,' protested Mara, 'you're not . . .'

'Mad? Of course I'm not. But Herbert's trying to make out I am. He wants me certified so he can run Rushton-Gaunt as he pleases.' He looked over at the window. Mara hadn't noticed the bars before. 'See what I mean? I'm glad you came because I want you to do something for me.' He produced two letters from under the bed-clothes. 'I want you to post these.' One was to Mr Griffin, the accountant, the other was to Mr Lewis, his solicitor. 'Now the men will get their shillings. And I also wanted to ask you something.' He hesitated. 'When I leave here, if I can get out, I would like to come and live at the Dower House with you and Alexander.'

Mara's immediate thoughts turned selfishly to what it might mean to have him in the house. Would she still be free to come and go as she pleased? Then she chastised herself. How could she be so disgustingly self-centred when the Old Man had welcomed her into his family? 'Of course you must come,' she said.

'We may have a problem with Herbert.' He gave her a craggy smile.

'He won't get the better of us,' she said, squeezing his hand. 'When can you get out of here?'

'I'll work on the doctor.' He squeezed her hand back and lay there looking at Mara. After a while he said, 'You're just what Alexander needs. I knew it the first day I met you.'

Mara smiled. She didn't know what to say, so she merely said, 'Thank you.'

'Of course you're not in love with him.' He was watching her again.

Mara flushed. He had caught her off her guard. It was as if Jamie – oh, no, don't let me think of Jamie now – were prompting him. 'I'm very fond of Alexander,' she said lamely. Then she pulled herself together and added more forcefully, 'I wouldn't have married him otherwise.'

'And your parents were dead.'

'Yes.'

'And your country in ruins.'

'Yes, but . . .'

'And starvation did not appeal to you.' The way he put it was much harder than the way Mara had put it to herself.

'Yes, that's all true. But it's also true that Alexander had been very kind to me. He was the first person after my mother's death to treat me as a human being. Without his help I'd never have survived.'

'Rubbish!' His eyes burned up at her. 'You survived before, you'd have survived again. That's why you're what he needs. You're good for him.' He paused. 'And I like you.'

Mara said nothing. She could think of nothing to say. The Old Man lay back against his pillows, his cheek resting on the crisp white cover. 'And I shall go on liking you just so long as you make my son happy.'

His words brought Jamie back to Mara yet again. Jamie! He was with her in the car on the way home: she closed her eyes and stretched her hand across the back seat, just as if he were there to take it. He was with her in the garden, where she wandered barefoot in the heat with the faithful Prince beside her. She felt Jamie as she felt the warm damp grass against her legs. He touched her as the hot air touched her face and arms, and when she went upstairs and lay down on her bed, it was Jamie who filled her mind and it was for him that she lay there, on her back, her legs languorous and seductive.

When Alexander came home he found Mara sitting primly beside the drawing room window. After hearing an edited version of her conversation with his father he said, 'He wants to come here? But that's wonderful. You don't mind, do you, darling? He'll be no trouble.'

Mara smiled. 'No, of course not.' Then she blushed because she remembered her earlier selfish thoughts, and added cheerfully, 'It'll be nice to have him.'

'Then I'll telephone Herbert and tell him,' said Alexander hurrying into the study to use the phone.

Mara ran after him. 'No, don't! Don't tell Herbert, not till the Old Man's here.'

Alexander stopped. 'Why not?'

'Because Herbert may object.'

Alexander picked up the telephone. 'Really Mara, you're being very silly. If we don't tell him he'll be . . . cross, and with every right. Now, I know Herbert lost his temper once, but . . .'

Mara went back into the drawing room, she couldn't bear to listen to him.

When Alexander came back, he said, 'Herbert's delighted, he's going to see the Old Man tomorrow afternoon to tell him so. The only . . . er . . . small change he's going to suggest is . . .'

'What?'

'That the Old Man spends a month at the Park before coming here.'

'But . . .'

'Herbert wants to make it up to the Old Man, darling. Perfectly understandable. After all, the Old Man is his father.'

It was pointless for Mara to argue with him, he wanted so much to believe in his brother. So she changed the subject. But the next morning, as soon as Alexander left for work, she telephoned her father-in-law and after endless explanations to various nurses she eventually managed to speak to the doctor, who agreed to run an extension through to Mr Rushton.

'What is it, Mara?' the Old Man asked her.

'Alexander told Herbert you want to come here, I couldn't stop him, and Herbert says he wants you to go to the Park for a month first.'

'So he can shut me in like a prisoner.'

'I know.'

There was a brief silence and then he said, 'Go and ask Elenora Harris to drive you over to get me. I'll be waiting.'

Mara was halfway to the cottage before she began to wonder why the Old Man had asked for Elenora. She realized they knew each other, everyone round Gaunt knew each other or knew of each other, but it seemed a strange request to make of a woman with whom he did not socialize. But he probably knows she's the only person who doesn't give a damn what Herbert or anyone else thinks, she told herself.

Luckily Elenora was alone and within five minutes they were driving away from the cottage, Mara still in the middle of her explanation which, now that she had begun, came pouring out in all its details. She told Elenora about the row over the Gemelli, about Herbert hitting the Old Man, about Alexander hitting Herbert, about Mark and how she had thought of him as a white knight because he hadn't made her feel a leper and how, in the end, he hadn't been a white knight, just another human being but she had been fond of him all the same. Mara even told

Elenora about herself and Alexander, though not about Jamie, and how she had hoped Alexander hitting Herbert would be the turning point but it hadn't been. 'I suppose I expect too much of people.'

They drew up in front of the nursing home and Elenora turned to Mara with an understanding smile. 'The only person you don't expect too much from, Mara, is yourself. You don't expect enough of yourself or for yourself.'

Mara had no time to answer because one of the nurses came running out to them saying, 'The doctor wants to see you.'

Inside the nursing home they found the doctor hovering round the reception desk. 'I'm afraid I really can't allow this,' he said. 'I sympathize with the problem but, although Mr Rushton's not certified, he can't just leave at the drop of a hat.'

'What's the matter with you all?' roared a voice from down the corridor.

They spun round to see the Old Man hopping towards them, his right leg held painfully to one side. He was wearing a brown cashmere dressing-gown tied tightly over his blue and white striped pyjamas. 'Ah, there you are my dears,' he called. 'Good of you to come so promptly.'

The doctor rushed to the Old Man's side. 'Please, sir, you must go back to bed.'

The Old Man laughed. 'I'm not going anywhere except to the Dower House. Bring me a wheelchair before I fall over.' A nurse hurried forward with a wheelchair and he sat down heavily in it. 'Now, take me out to the car,' he ordered, 'and if anyone says anything to you, doctor, you can say I escaped. After all, my son says I'm a lunatic and lunatics are always escaping.'

They took him out to the car and the doctor and nurses helped to lift him into the back seat. If they inadvertently hurt him, which Mara was sure they must have done, he didn't show it. 'Thank you again, doctor,' he said. 'And all of you charming nurses. I shall need two nurses, so perhaps you can recommend some. Well, off we go.' He tapped Elenora on the shoulder.

Elenora drove as slowly and carefully as she could but at each bump Mara saw the Old Man wince, although he didn't complain. 'Thank God I'm out of that place. Much longer and I'd have gone really mad. Well Mara, which room am I going to have? If it's all the same to you I'd like the bedroom in the old house, then I can pull myself up the stairs by the banister.'

'Of course you can have it. I'm afraid I forgot all about where you were going to sleep, I was in such a hurry to get to Elenora.' She smiled at Elenora and noticed that she was very quiet.

Alexander and Herbert were pacing up and down in front of the Dower House, their hands thrust deep into their pockets, their heads bent towards each other: Herbert angry, Alexander worried.

'Bad news travels fast,' muttered the Old Man as Elenora stopped the car and his sons hurried over.

'What is going on, Papa?' demanded Herbert. He ignored Mara and Elenora. 'I phoned the hospital and they told me you'd discharged yourself. Really, Papa, this is most unwise, you're not well.' He was furious.

Alexander was looking at Mara who was avoiding his gaze. 'Mara, darling, what have you done? Oh . . . er . . . good morning, Mrs Harris, I'm sorry that you've been . . .'

Herbert snorted. 'It's perfectly obvious what they've done. Papa, I must take you back, you'll never get well if . . .'

The Old Man had kept silent, but now he opened the

back door. 'You're not taking me anywhere. I'm home. Now, help your father out of the car.'

'But, Papa . . .'

'I said help me out of the car!'

Herbert stood there clenching and unclenching his fists as though he were about to hit his father again. Mara looked at Alexander, who was hovering uncertainly, then she opened her door, got sharply out of the car, pushed them aside and took her father-in-law's arm. Immediately Alexander bent obediently to help her.

'Oh, God, you make me sick!' said Herbert, and he marched over to his own car and drove off at high speed, so fast that the gravel erupted from behind the back wheels.

The Old Man shook his head. 'Let's go and have a good stiff drink. El . . . Mrs Harris?'

Elenora shook her head. 'I must be getting back.' She drove off, and it seemed to Mara that there was a certain sadness in the Old Man's eyes as he watched her go. But I'm imagining it, she told herself, he obviously likes her but if there were anything more than that, then surely he would see her openly. And surely I would have heard about it. Local gossip wouldn't miss that one.

'Well, Mara,' he said, turning to her, 'I suppose it's time I asked Smithy to teach you to drive properly.'

Chapter 22

Two days later Smithy arrived at the Dower House with a works saloon. 'I think we'll go up to the test-track,' he said, 'then I can see what young Mr 'atton taught you.'

Mara blushed. 'Oh, you know about that.'

Smithy turned his merry chipmunk face to her. 'Not much goes on that Smithy don't know about.'

He drove up to the test-track, then Mara took over the car. Muttering, 'Clutch. In gear. Accelerate. Engage,' she managed to start off without any rabbit hops.

''E taught you well,' said Smithy after one lap of the track. 'Now, go round again and speed up.' They went round again and when they drew level with the works they met the Old Man. He was being pushed down the ramp at the back of the van which collected him each morning from the Dower House.

'How's it going?' he called.

Smithy replied, 'Not bad at all. Now, brake! Slowly! Clutch out!'

But Mara had braked too quickly and the car stalled.

'You forgot the clutch.'

'I know.' Of course she would make a mistake in front of the Old Man. At that moment Alexander and Herbert came out of the office building. And in front of them! She heard Herbert laugh.

'You'll get the hang of it, darling,' said Alexander kindly. He gave her an encouraging smile. Whatever objections he might previously have had against Mara learning to drive, as far as he was concerned now, if the

Old Man approved then he was quite happy. Alison drove. Caroline drove. So why shouldn't Mara? He'd said as much to Herbert; he had had the courage to do so because he was no longer fighting a one-to-one battle against his brother. Automatically the power had shifted back to Samuel Rushton. He had taken over the reins, leaving Herbert with his hands impotent and empty. And there was nothing Herbert could do about it, for as far as everyone at Rushton-Gaunt was concerned the Old Man was their boss.

'Well, we mustn't hold up the lesson,' said the Old Man. 'When you think she's up to it, Smithy, you can take her out on the road. But you, young lady, are not to take the car out on your own till Smithy and I say so.'

That afternoon Mara went to the cottage. She was not satisfied with her own explanation of what lay between her father-in-law and Elenora, she kept remembering she'd once seen a car drive up to the cottage, and how, after church that first Christmas, his car had seemed to slow down as it drew level with Elenora. Then there'd been the evening when he'd insisted on walking home.

It was some time before Mara managed to steer the conversation in the right direction and she started by saying, 'My father-in-law's much better. He's back at work now.'

'Oh, good.' A pause. 'What about Herbert, is he still ranting and raving?'

'I haven't seen him, thank goodness.' Mara put on a casual voice. 'I didn't realize you knew my father-in-law so well.'

'Gaunt's a small village, I could hardly not know him.'

Mara was getting nowhere. Although she knew Elenora very well she didn't like to ask outright, 'Have you had an affair with him?' because she would have hated to be asked such a question directly. 'I was just surprised he didn't suggest the Taylors or someone else he sees a lot of,' she said. Of course he wouldn't have asked her to get the Taylors.

Elenora shrugged her shoulders. 'Oh, he probably realizes I'm one of the few people round here who's not afraid of Herbert's wrath.' She lit a cigarette. 'One of the advantages of being an outsider is that one makes one's own rules.' She stood up and walked over to the window. 'I'm glad you're learning to drive, you need the freedom.'

They went on to talk of why so many men were against women driving and Mara didn't mention the Old Man again. But she still wasn't satisfied, it was simply that it would have been boorish of her to persist.

Mara had a driving lesson whenever Smithy could spare the time, and the more she drove the more she enjoyed it. She loved to feel the car accelerate beneath her. She loved to put her foot down hard and take it up to forty on the track, which on the road Smithy wouldn't let her do.

One day when they were out, driving through the hilly lanes, he told her, 'You're a good driver, madam.'

'Am I really?' This was praise indeed from Smithy.

'For a woman.' He grinned at her. 'No, I mean it. In fact you're a better driver than Mr Herbert or Mr Alexander.'

Mara said quickly, 'You'd better not tell them.'

He laughed. 'Now, would I be so silly? You see, most women lack aggression and you need aggression to drive well. But there's one thing you're not good at, you jerk 'er round the corners. You want to ease 'er round. 'Ere's a good corner. If you get out I'll show you.'

Mara stood on the verge while Smithy backed down.

'Like this!' he shouted. He roared up to the corner, revved hard, double de-clutched to change down, and accelerated as he went on out of the bend. He did it all very smoothly and without losing momentum.

Mara tried five times and each time she did something wrong. But on the sixth try she got it right.

'That's better,' Smithy told her. 'But move with 'er. You tend to sit like a corpse, madam, if you don't mind my saying so.'

'Am I really that bad?'

'No.' His face became serious. 'It's because you're good that it's worth teaching you these things.'

Having the Old Man at the Dower House was like being visited by a tornado. He had dominated their lives at the Park but, as he told Mara, he had never enjoyed living there. Now he was on home ground, and he was not only the dominant force in the house but he swept them all up into the whirlwind of his activities. He was installed in the bedroom in the old house and the sitting room below it was allocated for his use. 'Won't interfere too much with your lives like this,' he told Mara, 'and the nurses will take it in turns to sleep at the Dower House. They'll get me up and dress me, so I won't make extra work for your staff. Lucky to find nurses living nearby. Nice women, too.'

But he didn't live a separate life. He was such a vibrant personality that both Mara and Alexander gravitated towards him. Occasionally he would say to Mara, 'I do hope I'm not in the way,' and she would answer, 'You're not. We love having you.' It was true. He had brought life to the Dower House and he made her feel lively; he did the same for Alexander, who no longer came slinking home, grey and tired, but came home with his father, the useful aide-de-camp of a powerful general. And in the evening when they dined at home, they no longer made small-talk down the length of the dining room table, they joked and teased or he told them stories of the early days at Brooklands, making the famous track, which Mara had yet to see, come alive in his words.

Occasionally Mara wondered what had happened to her long peaceful days, but she didn't really regret their passing. Each morning the van came for the Old Man and Alexander, and she was free to ride, to visit Elenora or to have a driving lesson if Smithy wasn't busy. Several times Mara said to Elenora, 'Why don't you come to the Dower House? I know my father-in-law would like to see you,' but each time Elenora shook her head, and Mara didn't like to probe. In the end she concluded that either there had once, briefly, been something between them, or else that the Old Man had known Mr Harris and Elenora didn't want to be reminded of that part of her past.

There was another advantage to having the Old Man in the house – he insisted on seeing his grandchildren. 'I want to see them in the daytime,' he told Mara. 'Sophia must bring them over.' Mara also knew, without him saying so, that he preferred not to see Herbert more than necessary.

The first time Sophia brought the twins there was awkwardness between her and Mara; they hadn't spoken since Herbert had hit the Old Man.

'I planted some roses outside the study,' Mara told Sophia, to try to break the ice, 'but they've not done very well. I don't know what's the matter with them, I only have six roses this year. And that's from three bushes.'

'Perhaps you should use Clay's Fertilizer,' said Sophia.

'My father always used it. You start using it when the buds are forming and carry on until the flowers are over.'

Solemnly Mara thanked her. She turned to watch the twins who were chasing each other round the garden and she wondered when Alexander would bring up the subject of children again, and hoped it wouldn't be just yet. Although she no longer saw their life together as being impermanent, she was still not ready for that final tie.

As the weather grew colder the Old Man would often work from the house and, although he didn't say so, Mara suspected the cold and damp made his leg ache. Most of the time he was cheerful, they even had to have another telephone line put in so he could talk freely to his friends and business acquaintances, but once or twice she would find him sitting in his wheelchair gazing despondently out of the window. On these occasions he reminded Mara of a lion, captured in old age and forced to accept that the human beings he used to terrorize were now his captors. 'Ah, Mara,' he would say, turning his white head to face her, 'come and tell me what you've been up to. How's the driving going?' Once he asked her, 'Have you seen Mrs Harris?'

In the middle of October Smithy announced that Mara was now a safe driver and on a crisp sunny morning, with the Old Man, Alexander, Herbert, and a couple of the mechanics watching, he put her through her paces on the track. Luckily nothing went wrong. She sped round the circuit, cornering just as Smithy had taught her, reversed, and sped round the other way.

When she finally stopped beside the spectators, the mechanics clapped and the Old Man said, 'I should think you're good enough.' He gave her one of his craggy smiles.

Mara was basking in his praise when Herbert spoke

375

up. 'Really, Papa, I can't understand why there's been so much fuss about Mara learning to drive. If she's as good as you say, why has she had to have all these lessons? Why has Smithy had to give up valuable hours teaching her? Alexander and I learned in less than six hours.'

'Because she's a better driver than either of you,' said the Old Man, 'and we need a good driver to test the Roadster.'

'Test the Roadster! Mara! But she's a woman!'

'Yes, Papa,' said Alexander, 'I mean, she might hurt herself.'

'Might hurt the car,' snapped Herbert.

It hadn't occurred to Mara that she was being groomed to test-drive the Roadster. She'd hoped she might be given a Roadster when he was satisfied with her driving. A saloon was all very well, Alexander had a saloon and so did Herbert, but for herself she'd wanted a sportscar. That had been her next goal. But to test the Racing Roadster was something else. She leaned back against the seat and stretched her arms against the steering wheel, and smiled.

Beside Mara the argument was drawing to its inevitable close. The Old Man was saying, 'Work on modifying the Roadster, which in my absence appears to have ground to a halt, will restart next week. It will be ready for testing in the spring, I mean testing at Brooklands. Since Mark's death we have no works' driver. I am too crippled to drive and Smithy is too old to go juddering round a track, and we both agree that Mara is the obvious choice.'

Herbert interrupted him. 'You mean Mara's going to test at Brooklands?'

The Old Man looked from Herbert to Alexander. 'I said test, not race.' He turned to Mara. 'Well, young

376

lady, you're very silent. Do you want to do it? It'll mean a lot of hard work.'

'Oh, yes,' she smiled at him, 'I want to do it.'

Mara was given a Roadster, and the first place she went was the cottage. 'Look what I've got!' she cried, dragging Elenora down the garden path. 'Look! Come on! Get in! Let's go for a drive.'

They set off along the valley, Mara chattering with excitement. 'And you'll never guess what.'

'What?'

'I'm going to test the new Roadster.'

'How terrifying! But how wonderful for you!'

'And how exciting.'

Elenora studied Mara's glowing face. 'I can see you've found something you want to do.'

'Yes.' Mara laughed. 'Doers and watchers.'

She had a couple of weeks' respite from the works because the Racing Roadster was still being modified, and when she wasn't at the cottage she either drove around the countryside, revelling in the Roadster's speed and her own sense of freedom, or else she hunted, usually with Alison and sometimes with Alexander as well.

'I hear you're going to test the Roadster,' Alison said one day as they set off.

Mara laughed. 'News travels fast.' She kept her voice down so Alexander wouldn't hear.

'It's the servants. Most of the local ones have some relation working at Rushton-Gaunt. I heard it from our cook.' She leaned towards Mara. 'I gather Herbert was none too pleased.'

Mara straightened her veil. 'No, he wasn't.'

'Jolly funny if you ask me.' They went through a

gateway and trotted across a field towards a distant wood. 'Everyone thinks it is.'

When they stopped beside the wood Mara asked, 'Does everyone know?'

'Of course they do. And they think it's funny. Herbert's not popular, as you must have gathered.'

It was a perfect day for hunting, warm and damp, and the hounds soon found a fox in the first cover and it gave them a good run before it got away by swimming the Oxford Canal.

'We'll have to find you another horse,' said Alexander when they stopped to eat their sandwiches and Lord rode up with his second hunter. He turned to Alison. 'If you hear of one, Alison, let me know.'

Mara stroked Mahogany's neck. She didn't want her to think she was to be usurped.

As they set off again a thin ferret-faced man barged past Mara, muttering, 'Bloody women!' and yanking his poor horse about.

'Who's that?' Mara asked Alison.

'Heaven knows! Not a member of The Banbury I'm glad to say.' Her eyes followed the man's horse. 'Actually, I recognize that animal, it belongs to the Rushtons.'

They were trotting side by side with Alexander following. Keeping her voice as low as possible, Mara said, 'Not those new people at Gaunt Hall? We met them a couple of weeks ago, she's rather . . .'

'Frightful! All that jewellery! She clanks like a galley-slave every time she moves.'

Mara giggled.

In the late afternoon the hounds picked up the scent again and in full cry they set off across a ploughed field with the riders streaming behind them. Suddenly Alexander's horse stumbled, almost unseating him. Mara tried to stop Mahogany but her little hunter had the bit between her teeth, and she only managed to slow down enough to hear Alexander shout, 'Gone lame. Go on. I'll see you later.'

Mara galloped on down the field, jumped a ditch, and charged up the next field. She had lost ground by slowing down but now Mahogany was catching up fast. As long as I don't fall off, thought Mara, and she felt like laughing aloud. It was the best run she'd ever had. It was so exciting. They didn't stop at the top of the hill but went down the other side, the fox running hard for the distant woods. I hope he gets there, thought Mara. At the bottom of the field was a very thick hedge with a gate. A local farmer was holding it open. The fox tried to push his way through the hedge but couldn't, then tried again. This time he succeeded but he'd lost ground and the hounds streaming through the gateway soon caught up with him. It was all over for the fox.

By the time Mara reached the gateway the mud was so churned up that it was only possible for one horse to go through at a time. She waited her turn, then steered Mahogany into the gateway, but at that moment the ferret-faced man urged his horse forward, barging into Mahogany. Mara tried to rein her horse in, after all if the man wanted to go first she didn't care, but he lifted his whip hand and shouted, 'Get that creature out of my way,' and brought the whip down on Mahogany's rump.

Scarlet with embarrassment, Mara was thrown on to Mahogany's neck as the horse shot through the gate and barged into two other horses which formed part of the circle around the kill. 'Sorry,' she muttered, straightening her bowler and collecting up her reins.

But the man hadn't finished with her yet. 'If you can't

control your horse, madam,' he shouted, 'you shouldn't ride to hounds in the English countryside.'

Around Mara conversations dropped to mere whispers. She looked at the ferret-faced man. She was his fox and he her one hound baying for her blood. This is it, she thought, if I don't get the better of him now I'll never get the better of any of them. She pushed up her veil and looked him full in the face. 'If you can't control your horse, sir, I suggest that you shouldn't ride to hounds in any country.'

There was silence. Then someone shouted, 'Bravo!' And before the man had time to answer, the Master rode up and said, 'Sir, Mrs Rushton is a competent horsewoman and a welcome member of The Banbury. You, sir, are a guest and no longer a welcome one. Kindly remove yourself and your unfortunate horse.'

'Well done, Mara,' said Alison, coming up beside her as they rode back to find Alexander.

They found him with Lord and the horse-box. 'Have a good run, darling?' he asked.

'Wonderful.' Mara gave Alison a don't-say-anything look.

But she had to tell him in the end because various people came up to her and said, 'Good show, Mrs Rushton, you put the bounder in his place.'

Then the Master came over and said, 'I must apologize, Mrs Rushton, never had that sort of behaviour before in The Banbury.' He turned to Alexander. 'I told him Mrs Rushton was a welcome member of this hunt and that he was a guest and no longer a welcome one.'

Alexander reached up and touched Mara's hand. 'How awful for you, darling, I didn't realize it was as bad as that.'

She put her gloved hand over his. 'I was perfectly all right.'

'A fine young woman,' said the Master. 'She gave as good as she got' – he winked at Mara – 'but then I gather she always does.'

It was that incident, the end of leper island which, coupled with the knowledge that the Old Man deemed her good enough to test the Roadster, gave Mara her final boost of confidence. She went to the cottage and told Elenora about the hunt. 'You should have seen the man's face when the Master told him to remove himself,' Mara chortled.

Elenora laughed. 'I wish I had.'

'I wonder if that's the end of it.' Mara wandered across the studio and picked up the lump of black rock, the thing which she had first admired in the cottage.

Elenora was filling the kettle at the sink. 'I don't think you'll have any more trouble round here, everyone says how popular you are, and even if you do, you've learned how to deal with it.' She put the kettle on the gas ring and joined Mara. 'You've made them like you despite the fact you're German, and that's no mean feat.'

Mara smiled. There was no praise which counted more than that of the Old Man or Elenora. 'Where did you say you got this?' she asked, waving the lump of black rock.

Elenora shrugged. 'Nowhere particular.'

Mara frowned. 'I thought you told me it came from France.'

'Did I? Yes, you're right. I'd forgotten.' Elenora went over to the pine table and lit herself a cigarette.

By January the Roadster was ready and one bright sunny morning Mara drove up to the works to begin testing her. She wasn't entirely sure what she would be expected to do, the Old Man had muttered that it was a long and tedious process and that all she had to do was to obey instructions. Mara hadn't been quite sure what to wear either, she didn't like to ask the Old Man in case he thought her frivolous, so she settled for a blue skirt and jumper and a three-quarter-length coat.

She found the Old Man, Smithy and two mechanics admiring the Roadster, which was parked in front of the offices. It was exactly the same shade of green as the Old Man's car, the one in which Owen had come to collect her and Alexander from the Ritz. 'See! Rushton green,' the Old Man called, waving at the car. 'Now, if you'd come up here in these past weeks instead of gallivanting around the countryside . . .'

Mara blushed. It hadn't occurred to her to come up and see how the car was getting on, all she had thought about was driving it when it was ready.

'Well, Smithy,' the Old Man turned to the foreman, 'shall we have a couple of slow laps first and then we'll have a look and see how the engine's bearing up. And you, young lady,' he looked at Mara, 'remind me to dig out my old flying-helmet and goggles. You're all right for the time being, but when we start getting a bit of speed up we can't have you careering off the track because a bit of dust got in your eye or your hair was covering your face.'

Mara lapped the track three times. Then she stopped and the men opened the bonnet and discussed the engine. Then they told her to do another ten laps. She stopped and again they opened the bonnet. 'Now, a bit faster,' said the Old Man.

Mara did another five laps, but this time when they opened the bonnet Smithy shook his head. 'Seems to be running a bit hot. We'd better 'ave a look at 'er.'

The Old Man said, 'That'll be all for today, thank you Mara.'

So Mara went home. It hadn't been nearly as exciting as she'd expected.

The second time Mara tested the Roadster something else went wrong, but this time she didn't go home, she stayed to watch them work on the car, and this set the pattern for all the test drives. In all honesty Mara wasn't terribly interested in the size of the bore of the carburation, it was the driving she enjoyed; but by staying she became a part of the team. There was the Old Man with his great knowledge of how a car should work and his brilliant ideas on how to improve its performance, there was Smithy who knew how to put those ideas into practice and the mechanics – fair-haired Terry and dark-haired Jackson – faithfully following Smithy's instructions, and there was Mara, the driver.

And as the testing hotted up, the exhilaration of speed spilled over into all aspects of Mara's life. Late one afternoon, when they'd had a particularly good session and everyone was saying how well the Roadster was going, she went home to find Alexander had arrived ahead of her. He was in his dressing room, wearing his dressing-gown and standing in front of the mirror combing his wet hair.

'You're back early.'

'Yes, I had to go into Banbury and I decided to come straight home. I had a bath.'

She smiled at his reflection. 'I can see.'

He put the comb down on the dressing-table. 'When I left the works you were going very fast,' he said.

Laughing, Mara turned to him and ran her forefinger down him, from below his neck to his stomach, that same intimate gesture which she had made towards him at the ball when Mark had seen her. 'Yes, it was wonderful.'

'I could hardly bear to watch.' Alexander pushed her uncombed hair back from her face. It was streaky at the sides where it had been pressed against her head by the goggles and the leather flying-helmet. 'I'm so afraid you'll hurt yourself. I couldn't bear it if something . . .'

'It won't.' She perched herself on the edge of his dressing table and slid her arms around his waist, pulling him towards her until he was standing between her legs, pushing her skirt up her thighs.

'Darling,' he put his hands on her shoulders, 'Rachel will be up soon to help you dress.'

'So?'

'Well, she'll come into our bedroom.'

Mara untied the cord of his dressing-gown. 'Who said anything about going into the bedroom?'

'But . . . we can't . . . I mean, not in here.'

'Why not?' Her skirt had ridden right up above her thighs, exposing the white silk of her suspenders and the bare flesh beneath them, and the wide, loose legs of her cami-knickers above that. She pulled him closer, gripping him with her knees, and forced him to take her, there in the small dressing room, with the sound of her maid moving around in the bedroom next door adding to her excitement because they had to be quiet, and she didn't want to be, and that gave it an erotically forbidden flavour.

Afterwards she buried her head in Alexander's stomach to smother her giggles whilst he stroked her hair and smiled, unsure what the joke was, just pleased that she had come to him. It made him love her even more, and he was even more afraid that she would kill herself.

That night as they were going to bed Alexander said,

384

'Everything's gone right since we moved to the Dower House, hasn't it darling?'

Mara thought of the months when the Old Man had been in hospital and Alexander had slunk home each evening, but she said, 'Yes, it has,' although she was thinking, no, everything's gone right since I began to test the Roadster.

All through the early months of that year, 1922, they tested the car. There were cold, wet days when Mara would drive and the others would cluster round the Old Man's wheelchair in the middle of the circuit, hunching their shoulders in their jackets and stamping their feet. There were cold days when Smithy and the mechanics would be fiddling with the Roadster and Mara would go to Mrs Wright, the receptionist, and order hot sweet tea for the team. And there were sunny days when the windows of the office building sparkled and the wind whistled across the plateau as Mara lapped the track. Sometimes, when she was waiting to drive, she would look down the track and the wind would catch her hair as it had when she'd stood on the Deutsches Eck and watched the rivers run by.

In April Lady Henrietta wrote to Mara asking if she should still expect her for the season. 'I don't think I can go,' Mara told Alexander, 'I hate to let her down, but how can I now I'm driving the Roadster?'

Alexander nodded. 'She'll understand.' He was delighted that Mara wasn't going to London but he wished it could have been because of him that she wasn't going.

'You can always go later on,' said the Old Man.

'Perhaps.' Mara was keeping her plans to herself, she hadn't even told Elenora. There had been talk of Rushton-Gaunt looking around for a driver to race the Roadster – there were plenty of young men who would have

385

jumped at the chance – but so far the Old Man had made no decision. 'Let's see her test first,' he said whenever the subject came up, 'then we'll know the sort of driver we're looking for.' Mara was absolutely determined that the driver would be herself. From gossip at the works and from studying the *Autocar* she knew there were very few lady racing-drivers, a Miss Ivy Cummings and a Miss Addis-Price and a couple of others, but that didn't deter her.

One afternoon towards the end of May the Old Man called the team together. 'We've gone as far as we can here, so we'll take her down to Brooklands next week.' He turned to Mara. 'And for once I'm going to suggest you spend money on clothes. We can't have you testing our Roadster in a skirt. Get Mrs Wright to order you some Rushton green overalls, and Smithy, make sure she has everything she needs, the things I used to have. She'd better have some new goggles – those are a bit scratched – and a corset.'

'A corset!' Mara looked at him aghast. She'd never had to wear a corset in her life.

'To keep your stomach from being shaken to pieces. Have you any idea what it's like to drive over those bumps at high speed?'

'No, but . . .'

'But! But! But! You're going to a race-track, young lady, not a fashion parade.'

A week later they set off for Weybridge, Mara and Smithy in the Roadster, the Old Man in the van driven by Terry, and Jackson in the works car piled with spares. It was evening by the time they arrived and they went straight to the Hand and Spear, where the Old Man had always stayed in his racing days. 'The racing crowd call it the Mitt and Dagger,' Smithy told her as they went over the railway bridge and turned sharp left for the hotel.

The Hand and Spear was a red-brick Victorian building, built on varying levels, with a tall thick tower sticking up in the middle of it. This gave it an industrial appearance, or so Mara thought, as if its architect had been undecided if he should build a house or a factory and had kept his options open till the last moment.

The proprietor and his wife came hurrying out to greet the Old Man, and as soon as Terry had propelled the wheelchair through the door, a waiter appeared from the dining room to shake his hand, and an elderly porter reminded him of his last great win. Not one of them saw him as a cripple in a wheelchair, their memories of him were yesterday, and they had not been blurred by seeing him grow old and crippled.

Smithy and the mechanics took the Roadster into the courtyard beside the hotel and immediately opened the bonnet and began to check the engine. Once Mara had settled herself in her room, which was at the back, over the tea room, she went out to join them. 'My father-in-law's having a wonderful time,' she told Smithy. 'He has the whole of the tea room spellbound.'

''E deserves to, miss.'

To her amusement Mara noticed that Smithy had called her 'miss' not 'madam', and she wondered if stately 'madams' didn't test cars or wear overalls. She asked him, 'When did Rushton-Gaunts last race?'

'Before the war. Did very well too. I remember 'ow we used to close the works for the day, and down we'd come to Brooklands, every one of us cheering 'im on.'

'Tell me about the drivers.'

And Smithy did. At one point he said, 'One mustn't criticize the dead, but you know, miss, that poor Mr

387

'atton, 'e didn't 'ave what Mr Rushton 'ad. 'E'd never 'ave made it to the top.'

Mara thought of Mark. Thank God he couldn't hear, at least she hoped he couldn't.

As she lay in bed that night, listening to the muffled thud of bowls from the bowling alley on the ground floor, Mara wondered if she had what it took to get to the top.

Early the following morning they took the Roadster down to the track, and as soon as Mara saw the great oval circuit, a hundred feet wide, with its banking like the inside of a wave, curving up to a height of thirty feet, she felt horribly nervous. I must be mad, she thought. But when they reached the Paddock and she saw the other cars and she heard the roar of engines and the sound of laughter coming from the clubhouse behind, she began to feel better. If others could do it and laugh so could she.

Even on a non-racing day Brooklands was full of people: people who lived and breathed racing: people for whom Brooklands was home: people who welcomed Samuel Rushton as their childhood hero. 'See what I mean, miss,' said Smithy, pointing towards the men who clustered round the Old Man.

And the Old Man wasn't the only one receiving attention. Although no one spoke to Mara, they certainly looked at her, but because she felt unsure of herself she fiddled with the buttons on her Rushton green overall and looked at the clubhouse. It was a two-storey red-brick building with all its woodwork picked out in white. On the top was a little dome, and on the left, with a clear view of at least two-thirds of the track, was a long balcony from where the press watched the races. The clubhouse looked exactly what it was meant to be, a centre for the devotees of a rich man's sport. It would have done equally well on a polo-ground.

Mara asked Smithy, 'Where's the Finishing Post?'

'Right 'ere, miss, in front of the Paddock. They start from 'ere too.' He pointed, his arm outstretched. 'They go up the end of the Finishing Straight, round to the left at the banking . . . the Members' Banking, along beside the railway line, behind the Aero Sheds . . . see them, at the bottom . . . through the Byfleet Banking and up till they get to the Fork, just this side of the Vickers Sheds. Then they either keep to the right at the Fork and go behind the 'ill or, if it's the end of the race, they keep to the left and come up 'ere . . . up the Finishing Straight. And the first one back's the winner!'

At that moment an enormous monster of a car left the Paddock and set off as Smithy had indicated. 'Look, miss! That's Count Zborowski's *Chitty Bang Bang*. Ugly brute, but she can't 'alf get some speed up.'

They watched the monster roar round the track. At the same time a small biplane left the Aero Sheds and came bouncing up the grassy centre of the circuit. Remembering the Gemelli, Mara watched in horror as it went faster and faster, lifting then falling back, until at last it dragged itself up, skimmed the clubhouse, and wobbled off into the sky. Mara had been convinced it was going to crash.

She realized that the Old Man was calling to her and she hurried over to him. 'This is my daughter-in-law,' he said, introducing her to Tom Sopwith. 'She's testing the Roadster for us.'

Mara shook hands with the famous aviator and smiled nervously. Having seen the Gemelli crash and the little biplane wobbling through the sky, she now regarded anyone who flew as having superhuman courage.

When he had gone and they were left alone, the Old

389

Man said, 'Now come along, Mara, let's get down to it. One of the mechanics, I think Terry, will ride with you. Don't want you breaking down with no one to help. And I want you to take her slowly for the first three laps, then if you feel confident take her faster. But not too fast! This isn't a race. Tomorrow, if all goes well, we'll try her on Test Hill.' He pointed to the hill which separated the clubhouse and the Paddock from the gully of the Members' Banking. A narrow road led steeply up the hill on top of which were the public enclosure, the restaurant and the terraced stands, which reminded Mara of the vineyards around Koblenz.

'Where's the corset?' demanded the Old Man, looking at Mara's waist.

She produced it from behind her back.

'Smithy,' he called, 'put it on her.' The little foreman blushed as he tightened the padded girth around Mara's waist.

In fact, the corset wasn't as unflattering as Mara had feared, it was more like a low-slung cummerbund with three buckles across the front.

Mara climbed into the Roadster, adjusted her flying-helmet and pulled on her goggles. Terry climbed in beside her. She set off slowly out of the Paddock and into the Finishing Straight, turning left at the top to go down the Railway Straight. At the bottom, she went into the Byfleet Banking, where the great concrete wave rose on her left, and Mara tightened her hold on the steering wheel and gritted her teeth. But she wasn't going fast enough to go up the wave. At the Fork she swung right and went into the deep gully of the Members' Banking, passing under the bridge, and back into the Railway Straight. At least I've got round once, she thought.

But the Roadster wasn't the only car on the track. The

390

Chitty roared past like a mechanized dragon, followed by a motorcycle which, to Mara's horror, swung right up to the lip of the banking wave, its rider leaning over, seemingly touching the ground with his elbow. Then two other cars passed, one on either side of her. At first Mara was terrified in case she smashed into some shiny monster, but gradually she grew more confident and she drove faster, so fast that on the tenth lap she too swung right up into the wave. When she got round to the Fork, Smithy was standing on the verge and he waved her into the Paddock.

'You're going much too fast,' the Old Man shouted at her as she drew to a halt beside his wheelchair. 'This isn't a race, Mara, and you're not trying to break a record. We're here to test the car, please remember that. Now, let's have a look at the engine – if there's one left to look at.'

Mara was suitably chastised but she felt frustrated. She had wanted to put her foot down and go even faster.

On the following day they attacked Test Hill, and Mara drove up and down it, sometimes slowly sometimes fast. And every day after that Mara either lapped the circuit or drove up and down Test Hill, always very careful to obey her instructions. And she enjoyed it. It was exhilarating to drive where famous drivers had raced and where she hoped she too would race.

It was not only the testing at Brooklands which Mara found exhilarating, but also the attention. Women who drove at Brooklands were a rarity, a breed apart from the girlfriends and sisters who hung around the drivers in floral dresses and too much make-up. And Mara, although she wasn't racing, with her Rushton Green overalls, her suntanned face and her sunstreaked hair, stood out among them like a wild stallion in a herd of well-tamed mares. Daredevil and slightly masculine, she challenged each man's masculinity.

'I suppose they think I don't know it's not just the car they're looking at,' grumbled Smithy after yet another young driver had wandered over to inspect first the car, then Mara, then had casually suggested she might like to meet him for a drink in the clubhouse. So far she had always refused.

'It's just because I'm a novelty,' Mara told him, smoothing the overalls down over her hips.

'And you do right to refuse 'em, miss,' he said, giving her one of his bright beady smiles. 'Young devils most of these drivers.'

But they're bloody attractive, thought Mara. Then she berated herself for swearing. She was picking up the language of the pits.

At the end of the week the Old Man said, 'Well, I think we have a pretty good idea of what the Roadster can do. She needs a few modifications and then she'll do nicely.' They were in the Paddock and the Old Man was in his wheelchair with his back to the clubhouse, with Mara, Smithy and the mechanics standing next to the Roadster. The Old Man looked up at her. 'Thank you very much, Mara, you've been a great help. Now, Smithy, we must see about finding a driver.'

This was Mara's moment. She waited until Smithy and the mechanics had moved away, then she took a deep breath and said, 'I would like to race the Roadster.'

The Old Man looked up at her from his wheelchair. 'I know you would but you can't.'

This was not how Mara had planned it. In her day-dreams he had answered, 'You're inexperienced but I'll give you a try.' 'Why can't I?' she asked hoarsely.

392

'For three reasons.' He screwed up his eyes against the sun.

'Because I'm a woman?'

'No, you're not a woman, Mara, you're a twenty-year-old girl who only started driving properly last autumn. That's one reason. You're a good driver but you're too inexperienced.'

'I could learn.'

'You could, but my second reason is that Rushton-Gaunt not only have to race, but to win, and we won't win with a beginner.'

Mara looked down at him, her shadow was waving on his lap. 'You've known for some time that I wanted to race?'

'Yes, I have.'

'Then why didn't you tell me you weren't going to let me?' She felt like hitting him and had he not been in a wheelchair she might easily have done so.

The Old Man replied calmly, 'If you'd asked me I'd have told you, but you didn't, and anyway I suspected that if you knew you might give up on the testing.'

'You can say that again!' She was furious, she hated him, she felt he had tricked her as Jamie had tricked her, as Herr Steiger had tricked her.

'That's what I mean when I say you're a twenty-year-old girl.'

'And what's the third reason?' she demanded.

'Alexander asked me not to let you race, and I may not always take notice of my son's wishes but I do over this.'

Mara relaxed slightly. 'I'm sure I can persuade him to . . .'

'It'll make no difference.'

'Why not?'

'Because you won't persuade me and that's what counts. You've forgotten my first two reasons.' He paused. 'And you should try to see it from Alexander's point of view. He's afraid you'll be killed, Mara, and because he loves you he doesn't want to lose you.'

Mara turned away and looked down the great sweeping oval to the Byfleet Banking at the far end. The sun was dipping behind some trees beyond it and long shadows lay across the concrete, but the curve no longer seemed to Mara like the inside of a wave. It was a prison wall and it was drawing closer. That the Old Man considered her too inexperienced to race was hurtful but almost acceptable, she could have gone all out to prove him wrong, practised on the works track with her own Roadster, persevered, and in six months . . . well . . . but she'd have hope. Only there was no hope, for however hard she tried Alexander would still hold the key to her prison. 'He has lost me,' she said, and tears of rage and frustration came into her eyes.

Chapter 23

Mara's obscene pursuit of pleasure began then. In it she became two people, the director and the actor, the detached guiding the involved through one hedonistic event after another. Go there! Wear that! Say that! Laugh! Drink! Smoke! But never have time to think. Never care. Never feel. Never try to make something of yourself. What was the point when a man who lay crushed beneath his brother's feet could, with a couple of words, prevent her from doing the only thing she wanted to do.

Was it her fault that Alexander was crushed? Was it her fault that without the Old Man's support he would disintegrate? She'd tried to help him, she'd done her best, but he hadn't wanted her help, he wanted to submit to others. But Mara didn't and she was forced to. And he had done it to her.

A week after their return to the Dower House Mara went up to London and immediately she was caught up in the Barrie-Leith whirlwind.

Charles and Cynthia. The greyhound and the poodle. They were just what Mara wanted. Never serious, never boring, always ready for the next excitement. With Cynthia she giggled over cami-knickers and who was sleeping with who. With Charles she listened to jazz, which he pretended to understand and she pretended to adore. Together, the three of them, they worshipped Scott Fitzgerald. He had written for them. They were *The Beautiful and the Damned* – not that any of them had

395

actually read the book. They were too busy, they didn't have time.

At first Lady Henrietta was delighted to see Mara, she arranged for her to be presented at court and took her to Ascot, but after Mara had been in London for six weeks she said, 'Really, my dear, much as I love having you I think you should go home. Samuel is rather worried about you and it is a little awkward if I let you stay on. Duty calls, my dear.'

But duty didn't call Mara, she didn't give a damn. Ignoring Lady Henrietta's 'This is most unwise, people will talk,' she went to stay with Charles and Cynthia who lived in their father's town house just off Brook Street, and on her first night there Mara went to bed with Charles. Why shouldn't she? But it meant nothing to her and she didn't particularly enjoy it. In everything Charles did, including making love, he was smooth, sophisticated but just a little too soulless. A couple of weeks later Mara went to bed with a tennis-player she'd picked up at Wimbledon, but she didn't enjoy that either, he battered away at her as if he were practising his volley. She left the tennis-player as soon as he fell asleep, creeping out into the flat dawn of casual sex. But she didn't go straight back to the Barrie-Leiths, who lived just the other side of Grosvenor Square. Instead she went into Hyde Park and wandered right across it, skirting the Serpentine, until she came to the monument to Prince Albert. She stood looking up at him, thinking how incongruous they both were. Two Germans in an English park, he sitting on his throne like some Eastern potentate surrounded by jagged red and gold turrets, she standing on the rough grass in a long evening dress which left her shoulders bare to the early-morning light. For a moment Mara wondered if the Victorians had got it right, that she might have been happier if her life had been arranged for her. Or is it that then I wouldn't have myself to blame, she thought, and she lit a cigarette and walked quickly back across the park to Mayfair.

When she reached the house she found Charles pacing up and down in the hall, for once without his usual sophistication. 'Where have you been?'

'Wandering around.'

'Did you go off with . . . ?'

Mara walked past him and into the drawing room. 'If you're having a brandy I'll join you.'

He followed her. 'Mara, I asked you a question.'

She ran her fingers through her hair, tousled by the tennis-player. 'Don't be a bore, Charles, you're getting as bad as Alexander.'

She was playing them all at their own game, and doing so quite unconsciously. She didn't think about Charles or about any of them, only about Mara. And about fun. Fun. Fun. Fun. That was all she let herself think about. They called her a bright young thing and, together with all the other bright young things, she flitted from man to man and social event to social event like a brilliantly plumed but mindless bird of paradise.

Eventually Mara had to go back to the Dower House, but even there she didn't slow her pace. Cynthia and Charles and other friends from London came to stay. She gave parties which lasted long into the night, and from which Alexander retired early, exhausted. She played tennis, drank cocktails, and smoked, ignoring Alexander's grimaces. Inevitably Mara saw less of Damon, he avoided her; the bond had gone. And she saw as little as possible of Herbert and Sophia. Why should she make the effort when they made it patently obvious she'd fulfilled all their gloomy predictions?

Mara had no feelings of remorse about having slept with Charles and the tennis-player, and if she didn't have many lovers it wasn't because of Alexander, it was because she'd found her experiences unsatisfying.

Perhaps if Elenora had been at the cottage that summer Mara could have poured her heart out and come to terms with life, but Elenora was away until October and by then Mara was set on her course. Their meeting was not a success. Somehow Elenora made her feel a failure in spite of her social victories, and when Mara left the cottage she had no desire to return.

Any mention of the Roadster also made Mara feel a failure. She didn't want to hear about cars or about racing, she even refused to go to Brooklands to watch the first Hatton-Gaunt Cup race. When Alexander begged her to go, saying, 'We're all going, Mara, and it'll look so odd if you won't,' she replied, 'I don't care what it looks like,' and went off to stay with Cynthia, roaring her Roadster through the country lanes as fast as it would go.

Mara's only consolation that year was that the new driver had failed with the Roadster. She overheard the Old Man tell Alexander, 'He has no feel for the car. We'll have to find someone else,' and she had to rush out into the garden so that they couldn't hear her laughter.

The spring came again. In was 1923. But this spring Mara didn't come alive. She had lost her spontaneity: the gap was filled with calculated fun. She could no longer hope: she knew the limitations of her life. And because she didn't want to think about those limitations, she threw herself into an even wilder whirlwind.

The Old Man said nothing about all this. Occasionally Mara would find him watching her, his eyes full of compassion, but most of the time they treated each other as if they were strangers. She because he could have overruled Alexander and hadn't; he because she was destroying his son.

Alexander was miserable. One morning he asked her, 'Is it because I wouldn't let you race?'

Mara was lying in bed with her eyes shut. 'What do you think?'

He came round to the side of the bed and looked down at her. He longed to take her in his arms, or even just to touch her, but he didn't dare, she was so cold towards him. But in spite of all this he still loved her. 'I was afraid you'd kill yourself.'

Mara rolled away from him. 'I'd rather be killed in a crash than die of boredom.'

The year passed and in the following April Mara and the Barrie-Leiths and their crowd went to the opening of the British Empire Exhibition at Wembley. It was tremendous fun and they, along with hundreds of other people, watched a rodeo, ate in the Hong Kong Chinese restaurant and marvelled at the reconstructed tomb of Tutankhamen. They also drank at every possible opportunity and ended up by singing, 'Yes, We Have No Bananas' beside the Gold Coast section, where huge bunches of bananas covered a little hillock like a lot of exhausted bodies slumped in the sand.

When Mara eventually returned to the Dower House she told the Old Man and Alexander about the exhibition – it was one of the few things about her time in London she could tell them. 'It was such fun,' she said. They were having dinner and she smiled down the dining room table. 'I've never seen so many people in one place.'

The Old Man shook his head. 'The exhibition's a waste of time. We're trying to justify having an empire by saying it's good for trade, but the dominions are straining to get away from us.'

'But they buy all our goods,' said Alexander.

'Oh, they will for a bit . . . until they've got the hang of our technology, but after that they won't, they'll buy from elsewhere and from each other. And why shouldn't they? We exploited them. I'm a patriot through and through, but I'm not blind to our faults. Crippled maybe, but not blind.'

Mara was furious with him for denigrating her fun. 'There were lots of Africans and Indians there,' she said, 'and none of them looked at all . . . cross or whatever.'

'You'd hardly expect them to,' he replied. 'It's we who are the fools. We're like the owners of a theatre who plan a season of plays whilst ignoring the fact that all our actors are out looking for better parts.'

I don't know why I bother, thought Mara, emptying her glass of wine.

She went back to London two weeks later and stayed away till August, and even when she came home she brought Cynthia and Jeremy with her, and they racketed around the countryside or played loud music on the gramophone, drinking White Ladies and not going to bed till the small hours. There was no time to think, but Mara didn't want to think. She didn't want to question her golden cage, for if she did, what was the answer? She had to shut her eyes, and she did: to Alexander struggling helplessly against ill health and with his father between him and Herbert's bullying: to the Old Man who hated what she was doing to his son but at the same time, irritatingly, felt sorry for her: to anyone who questioned: to anyone who criticized. For if they questioned her lifestyle and criticized her behaviour, why hadn't they criticized those who had pushed her into this trap and locked the door, and given the key to someone else, to a driver who wasn't even good?

In 1925, like everyone else, Mara and Cynthia read *The Green Hat*. It was the book of their age and it dared to mention 'one of those diseases'.

'I wonder if any of our friends have got . . .' said Cynthia with a giggle.

Even Alexander read *The Green Hat*, and afterwards Mara suspected he was wondering if she, like Iris Storm, had hundreds of lovers. Perhaps I will be like her, she thought, and I'll kill myself by driving into a tree – not in a yellow Hispano-Suiza but in a Rushton Roadster. Serve him right if I did! She made herself another White Lady with more Cointreau and gin than the recipe required, lit a cigarette and planned her next escape to London.

And so the social merry-go-round spun Mara round and round, and only just occasionally, as when she'd stood looking up at Prince Albert, would she admit that it felt more like a slippery slope.

Chapter 24

May 1926 – The General Strike

Mara had come to London to see Madame Cecile. She had arrived at Lady Henrietta's the previous evening and now, after breakfast, she was standing by the fireplace in the drawing room; her hostess was sitting on the sofa. 'So what if there is a strike?' said Mara. 'I simply *must* go to Madame Cecile this morning or I'll have nothing to wear this summer, you know how booked up she becomes. I can't possibly go and work in a soup kitchen.' She looked at herself in the mirror over the mantelpiece. She was nearly twenty-five and she looked it – looked even older – which was grossly unfair because she didn't do anything ageing and she spent a fortune on face creams. Raking her hair with her fingernails so that the fair and red of its tawniness separated from the dark underneath, she cursed the fashion of the short bob. She should have left it long, but how could she when no one else did? Everyone said short hair made one look younger, but it didn't on Mara; she looked hard, which was also unfair. Everything was unfair. Lady Henrietta was being particularly unfair.

'I'm very fond of you, Mara, but you do tend to think of yourself. There's a strike on and people are starving. We all have to do our bit.'

'Strikes! Strikes! Strikes! I'm sick of hearing about strikes. Anyhow, it'll be over tomorrow.'

'Then you can go to Madame Cecile tomorrow.' Lady

Henrietta stood up. 'It's time you learned, my dear, that wealth and position carry their own responsibilities.'

'Lady Henrietta, surely . . . I mean.' Mara smoothed down the skirt of her buttercup Chanel suit. The short skirt was the very height of fashion and she adored it, perfect for the lunch she had planned with Charles, the lunch Lady Henrietta had made her cancel. Dear Charles! She might even have let him make love to her that afternoon.

Her hostess picked up her bag and gloves and said sharply, 'Do stop making such a fuss! Frankly, judging by the brevity of that skirt, you could just as well buy your clothes in the children's department at Harrod's. Lady Barrie-Leith is expecting us at twelve. Hurry up, the car's waiting.'

Mara picked up her bag and gloves as slowly as possible. 'I'm sure Cynthia doesn't have to work in a soup kitchen. I'm sure she hasn't had to cancel her charleston lesson.' Mara was desperate to learn the new dance before the season began.

'Of course she'll be there.' Lady Henrietta straightened her shoulders and pushed out her large silk-covered bosom. 'Charity is the price women of our class pay for their boundless privileges and' – she gave Mara a hard look – 'we are expected to pay it with good grace.'

The journey from Mayfair to Whitechapel took nearly two hours. They were constantly held up as cartloads of giggling shopworkers and buses driven by university students bumped up against convoys of food destined for Hyde Park and other distribution centres. Why can't we go to Hyde Park, Mara wondered as she stared out of the window at the people and the placards: 'Join the strike', 'General Strike spreads'. It was more like a carnival than

403

a national emergency. So much for Lady Henrietta's starving masses.

The Whitechapel soup kitchen, on the ground floor of a seedy Victorian building, was easily identifiable by the smart cars parked outside, many with waiting chauffeurs, all belonging to the charity workers. The cars stood out with shining incongruousness amongst the bedraggled crowd of grimy children and grey-faced women who were grouped around the entrance.

'I do hope they don't attack the car,' said Lady Henrietta doubtfully. Her intentions were excellent, but how much easier it would have been to write a cheque.

Mara looked up at the faces. They stared back resentfully, taking in not only her face but her clothes, calculating the cost in food. For the first time Mara wished she had worn something less ostentatious. She knew what it was like to be on the outside looking in, and the memory gave her an unwelcome twinge of guilt. Outside the car the smell of poverty was overpowering, the cobbled streets thick with mud, and the disorderly queue muttered as she passed. Inside the kitchen things were better: at the far end, behind the trestle-tables, she recognized her own kind – her own kind now. She saw that they too were uncomfortable but covered it by brazening it out with the jolly bossiness of charity workers, though each had a nervous look as though afraid the French Revolution was about to be repeated in Whitechapel.

Beyond the trestle-tables and the women ladling out the soup, Mara caught sight of Cynthia. She pushed through the soup queue and the two friends fell into each other's arms.

'Mara, darling, thank God you're here,' squealed Cynthia. 'I couldn't bear it if there wasn't a single chum.

Now, find yourself an apron before you get that divine suit filthy.'

Mara asked, 'How's Jeremy?' To everyone's surprise, after years of gallivanting, Cynthia had settled for the faithful Jeremy and the previous summer they had had an enormous wedding at St Margaret's, Westminster. At the time Mara had wondered cynically whether Jeremy's recent and considerable inheritance had had something to do with it.

'Actually, darling' – Cynthia handed a knife to Mara – 'he's being rather tedious. He keeps talking about having children and I don't want them yet. I want to enjoy myself. After all, you've been married for years and you haven't any . . . oh, sorry, darling, I haven't put my foot in it, have I?'

Mara laughed. 'Not at all. Alexander wants them too, but I feel the same as you do. Now, tell me what I have to do.'

'Chop up this pile of veggies with me, that's all. And whatever happens, don't let mother drag you into ladling out the soup.'

Mara eyed the mountain of carrots and potatoes. 'Is that worse?'

'Of course. You can't gossip and you have to speak to THEM.' She waved her knife towards the never-ending stream of dirty faces which approached the trestle-tables with bowls outstretched like Oliver Twist.

By mid afternoon Mara had only two thoughts in her head: to have a bath and go to sleep. She couldn't remember when she'd been so tired and dirty and bored.

Just as she was wondering if she could pretend to be ill there was a commotion at the far end of the room and a distraught woman burst through the crowds. She was pale and unkempt and had been crying. 'Is there a nurse 'ere?'

she asked. 'Doctor sent me. My little boy's been 'urt. One of them cars knocked 'im down.'

Slowly the room fell silent. The charity workers looked at each other doubtfully. Most had vague notions of first aid, how to deal with a burn or a bruise, but not much more.

'A nurse!' The woman's voice wailed in desperation. 'One of you must know something about nursin'.'

Was it the boredom which made Mara stand up and say, 'I do!'? No sooner had she done so, and all eyes had turned to her, than she wished she had kept quiet.

'Do you, miss? Oh, miss!'

To be called 'miss' brought back best-forgotten memories. Mara frowned. 'I'm not a nurse, I only know a little, so perhaps . . .'

'Doesn't matter, miss. Come quickly!' The woman clapped her hand on to Mara's arm and dragged her towards the door. 'Please 'urry, miss. Please!'

The woman led her out into the street, weaving through the cars to the other side, then into a small courtyard at the far end of which was a building almost but not quite as seedy as the soup kitchen. Outside was a freshly painted sign: 'Clinic'. The door opened into a corridor: narrow, white-painted and surprisingly clean. Halfway up was a bench upon which were a couple of rolled bandages. The woman handed them to Mara. 'Doctor said 'e needed these. The lady upstairs gave 'em to me.' She nodded at a closed door a few yards further on. ''E's in there.'

Mara hesitated. 'Aren't you . . .'

'Coming? No. I'll stay 'ere. Can't bear to watch . . . my own little boy.' The woman smiled with pathetic bravery.

Mara nodded and walked to the door. She was very conscious of the beautifully pressed pleats of her yellow skirt as they touched the soft backs of her knees, and conscious too of how she must look to the woman. She knocked on the door.

There was a grunt from inside.

She opened the door. The room was small and shabby but quite orderly and, like the corridor, surprisingly clean. There was a bed against the back wall and the white-coated back of a man bending over its occupant, a small and very grubby child.

'Doctor . . . umm . . .' she said, thinking how rude he was to ignore her.

'Yes.' He sighed, resenting the interruption, and turned slowly, his thoughts still on the child. 'Yes.' He looked at her. Then he looked hard. Then he froze. And Mara froze.

Awkward with emotion Mara stood in the middle of the room and stared at Jamie. She couldn't believe she was seeing him, and in this terrible place, but that made no difference to the effect he had on her. He was older, six years older, thirty-one, and there were a few more laughter lines around his eyes, and other lines too across his forehead, and amongst his dark unruly hair was the odd grey one: he was a man not a boy. But he was still her Jamie. And as Mara stood there looking at him she was no longer surprised to see him. A little inner voice said, You always knew didn't you? and was answered, Yes, but I didn't dare believe.

There had been no proper end to their relationship. Jamie had never really left her though his allotted space had grown hazy. Koblenz had not been the final chapter. 'The End' had not been typed in neat black letters. The axe, though swift, had not entirely severed her. Or severed Jamie from her.

'Mara!' He said it so softly. 'Mara, I never expected
. . .' The smile, half mischievous, half apologetic.

'Jamie!' Nerves made her laugh.

He laughed too. 'And here, of all places. You.'

'How are you?'

'Fine. And you?'

'Fine.'

He shook his head slowly from side to side. 'We sound
like strangers.'

'Yes, we do.' She took a step towards him, but as she
did so her fingers relaxed and the bandages, so carefully
rolled, slipped to the floor and unwound across its dusty
surface. Jamie looked from Mara to the fallen bandages,
then back at Mara, and then, to her horror, the barrier
came down behind his eyes and the fondness in them
dulled hard and she knew he was seeing another her; the
rouged lips, the pencilled eyebrows, the expensive suit,
the wealthy lady treading on the much-needed bandages.
'Jamie, I didn't mean . . .' She stumbled over the bandages, desperate to reach him before he shut her out.

He looked at her feet and at the bandage caught round
one high heel.

'For God's sake, Mara,' he snapped, 'don't walk all
over the bandages. They're the only ones we have.' He
turned back to the child.

Mara retrieved the wretched bandages and in heavy
silence rolled them up, one by one, and put them on the
desk. Jamie still had his back to her, he was giving the
child an injection. She stood and waited for him to finish.
In all her thoughts of Jamie she had never imagined him
in such a place: a smart society doctor or an eminent
hospital physician, but not this. Not these mean surroundings. Not these poor unwashed people. What on earth
was he doing here? She looked at his back. Whatever he

408

did she still loved him. She looked at the child and his hands on the child's leg, and it was almost as if he were touching her leg.

'I've done the bandages,' she said quietly. She sensed he wanted her to go before he had to turn around and look at her again.

'Okay.'

'Can I do anything else?' She knew she was prolonging the agony but could not bring herself to leave, although she despised herself for staying.

'Sure. Find me a nurse.'

'There isn't one. That's why I came. I thought . . .'

'What!' Now he turned to look at her. 'You thought that six months as my secretary qualified you?'

'No, of course I didn't.' How unjust he was! 'I just thought I might be able to help, that's all, but as you're obviously . . .'

He held up his hand. 'Okay, okay, cut it out. If you want to help go and tell the woman to find Sarah.'

Mara hurried out of the room, found the woman, told her to find Sarah, then went back to Jamie although she knew he did not want her. But she couldn't just leave. She couldn't just walk away, coldly, as if they were strangers. Jamie was sitting beside the bed when she returned. The child was asleep.

'The woman's gone to fetch her,' Mara told him.

Reluctantly Jamie looked up at Mara. This time he did not look away again, but he sat there staring at her, and she stared back at him. The child was no longer with them: the carbolic-smelling room had disappeared: they were just two people suspended by their emotions – mixed emotions. Under his gaze Mara twisted her hands nervously. He made her feel gauche and ungainly. Gone was her indifference of the past years, gone her confidence, gone the pretending and the acting – the director and the actor. There was no uninvolved little voice telling her what to do or say, she was totally concentrated on Jamie and, as always when things were difficult between them, she had to rely on her instinct: without guidelines: without knowing if what she did or said was right until after she had done or said it. Nothing had changed. Not that, or anything else. She longed to touch him. She longed to go to him and put her arms around his tired shoulders and kiss the lines at the corners of his eyes. She smiled tentatively.

Jamie saw her smile and turned back to the child. 'Go away, Mara,' he said gruffly.

Mara swallowed hard. She couldn't believe he meant it. She went to him and stood behind him, her hand hovering above his shoulder as she summoned up the courage to touch him. 'Jamie . . . Jamie . . . please.'

He kept his eyes on the child. 'Go away, Mara,' he said again. 'Go back to your own life and leave me to mine.'

'But . . . but . . .'

Suddenly a familiar voice spoke from behind her. 'You wanted me, doctor?'

Mara spun round. Standing in the doorway was Elenora's friend Sarah Bucklethwaite.

Sarah said, 'Good heavens! Fancy seeing you down here, Mara. Visiting the deserving poor?'

'She's just going,' said Jamie. He was astonished they knew each other.

'I'm not surprised.' A smile of condescension flickered across Sarah's mousy face and she glanced at Jamie as though assured of his support. 'I didn't know Mara ever ventured beyond the boundaries of Mayfair.'

410

Mara was speechless with rage. They were talking about her as if she didn't exist. Sarah Bucklethwaite was mocking her in front of Jamie. She longed to smash the sweaty ratlike nose, to pulverize the smiling thin mouth. But she couldn't, not in front of Jamie. He'd think she was jealous. Jealous of Sarah! Without a word Mara swept out of the room and down the corridor, her head held high and her thoughts seething with all the puzzled anger an attractive girl feels when she suspects she has lost her man to a plain one.

Seeing Jamie again drove Mara deep into frustrated self-analysis. She'd loved him. She'd always love him. The deadness in her body had gone. Now she shivered with pent-up sexuality. Now she cared and wanted. Simultaneously she felt both weak and strong, nervously on edge but only half awake. She saw now that the bitterness she had felt towards him, which had driven her to marry Alexander, which had tinged her memories of him, had been nothing but the bare claws of rejection. Yesterday he had rejected her again. Again she was bitter, but not so much against Jamie as against her life. His reappearance made her question it and the deeper she dug with her questions the more she became aware of its superficiality.

On the morning after seeing Jamie Mara knew she could not go to the soup kitchen again even though she was expected. Luckily, with her white face and pink eyes, she had no problem in convincing Lady Henrietta she was unwell. 'I think I've picked up a bug.'

'Perhaps you have. You don't look well.' Lady Henrietta smiled down at Mara's hollow face. 'I must say it really was most admirable of you to offer like that yesterday. Lady Barrie-Leith was most impressed. I'd no idea . . . well . . . maybe someone did once mention

411

you'd worked in a hospital, but I think we kept off the subject when you first came to England. Germany and all that.'

Mara nodded. She remembered how the word 'war' had been studiously avoided.

'Though I must say, dear,' Lady Henrietta went on cautiously, 'I've always found it most odd you've never tried to trace your mother's people. I don't mean to pry, but . . .'

Mara watched the pale lilac curtains moving in the breeze. 'I did try, but the records of the orphanage where my mother was brought up had been lost.'

Lady Henrietta patted her shoulder. 'At least you didn't find you had some frightful cousins. Well, I must be going. I'll make your excuses. They must have been so grateful to you at the clinic.'

They must have been grateful. They. He. Her. Were they a 'we'? Jamie and Sarah. Sarah and Jamie. Surely he couldn't? Not with Sarah. Or would he? Did he? In the back of her mind Mara kept hearing Elenora say, 'Sarah is one of those girls whom men find attractive for reasons inexplicable to women.' But did Jamie find her attractive?

For two whole days Mara lay in bed and if-ed. If I hadn't dropped the bandages . . . if I hadn't worn that suit . . . if I'd said, not said, done, not done. If I weren't married. If I'd stayed in Koblenz. If. If. If. Mara relived, rewound and replayed her meeting with Jamie. She said. He said. She said. First fact, then fact and fantasy, then pure fictional fantasy. She would say. He would say. Do. Think. Feel. Touch. Her hands running down the softness of her body were his hands. Wonderful fantasy.

She planned their next meeting and saw it all before her like a moving picture for which she directed the

412

action and wrote the script. They were alone in a hotel bedroom. No, not a hotel. Too . . . sordid. A cottage. A cottage like Elenora's, miles from anywhere. Mara spent hours working out the position of the rooms and the decor right down to the smallest lamp – and the wall against which Jamie would suddenly press her, physically and metaphorically, to leave Alexander and be his.

With violently opposed emotions, and without having visited Madame Cecile, Mara went home on the third day. She was glad to go because in her present state the effort of being a guest, albeit an ill one, was a strain and an interruption to her fantasizing. But she was desperate about leaving London: London meant Jamie. It seemed incredible that nothing at home had altered whilst she had undergone such a momentous change: Jenkins opened the door for her and took her bag: Rachel unpacked her clothes: Alexander kissed her on the cheek and told her that the strike wasn't expected to last much longer. And Prince wagged his tail for her.

The question which haunted Mara most in the days that followed was what relationship, if any, existed between Jamie and Sarah. Were they? Did they? She thought she'd go mad if she didn't know the answer soon. Every couple of hours she went up to her room, opened the iron box, took out Jamie's locket, and twisted it through her fingers as though somehow it could tell her what she wanted. Of course there was one person who might know: Elenora Harris. The problem was, Mara hadn't been near the cottage in over three years and on the odd occasion when she'd caught sight of Elenora in the village, she'd simply pretended not to see her, so she could hardly call without good reason.

In the end providence dropped into her lap. She heard that the sort-of-spaniel, the one whose cold nose had once given her such a fright, had died recently and, armed with her excuse for calling, she went to the cottage. Elenora answered the door, paintbrush in hand. 'So you've come back.'

'Yes. I . . . er . . .heard about the dog.' Mara cursed herself for not remembering its name. 'I was very sorry and I thought . . . well . . .'

'The perfect opportunity?'

Mara blushed guiltily.

Elenora smiled, but there was a hint of amusement far deeper than a smile in her green eyes as she led Mara through into the studio.

It was all as it had been: the bright colours: the rough table: the lump of black rock gathering dust. Mara wandered round the room as Elenora made tea. She touched an easel. Touched the black rock. Ran her hand across the table. Picked up a magazine and smiled. It was good to be back in the cottage. She wasn't sure if she belonged, but it felt good.

As soon as was decently possible, Mara mentioned Sarah. 'I saw her in London, at a clinic in Whitechapel,' she said very casually. 'I was down there helping in a soup kitchen during the strike.'

'Yes, I had a letter from her and she said she'd met you.'

'Oh. Does Sarah . . . umm . . . work there all the time?'

'Every day except Fridays. There's an American doctor, I believe you met him. Sarah says he's quite brilliant and he seems impressed with her.'

If Mara had been watching Elenora, instead of trying to gaze nonchalantly round the room, she would have seen her friend's mouth twitch with controlled laughter. But as it was, she seethed with envy. Once, she had been

414

the one to know what Jamie did and where he went, now others did. Keeping her voice light, she said, 'I had the impression they were . . . er . . .'

Elenora laughed. 'Lovers?'

'Well, yes, I suppose so.'

'Not yet.'

Not yet, thought Mara, lighting a cigarette. Not yet! So I was right. There is something between them. Or maybe, she tried to cheer herself up, it's simply that Sarah has confided in Elenora. Unrequited love and all that. Whichever it was, she still had no answer.

As Mara was leaving she said with an uncharacteristic shyness, 'I've missed not coming here, I really have. I realize it now. This cottage. The studio. You.'

Elenora smiled. 'You could have come any time.'

'I know, but,' – Mara picked at the ivy which hung over the porch – 'it's hard to explain. I was afraid to come.' She bit her lip and studied Elenora's face, and wondered why she never thought of Elenora as being older than herself, only wise, when there were at least fifteen years between them. 'I suppose,' she said, carefully picking her words, 'I didn't want to question.'

'And now you do?' The green eyes were full of sympathy.

'I don't know, I really don't know. I think I'm afraid to question in case I find an answer I don't like. That probably sounds silly, but then I'm not as brave as some people . . . as you.'

'You underestimate yourself. Look at the way you rescued your father-in-law from the nursing home.'

'You came with me.'

'I didn't have to face Alexander or Herbert. And what about the way you drove the racing Roadster? I couldn't possibly have done it.'

Mara said, 'But that's physical bravery. I'm talking about mental bravery. If I'd been a little bit braver I'm sure I'd have left Alexander when he stopped me racing, and struck out on my own. I really hated him, you know, but I don't any more. I feel sorry for him. That makes it all the more difficult. But I can't spend the rest of my life acting a part and I can't shut out the world for ever, just because I'm afraid of being tempted by it.'

Had Elenora been anyone else she'd have said, 'I'd have thought you'd had enough of temptation,' but she didn't, she understood the difference.

Mara went on slowly, 'Sometimes when I'm going to a party or whatever, I see a queue of people waiting for a bus and I think, that's me. Waiting for something to come along. I used to think like that in Koblenz too.'

'Then Alexander came along?'

'Yes.' Mara smiled ruefully. 'But perhaps I caught the wrong bus.'

'And now you want to get off and catch another one?'

It was as if Elenora could read her mind and knew all her dilemmas. 'I don't know,' said Mara. She thought of Jamie: she loved him. She thought of Alexander: she didn't want to hurt him.

Elenora fiddled with a tendril of her grey-streaked hair. 'Only you can decide that one. But you must be sure before you . . . get off. You see, you're used to a way of life with the Rushtons you won't have if you leave Alexander. It's a battle when you're on your own.' She glanced back over her shoulder into the cottage as though expecting it to agree with her. 'Bills have to be paid, food and clothes have to be bought. And you're the one who's paying for them. And it's not only money. People! Their attitude towards you changes. Not all of them, of course, not your real friends. But the hypocrites of this world.

416

You soon find out what a lot of hypocrites there are. So you must be sure that freedom and the abstract things you'll gain are more important to you than the material ones you'll lose.'

Mara thought of Jamie. If he didn't want her what would happen to her if she left Alexander? Unlike Elenora she didn't have a particular talent. She couldn't paint or write. She hadn't the ambition or dedication which kept Elenora's clever friends going, even when the rest of their lives fell apart.

'And another thing,' Elenora said with a peculiar gentleness, 'it's not always a very good idea to jump straight from one bus to another.'

'Do you ever regret . . . being alone, I mean, regret . . . leaving?' Mara asked shyly. Elenora had never mentioned the absent Mr Harris.

'No, not at all. I'd thought about it a lot before I left my husband. It was a difficult decision because he was a kind man. But from the moment I stepped out of the house for the last time, I knew it was the right one.' Elenora smiled. 'So if things get tough, like they were to begin with, I remind myself of that exhilaration.'

'That freedom?'

'Yes. But you must remember, Mara, I wasn't leaving anything so grand as the Rushton Empire.'

Somehow, by moving along the pre-set patterns of her life, Mara got through the days without anyone noticing a change in her, except perhaps that she was less sharp than she had been for a long time.

When Alexander came home from work he would find her sitting in the drawing room gazing blankly into space, or in a deckchair under the oak tree, staring up into its

417

leafy branches. 'Had a good day?' she would ask, giving him a vague smile.

'Yes, thank you, darling.' He would pull up a chair. 'Actually it was quite interesting because . . .'

But Mara was miles away, with Jamie, and she didn't hear a word he said.

Different things annoyed her now, the telephone ringing, the pile of invitations waiting to be answered, people coming to dinner; but a day without a single social engagement, once so boring, was now a relief. Uninterrupted she could think of Jamie.

Once she came out of these thoughts to find that the Old Man had been pushed across the grass to the oak tree and was sitting in his wheelchair watching her.

'Can I get you anything?' she asked him.

He shook his white head.

But because Mara sensed that he, unlike Alexander, was not fooled by her outward calm, she left him as soon as she could.

Alexander saw nothing odd in Mara's behaviour, he was just relieved that she was back at the Dower House, that it wasn't full of people, and that she was being friendly. He told himself this was the real Mara, now grown up into the woman he had always known she would be. Ahead of them he saw years of peace and calm, he was sure he knew just what she needed. It was months and months since they had made love but one evening he tentatively approached her. She was sitting on the end of their bed and he came over and tried to kiss her.

Mara couldn't bear the thought of anyone except Jamie. 'I'm sorry,' she said gently pushing him away, 'in fact, I've been thinking I might move into the spare room. I sleep better when I'm on my own.'

418

'Oh, don't do that please, Mara.' He sat down on the far side of the bed and stared miserably at her back.

'Well, I'll see.'

Alexander didn't try to make love to Mara again and Mara didn't move into the spare room because she didn't want to hurt him more than necessary. In his behaviour towards her she saw all the mistakes she made in hers towards Jamie: the clutching at straws, the hope, the fear that one loves but is not loved. And subconsciously she felt that by not hurting him she was totting up credits in heaven and perhaps in return heaven would do something for her.

One weekend Damon came whistling down the field from the woods. Mara had not seen him since Christmas, and then only briefly. Now she noticed that he was no longer a little boy. There was something rangy about him, in the way he walked, his long legs in their grey flannels swinging out before him. 'Oh, hello,' he said, catching sight of Mara under the oak tree, 'fancy seeing you here.'

'And what about you? I thought you were at school.'

He flopped down on the grass beside her deckchair, then rolled over on his stomach, resting his chin in his cupped hands and looking straight up at her. 'I am at school but I've come home for the day. So has Atalanta but mother's taken her off to Oxford to do some shopping, so I thought I'd come over and see Grandpa.' He didn't say 'and see you' and Mara knew why: there had been no bond between them in recent years. 'You know Atalanta started at boarding school this term?'

'I suppose I must have been told.' She couldn't remember but then for years she'd been completely uninterested in the family. 'I'm a bit surprised though.'

'Because father doesn't approve of too much education for girls?'

'Yes.'

'That's right.' He picked a blade of grass and chewed it. 'But once Lady Henrietta told him that the best way for Atalanta to meet socially acceptable girls, who might have brothers of the right age, was to go to school with them, he couldn't pack her off quick enough.'

'Does she enjoy it?'

'She prefers it to being at the Park.'

'And do you enjoy Eton?'

He gave her an enigmatic smile. 'In some ways,' and then he stared at the blade of grass in his hand and his eyes became thoughtful.

Watching him, Mara thought, he's still beautiful but there's something different about him. It's not in his face or in his hair or just because he's taller, it's in him. He's lost his innocence.

After a short while Damon said, 'I'm so glad I'm not a child any more. Being a child is horrible, you spend your time having your arm yanked out of its socket and grown-ups are always cross with you.' He jumped up and imitated a child being dragged along by an adult, stretching his right arm as high as he could and tottering along on the tips of his toes, and saying in a cross, adult voice, 'Come along, Damon! Oh, do hurry up, you wretched child!' Then he fell down on the ground, laughing and rubbing his face against the grass in an intensely sensual manner as he looked up at Mara.

Mara laughed too and she told herself, he's only a boy, he's a young animal and all young animals flex their muscles, sexual and otherwise. 'You're not exactly an old man yet.'

'No, and grown-ups still get cross but I've learned how

to ignore them.' He glanced towards the house. 'Here comes Grandpa. Now he's unignorable. And so are you when you're being nice.'

After Damon had left the Old Man asked, 'Have you seen Mrs Harris lately?'

She nodded. 'Yes, I see her every few days.'

'Oh.' He turned his white head away from her and when he spoke it was of other things.

Elenora was the mainstay of Mara's existence throughout that month of May. At the cottage she rediscovered all that had fascinated, and her friendship with Elenora took on new dimensions. Before there had been little give on Mara's part, she had seldom considered Elenora as a human being but more as a sideshow for her own youthful curiosity. Now she was curious but in a different way. She asked, 'When did you start painting? How did you know you could do it?'

Elenora was whistling through her teeth as she slapped blue paint on to a blank canvas. 'I started painting when I was married and I took some of my work to Paul's gallery. It was run by his father then and his father liked it. He took a couple of canvases and they sold.'

'But did you believe you could do it?'

'I believed I had something.'

'Do you think lots of people have hidden talents and they never discover them?'

'Yes. Because it's not only a question of being talented it's having determination.'

Mara told Elenora what Smithy had said about Mark's driving. 'It would have destroyed him to find out he wasn't up to it.'

Elenora stopped painting for a moment. 'Then perhaps he had come to the end of his time.'

Of course Mara hoped Elenora would mention Jamie

421

again, but she didn't. And Mara could hardly keep asking after Sarah, whom Elenora knew she did not care for, without something being very obvious. So she was still left with her questions: did she want to leave Alexander for himself or was it only because of Jamie? And this led straight to, do I want to leave Alexander on an off-chance that Jamie will have me, or only for a certainty?

That was a question to which she had no answer.

One afternoon Mara and Elenora became so engrossed in their discussion that Mara didn't return to the Dower House until dinner time. As she came in through the front door she met Alexander, already dressed. 'It's terribly late, Mara. Where have you been?'

Mara looked him straight in the face. 'I've been with Elenora. I often go to see her.'

'Oh.' In his face was his disapproval.

Mara stood there willing him to criticize Elenora but he made no comment, and she went upstairs to change, infuriated because he hadn't done so. But why did I want him to criticize Elenora? To give me . . . what? A push into leaving? Or is it that he reminded me of how little I used to stand up to Jamie?

At the beginning of June Jeremy and Cynthia were giving a ball. When the invitation had arrived, the week before Mara had seen Jamie, she'd bullied Alexander into accompanying her, saying, 'I'll be going anyhow and it will look most odd if you don't come with me. After all, Cynthia is my dearest friend.' What she hadn't told him was that his presence was needed to quash the rumours about herself and Charles.

Now she wished she had not insisted. She wanted to go to London. She longed to be in the same city as Jamie. But she did not want to go to London with Alexander, or to Cynthia's ball. Nevertheless, London meant Jamie and it was with nervous excitement tinged with dread that Mara ticked off the days till their departure, then the miles till their arrival – for something totally irrational and completely unsupported told her she was going to see Jamie again.

Jeremy and Cynthia lived in Belgrave Square in one of those enormous white houses which always reminded Mara of very superior wedding cakes. As they drew up in their chauffeur-driven car Mara saw there were many people on the pavement, all bathed in the glow of light and the chatter and the music which reached out from the house and seemed to encompass the whole of that side of the square.

'Mara darling, you look simply rapturous,' Cynthia cried as she rushed to greet them. 'Quite divine.' They embraced. 'Wish I could slither around in white satin like you.' Mara's dress of white satin plunged at both front and back and clung to her like a second skin. 'Darling, it's absolutely IT.'

An automatic smile came to Mara's face, an automatic response from her mouth. 'And you look wonderful too, darling.' She found it easy to be effusive in an effusive world. 'I adore the dress. Wish I could wear pink.' But she was thinking, is this fluffy pink creature really my friend?

Cynthia was giggling beside her. 'Quite virginal, darling, if it wasn't so tight.'

Jeremy appeared and ran his hand down Mara's satin-encased bottom. 'Hello sweetie. Or should I say sexy?'

Cynthia linked her arm through Mara's and led her through into the already packed ballroom. Out of habit they paused in the doorway so as to be sure of making an entrance. 'Oh, I forgot to tell you,' said Cynthia, waving at various people as she talked, 'I've invited an old friend of yours.'

'Oh?' Mara froze.

'A divine American doctor called Jamie Turner. An absolute dream. Met him at that frightful place in the East End. Must find out where his practice is so I can get him to examine me. We had such fun together.' Giggle. Giggle. 'Can't think why you've never mentioned him to me. He said he knew you in Germany.'

'Yes.' Jamie and Cynthia? Jamie and Sarah? Jamie and Cynthia and Sarah? 'Yes, I did know him.'

'Don't tell me you forgot about him?' Cynthia looked at Mara curiously.

'Yes. I didn't know him well. He was stationed in my parents' house for a short time, that's all.'

Cynthia pursed her shiny rosebud mouth. 'Well, if he'd been stationed with me, darling . . .' She adjusted the pink tulle of her bodice until it clutched by a mere whisper to her nipples.

Mara saw Jamie before he saw her. He was standing with his back to the fireplace looking almost as much at home in a dinner-jacket as in a white coat. A group of people stood in a semi-circle around him, listening intently to what he said, as people always did with Jamie. Mara watched him surreptitiously: the way his eyes sparkled when he spoke: the way he tipped his head and listened, half smiling, when someone else spoke: the way he added to their words and made the speakers feel not belittled but enhanced as though they too were charming, witty and clever. She turned to smile at Alexander, who was approaching her, and wished that Jamie would make a fool of himself so she could feel sorry for him, so she could despise him as he had made it clear he despised her.

Alexander beamed down at her. 'Darling, have you seen who's here? Your old boss, Doctor Turner. Come on, let's go and talk to him. Always liked him. We must have him down to stay.' He took Mara's hand and led her forward.

She couldn't refuse to go or it would look peculiar. Of course Alexander had no idea she'd seen Jamie: it never occurred to her to tell him, just as it had never occurred to her she would meet Jamie again unless she initiated the meeting. Would Jamie tell Alexander of their meeting? Of course he would. He did.

'You never told me, darling.' Alexander looked puzzled. Jamie looked amused.

'Didn't I? I must have forgotten.' As soon as she could she left them together. It was like the attic with Alexander, rightfully, calling her 'darling'.

By sheer determination Mara got through the evening. She danced, she talked, she flirted, she drank a little too much champagne; and she forced herself not to watch Jamie. She hated him for coming. He had no right to enter her territory. She hated him for invading her life and for disturbing its shaky equilibrium. She looked across at him: he was dancing with Cynthia. The sight of that pink tulle pressed against that dark dinner-jacket made her sick with anger. He hadn't asked her to dance. They'd never danced together. Now Cynthia had had something she had never had: a dance.

It was inevitable she could not avoid him all evening. They met under the archway between the conservatory and the ballroom, she having abandoned a drunken admirer, he intent on departure. 'I'm surprised to find you at a ball,' she said.

He gave her a vague smile. 'Even doctors are allowed some free time, you know.'

'Really? I thought medicine was a full-time dedication.'

Jamie laughed. 'I'm not going to fight with you, Mara.'

'Fight? I don't know what you're talking about.' She pretended to be bored but really she was wondering what it was about him she found so attractive. He was not outstandingly good-looking; there were other more handsome men in the room. Nor was he a promiscuous charmer like Charles. And although he looked at home in his dinner-jacket, it did not slide down him in elegant lines. More, it was a covering to his vitality, to his power, to that magnetism which drew people, and Mara, to him. She longed to touch him. She longed to feel his arms and his body, around her, against her, and she wouldn't have cared if he had seized her there, with people milling all around them.

Jamie was studying her appearance. 'You've become old, Mara,' he said abruptly. 'It's all of this' – he nodded at the dancing and the champagne – 'that's done it.'

That really hurt. She wasn't twenty-five till August. Sarah was a good twenty-eight. Jamie himself thirty-one. And the way he said 'all this' showed that he saw her as having lived a mindless champagne-drenched existence. It was as though when they first met he had been a judge before whom she had come to trial accused of theft, and that now, seven years later, she was up again before him for theft, so he saw her as having lived a life of continuous dishonesty, whereas she had tried so hard to mend her ways. It was so grossly unfair that he should see only her present apparent self, and not the self which had been part of the Roadster team, or the self she was with Elenora. But Jamie wouldn't have believed her, Mara sensed, if she'd told him of her frustration when she hadn't been allowed to race, any more than the judge would believe the thief had wanted to be a missionary

426

but had been rejected, and, disheartened, had returned to old ways. To Jamie, if you wanted to do something badly enough, you did it.

'Oh, don't worry,' he said, laughing at her angry face, 'you may not be the prettiest woman here but you're by far the most glamorous. All the men think you're gorgeous. It's just that . . . you've lost that childish bravado I used to love.' He nodded to himself and looked at his watch.

Used to love. Used to love. With rising panic Mara realized he was about to leave. He was looking at his watch again. Now she was as desperate to stop him from going as previously she had been to annoy him. 'Jamie,' she began, 'I . . . umm . . .' Her arms and legs felt disconnected and her beautiful dress suddenly seemed vulgar and ostentatious.

Jamie had not noticed the change in her. He asked, 'Shall I escort you back to Alexander or are you chasing other prey tonight?'

She flushed. 'No, of course not. And don't go! Not yet. Tell me . . . tell me . . .'

'What?'

She wished she could sit down. That they could sit down. 'Well, how long you've been in England.'

'Three months.'

'Are you staying long?'

'A year at least.'

'Where do you live?'

'Hampstead.'

'Oh.'

He was fiddling with his watch. 'I must go, Sarah's waiting. We've a woman who's about to go into labour – one of my lung-disease patients.'

It didn't occur to Mara to wonder why he had bothered

to come if he had to leave so early, and if it had she would have answered, 'For Cynthia.' His apparent indifference to her had pushed her to a point where she believed everything he did was for other women; for another woman; for any woman but herself. 'I've met Sarah before,' she said.

'She told me.' He smiled over her head at the dancers. 'Sarah's a wonderful girl. I don't know what I'd do without her.'

'Such a pity she's so plain.' The words came straight from Mara's soul, angry and twisted and racked with jealousy.

Jamie looked at her with dislike. 'Is she? I hadn't noticed.'

'Of course she is. Everyone says so.' Mara was trembling with rage. Five minutes earlier she would have done anything, gone anywhere, for Jamie. But he hadn't wanted her. All he wanted was to get back to Sarah. With an effort she pulled herself together. She wasn't a doormat for him to trample on. She wasn't going to lie down quietly whilst he kicked her in the guts. 'Well, I mustn't keep you,' she said, giving him her sweetest, sugariest smile. 'But next time you're invited to a ball, Jamie, you must let me know. I'll make sure Sarah's invited too. And if she doesn't have an evening dress, tell her not to worry, I'll lend her one of mine.'

Mara stepped in front of him, smiling an even sweeter smile, and slowly ran her hand down over her hip to emphasize the snaking line of her own body and the impossibility of Sarah's buxom form fitting into her dresses. Then she turned and walked away from him, undulating her satin-encased bottom through the dancers.

But when Mara woke up next morning she cursed herself for being such a fool. Jamie thought her tough

428

and selfish, and that was exactly what she had been. 'But I'm not like that,' she muttered, burying her face in the pillow and thumping it with her fists, 'I'm no worse than anyone else. It's Jamie. Why can't he come when I'm being nice?'

Chapter 25

Mara's life hung on tenterhooks. She could not bear to be in London, she could not bear to leave it. She dreaded every social event in case she met Jamie, she could not stay away in case she missed him. Everywhere she went her eyes raked the crowd, every time she drove past a man with dark hair she turned to check if it were Jamie. But although, from time to time, she heard tantalizing mentions of his name and even saw his name in the newspaper in connection with a new form of treatment for lung diseases, their paths did not cross. And as the days passed and people began talking of where they would go when the season ended – the South of France, Scotland, the Italian Lakes – Mara slowly subsided into a relieved disappointment.

At the end of July Mara went back to the Dower House. She had no alternative, everyone was leaving town and in any case Alexander was pressing her to go home. He hadn't minded at first when she had stayed in London but as the weeks had passed he'd become miserably confused and his telephone calls to her had been stilted, with long silences.

But the rigid walls of her life seemed even closer, and she rebelled against them. The sympathy she felt for Alexander, his predicament being like her own, alternated with bouts of unreasonable irritation during which she silently blamed him for their situation. Why had he married her knowing she didn't love him? Why had he stood between her and what she wanted to do? He deserved to lose her. In this frame of mind, she demanded compensation from him. He took her to Deauville for a weekend and let her gamble although he didn't approve of gambling, especially women who gambled. He gave her a new Roadster for her twenty-fifth birthday, a long low sleek black bullet which she drove hard and fast. He gave her a new hunter called Nutcracker. He put up with her temper and her silences as well as he responded to her if she were being friendly. And all the time he watched her with his faithful brown labrador eyes, knowing something was wrong but not understanding what or why.

The Old Man watched Mara too, and felt desperately sorry for his son. And although Mara was making Alexander unhappy, Samuel also felt sorry for her.

On the rare occasions when Mara met Herbert, he watched her too and he was immensely satisfied. 'Not long now,' he assured himself. 'Another year and she'll be gone.'

One Friday morning Mara woke up and knew she couldn't go another day without seeing Jamie. Decision made, she called for Rachel to run her bath, leapt in and out of its scented waters, washed her hair, rubbed it dry, chose her dress – something flattering but not too obviously expensive, crêpe de Chine, pink tulips on black, soft and low waisted but not too short; chose her shoes, pink to match the tulips; chose her hat, small and cheeky in shades of pink. Decision made, she planned her absence. A visit to Cynthia? No, better not involve Cynthia. She pictured her friend's face contorted with excited gossip. A shopping spree, that was the answer. And possibly a night with Lady Henrietta. 'I'll telephone her if I'm running late,' she told Rachel, but all the time she was thinking, possibly a night with Jamie.

The drive to London seemed to last for ever. She cursed the cars not as fast as her own and the dust from the road – thrown up when she finally passed them – which filmed the shiny surface of her black car. Her car was beautiful and she wanted Jamie to see it beautiful, so that he knew what she would be giving up for him.

Through suburbia. Through West London. Past a sign pointing left to Hampstead. Through Holborn. Straight on at St Paul's. And on and on into the dilapidated streets of Whitechapel. Several times she lost her way and had to stop, turn, double back, and start again. But at last she found the street – no different from the others all around it – and the now deserted soup kitchen, and the clinic. This time, of course, there were no smart cars or waiting chauffeurs, just the grimy children, the tired women and the resentful out-of-work men milling around or sitting on doorsteps. They all looked up, first at the car, then at Mara with curiosity which turned to bitter surprise.

Mara parked the car in the courtyard outside the clinic, powdered her nose, patted some scent on to her wrists, adjusted her hat, and stepped out. She walked to the door as casually as she could with a hundred pairs of eyes boring into her back. Inside she found four women sitting on the narrow bench which ran along part of the corridor. They looked up at her in amazement.

'Is the American doctor here?' she asked, wondering yet again why Jamie chose to work in such a place.

They looked at each other, then back at Mara. ''E's busy.'

'And the . . . er . . . woman upstairs, Sarah?'

'Not 'ere Fridays.'

'I thought not.' It would have been just her luck if Sarah had chosen to come in that particular Friday.

432

Giving the women the benefit of her bright, social smile Mara asked, 'Do you mind if I have a quick word with the doctor before you? I'll only be a minute.'

They looked at each other again, then gave her a silent but reluctant nod.

A moment later the surgery door opened and an old man shuffled out. He looked at Mara in astonishment before muttering, 'Next one.'

So this is it, Mara told herself, her legs trembling against the pink tulips. This is it. She went inside and closed the door behind her.

Jamie was sitting at his desk jotting down some notes. It took Mara's breath away to see him, just as she had seen him so many times in the study at Koblenz. The clack-clack of her high heels made him look up. But the professional smile changed to a sort of naked bewilderment in which he showed neither pleasure nor anger – he was too surprised to think if he were pleased or cross.

'I had to come and see you.'

'Why? Are you ill?'

'No.' She laughed a little too brightly because she was so nervous. 'I just wanted to see you.'

Jamie's eyes never left her face, but Mara knew he was taking in every detail of her appearance though he gave no sign as to his opinion of it. 'Well' – he smiled guardedly – 'that's very kind of you.' He might have been talking to a casual acquaintance. 'But I am rather busy. Or at least I was. What happened to the four women out there?'

Mara knew then she had made yet another mistake. Why was it she never knew until afterwards? Why couldn't some kind little voice tell her at the time, 'No, Mara, don't do that! Do this!' And why was it she always made her mistakes with Jamie? 'I . . . er . . . asked if I could have a quick word with you,' she answered lamely.

'You mean you pushed in.'

'I did ask.'

'And they let you because they were overawed by you.'
He sighed. 'Look, Mara . . .'

But she stopped him. She knew he was going to tell
her to go, so she interrupted, 'Don't worry, Jamie, I'll
wait. I'll wait in the car. It's outside.'

Jamie nodded with tired resignation. 'Okay.'

Back at the car, the crowd had swelled. Dirty children
picked at the paintwork, adults muttered of its cost. They
backed away as Mara appeared and watched her climb
in, muttering again about her clothes, her hat, her silk
stockings. But when Mara did not drive off but sat stony-
faced in the car, they moved closer and began to discuss
her in loud voices, just as though she were a statue. Just
as she and her friends, she realized with a stab of guilt,
discussed 'the servant problem' in front of their servants.

Mara tried to ignore the crowd. She tried to shut out
their voices. But she couldn't. She tried to think of other
things, of Jamie, of what she would say to him. She
looked at her watch. Half an hour passed. She fiddled
with her watch strap. The sun had crossed over the clinic
building and now poured its heat down on to the black
roof of the car. Mara was boiling, she stuck to her dress,
her dress stuck to the seat, but she dared not open the
windows. Three of the women had left the clinic. Only
one to go, she thought, trying to control her nerves. Now
there was something about the crowd which had not been
there before. It was no longer just curious and envious,
but threatening and closing in.

Don't panic, she told herself. Don't let them see you're
frightened. Come on, Jamie! Whatever I've done surely I
don't deserve this. Come on! Please!

A young man pushed to the front of the crowd. Even

in the state she was in, and the state he was in, dirty, unshaven, Mara noticed he was quite attractive and she was appalled with herself. 'Come to visit the deserving poor, 'ave you?' he shouted, peering through the car window at her.

Mara tensed. Come on, Jamie!

The man banged on the car roof. 'Lost yer tongue, lady?'

'No, she don't speak to the likes of us,' said another man.

'She spoke to me,' one of the women from the clinic called out. 'She pushed me out the way, she did.'

Mara bit her lip. Sweat was pouring down her back. All around faces closed in. She couldn't drive forward or she would run them over, and if she reversed, the same. And what then? They would tear her limb from limb. She could not move. She was trapped – trapped like an animal.

'I'll teach the lady to push yer out the way.' It was the man again.

Suddenly the car began to rock violently from side to side. 'No, please!' Mara cried.

'No, please!' they chorused.

Then, just as suddenly, the rocking stopped and the crowd fell back. For a terrifying moment Mara thought they might have set fire to the car, but they hadn't, it was Jamie. He was saying something to the crowd which she could not hear and he was nodding and smiling good-naturedly, which infuriated her because she was sure he could not have seen what had happened. But at last he came to her, and she wound down the car window, sobbing with relief. 'Jamie, they tried to . . . they tried to . . . oh, Jamie, thank God you've come.'

'What the hell do you expect if you come down here in

a thing like this?' he demanded angrily. 'My God, Mara, are you a complete fool? Don't you have an ounce of sense? Is your brain completely soaked in champagne?'

The people backed off as though he were shouting at them. But they did not go far and their amusement was obvious; not often did they see a lady being shouted at. Mara no longer noticed them. She had forgotten their existence. She was sitting in a confused sweat, dripping from heat and fear, numbed into bewilderment by Jamie's anger.

He opened the car door. 'Move over! I'll drive.'

Obediently she slipped into the passenger seat as Jamie, with a casual confidence as though the car were his and he drove it every day, got in and backed out of the courtyard. In silence they passed through the cobbled streets, cut across the City, and passed Mansion House. For Mara it was a miserable silence. She had no idea how far he was taking her, or where, or when he would abandon her, except that she knew he would, because he was angry and blaming her for all that had happened. Which was unfair, just as it was unfair that everything she did where he was concerned went wrong.

On the north side of St Paul's he stopped the car. For a minute they sat, each staring rigidly ahead, watching the office workers scurrying past on their way to lunch.

Eventually Mara said, 'I'm sorry. Please believe me, I'm sorry.'

Jamie did not look at her. 'I can't think why you came.'

'I wanted to see you.'

'So you said.'

'Do you mind?'

'Frankly . . . yes.'

'Why?' Her voice was hoarse.

'Why!' He turned fiercely towards her. 'Because the

436

clinic is my life, that's why. I'm trying to find a cure for those poor sick people whose lungs are rotting inside them and after six months I've finally persuaded them to trust me, and I don't want to lose that trust because . . .'

'Because of me?'

'Because of you and what you stand for.'

'But Jamie, you're no different from me,' she protested. 'I mean, you're not . . . one of them.'

'Exactly. That's why it took them so long to trust me. You remember the child, the one who'd been knocked down by a car?'

'Yes.' How could she forget!

'That was the turning point. Till then I'd only seen a dozen patients. They wouldn't come near me . . . suspicious. But after they saw what I did for that little boy . . .'

'He's all right?' At least he was talking to her, even if it was only about his work.

'He's fine. But it wasn't just him I saved, I made the owner of the car pay compensation. That's when they realized I was on their side.'

'But why do you have to work there? Surely you could do it all just as well in . . .'

He grimaced. 'Harley Street?'

'Why not?'

'What? Dish out pills to hypochondriacs? No thanks.' He looked at her in disgust as if it were her fault hypochondriacs went to Harley Street, and Mara wished she could love someone who saw the best in her and not the worst. For she really wasn't that bad, and certainly no worse than most of the people she knew. If only Jamie could have seen the good in her, she was sure it would have risen over the bad; she would have become good because he saw her as good. Instead, even her most

437

innocuous words and actions were twisted into the natural behaviour of a paragon of selfishness.

'What is it you're trying to do?' she asked, desperate to regain what she had forfeited by her previous question.

'I'm trying to find out why people who live or work in that area have a particular form of . . .' he sighed and looked into her face. 'You wouldn't understand. You're not a doctor.'

She looked at him; at his face, his eyes, his hair, his mouth, and wished she could touch him. 'I might,' she said. 'Tell me.'

'No.' He shook his head and turned away from her, and did not meet her eyes when he said, 'Just stay away from the clinic, Mara. Please!'

'Very well.' She watched a young man and young woman cross the road, arm in arm. An insignificant couple. He, a bank clerk, in a cheap dark suit shiny at the elbows. She, a shop-girl or a typist, in a cheap cotton dress and carrying a canvas bag because she probably couldn't afford a leather one. Insignificant, but so very happy together. 'Perhaps we could meet elsewhere,' she said, smiling tentatively.

For a moment she thought Jamie was going to agree. He turned to her with a soft light in his blue eyes and a half smile hovering about his mouth. Then abruptly the light died and the smile disappeared, and he opened the car door and got out.

Mara sat very still. I've done it again, she thought. I've ruined everything.

With his hands resting on the window ledge Jamie looked down at her. 'I don't mess around with married women,' he said curtly. And he walked away, back towards Whitechapel and the clinic.

Mara sat for some time, still in the passenger seat, still

with the office workers' legs flashing past at the edge of her vision. She was a married woman. Well, she would unmarry. I'll leave Alexander. I'll tell him tonight. She started up the car and drove northwards. I'll tell him as soon as I reach home. I'll say, 'I'm very sorry but I want a divorce.' And he'll say, 'Why?' and I'll say, 'Because I love someone else.' And he'll say, 'Who?' And I'll say, 'No one you know.' No, he deserves the truth. I'll say, 'It was very wrong of me to have married you, Alexander, but I was very young at the time. I hope you'll meet someone who loves you as you deserve, as I love . . . this other man.' It all seemed perfectly simple, alone in the car.

But when Mara reached the Dower House, with her planned conversation bursting from her, it wasn't so simple. Jenkins met her at the door with the words, 'Thank goodness you're back, madam. Mr Alexander's taken a turn for the worse. Doctor Phillips is with him now, but he's afraid . . . oh, madam.'

'My husband's ill?' Her flushed face turned white and hard.

The butler saw the change and read it as anxiety. 'Poor madam, I tried to contact you to warn you but Lady Henrietta said . . .'

Mara cut him short. 'I decided not to stay, Jenkins, so I didn't telephone her.'

Alexander remained in bed for a month during which time Mara swung between frustration and relief. Had she been able to come home and say her piece straight away she would have done so and left. But now in the safety of her own home, and cocooned by the routine against which she rebelled but which was also a barrier between her and the hard world outside, she hovered in her

439

dilemma. For one thing she could not possibly say anything to Alexander until he was better, and she had no idea when that would be. Her solicitude towards him and his ill health, exaggerated by her guilt and the knowledge of the hurt she would do him, made her feel both martyr and traitor. She wished Jamie could see her as she mopped the fevered brow, though she sensed that somehow he would read the traitor – not the martyr – in her actions.

But the big questions remained and they had plenty of time to ferment in her mind, and there were no answers. Did she really want to leave? Did she want to be divorced? An inherent puritanism, unwelcome and previously unsuspected, rebelled against the word 'divorce'. Divorce was what happened to other people. It had tawdry associations of guilty and injured. She would be the guilty party, even if Alexander did what most gentlemen did and allowed her to divorce him. But why should he? Why should he when she was . . . She thought of Jamie. She loved him desperately. But if only she could have left for, say, six months, with the option of returning if . . . If what? If Jamie doesn't want me? There was that question too.

September was a beastly month. It was cold and wet, which didn't help. But October was glorious and Doctor Phillips encouraged Alexander to go out. In the angle of the house, sheltered from the wind, he would sit out after lunch, with a warm rug wrapped tightly round his emaciated body. Prince would lie beside him on another rug; he was an old dog now. Often Mara sat with them. She would perch on the low wall which divided the terrace from the lawn with her back towards the house, her knees bent to hold a book and her hands dug deep in the pockets of her coat. But she seldom turned the pages.

She sat there thinking of Jamie and gazing at the garden. Few gardens were as beautiful as the one at the Dower House. With its trees just tipped by autumn gold and the pale sun which stretched across the lawn turning the wet grass into a field of diamonds, it was magic.

'I don't know what I'd do without you,' Alexander said one afternoon when the peace of the garden seemed all the more poignant because winter was fast approaching and their days outside were numbered.

Mara looked across at him from her place on the wall. Why did he have to say that? And why did he have to look so ill and old, and so completely unabandonable? The bright light was cruel to his yellowish skin. It emphasized the lines of pain which cut down into his once-firm cheeks and picked out the strands of grey in his once-brown hair.

He continued, 'And don't think I don't appreciate what you've given up for me. I know how bored you are in the country.'

'Don't be silly!' Mara answered sharply. 'You can't help being ill.' She felt uncomfortable but could not believe he knew what he was saying. Not Alexander. Not kind but unimaginative Alexander.

'But I've kept you from London' – he gave her a curiously perceptive look which she could not bring herself to meet –''and from your friends.'

'It doesn't matter.' She shrugged her shoulders and stretched, saying, 'I think I'll go for a walk. I'll take Prince. He could do with some exercise.'

She escaped and went up into the woods, with Prince labouring behind her, his black barrel-like body willing but no longer sprightly. As always the beauty of the woods astonished her. The trees. The woodland path. The wet grass. And now, the fallen leaves which lay like

441

finely cut pieces of chamois leather on which some dainty hand had drawn the delicate pattern of their veins.

If only I hated him, she thought. If only he gave me reason to hate him. If he was cruel to me or made – what do they call it – perverted sexual demands. Shuffling her feet through the wet leaves, Mara wondered what counted as perverted. Did the things she had done with Jamie? Surely not. She had wanted to take him gently, in her mouth, and to know that what she was doing gave him exquisite pleasure, just as she had wanted him to take her brutally and grind her down with his weight on her back and her buttocks. There had been times when she had wanted him to hurt her, and he had. The memory of that delicious pain came back to her as she stood beneath the trees, and she felt as though someone were running a pencil up the inside of her thighs. And other memories came back too: the games they had played, taking it in turns to be the other's slave for just ten minutes, thinking up even more preposterous ways to join their bodies together, and falling about with laughter when their limbs became so entangled they could hardly move. All things she had done with Jamie, but never with Alexander.

If only Alexander kept a mistress, she thought, then I wouldn't feel so bad. Or if he chased after other women or abandoned me at parties or got drunk. But he doesn't drink much, at least not like most men do. And he never even looks at another woman, and he won't because . . . because he's married. She looked up at the waving branches and it seemed to her that in their whispering was a mocking 'And so are you.' It struck her then, like a blinding flash, and she could not imagine how it hadn't occurred to her before, that Jamie, however much he might want her, could never accept a woman who had abandoned a sick husband. A man who refused to mess around with married women would instantly reject one who had kicked a sick man in the face. It would not matter how much he loved her, or thought he loved her, or had loved her, he would not love her any more.

Prince pushed up against Mara's legs and she reached down to stroke him, rubbing the hairs on his back the wrong way, just the way he liked it, and watched his fat body wriggle ecstatically. If she left, she would never see Prince again, never rub his hairs the wrong way for him, never watch him gobble his food or see him watching her hopefully from the kitchen doorway as Mrs Kent crossed her arms over her ample bosom, and said, 'If that wretched dog so much as puts a paw in my kitchen . . .' And she would never stand, as she was now, beneath these trees. Or come back from her ride to find Damon waiting for her. Or see Damon. Perhaps, ever again. Or sit with Alexander in the study, or probably even see him again . . . ever. She would cut herself off from all these things. She would face poverty. Loneliness. Koblenz rose up inside her and she felt sick with fear. Jamie would reject her: she could almost hear his awkward laugh of rejection. He had never told her he wanted her: she saw that clearly now, and saw too that she had allowed fantasy to soften fact. Had he wanted her, he would have said so. He would have taken her. There would have been no need for her to fantasize excuses for him.

And she saw other things clearly. If she left Alexander when he needed her so badly, the sordid remnants of her cruelty would trail after her for the rest of her life. Every day she would be haunted by the mournful look in his brown eyes. She would wake up and wonder if he were still alive, because, of course, she would not know these things and no one would tell her. And she would go to sleep wondering if he sat alone in the study and if he had

443

remembered to take his medicine. Wherever she went, whatever happiness she found, would be tainted by the hurt she had caused him and the knowledge that she had hurt him when he was too ill to do anything to help himself. For she knew, in her heart of hearts, Alexander was very ill. And she knew too, as she stood there in the wood with Prince rubbing against her legs, that she could not leave her husband. Not now. Not when he was ill. Perhaps never. But certainly not now.

Chapter 26

That autumn was the plateau of Mara's life. There were no hillocks of excitement or deep troughs of anger or despair. The things which had excited her before – a ball or a visit to London – meant nothing now. She had no desire to go to a ball and anyway Alexander wasn't well enough. And she certainly didn't want to go to London or see her London friends. The things which had angered her before – a dress not being ready or the flowers for a dinner party not looking as they should – she shrugged off with a smile. What did it matter? Only despair yawned like a gaping chasm at her feet, ready to swallow her up and never let her go again if she once stepped into it. But somehow she avoided doing so. From the minute she had made her decision in the woods that October afternoon, she had refused to allow herself the luxury of daydreams. Daydreams, she had learned, lead to fantasy – and fantasy to a very real disappointment.

But the cure for daydreams is a busy life just as the cure for endless sleepless nights is physical exhaustion, and although Mara slowly picked up the threads of her life, hunting at least once a week, riding out most other days, discussing menus with Mrs Kent, and making polite conversation at her own table or at other people's, there was a void in her life as big as the gaping chasm at her feet, and to survive she had to fill it.

One morning in early November Mara heard Smithy talking to her father-in-law in his sitting room as she came downstairs. It was months since she had seen him, and then only briefly when he had come, as he had now, to see the Old Man. ''E's no better than the last one,' Smithy was bemoaning. ''E's got the men's backs up because 'e keeps saying the car's not right, but it's not the car, it's 'im.'

The Old Man grunted in agreement.

'Neither of them is a patch on . . .' The foreman hesitated. 'Well, that's not my business.'

Afraid they might come out and catch her eavesdropping, Mara tiptoed across the hall into the drawing room and waited till she heard Smithy leave. Then she went back through the hall to the Old Man. He was sitting by the window, gazing despondently out at the cold grey day, his craggy face set in lines of sadness. 'Hello, Mara,' he said, his eyes lighting with pleasure that she had come to him, for she so seldom did.

Mara positioned herself on the window-sill directly in front of him. Taking a deep breath and straightening her shoulders she opened her mouth to speak.

But he said, 'Smithy and I have been talking about Brooklands. Mr Locke King died not long ago. What a man, Mara! He gave up his whole estate to make Brooklands.' He smiled sadly. 'I remember going to the opening in nineteen hundred and seven. June the seventeenth, if I remember rightly. It was quite an informal affair and Locke King only spoke for a few minutes. A lot of people were disappointed. I suppose they'd expected him to tell them all about what he'd done. But I think he was right to keep it short. We could see what he'd done.'

As soon as he stopped, Mara took another deep breath. 'I understand that the drivers you found to race the Roadster haven't been a success.'

He nodded. 'Hamfisted fools.'

Well, this is it, thought Mara. 'Will you reconsider and let me try?'

The Old Man looked up at her, her perch on the window-sill made her some two feet above him in his wheelchair, and for a few moments he said nothing. Mara sat and waited. She wanted to take him by the shoulders and shake him and say, 'You must let me. Can't you see that it's my only hope?' But she knew that whatever she did would make no difference to his decision.

Eventually he said, 'It was only after I told you you couldn't race that I realized how much it meant to you and how much you needed it. Nevertheless, Mara, I believe I was right not to let you. You were too young and headstrong and inexperienced. You are still headstrong and inexperienced.' He paused. 'The new Roadster's a lot lighter and faster . . . but if Smithy thinks you can handle her and if . . .'

Mara leaned forward and hugged him. 'Thank you.'

'Let me finish. And if you can persuade Alexander to agree.'

Mara sat back deflated. 'What if I can't? You said before that he wouldn't agree.'

'That's up to you, but I think he'll be less adamant. He wants to save his marriage as much as I do.'

To Mara's intense frustration Alexander came home early feeling unwell and he retired to bed with a high temperature, so she had to wait for three days before she could tackle him. At first he said, 'You're mad, you'll kill yourself. No, darling, no.' Later he said, 'You can't be a racing-driver, darling, you're a woman,' shaking his head when Mara told him that Violette Cordery was only twenty-four and she had recently broken the fifteen-thousand-mile record at Monza. But finally she wore him down. 'Oh, all right then,' he groaned, 'if you insist. But . . .'

'But what?' She was sitting on the end of his bed munching her way through a piece of toast thick with delicious home-made marmalade.

'But if I let you race . . .'

Silently Mara shrieked, Let me! But she forced a smile, she felt she could afford it – she had won.

'If I let you race,' he repeated, 'can we start . . . er . . . a family?' He looked down into his coffee cup, his face red and puffy with embarrassment.

Mara was embarrassed too. She stared at the line of teeth marks in her toast. Alexander hadn't come near her since that night in May when she had refused him. In fact, when she thought about it, they hadn't made love since January and then it had only been a quick fumble, she'd only let him because she was a bit drunk. Love. Sex. Things she thought of as IT. They were best shut away. Open the door and she might discover . . . what . . . that after all she couldn't live without Jamie?

Alexander continued through her silence, 'Don't you want children, Mara? We've been married for seven years.'

'Seven years,' she whispered. 'Yes, I suppose we have.' And she thought, my God, I'm getting old. I'm twenty-five. I've been alive for a quarter of a century. She picked at the bedspread and wondered if she would die before it rotted and, if so, would other people sit on it in years to come, other women who would try to win a little freedom for themselves? A lump of marmalade dropped on to the bedspread but Mara didn't clean it up. She wanted it to sit there until it had made a mark: her mark.

'Well?' he asked.

Mara could not bear to look at him. Why couldn't he

448

just say yes, and let her do what she wanted? Why did everything always have to have its price? 'All right, but I don't think we ought to start until I've raced.'

'When will that be?'

'I don't know. It's up to your father and Smithy.'

His face became obstinate. 'We might wait for years. I want children while I'm young enough to enjoy them. I'm thirty-one now.'

Mara felt like strangling him. 'But it wouldn't be a good thing for me to be pregnant whilst I was racing.'

Alexander didn't look at her. His face was still obstinate. 'You might not get pregnant immediately,' he said, and closed his eyes. 'Now I think I'll have a rest, darling, I'm very tired.'

Mara went straight downstairs to the Old Man and said, 'Alexander's agreed.'

'He has?' He gave her his craggy smile.

'Yes.' Mara laughed out loud. But she didn't tell her father-in-law about Alexander's condition because she was sure he would see little point in wasting time with a driver who might become pregnant and be unable to drive. Even the Old Man wouldn't let her race if she were expecting a child. That, of course, was what Alexander was hoping for.

'Pass me the telephone,' said the Old Man, 'and I'll tell Smithy to expect you in the morning. No time like the present,' his eyes twinkled, 'especially as Herbert is off to America for a month tomorrow. But I want to make one thing quite clear, Mara. If Smithy decides you're not up to it, then that's the end of the matter. Understood?'

'Yes.'

'Good. Now you'd better go and look out your overalls – that is unless you burnt them in a fit of temper.'

Mara ran out of the room laughing.

It was wonderful to be back on the track, with Smithy grinning like a chipmunk and the two mechanics, Terry and Jackson, discussing pistons and axles. Mara felt a part of the team again, only the trouble was she wasn't yet, she was like someone who had applied for membership to an exclusive club and was waiting to hear if her application had been accepted.

Smithy was shouting, 'Pete! Pete!'

A freckled-faced lad with a mop of bright red hair appeared from behind the office building. 'Yes, Grandpa?'

'Come 'ere.'

The boy ran over and Mara was introduced to him. She liked him immediately for there was something endearingly cheeky about his face, he had Smithy's chipmunk eyes and Smithy's laugh but not, luckily for him, Smithy's stalactite teeth.

'Well, let's get on with it,' said Smithy. 'Now, miss' – he stroked the car's gleaming green bonnet – 'just remember she's a lot lighter than anything you've driven before. And a lot faster.'

Mara nodded and fiddled with the buttons of her overalls.

'Just get the feel of 'er,' Smithy went on. 'She's like a feather on the bends so don't let her fly away. Keep 'er tight in and 'old 'er steady. You're not racing today.'

Mara climbed in to the Roadster, pulled on her flying-helmet and adjusted her goggles. She felt horribly nervous and slightly sick. No longer was Smithy the foreman, he was her examiner. Like St Peter he stood at the gate and only he could let her in. But did he know how desperately she needed to enter?

He bent to turn the crank-handle. The car sprang into life, and Mara sat tensely revving the engine as he adjusted the carburettors. Satisfied, he snapped the bonnet shut, tightened the leather straps around it then stepped back and gave her the thumbs-up.

Gingerly Mara accelerated.

The engine responded with a roar.

Smithy yelled, 'Gently! Gently!'

Mara muttered, 'Gently, gently.'

The car shot forward. This time Mara didn't hear Smithy's 'Gently!' Before she knew where she was, she was halfway down the long side of the oval track and going like a bullet. The car was much, much lighter, it was slithering from side to side as she corrected, over-corrected, then over-corrected again.

'Oh, Christ!' The first bend was in sight, approaching fast, far too fast. In desperation Mara pumped the brakes. But even then she swung right out as she turned, hitting the grass verge and bouncing back across the track. Now it was not only the car that slithered, but her hands, wet and sticky on the steering wheel. She tried to remember what Smithy had told her and cursed herself for not having paid more attention when he had talked of the car being light. Now she knew what he meant. It was just like trying to drive a feather.

She hit a bump and for a moment lost her grip on the wheel. I'm hopeless. I'll never . . . But I must. Please God, I know I don't often think about you or speak to you, and I know I don't go to church except when I have to, but this is really important.

She flashed past Smithy but did not dare look at him. 'Slow. Brake. Hold her tight. Accelerate,' she murmured. 'Slow down, speed up, turn now, accelerate.' She passed Smithy again. The second lap hadn't been so bad. The third was better still. By the fourth she began to relax, she was no longer afraid. On the sixth she increased her speed on the straight. By the twelfth she was in complete control, her concentration icy, her movements precise – and she was enjoying herself.

Only when she stopped did she begin to tremble, but not with fear, with excitement. Pulling off her goggles and helmet, she rubbed her sweating, dust-streaked face on the back of her hand and started to laugh. Whatever exhilaration she had felt when she had test-driven the old Roadster was nothing compared to what she had felt driving this gleaming thoroughbred.

Smithy grinned at her and scratched his greying head. 'You lapped 'er in under seventy-five seconds on the last one – that's just over fifty miles an hour!' He shook the stop watch as though he believed it to be broken.

'Well?' Mara looked up at him. 'Did I . . . do I?'

'Get to race? I think we should give you a try.'

Relief and excitement flooded over her. 'Do you think I'll win?'

'If you find yourself up against Henry Segrave or Malcolm Campbell or Parry Thomas or any of the other big 'uns, you won't,' he teased. 'Not unless you're very, very lucky.'

'You mean if they all break down?'

Smithy laughed. 'Something like that.'

'What about other lady drivers?'

'There's only a couple of 'em, but let's face it, miss' – he gave her his chipmunk grin – 'they've got to be pretty good to get a ride in the first place. There's still plenty of men who think the track's no place for a lady.'

'And what do you think, Smithy?'

'I think if a lady knows 'er stuff she should be allowed to. Mind you, I didn't always think like that. But over the years I've seen a couple of ladies . . .'

'Violette Cordery?'

'Now you're talking! But I don't think you'll come up against Miss Cordery, she mostly does long-distance now though she used to drive at Brooklands, in a Silver 'awk, if I remember rightly, and she weren't yet twenty.'

'And Miss Addis-Price and Miss Ivy Cummings?'

'They're another two who could 'andle a car as well as any man, but I don't think they're driving at Brooklands much now. No, apart from the men you'll 'ave tough competition from Mrs Nicholls.'

Mara said, 'Oh, didn't she come third in the Rushton-Gaunt Cup?'

'She did indeed, but with practice you'll give 'er a run for 'er money.'

'But will I beat her?'

Smithy chuckled. 'If I knew who was going to win, I'd know who to put my money on, wouldn't I? Now, I'll see you up 'ere tomorrow morning, miss.'

Mara stretched her arms and pushed herself right back into the driving seat. I don't just want to beat the women, she thought, looking down the track, I want to beat the men too.

At home she went straight to her father-in-law, not bothering to change out of her overalls first or even to wash the sweat and dust from her face. 'Smithy says I can race,' she told him triumphantly.

'Oh he does, does he?'

'Yes.' She pushed back her streaky hair and laughed.

'Now we have to decide how we're going to teach you,' he said. 'Smithy'll teach you to drive well but it takes more than that to win. You need precision, anticipation, patience and aggression. Now you accelerate. Now you decelerate. Into the bend. Accelerate out of it. Every second counts.' He was gripping the arms of his wheel-chair and moving from side to side, just as though he

453

were driving a car, and Mara knew he wished he could race again. 'Who's going to teach you these things?' he asked.

She laid her hand on his arm. 'You could.'

'What! An old man in a wheelchair who can't even get downstairs.'

But nothing could stop Mara now. She was fired with enthusiasm and enthusiasm brooks no obstacles. 'The van could drive you into the middle of the track and you could sit at the top of the ramp in your wheelchair and watch me go round.'

He smiled. 'I'm thinking about when you go to Brooklands. You'll need to practise there because you'll have to learn how to handle those bankings at speed.'

Going upstairs to have a bath Mara spared a few minutes from her elation to wonder how Herbert could ever have imagined the Old Man could be cut off from his beloved Rushton-Gaunt. He *was* Rushton-Gaunt and anyone who thought he could be ousted was a fool.

She lay in the bath for an hour, luxuriating in the scented steam which rose from the hot water which she constantly topped up by turning the tap with her toes. Finally she stood dripping in front of the bathroom mirror. 'You see, you can do something,' she told herself with immense satisfaction. 'You're not just another bloodsucking little parasite after all. You're a racing-driver . . . well . . . almost.' She hugged herself and remembered the fear and the speed, and the thrill which had left her feeling vibrant and sexual.

Wrapping a towel round herself, Mara padded into the bedroom. Alexander was lying in bed reading a book.

'Well? How did it go?'

'It was wonderful. Incredible.'

Alexander smiled. 'You picked a good day, Herbert went to America this morning.'

Mara laughed. 'Yes, I know.' She sat down beside him. She couldn't be cross with anyone today. So what if he wanted to have children? That was in the future, she was only interested in the present. Pushing Alexander's book away, she draped her arm over him. 'How are you feeling?'

'Better. Doctor Phillips is coming soon.'

'What a bore!'

'Why?'

Mara kissed him on the cheek. 'Why do you think?'

'Oh . . . er.' Alexander ruffled her damp hair. He was bemused, it was months since she had let him touch her and the previous morning when he had mentioned children he had seen her reaction. Now he was so afraid she would suddenly push him away that he held himself back although he longed to make love to her.

But Mara had no intention of pushing Alexander away. She pulled back the bedclothes and wriggled up until she was almost on top of him and her mouth was just above his chin.

'The doctor's coming in half an hour.'

'Really?' She nibbled at his chin and deftly unwrapped her towel.

'And he doesn't usually find his patients lying naked in bed with their wives.'

'You mean' – Mara undid the buttons of his pyjama top – 'he expects to find them in bed with ladies other than their wives?'

'You are funny,' he murmured, running his hands up and down her bare back and feeling each bump of her vertebrae from the base of her neck to her bottom, where he took a cheek in each hand and squeezed. 'And he said

455

I wasn't to do anything tiring,' he said into the corner of her mouth.

'But you're not.' She twitched the muscles of her bottom under his hands. 'You're not. All you have to do is just lie there. You see. You see.'

Mara drove every morning, at first with Smithy watching her, but as she became more competent the Old Man took over. Two hours. Three hours. Round and round, lap after lap under the critical eye of her father-in-law, who sat in his wheelchair at the top of the ramp, with the van doors wide open to give him a perfect view. He watched. He criticized. Occasionally he praised. But like Mara he was always enthusiastic. And through Mara and her enthusiasm he came alive for the first time since the Gemelli.

For Mara racing was all that mattered; all she thought about; all she talked about. Nothing could compare to the thrill of speed. Nothing made her feel so alive. So sexual. Day after day she returned home to Alexander, hardly able to wait until her father-in-law was back in his room before she was in her husband's bed. Their sex life had never been so good. To her astonishment she found Alexander liked her to take the initiative, and if only they had been able to talk of such things, she would have known that he too found it astonishing, and that he waited all day for her to come home and that from the moment he heard the van draw up, he could think of nothing but when she would come striding into his room, aggressive and demanding.

Mara wished she could have told Elenora about the racing but Elenora was spending the winter in Florence,

456

so she had to make do with writing her a long letter, and getting one back in return.

'I always knew you had it in you to *do* something,' wrote Elenora, 'and now you are. Painting, writing, racing, it doesn't matter what one does so long as one *is*. So long as one doesn't just *exist*. And now you *are*.'

Of course Mara thought about Jamie. He didn't just disappear from her thoughts because she had found an interest, however all-absorbing. He had been with her too long for that and she had loved him much too deeply and desperately, but because he had no part in what she was doing and she had little time to mooch around and think, when she did think of him it was with much more understanding. Now she too had her medicine, her dedication and her ambition.

Herbert's return from America in early December was something about which no one spoke but all dreaded, particularly Mara. She told herself there was nothing he could do to stop her racing, she had the Old Man's permission, but during his absence everything had begun to go right: she and Alexander were much happier, in the Old Man she had her kindred spirit, on the track she had her excitement, and at the works she was part of the team.

Mara was on her tenth lap next morning when Herbert arrived. She saw his bulky form marching across the grass to the van and she roared round there, arriving just as he reached the Old Man.

'I might have guessed you'd be up here the minute my back was turned,' he shouted, glaring first at Mara, who sat in the car with her goggles pushed up on her head and her cheeks glowing pink under the film of dust from the track, then at his father, who sat impassively in his wheelchair at the top of the ramp.

Mara climbed out of the car. 'I have your father's permission. And Alexander's.'

'I wonder how you managed that, you wheedling little minx.'

'That's enough, Herbert!' roared the Old Man.

'But, Papa . . .'

'I said, enough. I make the decisions on who races and who doesn't. Your job is to sell.'

Herbert tried to control his temper. 'But, Papa, I'm thinking of you. You'll exhaust yourself with all of this and anyhow Rushton-Gaunt can't have a woman driver, let me try to find . . .'

'Find what? Another fool like those other two we had? Mara's going to race next season and that's the end of it. Now, kindly let us get on with our work and I'll see you in an hour to hear how your trip to America went.'

Herbert wasn't beaten yet. 'I think we should take a vote on it, Papa. I'm sure if I talk to Alexander . . .'

The Old Man shouted him down. 'Rushton-Gaunt will have what I say, I still control this company and don't you forget it. Now, Mara, get back in that car and let me see if you can lap her in one minute – sixty miles an hour. Come on!'

After this confrontation there was a sort of angry truce between Mara and Herbert. He did not dare attack her directly, though she knew he longed to, and he made a point of being particularly nice to Alexander – Mara suspected he worked on him to end her racing hopes. But Alexander was besotted with his wife. He was happier than he had been in years and felt better than he had for months; well enough to go to work each morning, to lunch with his father and Herbert, and sometimes his wife, then to go home in the afternoons to rest. Or, more often than not, to make love. Nothing Herbert said could have made him deny Mara whatever she wanted. The Old Man would deny her nothing either. To Herbert it was as though Mark had returned, the son who wasn't a son but whom the Old Man liked better than his own. For this to happen with Mara who, six months earlier, he had been sure was on the point of running off, was more than he could bear. His only recourse was to grumble that Mara would be the death of his father.

Just before Christmas Damon, home from school, came up to the works to watch Mara drive. Afterwards she said, 'I didn't know you were interested.'

He laughed. 'I'm not but I wanted to see you drive, and anyhow it's a good excuse to get out of the Park.'

'Is it that bad?'

'Uhhh!' He lifted his hands to his head and pulled his hair down over his face as if drawing down a curtain. Mara watched him. Adolescence was still doing nothing to mar his looks, he had no awkwardness or spots, and his eyes were just as thoughtful, the brooding quality was still there. Once again Mara had a suspicion he had learned to twist it to his own advantage.

'Is Atalanta home as well?' she asked.

'No, she's gone to stay with a schoolfriend and she's not coming back till Christmas Eve.' Suddenly he looked up at Mara and laughed. 'Father's delighted because the friend's father is a baronet, although not as delighted as he would have been if she had a brother. But, alas' – he held out his hands, palms upward, in a dramatic gesture – 'she's an only child.'

Mara laughed. 'You are dreadful! Now, I must go and have a word with Smithy. I'll see you on Christmas Eve if not before. We're dining at the Park then.'

'Yes.' He turned and walked away down the drive, kicking at the gravel as he went.

On Christmas Eve Mara, Alexander and the Old Man arrived at the Park just after tea. Stepping from the car it seemed to Mara incredible that it was seven years since that first Christmas Eve when she had arrived at the Park and looked up at the house with its big sightless windows. And as on that first time, Mortimer opened the door to them and took their coats and they went through into the drawing room, where Sophia was lying on the chaise-longue.

'You'll forgive me for not getting up,' she said. 'I've had a bad cold and it's taken rather a lot out of me.'

They all murmured their sympathies and sat down.

'Oh, you've arrived,' said Damon, coming into the room. 'I thought it was Atalanta when I heard the car. Father's gone to collect her from the station.' He sat on the arm of Mara's chair. 'Well, how's it going?'

'All right I think.' She looked at her father-in-law and waited for him to say something.

'Not bad at all,' he growled. 'In fact, I was just telling Mara this morning that it's time we had a few days down at Brooklands.'

Damon asked, 'Can I come?'

'I don't think so, dear,' said Sophia, nervously twisting her long white fingers.

'You can come when you're older,' the Old Man placated him, 'you're a bit young at the moment and we'll be too busy to keep an eye on you. You see, Mara has to improve her speeds and she can't do it here, but at Brooklands . . .' His eyes lit up as he spoke of the joy of coming out of the Members' Banking and going into the

460

Railway Straight, where you could put your foot down and give your car its head.

As he was talking the door opened and Atalanta came in. 'Hello,' she said, walking a little self-consciously into the middle of the room. She was wearing a purple dress with a low waist and a long yellow sash, and high-heeled yellow shoes. Her outfit was obviously new and Mara's immediate thought was she had bought it herself, for it was quite unsuitable for a girl of fifteen. And when Mara looked closer she saw that Atalanta's hair, although unfashionably long, had been subjected to a crinkling perm and that she was wearing a slight touch of pink lipstick and not very well applied eye make-up.

Damon started to laugh. 'Good God!' he exclaimed, but when he saw Atalanta was upset he stopped laughing and said, 'Oh, twinny, you do look grown up.'

'Yes, dear, it is quite . . . where did you buy it?' Sophia gave her daughter a nervous smile.

'What's the matter?' demanded Atalanta defensively. 'All the girls wear this sort of thing. You told me to buy something new, surely you didn't expect me to buy one of those baby dresses you . . .'

Before she had time to finish, Herbert stormed into the room. 'I told you to take that dress off and wash that muck off your face,' he roared.

'But, Daddy . . .'

'You look like a tart!'

For a moment Atalanta hesitated, and then she turned and ran. They all sat in silence listening to her footsteps as they sped up the stairs and along the corridor, and for the first time Mara felt some sympathy towards her niece. Had I been able to buy clothes when I was fifteen I would have experimented too, she thought. She looked across at Herbert and found him watching her, daring her to speak up for Atalanta's outlandish clothes. But Mara said nothing; she was sure that if she did so they would most certainly be burnt.

The team went down to Brooklands for a week in late January and again they stayed at the Hand and Spear. To Mara there was something different and in many ways nicer about being at Brooklands in the winter. The weather was cold and there were few spectators, just the close-knit core of the racing fraternity preparing their cars for the coming season. Everyone was busy, everyone had a job to do, everyone got dirty and oily. There was little glamour about the place in the winter, but what Mara liked was that same sense of the heart pumping the life blood through the arteries which she had felt when she'd first visited the works. Only here there wasn't just one heart, there were lots of little hearts. Each team was a heart.

The Rushton-Gaunt team had only a week at Brooklands and they used every hour of it. Round and round the circuit Mara drove, her goggles and her balaclava protecting her face from the cold wind and her heavy leather flying-jacket buttoned over her overalls and corset to keep out the cold. Seldom had she looked less glamorous, never had she enjoyed herself so much. Now it was no longer, 'Don't go so fast!' but 'Speed up on the straight! Keep those revs up!'

Every twenty laps Mara would turn off at the Fork and head up Test Hill, to where the Old Man sat watching her through binoculars, and from his perch at the back of the hill overlooking the Members' Banking, Smithy would come scuttling through the trees. First the Old Man would tell her what she was doing wrong on his side of the hill, then Smithy would do the same for his side, all this while the mechanics checked over the car. Then Smithy would produce a thermos of hot sweet tea and pour a mug for Mara, and as soon as she had drunk it, off she would go again, Terry and Jackson taking it in turns to ride with her. And she certainly needed a mechanic. Twice she had a puncture on the Railway Straight and on the second occasion the force of the tyre bursting spun the Roadster right round.

'Oh, no!' cried Mara as she found herself staring at two cars which had been following. She closed her eyes as they roared past, opening them only when Terry shook her arm, and said, 'We must push 'er into the pull-in bay, miss.' Getting out and pushing calmed Mara down.

One of the things which Mara liked about Brooklands in winter was the attitude of the other drivers towards her. They were more friendly, not because they were trying to pick her up but speaking to her as though she'd always been there. Or perhaps it's because I'm more confident, she thought. I'm racing. I'm one of them.

She met Parry Thomas, to whom Mark had been introduced at the Motor Show. He was a big jolly man who drove a blue and white car nicknamed *Babs*, and always wore a Fair Isle sweater. Often if they were working on the Roadster he would wander over, followed by his Alsatian, Togo, and exchange a few words with herself or the Old Man or Smithy. Then there was Henry Segrave who was incredibly good-looking in a debonair and aristocratic way, and Malcolm Campbell who had a lovely way of wrinkling his nose when he smiled.

'At least the big 'uns don't 'ang around you like a lot of dogs,' Smithy said to Mara one morning. 'Got too much to do, they 'ave.'

Mara laughed and looked down at her dirty hands and

her even dirtier overalls. 'I don't think they'd take much notice of me now, Smithy.'

'Don't you believe it, miss! Why, we were only saying yesterday you looked a treat in our Rushton green.'

'Were you?' It was always odd to think of oneself being discussed behind one's back.

During February the Rushton-Gaunt team had a further two sessions at Brooklands, each lasting a week, and in between Mara continued to practise on the works track. With Herbert there was still the truce. With Alexander she was still quite happy.

But one morning, very early, he suddenly asked her, 'Do you think you are . . . pregnant?'

'Pregnant! Good heavens I hope not. Not with the racing season starting in a month's time. Pregnant! That's all I need. Being sick and all that.' The exhilaration of driving had taken her over to such an extent that only from time to time had she remembered their earlier conversation and immediately felt heartily relieved that she hadn't become pregnant. Thinking about it now, she wondered why she hadn't. She said, 'Why? Did you think . . .'

He kissed her cheek. 'But of course I thought . . . well, imagined . . . that was why you suddenly . . . you know. I mean, we talked of having children and that very day you came and . . .' He kissed her again.

Mara lay perfectly still with her eyes shut. If she had not felt so depressed she would have laughed.

'Perhaps you should see a doctor,' Alexander said after a few minutes.

'Why?'

'There might be something wrong.'

Mara buried her face in the pillow. 'I'll go when the season's over.'

'Mara, you said that if I let you race . . .' It struck Mara as extraordinary that Alexander could be so weak in some ways and so obstinate in others. She felt like screaming at him to shut up, but he went on unconcernedly, 'Doctor Phillips is meant to be very good at this sort of thing, he's very discreet, but perhaps you'd rather see someone else. What about your old friend Doctor Turner?'

'No!' It came out in a shriek.

'All right, all right.' Alexander was miserably confused. 'It's just that he's meant to be so good.'

'How do you know?' Mara was wide awake now.

'There was an article about him in the newspaper . . .'

'Oh?' She longed to shout, 'Where? Where? Show it to me! How could you have kept it from me? Have they burnt the paper yet? Has it gone to light a fire?'

'I read it a couple of weeks ago, I meant to keep it for you but I forgot. You were down at Brooklands at the time.' Mara groaned inwardly: it would have gone to light a fire by now. Alexander yawned. 'Of course the man's a socialist, he wants to nationalize health and set up free hospitals paid for out of income tax. It's all nonsense because the people who can't afford to pay aren't the ones who pay income tax, so where's all the money going to come from? People like us! And we pay quite enough as it is.' He paused. 'But getting back to Turner, the article said he was brilliant in his field.'

Mara collected herself and spoke calmly. 'His field is lungs not . . . er . . . babies.'

'Then perhaps I should see him.'

She shrugged her shoulders. 'Why not? But I don't want to see a doctor I know socially . . .' She gave a brittle laugh. 'So embarrassing if we were to meet him at a ball. I wouldn't mind so much for me, of course.'

'What do you mean?' he asked.

She had his full attention. 'Only that . . . er . . . if something is wrong it might not be me and I would have thought if it isn't, you'd prefer only Doctor Phillips to . . . er . . . know.'

But Alexander was so appalled he missed her point. 'You're not suggesting it's me! These things are always the woman.'

What could she say? She could not even bear to look at him.

Mara would have been happy to let the matter rest until after the racing season. But for a whole week Alexander went on and on and on about wanting her to see Doctor Phillips until, just to shut him up, she went. After submitting herself to an undignified examination and a series of tests, she was called back for the result. 'There's nothing the matter with you, Mrs Rushton,' Doctor Phillips told her. 'Perhaps it's your husband.'

Mara was sitting in front of the doctor's desk. He sat the other side, smiling, in his white coat. Jamie. Jamie. Jamie. The realization that Alexander had not understood her and would never understand her had pulled her deep into the despondency of Jamie, alleviated only when she roared around the track.

'Mrs Rushton, did you understand what I said?'

'Yes, but my husband believes these problems are always the woman's fault.'

'But he's been very ill and often a man who has been ill finds that . . . er . . . other parts of his body don't work as they should. Would he agree to an examination?'

'No. Never. He would be humiliated. In fact, Doctor Phillips, I would prefer to say I had some small problem – something which rights itself with time – something which doesn't require treatment.'

Doctor Phillips smiled. 'I quite understand, Mrs Rushton. I'll prescribe you a tonic and say you needed plenty of exercise. I know you take it, what with your racing. Unfortunately most men share Mr Rushton's view, though I must say the ladies who are really keen to have children usually try to persuade their husbands to be examined.' He paused and fiddled with his prescription pad. 'It all depends on how much you want to have a baby, doesn't it?'

When Mara returned to the Dower House she found the Old Man sitting in his wheelchair by his sitting-room window with tears rolling down his leathery cheeks. 'What's the matter?' she asked, laying her hand on his shoulder.

'Parry Thomas has been killed.'

'Oh, no! How did it happen?'

'He was trying to break the Land Speed Record in *Babs* and something went wrong with a wheel.' He wiped the tears from his face with the back of his hand. 'Brooklands won't be the same without him.'

Mara thought sadly of the big kindly man in his Fair Isle sweater with Togo trotting behind him. And suddenly she was afraid. If a driver of Parry Thomas' calibre could be killed, what chance did she stand? But even as fear came creeping up her legs and arms she knew there was no question of her giving up. Racing had become such a part of her that the idea of a life without its excitements and exhilarations was no life at all.

Chapter 27

The Old Man decided that the sooner Mara raced the better, and he chose the Short Handicap at the Brooklands Easter meeting for her first race. 'I don't expect you to win first time out, but you need to get the feel of the track and as long as you acquit yourself well, I'll be satisfied.'

The plan was that Mara and the team, including the Old Man, would go down to Brooklands ten days before the race so as to give Mara plenty of time to practise; the rest of the family would come down on the morning of the race. 'I don't want anyone upsetting you,' the Old Man told Mara when he made the arrangements.

She gave him a grateful smile. The last thing she needed was Alexander's worried face or Herbert's disapproving one.

On the Sunday before they were due to leave the whole family went to church and Mara, sitting between Alexander and Damon, mused on the strange family into which she had married and to whom, although she had always felt distant, she was intrinsically tied. During the sermon she studied each member out of the corner of her eye. Were they any different to any other family, she wondered. Didn't all families have both love and hate, and guilt where hate existed because the very notion of the word family suggests love. And when people find they don't love each member of their family they feel they have failed the notion, and feel guilty. She looked at Alexander. As a marriage they had failed and knew it.

He turned and saw her watching him and smiled. She smiled back and gave him a slight wink. He was so good and kind, sometimes she asked herself why. He put up with far more than most people would have; from herself; from everyone.

The pattern of the light on the pulpit reminded her of that day in the woods of the previous October. She hadn't left him then because he was so ill. Now he was better, much better, but the time for her to leave him had passed. The alternative, Jamie, had receded – if it had ever been there. She wondered if God favoured Alexander and had made him ill to thwart her, then better only when she could not go. 'That is,' she thought, 'if God exists. Which I think he probably does. But does he exist because people want to believe in a higher being or do they believe in him because he exists?' She stared at the light-pattern on the pulpit and pondered. Then, suddenly, she remembered where she was and looked up quickly at the ceiling, half-expecting it to come crashing down on her irreverent head.

As Mara left the church, the vicar clasped her hand with extra warmth. 'I'll be at Brooklands, my dear Mrs Rushton,' he assured her. 'I'll be there.'

'To give you the last rites,' Atalanta whispered as they moved on. She was shaking with laughter under a ridiculously demure dress.

Mara glanced round at her. 'Thanks very much.' But Atalanta did not hear her, or pretended not to. Studying her niece, Mara wondered why on earth Sophia dressed her luscious, over-developed daughter in a white muslin dress cut for a childish figure. It made Atalanta look like Jezebel masquerading as a nun, whereas the purple dress in which Atalanta had turned up at the Park the previous Christmas had made her look like a child masquerading as Jezebel. Surely, she thought, they could find a happy medium. Or is Herbert's hand in this too? Atalanta was standing next to Sophia, whose aristocratic head was bent to hear the words of some little old lady, and Mara noticed there was a smile on the girl's sultry red lips as she played with the ends of her unfashionably long hair. It was just as though the old lady was a man who was saying something that excited her intimately. But Atalanta's smile was not for the old lady, she was looking directly across the graveyard at someone for whom her smile and all her movements were intended. And that someone was Pete Smithy.

He was standing under a yew tree, cap in hand, pretending to be watching the people; but there was only one person he had eyes for. And he was not looking at Atalanta as a man might look at his boss's daughter, a girl beyond his humble reach, in class and money. Nor was Atalanta looking at Pete as a boss's daughter looks at an employee, flattered by his lowly admiration and exciting his lust, which she has no intention of satisfying. In their faces and their eyes was the awakening to that incredible feeling, such as Mara had experienced when she had first seen Jamie.

Mara was too busy to wonder about Atalanta and Pete. In any case, as she'd told herself at the time, it seemed highly unlikely they knew each other and whatever the attraction, when they did meet their differing status would kill off anything other than polite detachment. Fleetingly Mara felt sorry for Pete, but then she turned her mind to other things: to telling Rachel what clothes she would need at Brooklands and to arranging with Lord to put her neglected hunters out to grass. 'I just don't have the time to ride now,' she told him, 'so they may as well enjoy themselves in the field.'

470

Two days later they drove down to Brooklands and on the way down Mara had another attack of nerves. Why am I doing this? she kept asking herself. I must be mad. But when they reached Brooklands and she saw the oval track and heard the engines being tuned and the laughter coming from the clubhouse, she started to feel better. They took the Roadster straight into the pits and immediately Smithy and the mechanics began to check her over. Whilst they were doing that, Mara went over to the clubhouse and changed into her overalls. When she came back, striding across the Paddock, her tawny hair ruffled by the wind, she saw a few familiar figures and waved cheerfully. They waved back. Confident and happy she walked down the straight towards the pits, swinging her bag and thinking how different it was this year and how much she now felt a part of this place.

Once again Mara stood out amongst the sisters and girlfriends, and soon Smithy was having his favourite grumble. 'Young devils, coming over 'ere and pretending they're interested in the car. What do they think I am? Barmy? At least you stand no nonsense, miss. Nor does Mrs Nicholls.'

'Which is Mrs Nicholls? Is she here? Has she been practising?'

'I've not seen 'er yet' – he scratched his head – 'and she's cutting it a bit fine.'

Mara picked up a spanner and ran her finger down its groove. 'Oh, Smithy, I hope I don't let everyone down.'

'Eh, nothing to worry about, miss.' He patted the Roadster's shiny green bonnet. 'She'll do it all for you.'

In the Paddock the Old Man was in deep conversation with a grey-haired man in a dark suit and a black felt hat whom Mara had noticed before. He was very much a part of the place, with an air of calm authority. She

471

watched him put his hand on the arm of the Old Man's wheelchair as he bent to say something at which the Old Man laughed. 'Who's that with my father-in-law?' she asked Smithy.

Smithy glanced up. 'Why, that's Ebby . . . Mr Ebblewhite. 'E's the one who decides on the 'andicaps. A real character is Ebby. The number of times some young rogue's tried to pull the wool over Ebby's eyes and make out that a car's not as powerful as it is don't bear thinking about. But Ebby catches 'em every time.' He chuckled and turned back to the car.

Mara was standing near the car, half in the shade and half in the sunlight, spinning the spanner in the palm of her hand, when one of the journalists she had seen talking to her father-in-law earlier came hurrying up to her. 'Mrs Rushton, I'm from the *News Chronicle*. Just a quick word if you please.' His pencil hovered above his notepad. 'This is your first race? What do you think of your chances? You know Mrs Nicholls won't be racing?'

Mara said, 'No, I didn't.'

'Her car cracked its chassis in practice. Jolly bad luck! Now, how do you feel about being the only lady racing this meeting?' He fired his questions one after the other, hardly giving Mara time to answer. Finally, he said, 'A photograph of you beside the car.' He beckoned to a photographer who came running over and Mara found herself being ushered back to the Roadster whilst Smithy was pulled away from it, and the photographer called, 'Lovely. Smile. Another one. Head up. Perfect.'

When they had gone Smithy muttered, 'Anyone would think we'd no work to do. Cheeky devils!'

Mara nodded. She was wondering if Jamie read the *New Chronicle* and imagined him sitting at his Hampstead breakfast table and seeing her face staring back at him.

472

Would he think, I never knew Mara had it in her, I was a fool to let her go?

The day before the race was warm and sunny and, what with the heat from the sun and her sporadic bouts of nerves, Mara was soon dripping with sweat. At lunchtime the Old Man excused himself. 'I'm going back to the Hand and Spear. All this excitement's wearing me out.'

Mara looked at him anxiously. His face was pale and slightly like parchment and the shadows under his eyes had sunk into the hollows of his skull. 'Are you all right? Shall I drive you back? Do you want a doctor?'

'No, no, just a rest. Pete will drive me back. Last thing you need is to hang around the hotel feeding your nerves on boredom. Bad enough staying here. Remember, I know what it's like.'

He was right. By late afternoon Mara was not just nervous, she was hot and tense and shivery. Her last practice lap was appalling. She made every elementary mistake, and when Smithy flagged her down he told her firmly, 'Enough's enough.'

But Mara still had hours to kill. Normally she went straight back to the hotel but today the thought of the long, unsleeping hours ahead was more than she could bear. To pass time she had a tepid shower and changed her overalls, toying with the idea of going to the clubhouse in the hope of finding one of the men who had chatted her up. But they would think she was trying to pick them up, and all she was after was company. Someone with whom to kill the hours. Hopefully she looked around outside the clubhouse to see if there was anyone she knew whom she could join, but there was no one. Just a lot of strangers who all seemed to know each other. With her hair dripping on to the shoulders of her fresh overalls she made her way despondently across the Paddock towards Test Hill, from where the bridge over the Members' Banking would take her towards Weybridge and the hotel. At least the walk will kill a bit of time, she thought. But she wished she didn't have to go back to the hotel, she longed to be part of one of the groups, drivers in overalls and girls in pretty dresses, lolling around on rugs or flopped in chairs, all drinking champagne and enjoying themselves: oases of colour whose laughter made her feel intensely lonely.

Mara was standing watching them when she realized she, herself, was being watched, by a man she hadn't seen before. He was standing a few yards from her and, when she looked round at him, he gave her a flash of perfect teeth in a perfect smile; white teeth like his white overalls and his white-blond hair.

'You're Mara Rushton,' he said, with a French accent.

'Yes. Who are you?'

'Yves Lejeune.' He sauntered over to her with the confidence of a successful driver and the suntan and the glamour which were the hallmark.

Mara was thinking, Yves Lejeune. The hero of the French Grand Prix – was it last year or the year before – and the meat of the gossip columnists. What is it they say about him? 'Yves Lejeune with yet another blonde beauty.' She knew then that she should leave.

'I want to tell you how much I admire you,' he was saying, bending down to her as though she were a precious object and he wished to protect her. 'I admired your father-in-law and now I admire you. And now I am hoping you will come and have a drink with my friends.' He waved his hands in a very Gallic gesture towards one of the groups of young men and women.

Mara looked at them. Like him, they had that casual

474

sophistication which only a long and harmonious relationship with wealth can produce. 'I'd love to.' She tossed
back her wet hair and smiled up at him.

The nagging little voice which kept telling her to go
home was soon forgotten. But an hour and a bottle
of champagne later Mara not only knew that she
should have gone, but that having failed to do so,
she should leave now. She was sitting on a rug, leaning
against a car, and she was talking and laughing, high on
alcohol and nerves, with the adrenalin pumping through
her veins. Never had she been funnier. Never had she
laughed so much. Never could she remember having
drunk so much so quickly. Empty bottles were strewn
everywhere. Full bottles sat in the ice-box. She ought to
go home. But she didn't. She held out her glass for a
refill and leaned very slightly towards Yves.

Another hour and it was almost dark and growing cold.
Yves was talking softly in Mara's ear. The others were
talking about going to eat. One of the girls, French with
a black, geometric haircut, was smoking a cheroot. But
Mara was on a planet far above them, racing through the
sky, laughing quietly to herself as the wind seemed to
take her arms and legs and blow them around her and
the champagne took her head and made it both heavy
and light.

Another hour and they were in a restaurant, twelve of
them at a long table. Behind them the restaurateur
hovered. He had been torn between his desire for their
custom – he knew the money such a glittering crowd
would spend – and his fear that they would get even
drunker and upset the other diners or throw food at his
new red flock wallpaper or break his art deco lamps, or
all three.

Mara was sitting on a cushion-covered bench with her

back against the wall; she was squashed between Yves and another man. But it was Yves who had her attention, though she purposely did not look at him. And it was Yves whose hand was moving competently up the inside of her thigh, hidden from view by the tablecloth. Mara leaned forward to talk, aware that by doing so he could see right down the valley between her breasts. She stretched out her trousered legs and his hand crept up, so much higher than if she had been wearing a skirt. She took a peach and peeled it, ripping through the skin with the sharp ends of her fingernails, and sank her teeth deep into its soft yellow flesh, then turned towards Yves with the half-eaten peach in her hand and the juice of it still on her lips. She licked it up with the tip of her pink tongue.

At midnight they left the restaurant and its restaurateur whose fears had been unfounded, and staggered out into the night.

In a clear voice Yves asked Mara, 'Can I give you a lift back to your hotel?' It was a mere formality. He was being careful – he knew she was married.

'If it's not out of your way.' She stifled a giggle. She was feeling very sexy, but the sexier she felt the more she wanted to giggle.

'Not at all. You're staying at the Hand and Spear and I'm with friends nearby.' For a split second their eyes met, then Mara lowered hers so the others could not see the sparkle of anticipation as they wished her goodnight.

Yves drove with one hand on the wheel and the other on Mara's thigh. 'Unfortunately I'm staying with friends so I don't think I can . . . umm . . .'

'Take me there?' She ran her hand down his leg. She could feel his muscles harden as he trod the clutch.

'Yes.' He smiled at her in the darkness. 'What about your hotel?'

She rolled her head across the back of the seat towards him. 'I think not.'

'Your . . . er . . . husband?'

'No, but . . .' She turned sideways to him and began to undo the buttons of her overalls, slipping them through their holes, one by one, till the green overalls were slashed to the waist and her breasts gleamed in the night, and her nipples were just dark patches on the very white half-moons where her bathing-costume always covered her.

Suddenly Yves swung the car off road and into an open gateway. 'I cannot concentrate on my driving,' he said in his over-correct English.

The sudden movement had thrown Mara towards him, and she was lolling all over him as he turned off the ignition, and supple and willing as he took her in his arms. And she could hardly bear to let go of him when he got out of the car, and clung to him hungrily when he came round to her side and pulled her out, and down, on to the grass, which was cold and damp beneath her half-naked body. Mara had a rather hazy recollection of what happened next, for she had looked up at the branches of a tree waving above her and her head had begun to go round and round as if it too were suspended, not on her neck but on a thin branch. One minute she was lying half-naked on the ground and Yves was kissing her, the next she was totally naked and Yves was half on top of her, and the next she was pushing him away, because her stomach was churning and her head was spinning and she knew she was going to be violently sick.

'Let me go! Let me go!' she hissed through gritted teeth as she staggered to her feet and stumbled through

477

stinging nettles to the safety of the tree. 'I'm going to be
. . .' Steadying herself against the tree trunk she retched
into the nettles.

When Mara came back to Yves some five minutes later
she found him sitting in the car fully dressed. In silence
she picked up her overalls and began to pull them on,
pushing her scratched and stung legs into the rough cotton
material. She felt utterly miserable. Her mouth tasted
revolting, her body was covered in cold sweat, her bare
feet were freezing and muddy, and her stomach ached
from retching. 'I'm sorry,' she muttered as she got into
the car, keeping her head turned well away.

'I am sorry too.' He gave her a look of disappointment,
like that of a child whose new toy proves not as exciting
as it looked in the shop window.

Yves dropped Mara a discreet fifty yards from the
hotel. She kept her head turned away from him as he
said goodnight, and she wasn't surprised when he didn't
try to kiss her. Who would? But she was surprised when
he said, 'Can I see you again, Mara?'

Mara shook her head and felt for the door handle.

'Is it because of your husband?'

'No.' She opened the door.

'Then?'

She got her leg out of the car. 'It's just that, well, I
don't usually . . .' She stopped abruptly, knowing she
sounded like the sort of pathetic fraud who says, 'I'm
not that kind of girl,' when she, like everyone else, *was*
that kind of girl given the right man and the right circumstances.

Yves touched her arm. 'Fear makes people do strange
things,' he said kindly. 'Don't worry. It happens to all of
us.'

'Does it?' She gave a brittle laugh to cover a sudden

desire to burst into tears and hurried off, through the trees and into the courtyard where some of the drivers serviced their cars. From there she crept up the wrought-iron stairs which led to the first floor and in through a door, luckily left unlocked, and on up to her bedroom.

Mara didn't wake up till nine o'clock next morning, and then only because Smithy sent the porter up to find out what had happened to her. 'Sleeping like that before your first race! Why, you've the nerves of an old-timer,' he told her proudly when she came downstairs some twenty minutes later.

The cold bath had done its trick. Her face was glowing and her eyes were hardly bloodshot at all. In fact, she thought, catching sight of herself in a mirror, I look remarkably healthy . . . considering. No one would know that I'd . . . well . . . after all, they can't see my hangover.

'I've just seen old Mr Rushton,' Smithy carried on cheerfully, 'and 'e said to tell you 'e'd be along later. 'E's going to wait for Mr Alexander and Mr 'erbert. And you're not to go up and see 'im because 'e's going to 'ave a bath now.'

Mara nodded and wished he would stop talking. The oppressive bright light of the hazy morning sunshine and the warm air which was building up under the thin layer of white clouds were bad enough, without his cheerful voice pounding in her head. By the time they reached the track she was feeling even worse. The Roadster was parked in the Paddock, and she sank down on the grass nearby and closed her eyes. Her race was scheduled for early afternoon and was expected to last less than half an hour. But I'll be lucky to get round the first bend, she thought. Lucky if I'm not dead by then. God, I wish I'd gone to bed early. I must have been mad.

But she couldn't rest. People kept coming up to her, to

shake her hand, to wish her luck, and for each person she
had to stand up and smile and talk and nod her aching
head. There were tests and trials and people, and black
coffee. There were officials and photographers and
journalists, and more black coffee. And sandwiches. And
more black coffee. She began to feel better. No longer
sick; just nervous.

At one point the Old Man wheeled over to talk to her.
'Now just remember, keep her steady when you're on the
bankings' he said. 'Ease her round. Don't jerk her!'

Mara nodded her aching head.

A few minutes later Alexander arrived with Herbert,
Sophia and the twins, and she tried to look confident – or
at least alive.

'You look terribly pale, darling,' said Alexander, kissing her on the cheek. 'I think you should have some
lunch.'

'Oh no, I couldn't.'

'Mara, you must. Come along.'

The last thing she wanted was a hot noisy restaurant
and food, but they insisted and she found herself being
dragged along. Hardly had they sat down before there
was a shriek behind them and Mara turned to see Cynthia
wafting towards her in a cloud of scent and chiffon,
crying, 'Mara, darling, here we all are. Why didn't you
tell us you were racing today? If we hadn't seen the
newspaper . . . Alexander! And everyone! What a Rushton gathering! How sweet!' She was followed by Jeremy
and Charles and Jeremy's sister, Sybil. They all engulfed
Mara with cries and hugs, telling her how brave she was
and how they all knew she was going to win, while Mara
sat there like some unfortunate pet dog whom everybody
wants to cuddle.

An hour later the Roadster, in line with the other four

entrants, was taken round to the back of the clubhouse, filled up with petrol, and then pushed through the back doors of the clubhouse and on to the weighbridge in the centre of the ground floor so that Ebby could decide Mara's handicap.

'You have a twenty-second start,' the Old Man told her as the Roadster was rolled forward into the Paddock, 'but remember the others will be coming up fast behind you, so don't go up to the top of the banking till you're sure no one's overtaking you on that side or you'll push him over the top.'

Mara nodded. She looked nervously at the other drivers. They were all men and they were all excellent drivers. There was Cobb driving a Vauxhall, Meeson with another Vauxhall, Poppe with an orange Rover and a Frenchman called Goutte with a supercharged Salmson. I must be mad, she thought.

Alexander touched her arm. 'Look, darling, there's the cup.' She looked at the trophies in their glass cases on the front of the clubhouse.

They all followed the Roadster which was being pushed up to the starting line by Terry and Jackson. Mara wished that she could have been alone with the Old Man and Smithy and the mechanics, just the team, not all these people talking and laughing.

Cynthia came rushing up to her. 'Darling, we've been to the bookies and you're twenty to one. But don't worry, we believe you'll win. I've put five pounds on you and so has Charles. Jeremy's so mean he won't bet. Isn't that mean?'

To be gabbled at about people risking their money on her was just what Mara didn't need.

The Old Man came to her rescue. 'Leave the girl

481

alone!' he roared. 'Alexander! Herbert! Get everyone off the track.'

Alexander gave Mara a quick kiss on the cheek. 'Good luck, darling.' There were other subdued 'good lucks' as the entourage beat a hasty retreat.

Terrified but relieved the waiting was over, Mara climbed into the Roadster and pulled on her helmet and goggles. Smithy cranked the engine which sprang into life with a loud roar. She heard the other cars start and glanced quickly round at the other drivers; their faces like hers were strained in concentration.

'Keep 'er steady on the corners!' shouted Smithy. His voice was almost drowned by the engines. ''Ere comes Mr Ebblewhite. Watch the flag!'

Ebby stood beside the track just ahead of the Roadster. He raised the flag. In those few seconds before he lowered it a surge of terror and excitement swept up Mara's legs and arms. Foot on clutch. Into gear. Increase the revs. Then the flag was down. With a roar the Roadster shot forward and, before Mara was really aware of what was happening she was speeding down the Finishing Straight, heading for the Members' Banking. Behind her she could hear the other cars and as she went into the banking, she glanced quickly to her right, the track was clear, and she swung up into the lip of the concrete wave. Down off the banking she came and into the Railway Straight, now nearly at full speed, round behind the Aero Sheds, into the Byfleet Banking, past the Vickers Sheds, swinging left at the Fork and on into the deep gully of the Members' Banking. Now she could hear the cheer from the spectators high above her and she glanced up quickly and saw the mass of faces peering down from the top of the gully. Then suddenly, and it happened so quickly, Cobb shot past her in his Vauxhall. As long as Mara had been out front she had felt she stood a chance but although there were still three other drivers behind her, she began to panic. The icy precision went, and she jerked the car out of the Members' Banking and back into the Railway Straight, causing it to skid sideways and almost hit Meeson who flew past her in the other Vauxhall.

'Come on!' she muttered. 'Come on!' Inside her overall she was dripping with sweat and behind her goggles the perspiration was running into the corners of her eyes. On the straight she did a little better and she began to catch up, but when she came into the Byfleet Banking she jerked the Roadster so hard that the back slid sideways up the track as Poppe flashed past in his orange Rover. And to make matters worse she had stalled the engine. For a moment she sat there, her body slumped in the seat and her eyes fixed on her hands where they held the steering wheel. What a fool she'd made of herself! How they must all be laughing! She wished she could creep away into the trees and make her way home without having to see or speak to anyone. But she couldn't, she was stuck across the track in full view of hundreds of spectators.

But she didn't stay there for long. Four men rushed up and pushed Mara and the Roadster off the track and on to the grass verge, from where she had the added humiliation of seeing the other three cars flash past before she even had time to climb out of the car.

There were murmurs of, 'Bad luck! Bad luck!' and Mara tried to smile but she felt sick with disappointment and shame.

Someone said, 'Goutte's out of it too. Poor chap, he took the wrong turning,' and Mara thought, at least he didn't do what I did.

The van was coming slowly towards her across the grassy centre of the oval track. She saw it reach the runway down the middle and speed up. The Old Man. Smithy. Terry. Jackson. Even freckled-faced Pete. She'd let them all down. She leaned against the Roadster and closed her eyes.

The van stopped beside her and Smithy leaned out. 'Bad luck, miss.'

She gave him a weak smile. He was such a kind hardworking little chipmunk, he deserved far better than what she'd given him. They all did.

Terry and Jackson and Pete gave her sympathetic smiles. 'Bad luck!' they said, their disappointment obvious in their subdued voices. With shoulders hunched and heads bent they went round to the back of the van and lowered the ramp.

'Mara!' shouted the Old Man. 'Come here!' Mara could hardly bear to look at him she was so ashamed. 'Bad luck,' he said gently. 'You did jolly well to begin with.'

They were all being so nice about it, that's what made it worse. Mara looked at the ground and bit her lip as tears pricked her eyes. She longed to be alone and to cry, but she couldn't cry, not in front of the team.

'Now don't get disheartened,' he said. 'I didn't expect you to win first time out, especially with such stiff competition. You'll do better next time, you wait and see.'

Mara shook her head. She never wanted to race or come near Brooklands again. The idea of subjecting herself to further humiliation was appalling, she wanted to go away and forget the whole thing.

The Old Man looked down at her bowed head. 'You don't mean you want to give up?'

She murmured, 'Yes, I do.'

'Why?'

'Because I'm not good enough.'

'Of course you're good enough, if you weren't I'd never have let you touch the Roadster in the first place.'

Mara raised her head to him. 'No I'm not, and I couldn't bear to do it again.'

As they reached the Paddock the loudspeaker announced that Mr Cobb, lapping at 111.42 mph, had won by a quarter of a mile, with Mr Meeson in second place and Mr Poppe in third. Mr Goutte and Mrs Rushton had both retired early. Mara had the added humiliation of hearing Herbert laugh and say to Sophia, 'Well, let's hope the Old Man's seen the light.' Then she had to put up with Alexander trying to appear genuinely upset for her, with Atalanta who clearly relished Mara's fall from stardom, and with Cynthia who seemed to think the whole thing was a big joke.

'You owe both Charles and me five pounds,' she giggled.

Only Damon, apart from the team, seemed to understand how miserable she was. 'Bad luck,' he said, giving her a sympathetic smile.

The other competitors came over and shook her by the hand and said, 'Bad luck,' and she congratulated Cobb. But as they walked away she felt like a little girl who had gone to a grown-ups' party. From the starting line came the loud revs of cars waiting to begin the next race, then shouts of 'They're off', and the distant roar of highly-tuned engines as the cars went up the Byfleet Banking. Listening to them Mara felt intensely lonely. She was no longer a part of that sound – or of this place.

A short while later the Old Man beckoned her over. 'The others are going in a minute, but you and I are going to stay and watch the last race.'

'I'd . . . I'd much rather go . . .' The last thing Mara wanted to do was to watch another race.

'Well you can't,' he said shortly. 'You'll have to come in the van with me, and I'm not leaving till I've seen Campbell race his Bugatti in the last race. And I expect you to watch it with me. Even if you don't intend to race again you might at least see it done properly.'

In that moment Mara hated her father-in-law. His implication was that having ruined their day the least she could do was to shut up and do what she was told. With her face burning from anger and shame she clambered into the front of the van and Smithy drove them all up to the top of the hill where they would have a perfect view of the track. They unloaded the Old Man and he sat in his wheelchair, just by the top of Test Hill. I wish he'd roll down it, thought Mara, and moved some ten or fifteen yards away from him in case she should be tempted to give him a push.

She was standing there wondering when the race would begin and how much longer this torture was to last, when someone walked up beside her. She turned, expecting it to be Smithy or Pete or one of the mechanics, but it was Jamie. 'Hello, Mara. I've been looking for you. I wanted to tell you how sorry I am about your race.'

Mara didn't know what to say to him. She was aware that her face was still streaked with dust and sweat and her overalls were oily and her hair matted and uncombed, whereas he was looking clean and smart, in grey flannel trousers, navy-blue blazer and a crisp white shirt, which seemed to emphasize her own grubby state. 'I didn't know you came down here,' she said eventually.

He smiled. 'It's the first time. Cynthia phoned me this morning to say you were racing.'

'But you didn't come with them?'

'No.' Their eyes met and Mara didn't have to ask him why. 'In fact, I have to leave in a minute and get back to the clinic.'

Mara nodded and looked at the ground. She didn't know what she felt for him, or even if she felt anything at all, but she kept thinking, why does he have to come when I'm down? Why can't he come when I'm up?

'You must let me know next time you race,' he said, 'I'd like to watch.'

Mara said nothing. She was very aware of him standing next to her, of his long legs in their grey flannels, of his body, of his shoulders, of his slightly tanned hands below his white cuffs.

'You're not going to give up, are you?' he asked gently.

She shrugged and swallowed hard. 'I don't know, I made such a fool of myself and I feel so ashamed in front of the rest of the team, they've all worked so hard and I let them down.' She looked up into his brilliant blue eyes which were full of sympathy and also something else: admiration. And suddenly she longed to throw her arms around him and bury her grubby face on his white-shirted chest, but then a little inner voice said, 'What are you doing telling him these things? He's rejected you twice. Remember how he mocked you.' 'My father-in-law's waiting for me,' she told him abruptly. 'Goodbye.' And before Jamie could say anything Mara turned and hurried back to the Old Man.

A few minutes later Mara looked over. Jamie had gone. It was as though she'd dreamed it.

The Old Man said nothing to Mara, not even when the race began. He followed it through his binoculars and she beside him with her eyes. Over the loudspeaker she heard the drivers' names: Eyston in the Halford, Goutte in the Salmson, Cobb in a Fiat, Kaye Don in a Sunbeam, and

Malcolm Campbell with a Bugatti, Vaguely she hoped Campbell would win because she liked his crinkled smile, but she wasn't that concerned, the cars were just little screaming dots which now meant nothing to her. Nevertheless, her eyes were drawn to them as they sped down the Railway Straight and into the Byfleet Banking, where she'd come adrift but where they didn't. Even from this distance she could see the way they cornered, not jerkily but smoothly and without losing momentum. They came round again and she watched, this time more closely. If only she could have done it like that!

Over the loudspeaker came, 'Eyston's in trouble and Cobb's retired with the Fiat, Goutte's still going strong in the Salmson but it's Campbell in the Bugatti and Don in the Sunbeam battling it out for first place. Yes it's one of those two.' Mara clenched her fists. Come on Campbell! 'As they come into the finishing straight it's Campbell leading by less than thirty yards. And it's Campbell the winner. Yes, it's Campbell in his Bugatti.' The spectators cheered. And Mara cheered too.

When the initial excitement had died down she turned to find the Old Man watching her. 'You have to get straight back on, just like you did when you fell off old Blackie,' he said.

Mara saw now that he'd engineered the whole thing: he'd made her feel she'd ruined his day so she'd not dared insist on leaving. And so she'd seen another race. 'But I still don't want to race again,' she said firmly. 'I'm sorry.'

When they returned to the Paddock the Old Man said, 'I want to go and have a word with Colonel Mackintosh. Mara, wheel me over please!' He pointed to a large man with pepper-and-salt greying fair hair and a military aspect, in the way he stood fiercely straight and in the way everything about him was orderly. He was wearing overalls like all the other drivers and he was standing next to a white Hispano-Suiza, the car which the Old Man had once said looked like a matinée idol.

Mara pushed the Old Man across the Paddock. It was the first time he'd ever asked her to do so, he usually asked one of the men. They hadn't gone more than a yard or two before, to her horror, she saw Yves come out of the clubhouse, see her, and turn in her direction. Frantically she gave him a don't-talk-to-me-now look and to her relief he walked straight past her.

'Tim Mackintosh was one of the best in his day, in our day,' the Old Man was saying. 'Mind you, he's a good ten years younger than me. And he's taught some of the best to get their speeds up. Has the knack of showing people where they go wrong. Ah, it's good to see him again. Mackintosh!' He waved and the big man looked over and waved back.

'I hoped I'd see you, Rushton,' he said, pumping the Old Man's hand. 'So many people around, one always ends up talking to those one doesn't want to talk to, and not to those one does.'

The Old Man introduced Mara. 'Perhaps you saw her race this morning,' he said.

Mara blushed. She hated to be reminded of her shame.

Colonel Mackintosh looked over at her. 'I did indeed, and I must say I've seldom seen such aggression in a woman driver.'

Mara said, 'But I did really badly.'

The Old Man patted her arm. 'She wants to give up.'

'Give up! My God, if most drivers had your talent, Mrs Rushton, they'd be down on their bended knees with gratitude. You're erratic, that's your trouble. You need to learn to drive smoothly, to ease the car through the

489

corners. You have to treat her as though she were a thoroughbred and not some hard-mouthed mule.' He paused, 'And you could learn. You've got what it takes.'

'Well I'm glad you think so,' said the Old Man, 'because I want you to teach her.'

Mara shook her head. 'No. Thank you.' She was standing in front of the white Hispano-Suiza and she stretched out her hand to touch the strange silver bird perched at the front of its bonnet, poised as if it were about to raise its wings and propel itself forward. The two men were watching her. 'What's this bird?' she asked.

Mackintosh smiled. 'Ah, that's *La Cicogna Volante*. It was the Emblem of George Guynemer, the great fighter-pilot, and his squadron. Their fighter-planes were powered by Hispano engines and Hispano-Suiza have been sticking his emblem on their cars ever since the war ended. Beautiful, isn't it?'

'Yes.' She stroked the bird's long neck. 'What does *La Cicogna Volante* mean?'

'The Flying Stork.'

Mara lowered her hand from the emblem and turned her face away so that she was looking down the track, to the distant Byfleet Banking, just as she'd looked that day when the Old Man had told her she couldn't race. Only now her eyes were fixed on the spot where she'd cornered too hard and sworn she'd never race again. 'I'll race again if you'll teach me,' she said. 'I'll race, and this time I'll win.'

490

Chapter 28

Colonel Timothy Mackintosh organized Mara's training with the precision of a military manoeuvre, leaving her little time to think about Jamie or anything else except racing. 'I can give you two weeks now,' he told her, 'and two weeks at the beginning of June, so I think we should decide on a race at the end of that two weeks and build up to it.'

'That's only two months away,' Mara protested weakly.

'So much the better. You have to get back on that track as soon as you stand a reasonable chance of not disgracing yourself. Now I think we should go for the Hatton-Gaunt Cup.' He looked at the Old Man, who nodded his approval.

'But if I do badly in that it'll be . . .'

'Worse than in another? Nonsense. Stop being such a pessimist, Mrs Rushton. Now, I want you down at the clubhouse by seven each morning, having had a decent cooked breakfast first. And when I drop you back to the Hand and Spear each evening I expect you to have your supper and go straight to bed, by ten at the latest. Understood?'

Mara nodded. She felt as though she had inadvertently applied to train as an athlete for the Olympics.

On the following morning she said goodbye to the Old Man, who was going home to the Dower House, and went down to the track. She arrived on the dot of seven to find Colonel Mackintosh's white Hispano-Suiza parked in front of the clubhouse and the colonel himself round the back, talking to Terry, Jackson and young Pete who were staying to look after the Roadster.

'Ah, good morning, Mrs Rushton,' he boomed. 'Lovely sunny day again. The men are going to service the car and you and I are going to spend today walking round the track. Have to learn every bump and groove. Come along!' He set off briskly in the direction of the Members' Banking. Mara gave the men a wry grin, and they hid their laughter under the bonnet of the Roadster as she scuttled after the colonel.

It took them all morning to walk the three and a quarter miles round the course, because every few yards the colonel would stop and say, 'Show me your correct position, Mrs Rushton.' Mara would take her stand on the track. 'No. Lower!' She'd move down a few paces. 'Now. Into the banking!' And she would run up the concrete curve as he shouted, 'Up! Up! Hold her steady!'

In the afternoon he took her up Test Hill, to the very place where the day before she had stood with Jamie. 'See how the Railway Straight swings round into the Byfleet Banking behind the aerodrome.' He pointed to the far end of the track. 'That's where you began to go wrong.' He went on, talking about how Campbell had taken the bend in the Bugatti and Mara tried to concentrate, but Jamie kept floating in and out of her thoughts. What was he doing now? Was he thinking about her? Why hadn't he come down with Cynthia? Because, as she had first thought, he didn't care for Cynthia's wafting muslin type? Or was it because to watch her drive was such an intensely personal thing that he had to do it alone?

'Understand?' bellowed Colonel Mackintosh.

'Yes.' She answered a little too quickly, as people do

when they haven't heard a word and are afraid of showing it.

On the following day Mara drove. It didn't take her long to discover that to be taught by the Old Man sitting in the van or by Smithy standing on the verge was one thing, to have this big fierce man sitting beside her shouting his criticisms in her ear as she went round the track was another. He didn't miss a single error.

And it was like that every day. On the track by seven, collapse into bed by ten.

One morning during the second week, by some miracle Mara arrived at the clubhouse before Colonel Mackintosh. It was a beautiful sunny morning and she sat down on the grass near the Paddock, closed her eyes, and thought of Jamie, picturing him in his navy-blue blazer and his grey flannels and his crisp white shirt. What is it about him that I can't forget him, she wondered. When he first came up to me I wasn't sure what I felt, if anything, I suppose I was too ashamed at the way I'd driven. But he made me feel both better and worse; I wanted to cry but I wasn't numb any more. She yawned and stretched out her legs, feeling the faint warmth of the morning sun on the insides of her thighs. And what is it about him that I still want him? He's the only man I've ever really . . . wanted. He's the only one I've wanted, both when he's with me and when he's not. She rolled over on her stomach. The trouble is, now he's been here once I'll always wonder if he'll come again. She picked a piece of grass and chewed it.

'Not had enough breakfast, Mrs Rushton?' Colonel Mackintosh bellowed at her.

Mara jumped up. Although he shouted at her, she sensed that in his gruff way he liked her. And she liked

493

him too. He made her strive to do her best, and when he praised her she glowed with pleasure.

At the end of a fortnight Colonel Mackintosh declared himself reasonably satisfied. 'Go home and practise what I've taught you,' he told Mara, 'and I'll see you down here, seven o'clock, June the first. Right?'

'Right.' Mara felt she ought to salute and stand to attention until he'd driven off, but she held out her hand and he pumped it hard, almost breaking the bones in her little finger.

When she arrived at the Dower House, Jenkins came out to the car and told her, 'I'm afraid your father-in-law isn't too well, Mrs Rushton. He felt poorly this morning and Doctor Phillips is with him now.'

'What's the matter with him?'

'Exhaustion I think. And he's had a touch of flu.'

'So it's not . . . serious?'

'Oh no, madam, he just needs a good rest.'

As soon as Doctor Phillips left Mara went to see the Old Man. 'How are you?' she asked, walking over to his bed and looking down at him. He was much thinner.

'I'm all right.' He passed a weather-beaten hand over his face. 'Now tell me about you. How did it go?'

Mara hesitated. 'Perhaps I should wait till you're better.'

'Rubbish! Nothing makes me feel so good as to hear about Brooklands and racing . . .' He chuckled. 'How did you get on with Mackintosh? Not got you saluting yet, has he?'

Mara laughed. 'Not yet, but almost.'

When Alexander came home he found them still talking and laughing. He kissed Mara on the cheek. 'Hello darling, nice to have you home. Hello Papa, how are you? Don't you think you should go to sleep?'

494

The Old Man looked at Mara as if to say, 'We can't talk in front of him anyhow, so I may as well go to sleep.'

Over dinner Mara asked Alexander, 'How's your chest? It seems to be better.'

'Yes it is.'

'Everything all right with the house? I haven't had time to see Mrs Kent yet.'

He nodded. 'Everything's fine.'

'And at the works?'

'All right.'

Isn't he going to ask me how I am or how I got on, Mara wondered. She cut herself a piece of brie and squashed it down on top of a biscuit and waited for him to speak, but he said nothing.

They went through into the drawing room to have their coffee and still Alexander said nothing.

Mara tried again. 'Have you ever met Colonel Mackintosh? I must say he's fairly terrifying.' She sat down on the sofa.

'Yes, I have.' Alexander was standing by the window. He turned to look at her then began pacing up and down in front of her.

It was obvious to Mara that he had something to say, and for a wild moment she wondered if he'd found another woman and wanted a divorce and didn't know how to tell her. 'What is the matter?' she asked him.

'Nothing.'

She bit back her irritation. 'Come on, tell me!'

He stopped dead in front of her and looked down into her eyes. 'When you were at Brooklands you said you weren't going to race any more.'

'That was straight after the race.'

'But I heard you say you wouldn't do it any more.'

495

'And later your father and Colonel Mackintosh persuaded me to try again. I only said I wouldn't race again because I was ashamed,' she explained. 'I thought I wasn't good enough.'

Alexander walked over to the window. 'I came back here thinking you wanted to give up.'

Mara clenched her fists into the soft yellow silk of her skirt. 'Well, I'm sorry if you're disappointed.'

He parted the curtains and looked out at the dark garden and said, 'I'd never have let you do it in the first place if I'd known it was going to go on and on like this.'

Mara ground her teeth in anger. Everywhere else she was a person in her own right with full control over what she did and said. At Brooklands, even though she'd disgraced herself, she was considered brave merely for having driven. At the cottage she and Elenora weren't always in agreement but they respected each other's right to differ. Jamie had never told her she mustn't do things because he was afraid they might take her out of his level, he'd wanted her to do things so that she would find her own highest level. With the Old Man she said what she thought, his only criterion being that she should believe in what she was doing. But with Alexander, she had to wheedle every ounce of freedom, bargaining for it as though it were not hers by right but something he generously allowed her, as a child might be allowed a chocolate after lunch on Sundays. 'I'm not your prisoner,' she snapped at him, 'and I'm fed up with you telling me you'll let me do this but won't let me do that. If I'm good enough to race, then I'm going to do it for as long as I want to, and if you don't like me being down at Brooklands then perhaps you should try to make me feel a bit more welcome when I come home.' She stood up and without looking at him marched straight upstairs to the spare bedroom.

It was the first time Mara had ever shouted at Alexander and she felt guilty for having hurt him. What she'd said to him was true, but because she'd bottled it up for so long it had come out far too viciously. But he drove me to it, she told herself as she slipped into bed. Oh God, if only I was back at Brooklands!

Mara was just drifting off into a guilt-ridden sleep when there was a soft tap on the door. 'Come in,' she murmured, half opening her eyes.

The door opened and Alexander stood dejectedly on the threshold. 'I'm terribly sorry . . . very sorry,' he stammered, 'I didn't mean to . . . upset you.'

Mara said, 'I'm sorry too. I didn't mean to shout at you.'

He hesitated, swaying from foot to foot, then he plucked up courage and came over to the bed. 'Goodnight, darling.' Tentatively he bent to kiss her on the cheek. 'Are you sure you . . . er . . . want to sleep in here? I'm quite well now.'

Mara felt sorry for him but she really didn't want to share a bed with him that night. 'I'll stay here now,' she said as kindly as possible, 'I'm all nice and warm.'

'And I expect you're tired.' He said it hopefully, wanting her to agree, to give him an acceptable reason for her outburst.

Oh, what's the point, thought Mara, and she said, 'I am quite tired. Goodnight.'

The next day Alexander said, 'Feeling better, darling? Had a good sleep?'

Mara said, 'Yes, thank you.'

That was the end of it as far as he was concerned.

But it wasn't the end of it for Mara. Now she had put

into words her pent-up frustration, she wondered why on earth she'd kept quiet for so long. The situation, she saw, was partly her own fault: she should never have let him think he held the key to her freedom. What struck her as odd was that although he'd been unhappy when she'd been gadding around in London he'd never tried to stop her. She remembered how she'd once thought he couldn't help her because he didn't know she wanted anything, and she couldn't tell him because she didn't know what she wanted. But now she did know. And he didn't want to help her. He wanted to stop her.

The Roadster was being overhauled, giving Mara a week's break from driving.

She longed to see Elenora but the Old Man was still unwell and she felt she couldn't disappear all afternoon, so she sat in his room and talked to him or wandered round the garden. The roses she'd planted by the study had really come into their own at last, perhaps due to the fertilizer recommended by Sophia, and Mara buried her face in their soft red petals. But they're still not quite as good as the ones in Koblenz, she decided. Almost. But not quite.

There were plenty of little jobs which had accumulated whilst Mara had been away: letters and invitations on her desk: from Lady Henrietta asking if she was still coming to London for the season, from Caroline who'd had another baby, from Alison asking Mara and Alexander to dinner. They all had to be answered. There was also a polite note from Madame Cecile telling Mara that she had some wonderful new creations.

'Madame Cecile will think I've taken my custom elsewhere,' Mara told Rachel as they went through her summer wardrobe. 'I only ordered two dresses last winter and I really can't be bothered to think about clothes at the moment. I have more than enough.' She shut the wardrobe door and went down to the kitchen, where Mrs Kent informed her that Prince hadn't eaten his breakfast. 'Never known 'im off 'is feed before. Wouldn't even look at it.'

Mara found Prince lying on a rug in the study. He looked up as she came in, wagging his tail so that it thump-thumped on the floor. 'Poor old Prince.' She felt his nose – it was cold – then rubbed his hair up the wrong way while he wriggled in ecstasy. There didn't seem much the matter with him.

On the fourth day, a Saturday, the Old Man was much better and Mara told him she was going to ride over to the cottage and see Elenora. 'I haven't seen her for ages, and I haven't ridden either. I'll ask Lord to bring Mahogany up from the field. The exercise will do her good.'

As she went out of the room he said, 'Give my regards to Mrs Harris.'

Elenora was alone and painting and she came running to the door, paintbrush in hand, and hugged Mara. 'Come in and tell me all about the race. I've been longing to see you.'

Mara told her about the race, ending with, 'It was ghastly. There I was, stuck across the track.' She stood in the middle of the room and demonstrated how she had sat stranded in the Roadster. 'I felt such a fool, Elenora, I just wanted to crawl away and cry.'

'Weren't you frightened?'

'I was beyond fear.'

'So you're not going to do it again?'

'Oh yes I am.' She told Elenora about Colonel Mackintosh. 'Why did you think I was going to stop?'

Elenora passed a cigarette to Mara and lit one for

herself. 'Because a friend of yours was here just after the race and he'd seen you there and said he thought you wanted to give up.'

'Who was that?'

'Jamie Turner.'

'Jamie! What was he doing here?'

'Sarah brought him here for lunch, they were on their way to Oxford.' Elenora hesitated. 'You never told me you knew him in Germany.'

Mara drew on her cigarette to calm herself. 'Oh, didn't I? I thought I had.' She picked up her coffee and casually took a sip. She longed to ask Elenora all about Jamie's visit, what he'd said, what he'd done, what they'd eaten, and if there was anything between him and Sarah. But she didn't. 'My father-in-law sent his regards,' she said eventually.

Elenora got up and went over to the canvas on the easel, picked up the paintbrush from where she'd left it on the window-sill, and began adding colour to the already colourful picture. 'How is he?' she asked. 'I heard he wasn't well.'

'He's better. I would have come to see you before but I didn't like to when he wasn't well. He's had a sort of flu, I think.'

'And how's Alexander?'

Mara sighed. 'We had a bit of a row the night I came home. Well, it wasn't really a row, I shouted at him.' She told Elenora what had happened. 'The odd thing is, although he didn't like it when I was gadding around in London, and sometimes I was away for two or three months, he never tried to stop me. I used to fill the house with people, which he hated, but he never told me not to. You'd have thought if he was going to complain, he'd have done so then. But, oh no, he tries to stop me from doing the one thing I want to do.'

'Perhaps he's afraid you're going to kill yourself. As one who can't even bear to watch a race, I find that understandable.'

'Yes, he is afraid, but I'm beginning to think it's not so much he's afraid I'll kill myself as that I'll be beyond his control.' Mara paused and reflected. 'That's a horrible thing for me to say, because he does love me, I know he does. If anything he loves me too much. He lets me get away with murder. But that's it. *Lets me!* I don't want him to *let* me do things, I want him to *want* me to do them.'

'The trouble is,' said Elenora, 'he hasn't developed and you have.'

Mara went over to the window and looked out. It was drizzling and the garden had a soft, misty quality. 'The other thing is . . . oh, God, moan, moan, moan.'

Elenora laughed. 'Moan away!'

'He wants to . . . umm . . . start a family. That was one of the conditions of letting me race.' She picked up the lump of black rock and passed it slowly from one hand to the other. 'I suppose you might say we're . . . trying, though we're not really, but you know what I mean. Luckily I'm not pregnant yet.'

'Don't you want children?'

'I don't know.' Mara sighed. 'It's not that I don't want them, it's just that . . . I don't feel we're enough of a couple.'

Elenora nodded and carried on painting.

Moaning about Alexander had driven Jamie temporarily from Mara's mind, but now she longed to get back to his visit. 'What were Jamie and Sarah going to do in Oxford?'

'They were going to hear William Beveridge speak.'

'Who's he?'

'Ignoramus! He's head of the London School of Economics.'

'What Alexander calls one of those damned socialists?'

'Oddly enough I believe he doesn't belong to any particular party, at least that's what Jamie says. But they weren't going to hear him talk about politics, they were going to hear him talk about how to get rid of poverty and disease. Free hospitals. Free doctors. Subjects very dear to Jamie's heart, as I expect you know.'

Mara nodded. She wished she'd been there when Jamie had talked about this man Beveridge, she hated to think of him sharing his innermost thoughts, what was dear to his heart, with others, even with Elenora, but particularly with Sarah. She wished too that she could have gone with him to hear Beveridge speak. It wouldn't have mattered if she hadn't understood a word, just to be there, sharing something which Jamie cared about. She remembered how, in the car, he'd started to explain what he was trying to do then stopped, and said, 'You wouldn't understand,' and she thought, I bet he doesn't say that to Sarah.

The sun had come out by the time Mara left the cottage and rode into the woods, Mahogany's hooves swishing through the wet grass in which raindrops lay like trapped diamonds in the inner curve of each blade. They were ambling along, Mahogany snatching occasional mouthfuls of grass and munching them against her jangling bit, Mara deep in her thoughts about Jamie, when she noticed two figures half hidden by a tree trunk some little way ahead of her. They were standing very still and it was obvious they were hoping she wouldn't see them. Thinking they must be from the village, she pretended she

502

hadn't noticed them. But as she passed their tree trunk she decided that if they knew they'd been seen, they would be less likely to come back, so she glanced round at them. And she found herself looking straight at Atalanta and Pete Smithy. They were standing side by side, holding hands, and they were looking up at her with a mixture of fear and bravado. Mara reined in her horse.

Atalanta was the first to speak. 'I suppose you're going to tell them.' She glared mutinously up at Mara and shook back her dark curls which bore all the signs of having recently been ruffled.

Except for Herbert, there was no one Mara wanted less in her woods than Atalanta. This place was sacred to the cottage and to her thoughts. She wouldn't have minded finding Damon, he was a part of her thought world. But Atalanta! She looked at Pete and he gave her a nervous smile, although he didn't release Atalanta's hand. 'Of course I'm not going to tell anyone,' she said crossly. 'You're lucky I found you. It might have been someone else.' She nearly added, 'Don't you think you're a bit young for this sort of thing?' when she remembered that Atalanta was nearly sixteen and Pete was about seventeen, and that she had been seventeen when she'd met Jamie.

Pete's face relaxed but Atalanta was still wary. They stood together like two naughty children waiting for Mara to tell them off. Suddenly Mara felt sorry for them, even for Atalanta, for in their faces she saw the innocent hope, the conviction that nothing would part them, which she had once known with Jamie, and she said, 'Why don't you come back and have tea at the Dower House? I'll run you home later.'

Atalanta said, 'What? Both of us?'

'Yes.'

She looked at Pete but he shook his head. 'It's very kind of you, miss . . . er . . . madam, but I 'ave to be getting 'ome. I was just about to take Lani over to the other side of the wood so she could walk back to the Park.'

Mara noticed the way he said Lani, a nickname for Atalanta she'd never heard before, and she saw that he said it naturally as though he had often used it. 'Would you like to come, Atalanta?' she asked. 'Alexander's gone to Banbury and your grandfather's in bed. You can pretend you came over to see him, it'll look less obvious than if you go creeping out of the woods.'

'I've done it before and I haven't been caught,' said Atalanta. 'But all right. I'll come to the Dower House. Only I mustn't be long, I have to take the six o'clock train back to school.'

'Catch me up!' said Mara, turning and urging her horse forward so as to give them a few moments alone. 'I'll see you at the works tomorrow, Pete.'

'Yes, miss. And thank you, miss.'

Atalanta caught up with Mara where the path divided, the left-hand fork leading to the gate and the field above the Dower House. 'I suppose you think it's wrong because Pete's . . . working-class,' she began, 'and I suppose you think we're too young. Well, we're not. We love each other and no one's going to separate us.'

Mara looked down at the girl's flushed face. 'You are a bit young, that's true, but as for the bit about Pete being working-class, so is your grandfather, and look at him.'

'Exactly, that's what we say.' She paused. 'But I'm surprised you think it doesn't matter.'

'Why?'

'Because . . . oh, I don't know.'

They went down the field in silence and when they

504

reached the house Mara handed her horse to Lord and asked Jenkins how the Old Man was.

'He's asleep, madam,' replied the butler.

'What a pity! Miss Atalanta's come over to see him, but I think perhaps we won't wake him. Could you bring us tea in the drawing room? And, Jenkins, please phone the works and ask Owen to collect Miss Atalanta in half an hour and take her back to the Park.'

Jenkins eyed Mara's jodhpurs. 'Will you change for tea, madam?'

'No.' She ushered Atalanta through into the drawing room.

Atalanta walked over to the long windows while Mara sat down on the sofa. 'I don't know why you're helping us but it's kind of you,' she said. 'I really thought you'd go and tell them.'

Mara leaned back into the sofa. 'Surely you didn't think I'd tell your father.'

Atalanta thought for a moment. Then she started to laugh. 'No, of course you wouldn't, you never even speak to each other.' She went to the sofa and sat down next to Mara. 'As soon as I'm twenty-one Pete and I are going to be married. I come into some money on my twenty-first birthday and we're going to buy a garage with it.' She smiled happily. 'And we're going to have . . . lots of children.' She blushed and giggled. 'And no one's going to come between us. Ever.'

Mara smiled. It was all a beautiful idea.

Atalanta demanded, 'You don't think it'll work, do you?'

'I didn't say that.'

'You married when you were very young.'

Mara nodded. 'I know I did.'

505

'But you weren't in love with Alexander like I am with Pete, were you?'

Mara shrugged.

'I shouldn't have asked you that.' Atalanta tentatively touched her arm. 'I'm sorry . . .'

After Atalanta had left Mara wandered round the garden thinking about them. It was strange to find, after all these years of not liking Atalanta, that she was very likable. In fact, she was not unlike herself in many ways. Perhaps if she hadn't been so . . . jealous of me, we'd always have got on well, thought Mara. She pondered this, and Atalanta and Pete. She was pleased for them, but she couldn't help being a bit envious of their happiness.

Mara's relationship with Alexander was still strained on her part. She hadn't moved back into the main bedroom, telling him, 'I sleep better alone.' It wasn't only that she didn't want to share a bed with him, it was that she wanted to be able to think of Jamie without interruptions.

Alexander accepted Mara's decision in silence. He saw it as part of whatever it was which had caused her outburst, female inconsistencies.

On the last afternoon before the Roadster was ready for Mara to drive, she and the Old Man were sitting under the oak tree when Mrs Kent came hurrying out of the house. 'There's something the matter with Prince, madam,' she cried.

Mara ran into the house. The big black dog was lying on the floor just outside the kitchen, in the exact spot where he had so often sat and watched hopefully as meals were prepared. She bent down and pulled back one of his eyelids. The brown pupil, once so shiny, was dull and cloudy. 'I think he's dead,' she said, 'I'd better telephone my husband.'

Alexander was heartbroken. 'I can't believe it,' he told Mara as they watched the gardeners carry Prince to his grave at the bottom of the garden. 'I know he was getting on but . . .' He swallowed hard.

Mara put her arms round him. 'Poor Prince, but I'm sure he'll soon find the great kitchen in the sky.'

He smiled gratefully. 'Yes, I expect he will.'

That night, out of pity, Mara slept in the main bedroom and when Alexander turned to her and kissed her she moved close to him and comforted him, and they made love, but on her side there was only pity.

Mara drove the Roadster every day, trying to put into practice what Colonel Mackintosh had taught her. To some extent she succeeded, but the works track was not the challenge of Brooklands. Nevertheless she felt she'd learned a lot from the colonel. Smithy thought so too. 'Now you really do stand a chance,' he told her one morning, 'might even put a shilling on you meself.'

The race was looming nearer and Mara faced it with a mixture of dread and anticipation. She was determined to do well this time, she felt much more confident about her driving, it was only when she remembered the shame of being stranded across the track that she asked herself why she was doing it.

At the end of May, on the day before she was due to leave for Brooklands, she and Rachel were upstairs deciding what she would take with her when Jenkins brought her a letter. It was from Elenora. I don't know why she doesn't get a phone installed, thought Mara, opening it. Inside were just five lines:

507

Jamie is coming to stay tonight. He's going to a dinner in Oxford so he won't be arriving till after ten. Come over then or before if you can. If not, good luck. I'm not coming to Brooklands because I can't bear the noise! But I'll be thinking of you. Love, Elenora.

For the rest of the day Mara planned and schemed how she could go to the cottage. Her first idea was to tell Alexander, but she rejected it because he would be mortified if she went off on her last night, and she certainly didn't intend to take him with her. Her next plan was to creep out and take the car, but that was no good; someone would hear the engine start up and raise the alarm. Dinner was agonizing. The Old Man talked of Brooklands. Alexander smiled at her. Mara still had no plan. She sat at the end of the table, twisting her hands in her napkin, frantic to get to the cottage, terrified in case she missed this chance of seeing Jamie.

After dinner they had coffee in the drawing room. Mara was so restless she couldn't bear to sit down. It was after nine. In an hour Jamie would be there. She went over to the window and pulled back the curtains and looked out on the garden. It was bathed in bright white moonlight. 'I really think I must go to bed,' she said, 'I'm very tired and I have a long drive tomorrow.'

To her relief the Old Man agreed. 'I think I'll turn in too. Alexander, push me to the bottom of the stairs, will you, and give me a hand up.'

Mara followed the slow procession of the wheelchair out of the room to the bottom of the stairs. There she had to wait while Alexander called down the nurse and the two of them half carried the Old Man up. Another wheelchair was waiting for him at the top. 'A pity there's no room for me to sleep downstairs,' he said. 'Save you all a lot of bother. Well, goodnight Mara, come and say goodbye to me in the morning. And remember when you get to the Hand and Spear, tell them we'll all be down the night before the race.'

Mara bent to kiss him on the cheek and as she did so she heard the hall clock strike nine-thirty.

Outside their respective bedrooms Alexander turned to her. 'I suppose you . . . er . . .'

She reached up and kissed him. 'I'm so tired. I must get a good night.'

Dejectedly he went into the main bedroom and closed the door. Mara went into her room, pulled off her dress, took her jodhpurs and a sweater from her wardrobe and put them on, then lay on top of her bed listening to Alexander's heavy tread as he moved between the bedroom and his dressing room. Eventually she heard him go into the bathroom, close the door, water running, door open, back across bedroom, bed groaning as he climbed into it. Impatiently she waited till she heard the muffled sound of the hall clock strike ten then, carrying her riding boots, she opened the door and crept downstairs through the silent house to the study. There she opened a window and slithered out of it, flinching as her bare foot came down on a rose thorn.

Once outside, Mara closed the window to within an inch, jamming it with a twig so it could not shut completely. Then she pulled on her boots and made her way round the house to the tackroom, trying to ignore the rustling of leaves, which in the daytime she wouldn't have noticed, but which by night were magnified into unseen persons creeping after her. She found the key on the ledge above the door. The well-oiled door seemed to creak on purpose as she opened it.

The tackroom was dark and Mara had to feel her way along the wall until she came to the hook where Lord

509

kept Mahogany's bridle. Carefully she lifted it down. The saddles were on a rack on the other side of the room. I'll never be able to find the right one she decided, and went back out of the tackroom, locking the door behind her.

Mahogany, Nutcracker and one of Alexander's horses were in the field on the other side of the garden. When she reached it she could not see the horses, for although the centre of the field was so brightly lit by the moon that she could see each blade of grass, there were big trees on each side casting concealing shadows. Mara whispered, 'Mahogany!' Nothing happened. She tried again a little louder. This time three shapes detached themselves from the shadows like great four-legged ghosts. They came right up to Mara and nuzzled at her.

Mara slipped the bridle over Mahogany's head and led her to the gate. Nutcracker followed. At the gate Mara wasted precious minutes trying to slip Mahogany through without the other two. 'Go away!' she hissed at them. 'Go away!' Eventually she succeeded in shutting them in and, with the help of the gate, scrambled up on to Mahogany's bare back and set off, keeping on the grass verge so that the clip-clopping of hooves would not go echoing back to the Dower House.

There was something very exciting and rather frightening about the countryside at night: the rustlings of unseen little animals: the whisper of the hedgerows: the occasional cry of a bird. And there was something about the white light of the moon and the dark shapes, unearthly, which gave her the feeling of being the only person alive on earth; as if she'd woken up to find everyone else had been wiped out by a disaster.

Although Mara was impatient to see Jamie she did not dare go faster than a trot in case Mahogany stumbled, so it took her a good twenty minutes. But at last she saw the black shapes of the trees and the lights twinkling through them. At the garden gate she dismounted and tried to tidy her hair with her fingers, wishing she had brought a comb, and then, still leading the horse, she walked up the path to the door and knocked. Footsteps approached her from the other side of it. Mara took a deep breath and dug her fingernails into her hand. The door opened and silhouetted against the light stood Jamie in a white evening shirt, open at the neck and without the bow tie, and a pair of black evening trousers. He looked at Mara, then beyond her to Mahogany's big brown inquisitive eyes, and he smiled his beautiful mischievous smile. 'Paul Revere,' he said, his voice breaking out into laughter, 'don't tell me the British are coming again!'

Elenora appeared behind him. 'What's all this rubbish?'

Jamie winked at Mara. 'How ignorant the English are! "Listen my children, and you shall hear of the midnight ride of Paul Revere." I won a prize at school for reciting it.'

'Take no notice of him,' Elenora said to Mara, laughing, 'he's been like this all evening. Tie up the trusty steed and come on in.'

Mara tied Mahogany to the garden seat and Jamie stood aside to let her pass before following her through into the studio. She hadn't yet said a word, she could think of nothing to say, but she was terribly aware of Jamie walking behind her. She walked into the centre of the room, her long legs swinging in her tight cream jodhpurs and the highly polished tan of her boots gleaming in the light at each step.

'Why didn't you come by car?' he asked, sitting down at one end of the pine table.

Mara shrugged and lifted her hand to push back the tawny tips of her untidy hair.

'Doesn't . . . Alexander know you're here?'

'No.' She didn't want to talk about Alexander with Jamie, she didn't want him to remind her that she was tied to another life to which, within an hour, she would have to return.

'But surely he . . . er . . . heard you leave?'

'No, he didn't.' Mara glanced at Elenora who was making coffee by the sink and their eyes met in understanding. A few moments later she looked at Jamie and saw he too had understood that she and Alexander didn't share a bedroom. She sat down at the other end of the table, sideways to it, stretching her legs out and crossing her feet at the ankles and leaning her elbow on the end of the table, so she was looking towards the room and Elenora, who was putting the pottery mugs on a tray. In this way she didn't have to look at Jamie. He wasn't looking at her either. But there was between them that same little dance which she and Alexander did around each other's half-dressed state, only this wasn't for something as superficial as a bare breast or a naked thigh. It was a dance along the undercurrent of hostile sexuality between two people who once cared deeply for each other but are unsure if that chapter has ended; for themselves; for the other person.

To break the tension Mara asked him, 'Did you have a good dinner?'

'Very.' He looked at Mara curiously as if he were surprised she could remember or think about anything which didn't directly concern herself. 'But it wasn't as interesting as when we went to hear Beveridge speak, that was fascinating for me. I wrote to him afterwards to say I agreed with all he said.' He smiled in the embarrassed way people do when they admit they have written to someone famous.

'How did you persuade them?'

'I managed.' Mara's face closed in as she remembered Alexander's condition.

Jamie saw that she wanted to pull down the shutters on whatever had happened, and he said, 'I admire you for racing. I admire your courage and your tenacity.'

'You do?' His praise meant more to her than that of anyone. He was all she wanted. She didn't care if what she felt or if what she were about to do were wrong in the eyes of others, nothing she could ever feel or do with Jamie was wrong. She put her hand on his arm and moved her fingers slowly up and down against the sleeve of his shirt.

He laid his hand on hers in acceptance of what they were to each other. 'I'm glad I've seen you here,' he said, 'because when I'm not with you I'll be able to think of you in this cottage, just as you are now, with your big grey eyes looking up at me and the light shining on your ruffled hair.' He linked his fingers through hers. 'If only you hadn't done it, Stork.'

Mara felt the tears prick her eyes but she didn't brush them away.

'And when I'm in America,' he went on, 'I'll be able to read about your races' – he squeezed her fingers – 'and your wins.'

'When are you going back to America?' Mara asked in a small voice.

'Next Christmas. But I'll probably be back after a year.'

Mara pulled her hand away from his and walked over to the table and picked at the grain in the wood. She saw that whatever happened between them that night, or any other night, he would still go and she would be left behind. Suddenly, she wished he had not come to the cottage, he had invaded her oasis, the one place where she had been free from him and from Alexander. Now he

515

had permeated this place, as he had permeated the hill at Brooklands and the London season of the previous year. She watched him pick up the lump of black rock. He had permeated that too. Never again would she be able to come here without seeing Jamie in every angle of the room. She was furious with him for the way he was surrounding her and intruding on her life, pushing her back from all her outlets, Brooklands, London, the cottage, and imprisoning her in the Dower House: the only place where he had never been. If he didn't want her enough to take her with him, then why couldn't he leave her territories alone?

'I must go,' she said abruptly, and without waiting for him to speak she marched out of the room, through the hall, and out into the garden to Mahogany.

Jamie followed her. 'Do you want a leg up?' he asked from the doorway.

'No.' Mara took a running jump and, for the first time in her life, managed to get up unaided on to her horse. It gave her immense satisfaction to do so in front of Jamie. She looked down to where he stood and had she had a whip she would have lashed him with it, right across his face, for having made her want him only so that he might reject her once again.

Jamie said, 'Perhaps one day you and I will be friends. It's sad that we don't seem able to be, after all that's happened between us. I feel we should be, because our lives run on the strangest of parallel lines. Who would ever have thought we could know each other in Germany and then, by chance, meet again in the East End of London? And then again here because, by chance, Sarah knows Elenora.' He paused. 'But every time our parallel lines meet we seem unable to run smoothly, we always crash.'

'Is it surprising?' demanded Mara. 'At the clinic both times you told me to go away.'

'You were different then.'

'That's beside the point, you still told me to go away.'

'I didn't tell you to go away tonight.' He took a step towards her, coming out of the shadow of the doorway and into the full light of the moon, which picked up his features, reminding Mara – as it had the first time she'd met him – of an eagle about to attack its prey.

She turned Mahogany round to face the gate.

'That's what I mean about us not being friends.'

'What?'.

'That the only time you come running is when you've nothing else in your life.'

Mara was furious. He was wildly unjust. Hadn't she crept out of the Dower House and ridden through the night to see him? And wouldn't she have willingly made love to him on the floor of Elenora's studio had he not mentioned America? She was leaving only because she had seen the inevitable unhappiness ahead of her, but she'd no intention of telling Jamie that. Let him think she didn't need him any more, it would do him good. She snapped, 'You've never stopped telling me I ought to do something with my life, and now I am you don't like it.'

'That's ridiculous!'

'Is it? Oh no, Jamie, you're sorry I'm not lying at your feet for you to trample on as usual. Well, I don't need you now. And if I ever do need any help, I can assure you you'll be the last person I'll come to.' She dug her heels into Mahogany's sides and the horse shot forward down the path. 'Come on!' she shouted.

They jumped the gate, horse and rider black against the moonlight, Mara too angry to care about the danger, Jamie too angry to try to stop her.

517

Chapter 29

Two days later Mara was back in training with Colonel Mackintosh, and once again he gave her no time to think of anything but racing. Even when she went to bed, in that moment between snuggling down under the bedclothes and falling asleep, she did little more than call up Jamie's face before she was asleep. And as the race drew nearer, frankly, she didn't want to think of anything but racing. Not of the spectators or the other drivers, but of how she would drive in it: of her position on the bankings, of how she would ease the Roadster round each bend and accelerate out of it, and, of course, of how she would put her foot down flat on the accelerator as she sped down the Finishing Straight. 'If I don't do well this time,' she told herself, 'I never will.'

On the evening before the race, as Colonel Mackintosh drove her back to the Hand and Spear, he said, 'My dear Mrs Rushton, I do hope you've found our lessons useful.'

'Oh yes, I can't thank you enough. If I don't disgrace myself it will be entirely thanks to you.'

'Now don't think about disgracing yourself, think about winning!'

Mara smiled. He was a gruff and kindly old bear. This time tomorrow it'll all be over, she thought, this time tomorrow I'll know. 'Ah, they've arrived,' she pointed to the two Rushton-Gaunt saloons parked on the forecourt. 'You will come in, won't you? I know my father-in-law would like to see you.'

He stopped the car. 'I won't.' He leaned towards her,

lowering his voice. 'Can't stand your brother-in-law. I had a row with him in nineteen-thirteen and swore I'd never speak to him again. Can you imagine it, my dear! There was dear old Samuel Rushton heading down the Finishing Straight, leading the field by three hundred yards, and that oaf was standing outside the clubhouse, glass of champagne in hand, complaining about the cost of racing. I can tell you, I gave him a piece of my mind.'

Mara laughed. 'I wish I'd been there.'

He held out his hand to her. 'Good luck, my dear.'

'But won't I see you in the morning?'

'Yes, but it won't be the same, will it? There'll be other people around.'

She took his hand. 'I know what you mean,' and she leaned towards him and kissed his leathery cheek. 'Thank you. Thank you for everything.'

'It's been a pleasure,' he said with gruff emotion. 'Haven't enjoyed myself so much for a long time.'

Mara left the car and watched him drive away, the beautiful white Hispano-Suiza and its flying stork emblem twisting in and out of the big rough tree trunks.

She found Alexander and the Old Man sitting at a table in the otherwise deserted tea room at the back of the hotel. Alexander smiled and stood up when he saw her. 'Hello darling.' He kissed her on the cheek. 'Finished for the day?'

'Yes.' She sat down and stretched out her hand to the Old Man.

He took it. 'Everything all right?'

'Yes, thanks. At least I hope so.'

'Mackintosh not come in with you?'

'No, he was . . . in a hurry.' She looked round the deserted tea room. 'Aren't the others here?'

Alexander said, 'Sophia wasn't well enough to come,

you know how tired she gets. but Herbert's here. He's playing bowls.'

'What about the twins?'

Alexander frowned. 'Damon's in the middle of doing exams and Herbert didn't feel he should take time off.'

Mara said, 'I know, I didn't expect him to come.' She hesitated. Atalanta's school was only about twenty miles from Brooklands and she had meant to tell the Old Man before she left the Dower House that she would like her to come. But Jamie had driven everything from her mind. 'Couldn't Atalanta come?' she asked.

They both looked surprised, and Alexander said tentatively, 'We . . . er . . . thought you might find her annoying, you usually do, but of course if you don't mind we could easily fetch her in the morning.'

Mara thought of Atalanta and Pete standing side by side and holding hands. 'I'd like her to come. We got on very well last time I saw her' – she looked at the Old Man – 'you remember I told you she came to see you when you were ill but you were asleep so she stayed and had tea with me.'

The Old Man smiled. 'Then she must come.' He passed his hand over his forehead. 'This muggy damp weather makes me feel so tired.'

Alexander and Mara studied him with concern. 'Are you all right?' she asked. 'You look very pale.'

'I'm fine but I think I'll dine early. You should too. We'll have a quiet supper together and the other two can have dinner later.'

Alexander smiled at Mara. 'I'll come and talk to you whilst you're eating. In any case, darling, Herbert and I are sharing a room. The hotel's so full it was either that, or moving you in with me and Herbert into your room.' He touched her arm. 'I thought you'd rather stay where you were and have a good night's sleep in the bed you're used to.'

Mara nodded gratefully. At times like this she wished the fondness she had for Alexander could suddenly expand to include the furious passion she felt for Jamie. How much easier her life would be if it were Alexander, her kind, considerate legal partner, whom she wanted. If only he were not afraid of losing me emotionally, she thought, perhaps he would not need to hem me in physically. But I can't change Alexander, I've tried and it didn't work. And I can't forget Jamie however much I tell myself I want to.

After their supper Mara and the Old Man went straight upstairs to bed. They paused for a moment on the landing outside his room. 'Good luck tomorrow,' he said, giving her a tired smile.

Mara bent to kiss him on the cheek. 'I hope you feel better.'

'I will.'

She set off along the corridor to her room as the Old Man's nurse steered his wheelchair through the doorway of his bedroom. 'Mara!' he called.

'Yes.' She started back towards him.

'I just wanted to tell you that if I can't have you as my son I'm glad to have you for my daughter-in-law.'

She smiled down at him through the gloomy electric light. It was the greatest compliment he could have paid her.

Smithy came to collect Mara in the morning just as he had for her first race. 'There's a big crowd 'ere today, miss, and there's already five up on the board for the 'atton-Gaunt, Mrs Nicholls among them.'

'Has she arrived yet?' Mara asked anxiously.

521

'She arrived last night just after you'd left. But you've nothing to worry about, miss, you just do as the colonel's taught you.'

They went through the tunnel and on to the course. It was still quite early, the first race didn't start for another hour but, as Smithy had said, there was a big crowd. Down in the Paddock and round by the workshops, behind the clubhouse, drivers and their mechanics were frantically tuning engines, up on the hill in the public enclosure people were staking their claim to the terraced seats, inside the clubhouse Ebby and the other officials were busy with the last details of organization, and on the clubhouse balcony the members of the press were about to begin a hard day's drinking: the long black nostril of the Pathé News camera looked gloomily down towards the Byfleet Banking.

But it was the bright young things, the crowd she'd known in London, who made Mara feel most nervous. They kept rushing up to her. 'Darling, you look too too divine in your overalls, you will wear them at the *thé dansant*, you simply must!' The *thé dansant*, held in the late afternoon in the Members' Room on top of the Hill, was the last thing Mara was interested in. She tried to smile but felt completely detached from these people, the pretty Cynthia-type girls in their muslin dresses who fluttered between the men like a lot of brightly-coloured butterflies looking for a congenial perch, the men in their crisp blazers and inevitable Oxford bags, grey flannel and trailing in the dust. To avoid them Mara joined Smithy and the mechanics at the Roadster, which was parked near the workshops behind the clubhouse, and she hung around as they muttered inside the bonnet. There was nothing she could do to help but she felt safer here, she was with her team.

'Ah, here you are,' said Colonel Mackintosh, appearing from behind one of the workshops. He looked up at the sky. 'A bit overcast but they say it'll clear up by this afternoon. Not nervous, are you?'

Mara smiled weakly. 'A bit.'

'Nothing to worry about. Just remember the others will be equally nervous.'

'Even Mrs Nicholls?'

'Everyone gets nervous. I see there are two other women in your race. Mrs Nicholls and a newcomer. Three women in one race! Oh, well, I suppose it had to happen sooner or later.' He gave her a gruff smile. 'You and this other woman are twenty to one but don't let that worry you.'

Mara asked, 'Who's the favourite?'

'Mrs Nicholls and the Frenchman, Lejeune. Good drivers both of them.'

Mara thought, oh God, it would be!

The colonel asked, 'Is Samuel here? I haven't seen him.'

'No . . . umm . . . not yet.' She turned to Smithy. 'Have you seen my father-in-law?'

''E'll be down late morning.'

For Mara the morning passed appallingly slowly. The first race had begun and the loudspeaker boomed out over the roar of the engines, increasing and decreasing as the cars went round and round the track. Cynthia, Jeremy and Charles came over but Mara could hardly speak to them, so they left her as soon as they could. Two journalists asked her if she thought she stood a better chance this time and she nodded and tried to smile. Several people she had known in London shook her hand and wished her good luck, but she was so distracted she couldn't remember who they were. Several times she caught sight of a tall dark man and for a moment, until he turned to face her, she thought it was Jamie and she felt even weaker. On the one hand she desperately wanted him to come, to prove to her she was wrong and that all his urgings for her to do something with herself had not been merely to make her feel more inadequate. If he came it would show he'd really wanted her to make something of herself and he didn't just want a body to trample on. If he didn't come, then she was right – and for eight years she'd been wrong.

Suddenly Mara saw Yves approaching. Oh, God, she thought, not now. He strolled up to her, flashing his brilliant white-teeth smile enhanced by his Mediterranean suntan. 'I see we're racing against each other.' His eyes drifted down to her mouth. 'Perhaps we can have a drink afterwards.'

Mara shook her head. 'I don't think so.'

'Husband?' he whispered.

'Yes.' It seemed the easiest excuse.

'Pity.' He ran his tongue over his lower lip. 'Well, another time.' He walked off, turning once to give her his most sexy and understanding smile.

Mara didn't respond. She turned to Smithy. 'My father-in-law still hasn't arrived.'

'Stop fretting, miss!' He looked at Yves' disappearing back. 'Cheeky young devil! Them Frenchmen are all the same.'

Just before midday two women in racing-overalls came over and introduced themselves. One was hearty and masculine with big flat teeth and a well-scrubbed face, the other was gentle and friendly, with a sweet, very white face and wispy tobacco-coloured hair.

'I'm Kate Stock. We're in the same race,' said the

hearty one, crushing Mara's hand in her own. 'Good crowd here today. Excellent sign for women's racing.'

'Yes, yes,' replied Mara, wondering if some reciprocal feminist statement were called for and feeling inadequate because she couldn't think of one. Elenora would have thought of one.

Kate was watching the crowds picnicking on the grass. 'Got to give us all the vote soon,' she said. 'None of this nonsense about only householders and university graduates' – she looked at Mara – 'and married women. Well, can't stand here talking all day. Must be off. See you later, girls.'

The tobacco-haired girl whispered to Mara, 'Watch Kate! See! People step aside for her. They never do that for me.' She spoke with admiration, not envy, and smiled gently.

Mara smiled back. She had taken an instant liking to the tobacco-haired girl. 'They don't do it for me either,' she said.

'Oh, by the way' – again that gentle smile – 'I'm Maggie Nicholls.'

'Are you? Good heavens, I expected you to be . . . I mean . . . you're not nearly as fierce as I . . .'

'Oh, I'm fierce on the track all right. Well, lovely to meet you, Mara. I must go because I promised to buy the children an ice-cream.'

Mara was still trying to equate the gentle form of Mrs Nicholls with her awesome reputation. 'How many children do you have?' she asked.

'Three.'

'And you still find time to race?'

'Of course. My husband and my children are my greatest fans. Good luck!' She hurried away leaving behind her a feeling of warmth and happiness.

Shortly afterwards Alexander appeared and carried Mara off to lunch.

'What's happened to the Old Man?' she asked.

'He's having lunch at the hotel with Herbert and Atalanta.' Alexander gave her a breezy smile but his voice sounded strained.

Mara thought, I bet there's been a row. The Old Man must know I want him with me, he's a part of all this, and doubtless Herbert knows it too. He's made them have lunch at the hotel on purpose, anything to spoil my day and put me off the race. But surely the Old Man could have insisted? She felt bereft and abandoned and intensely lonely.

Alexander took her arm. 'I met Colonel Mackintosh and suggested he joined us.'

They went up to the restaurant and found the Colonel sitting at a table. 'Now you need a good steak,' he told her, 'and some of these delicious potatoes.'

Mara sat down. 'I couldn't eat all that.'

'Nonsense.' He ordered for her.

It was the colonel who kept up Mara's spirits during the last hour and a half before the race. He wouldn't allow her to sink into nervous silence but made her talk, almost as much as he did. 'At least it's not a handicap race,' he said. 'Very sensible of Samuel to have it this way, saves all that fiddling around on the weighbridge and all those young devils trying to hoodwink Ebby into giving them a better placing.'

The minutes were ticking by. It was time to go down to the Paddock. They walked down the hill. 'Better go and spend a penny, my dear,' the colonel whispered in Mara's ear. 'Don't want to find you need to go when it's too late.'

When Mara came back she found the colonel and

Alexander admiring the elegant silver Hatton-Gaunt Cup in its showcase attached to the wall. 'I still haven't seen your father,' she said to Alexander.

'He's gone straight up to the top of the Hill. There are too many people down here and he was afraid someone would trip over his wheelchair.'

'Seen the cup!' The colonel patted her shoulder. 'Now, let's check you out. Corset in place? Tight enough?' He stuck two fingers between Mara and the corset and tugged at it, just as he might have tested a horse's girth. 'Goggles? Helmet? Good. Let's find the Roadster. Ah, there she is. Good man, Smithy. A good team altogether.'

Smithy and the mechanics were pushing the Roadster towards the starting line and the others followed, Mara walking between Alexander and the colonel. This is it, she thought. Oh, God, let me do well!

Because the Hatton-Gaunt Cup wasn't a handicap the cars would be flagged off together. Mara had drawn the inside, Kate was next to her, Yves the other side of Kate, then Maggie, and then the two men Mara didn't know. She glanced up the line. Maggie was just climbing into her Lagonda. Yves was wiping a speck of dust from the gleaming bonnet of his Talbot.

'Now, remember,' the colonel was saying, 'don't jerk her. And don't move over till you're sure no one's on your outside. You've got thirty laps so you've plenty of time.' The last sentence was drowned in the sudden roar of engines coming to life.

'Good luck, darling.' Alexander kissed her on the cheek.

'Good luck, my dear!' shouted the colonel.

Mara settled herself into the driving seat. She was so nervous she could hardly think.

'Watch the flag!' shouted Smithy.

She nodded.

The flag went up. Mara pressed the clutch and engaged first gear, the engine racing. The flag came down and the car leaped forward. She was off, but so were the others, Maggie and Yves taking the lead. As Mara roared up the Finishing Straight she just had time to think, oh no, the banking, before she was into it. But she couldn't let the Roadster go up the wave because Kate was on her outside, and so presumably were the other two, for only Yves and Maggie were ahead of her. They were a good fifty yards ahead, neck and neck as they raced down the Railway Straight, tyres screaming as they swung round behind the Aero Sheds and into the Byfleet Banking. At least don't let me come last, thought Mara as she followed them up past the Vickers Sheds to the Fork, where in another twenty-nine laps she would peel off left for the Finishing Post. But now she swung to the right and into the Members' Banking, where she could hear the cheering from the Hill and caught a quick flash of faces peering down at her. Coming out of the banking and into the Railway Straight, Mara saw that Yves and Maggie had gained another twenty yards. She put her foot down hard and the Roadster responded. She began to catch up and as she hit the Byfleet Banking for the second time a quick glance to her right told her that Kate had fallen back and so had one of the other men, but the other one was still level, preventing her from using the whole of the banking. She was dripping with sweat, it was pouring down between her breasts and running down inside her helmet, into the corners of her eyes. She had to get away from the man who was level with her or she'd never be able to take advantage of the whole track. Back in the straight she put her foot flat down and just as they came to the Byfleet Banking for the third time she saw him drop back and, with a sigh of relief, she swung up into the middle of the track. Now she had to catch the other two. But she was doing better, she knew she was, getting away from that man had given her confidence and made her feel she could do it. With twenty-seven laps to go Mara finally settled down into that state of icy precision where the Roadster was no longer an independent mechanism to be battled with, it was a part of her, responding to her every touch and nerve.

On the twenty-third lap Mara drew level with Maggie. On the Railway Straight she passed her – just – then fell back on the banking, then drew level past the Vickers Sheds, only to drop back again on the Members' Banking. For three laps the two women battled it out. On the straight Mara was the winner, on the bends she was the loser, until, finally, with her wheels screaming as they slid across the track, she managed to hold her own through the Members' Banking and the Roadster drew away from the Lagonda. For a moment Mara could not believe it. She had overtaken Maggie Nicholls! She was so stunned she almost lost her advantage. Now only Yves was ahead, but by a good two hundred yards. With four laps to go Mara put her foot flat down on the accelerator. She didn't just want to win for her own sake and for the sake of the team; beating the confident, sophisticated Yves would be an added twirl of icing on top of the winning cake. But first she had to win. The Roadster was rattling at every joint as she went round the Members' Banking for the twenty-sixth time. The crowds were cheering and leaping up and down, but Mara didn't see or hear them, she only saw the gap between herself and Yves and heard the roar of the Roadster's engine. On the straight she caught up a little, decreasing his lead to a hundred and fifty yards and somehow she managed to hold it through the banking. She caught up a little more on the next straight, holding that too, she was now less than a hundred yards behind Yves. Round they went again, the twenty-eighth lap, tyres screaming on the concrete track. Into the penultimate lap. Mara was less than fifty yards behind. 'Come on! Come on!' she muttered.

They came into the Railway Straight for the last time. This was where Mara should forge ahead. But her foot was flat down and she couldn't catch the Talbot. With a feeling of despair and disappointment she went into the Byfleet Banking with half a lap to the Finishing Post and the Roadster still twenty yards behind. But I must beat him. She swung the car round the huge curve. Come on Roadster! Yves had gone high into the curve and for the first time since she had been chasing him, Mara found her exact position on the banking, not too high and not too low, just as the colonel had shown her that day when they had walked the track. And for once she gained on the banking. It gave Mara an incredible boost that the Roadster was catching up on the very spot where she'd once sat stranded and dejected. She drew level with Yves as they came to the Fork. Where previously they had borne to the right, she turned to the left and into the Finishing Straight with Yves, who had had to come down off the banking, just level with her back wheel.

Now Mara could hear the cheering. Now she could see the faces. With eyes full of tears and sweat she shot past the Finishing Post, to win by a car's length.

Chapter 30

The crowd surged forward as Mara drew to a halt in front of the clubhouse. Cameras were held high to capture her winning smile, flowers were thrown round her neck, a glass of champagne was pushed into her hand. She drained it and handed it back, then pulled off her goggles and her leather helmet, raking her fingers through her damp hair as she laughed up at the admiring faces around her.

Journalists shouted their questions. 'How does it feel to beat the great Yves Lejeune? To beat Mrs Nicholls? Did you think you were going to win? When will you race again?'

Alexander pushed his way through the crowd. 'Well done, darling.'

'A little nearer to the car, sir!' urged a photographer. 'That's right. Hold it.'

Alexander helped her out of the car. 'Darling, I must talk to you.'

'What?' She could hardly hear him.

Smithy, Jackson, Terry and young Pete struggled up to Mara. 'Well done, miss! What a race!' Proudly they patted the car. 'Ah, she's a real little beauty.'

'I never doubted you'd do well, my dear.' Colonel Mackintosh gave Mara a bear hug.

'When did you realize you were winning?' A journalist again.

'Darling, I must talk to you.'

'Yes, later.' She smiled at the journalist and said, 'Not till I'd passed the Finishing Post.'

'Darling, I must talk to you.'

'Yes, yes.' She was too excited to listen.

'Darling, it's important.'

'Well done, Mara.' Maggie Nicholls shook her hand.

Mara bubbled over with excited laughter. 'Thank you, thank you. Oh Maggie, this is my husband, Alexander. Alexander, this is Maggie. We must meet again, Maggie, we really must. I don't mean just on the track, I mean . . . you must come and stay, you and your husband.'

Kate Stock pumped her hand. 'As I said before, a good day for women's racing.'

'And not such a good one for us men.' Yves gave her hand an intimate squeeze.

'Darling, I *must* speak to you.' Alexander spoke urgently in her ear.

'Why? What about?'

'It's about . . .'

He was interrupted by the loudspeaker announcing the presentation of the Hatton-Gaunt Cup to the winner, Mrs Mara Rushton, and he drew back, saying, 'I'll wait at the back of the Paddock. Come as quickly as you can.'

Amid shouts and cheers and more flowers, tossed up at Mara on the platform, she received the cup. It was half full of champagne. 'Do I drink it?'

'Yes. Yes.'

'Very well.' She looked down on the sea of upturned smiling faces. 'Then before I become totally incoherent I would like to thank you,' she bowed to the judges and the officials, 'and you,' she bowed to the crowd. 'I am very honoured.' She lifted the big silver cup to her lips and drained its contents as the people clapped and called out, 'Well done! Well done!'

Hardly had Mara drunk the champagne than she was lifted bodily from the stand by two large men and carried shoulder high through the crowd. From her perch she looked across towards the stand and saw Alexander waiting there. What did he want? Why couldn't he let her enjoy her triumph in peace? She smiled, and a hundred faces smiled back at her. Then suddenly she caught sight of Jamie. He was standing just inside the Paddock fence, some twenty yards to her right, and he was watching her and smiling. Mara forgot everything else: Alexander: the people: she forgot them all. She jumped down and pushed her way through the mass of bodies until she reached him.

'You came.' She stood in front of him, her eyes blazing with pleasure and excitement, her hands still clutching the silver cup.

'I had to.' That beautiful half-mischievous, half-apologetic smile. 'I couldn't let you think . . .'

'That you only wanted me to trample on.'

'Yes.' He stretched out his hand and ran his fingers down the silver cup. 'You won, Stork.'

Mara was aware that her face was streaked with dust and sweat and her overalls were oily and her hair uncombed, but she didn't care. 'Did you see it all?'

'Sure. You were brilliant.'

'Was I? I think I was lucky too.'

'It wasn't luck, you were the best.' He took a step towards her. It was as if they were entirely alone, for neither of them noticed the curious glances cast in their direction. 'But you were mad to jump the fence,' he said softly, 'you could have been killed.'

Mara laughed. 'The only person I wanted to kill was you.'

'Mara, I was waiting for you.' Alexander's hand

533

encircled her waist. 'Oh, hello, Doctor Turner, I didn't realize it was you. Nice to see you again.' He frowned. 'Mara, I must talk to you.'

Jamie took a step back. 'I'll see you later.'

'Don't go!' Mara called to him. She could not bear to lose him so quickly. Inwardly she cursed Alexander for breaking the spell, for cutting short whatever might have come next. But Jamie either didn't hear, or pretended not to; he carried on walking. 'Well? What is it?' she demanded of Alexander.

'It's the Old Man. He had a stroke this morning. We didn't tell you because we were afraid it would put you off.'

'Oh no. You mean, he didn't come? You mean you were all telling me . . .'

'Yes. An ambulance has taken him to London. The hospitals round here don't have the right equipment. Herbert's with him.'

'Will he be all right?' Now she understood Smithy's strained face and Alexander's strained voice.

'We hope so. But the thing is, darling, I've promised to drive Sophia and Atalanta up to London and I have all the luggage and . . . I feel terrible, darling, but there's . . . umm . . . just not room for you too in the car. Do you mind asking Smithy to drive you up? I know you're one of the family and you should be with us, but it was all such a rush and Herbert asked me . . .'

And Herbert organized it so I was left out, Mara thought bitterly. Thank God I won the race. At least I don't have failure to cope with as well.

'You do understand, don't you?' Alexander was saying. He knew he should have insisted on staying with his wife. Smithy could easily have taken Sophia and Atalanta, and he knew he was wrong to abandon Mara in the aftermath

534

of her victory, expecting her to hang around on her own, waiting for the foreman to give her a lift. She deserved better than that, she'd brought life to Rushton-Gaunt and to the Old Man with her racing; by leaving her he was giving in to Herbert's 'I knew she'd kill him.' He tried to exonerate himself by gabbling out a list of arrangements. 'I've settled up with the hotel and they know all about it and you have your room till tomorrow if need be. And I've phoned Lady Henrietta and she's expecting you and I'll leave a message for you there.'

Mara nodded wearily. 'Yes, yes, don't worry.'

Alexander kissed her cheek and hurried off.

Feeling thoroughly deflated Mara stood by the fence and looked down towards the Byfleet Banking. The idea that the Old Man might die came over her in waves of horror. He was the mainstay of all their lives, but particularly of hers. And she loved him. She loved him as she might have been able to love her own father had she been old enough to appreciate his reasoning and not resent him for being different. She'd wanted to do well for the Old Man as much as for anyone and she'd longed to hear his praise. Did he know she had won? She wished she could be the one to tell him but even that was being taken away from her.

'Is anything wrong, Mara?'

She had not heard Jamie approach. 'It's my father-in-law. He's had a stroke.'

'I'm sorry.'

'He's a wonderful man. He and Elenora are the two people who've . . .' she hesitated, but she was desperate to talk to someone, '. . . helped me. I don't think I could have stood . . . it if it hadn't been for them. You'd like my father-in-law.' She smiled fondly. 'He can't walk and he's in a wheelchair but no one ever thinks of him as being a cripple. He's a lion.' She sighed. 'The trouble is, they'll blame me because he's had a stroke. He was a sort of . . . invalid, at least people said he was, though he wasn't really, and ever since I persuaded him to let me race they've been saying I'll be the death of him. I know he's not dead but . . . How could I have done it without him? He is Rushton-Gaunt.'

'He wouldn't have been involved if he hadn't wanted to.'

'I know.' She pulled a face. 'But try telling that to my brother-in-law.'

'Elenora told me he was . . . Oh, here comes Alexander.'

Alexander ran up to them, flustering with his hands, still unable to look Mara in the eye. 'Mara, I . . . er . . . Doctor Turner I was wondering . . . er . . . you live in London, don't you? It's just that my father's had a stroke and I . . . er . . . can't take Mara back to London and I thought perhaps . . . I mean, would you mind?'

Over Mara's head went the conversation. Jamie replied, 'My pleasure.'

Alexander said, 'Would you? Collect her luggage. Deliver her.'

Jamie replied, 'Of course. So sorry about your father.'

So Mara was left with Jamie, with her husband's inhibiting permission. They stood in silence, watching the people gather up their picnics and pack them away into baskets or hampers. From the *thé dansant* on the Hill came the ridiculous 'Felix Kept on Walking', to be replaced a few minutes later by the beautiful 'Rhapsody in Blue'. From time to time Mara and Jamie turned to each other, their eyes meeting, then they hurriedly looked away again as the image of Alexander, anxious and stammering, rose up before each of them. But in spite of

536

that, there was a warmth and understanding, which had appeared only fleetingly in their meetings since Koblenz.

After a while Jamie said, 'Shall we go?'

'Yes.'

In silence they walked across the grass towards the car park. Mara was careful not to touch him, though she was infinitely aware of him: of his hand with its long slender fingers, suntanned on the tops but white below the knuckles: of his long and muscular legs: of the angle of his hip which was exposed each time he moved his foot forward and his unbuttoned jacket flapped back. In the world of racing, which attracted a smart and moneyed crowd, there were many men better dressed and better looking, but to Mara they seemed tame in comparison. Jamie moved with an animal grace and his clothes were not a pretty wrapping to enhance him, they were a covering he was obliged to wear, which happened to look good but which, like the dinner-jacket he had worn at the ball, though not tight, appeared strained by his energy and his vitality.

Mara was surprised to find Jamie drove a Riley. She had expected something more sedate, like a Ford or a Morris, and she was annoyed to think he had accused her of flaunting the trappings of wealth when his car was not that of a humble doctor. But perhaps Jamie could get away with it, she thought with a mixture of irritation and fondness.

As she was getting into the passenger seat someone called her. It was Yves. He came striding over to Mara and clasped her hand in his. 'I wanted to congratulate you again, there were too many people around you after the race.' He gave Jamie a polite but puzzled nod. 'Good evening, Mr . . .'

Jamie said, 'No, I'm not "Mr Rushton",' and got into the car.

A gleam of comprehension came into Yves' eyes as he bent to kiss Mara's hand. She knew he was thinking that if she went around with other men there was still hope for him, so she said, 'Doctor Turner is a friend of my husband's.'

'I understand.' Yves gave her an intimate smile which she hoped Jamie could not see. 'Well, goodbye, Mara.'

Mara was relieved when they drove off, and relieved too that Jamie did not comment on Yves. But she sensed he knew. The warmth between them had been replaced by a distant politeness.

They went to the Hand and Spear. Jamie waited in the bar while Mara bathed, changed, packed and telephoned Lady Henrietta, who told her the Old Man was weak but stable.

'Does he know I've won?'

'I don't know, but we're all full of admiration for you, Mara. I'm going to the hospital now and if your father-in-law's well enough for me to see him . . .'

'Will you tell him, please. I want him to know as soon as possible and if I can't see him tonight, I'd like you to tell him for me.'

When she came downstairs Jamie said, 'Ready?'

'Yes.'

'Let's go.'

'Yes.'

They headed back to London, in silence again. Cool and clean at last, in a blue silk dress and red open-toe high-heeled sandals, Mara stretched out her bare legs, rested her head on the back of the seat, and closed her eyes. If Jamie didn't want to talk to her, far be it from her to make him. But where, oh, where had that lovely feeling gone? Where was that fond admiration she had seen in him when she had stood before him clutching her silver cup? Across her legs, just above her knees, the hem of the dress rippled on her skin as it caught the breeze. She pictured it as little blue waves caressing her skin as the sea caresses the beach on a still night. Further up her legs, at the tops of her thighs, the wide bottoms of her cami-knickers made other little ripples, soft down her soft skin. She opened her eyes and looked across at Jamie. His head was silhouetted against the grey window of the night sky. Why did things have to be as they were? Why did Yves have to come along when he did? Why couldn't she and Jamie be a couple, and she have the right to reach out and touch him?

Halfway to London Jamie suddenly said, 'Look, it's pretty late and I'm hungry. How about picking up something to eat?'

Mara had been thinking he could not wait to be rid of her. She was so surprised by his suggestion she could only stammer, 'Yes . . . er . . . what . . . whatever you like,' and wait for him to say he'd changed his mind.

They stopped at a restaurant, an old timbered place with a garden lit by red art deco lanterns in which tables and chairs were half hidden by creepers. It glowed at them through the dark, warm and red and inviting.

'Perhaps I'd better telephone,' said Mara as they walked towards it.

Jamie nodded. 'I'll be over there.' He pointed to a secluded table beside a wall over which honeysuckle was draped like the hangings of a four-poster bed.

When Mara came back after telephoning he stood up and held her chair. 'Okay?'

'Yes. He's a little better.'

They ordered their meal. Jamie ordered the wine. They

talked: he asked her about racing: she told him; she asked him about his work: he told her. It was all perfectly friendly, the conversation of two acquaintances meeting after a long time. Mara felt depressed. She began to wish they had driven straight to London, that he had delivered her quickly and gone on.

It was over the coffee when Jamie suddenly asked, 'Who was that blond god who came up to you?'

Taken by surprise, Mara blushed and hoped it was too dark for him to see. 'Oh, that was Yves Lejeune,' she answered, trying to sound casual. 'Just another driver.'

'Know him well?'

She knew Jamie was looking at her but she could not bring herself to meet his eyes. 'Not very.'

There was a small pause, then he asked, 'So what excuse did you give yourself this time?'

She took a sugar lump and crunched it with her teeth, took another and put it in her coffee cup. 'Excuse?'

'Yes. Excuse. You weren't looking for security or trying to save your father's life, so what was it?'

Mara's eyes narrowed. 'That's a very cruel thing to say about my father's life.'

'I want to be cruel. You make me want to be cruel to you.' He pushed back a lock of dark hair. 'It's all part and parcel of the same thing that made you jump the gate. Us.'

Mara looked down at her coffee where the movement of the spoon had left trails of cream, white whirls in the black. He was right, it was them. 'If you must know, I was drunk,' she said.

Jamie was leaning back in his chair and his face was hidden by the shadows of the honeysuckle. 'Do you often get . . . drunk?'

'No.'

'Oh?'

'I was drunk and frightened!'

'So it happened last night?' His voice was flat and unemotional as he interrogated her.

'Oh no, before the other race, the one when I got . . . stranded. My just desserts, I suppose. Not that anything actually happened between us, I was too drunk.' She pulled a face. 'And I was sick.'

Jamie gave a dry contemptuous laugh. 'So, are you now on the slippery slope of marital infidelity?'

Mara was sure she had lost him now, even if she hadn't done so long ago, but she was still glad she'd been honest. Playing games with Jamie had never really worked – except the time when she had played at not being a limpet. 'I was for a bit,' she answered truthfully, 'a couple of years ago, when I wanted to race the Roadster and I wasn't allowed to.'

'So you got your own back?'

'I suppose that's what I thought I was doing,' she sighed, 'not that I stopped to do much thinking. I didn't want to think.'

The waiter brought some port and after he had gone Jamie said, 'There's one thing I've always wondered about?'

'What?'

'You gave in to Steiger because you thought you were saving your father's life and you married Alexander for security and you went with these other men in a time of great frustration but' – he studied her face very carefully – 'why me? I'm curious because you're not promiscuous. It doesn't matter how many lovers you've had, you've always had a reason, however misguided.'

Mara lit a cigarette. Now was the time to tell him she loved him, but she was afraid. He might laugh at her. So she made him laugh by answering, 'It was the lamb stew, of course. Lamb stew and potatoes.'

He stared at her for a moment, then began to laugh. 'Lamb stew.'

Mara smiled nervously and shook her head, and her sun-bleached hair caught the lamplight and turned to threads of finest gold. What a fool I am, she thought. Why did I turn the most serious thing in my life into a joke? Why didn't I say that what I had felt for him was something which does not always join itself to love, but when it does, as it did with me, it makes that love so very much more desperate.

'And I suppose I just keep on feeding you,' he said, his eyes twinkling at her.

'Exactly. But that wasn't all.' She reached out to touch his cheek.

He took her hand and kissed its soft palm. 'Don't tell me you felt sorry for me – a poor lonely young doctor.'

She took her hand from him and leaned back in her chair. She had to tell him how she felt, even if he rejected her, even if it meant she never saw him again. She had to force out the words. 'You're the only man I've ever loved,' she said quietly. 'I still love you. I always will.'

He looked at her and frowned. 'I wish you wouldn't smoke.' A pause. 'And I wish you hadn't said that.' Another pause. 'Because . . . I suppose . . . I love you too.' A sigh. 'No, that's wrong. I do love you. I probably loved you in Koblenz, only I was so tied up with my work that I didn't realize what you meant to me till you'd gone. Then it was too late.'

'Yes. Too late,' Mara repeated, longing for him to contradict her and say, 'No, it's not. Let's start again.'

But he didn't. He went on. 'I was so busy and so ambitious I didn't see it at the time.'

'When did you realize?'

'After you'd gone.' He took her hand again. 'I used to sit in your father's study, night after night, thinking. Everyone thought I was working hard – but I wasn't. I was missing you. I missed you very much.'

Mara linked her fingers through his and stroked his thumb with hers. 'But you must have got over it . . . me . . . eventually.'

He stubbed her still burning cigarette firmly in the ashtray. 'Revolting habit. If you knew what it does to your lungs . . . well, anyhow, I thought I was over you by the time I left Koblenz. You know, going home, seeing my mother and my old friends. Oh, I haven't told you, my father died a month after you left. That made things even worse. We were very close.' He gave Mara no time to interrupt and say she was sorry. 'But one day I was looking at a magazine of my mother's and I saw a photograph of you and Alexander, something to do with an aeroplane crash.'

'The Gemelli.'

'Yes. At first I thought you'd been killed and I felt . . . I can't tell you how I felt, I sat there, staring at the photograph. Thinking. Regretting. I remember I blamed myself. I thought your death was all my fault. If only I'd agreed to take you to America. But then I read on, and I knew you were alive. I burnt the magazine up in the woods behind my mother's house. I couldn't bear the idea of your picture. You and him. The perfect couple.'

Mara took a sip of port, then ran her tongue round the edge of the glass, revelling in the sticky liquid which slid down her throat and filled her with its sultry warmth. 'When you came to England you must have wondered if you'd . . .'

'See you? Yes of course I did. But I never thought you'd turn up at the clinic.'

'Were you surprised?'

'You can say that again.'

'And you were so . . . horrible to me.' She longed for a cigarette but did not light one.

Jamie laughed at her. 'Not as horrible as you'd become.'

'You mean, you didn't love me any more?'

'Love you! Frankly, no. Want you? In all honesty, yes. You were everything I'd feared you'd become. Vain. Superficial. Selfish. And when you came flaunting your wealth in front of those poor women, my God! But I was pleased, you see. I thought, now I can finally bury a ghost.'

Mara took another sugar lump and crunched it slowly. 'And don't tell me sugar lumps are bad for my teeth' – she gave him a naughty grin – 'you're not my dentist or my doctor.' She puzzled as she crunched, and when she had finished the sugar lump, she asked, 'Why did you come down to Brooklands the first time if you thought you'd buried a ghost?'

Jamie smiled disarmingly. 'I suppose I was curious. Surprised . . .'

'That the little parasite was actually doing something?'

'Something like that. Now, when you've finished smoking, munching and drinking, may I have your hand back?'

Mara gave it to him.

'But when I saw you standing on the edge of the hill looking so dejected I knew the ghost was still unburied. I'd expected you to be sophisticated and laugh it off, but you weren't, you were so ashamed because you'd let down the rest of the team. And you weren't talking about the Rushton family, you meant the mechanics, the little people. I wanted to hug you, there and then, with everyone milling around.' He paused for a moment. 'I couldn't wait to see you again. That's why I stayed at the cottage. I could easily have driven back to London.'

'How could you be sure I'd be at the cottage?'

'I asked Elenora to tell you.'

'Did you tell her about . . . ?'

'Us? No. But I think she suspects.' He lifted her hand to his mouth and nibbled the ends of her fingers. 'Frankly I didn't give a damn who suspected, so long as I saw you.'

Mara remembered how difficult it had been for her to slip away from the Dower House. 'I might not have been able to come.'

Jamie smiled. 'Mara, if you want to do something badly enough nothing's going to stop you.'

Mara stretched out her right leg until her foot found his foot and her toes his ankle. 'You know,' she said, wriggling her toes against his ankle, 'sometimes in these past years I've felt as though I'm in a bus queue, waiting for life to come along. I've seen people in queues and thought, that's me. Waiting and waiting, but without the courage to move on. To take a risk. It's as though I'm outside myself, watching myself, directing myself and acting out my directions. But all the time I've been detached.'

'And now?'

'I don't know.' She held tightly to his hand as if it were her lifeline. 'I really don't know. Except that . . . I can't go back to what I was – to nothing. Seeing you again made me question, tonight makes me question more deeply. Perhaps I'd always questioned but I was afraid to hear the answer.'

'That you must leave Alexander.'

'Perhaps.'

'Would you?'

'I wanted to after I saw you last. When you said, "I don't mess around with married women," I thought, that's it. I'll leave. But then I went home and found Alexander was ill and I couldn't tell him. He needed me.'

'You're fond of him?'

'Yes.' She looked deep into his eyes. 'But it's you I love. I'll . . .' Her mouth trembled. 'I'll always love you, Jamie.' The warm night closed in round them and the smell of honeysuckle was thick and heavy in the secluded bower. 'And now it's too late,' she said, again willing him to contradict her.

Jamie released her hand and looked at his watch, and broke the spell. 'Yes, it's nearly ten. We must go. Do you want to telephone while I settle up?'

Mara nodded and stood up. She went inside the restaurant and dialled Lady Henrietta's number. Alexander was at the hospital. Her father-in-law was still weak but stable. If anything, a little better. 'Did you tell him about the race?' Mara asked.

Lady Henrietta's reply was gentle. 'I couldn't, Mara dear, Herbert wouldn't let me see him.'

'So he doesn't know I've won?'

'I don't think so. I know what it means to you for him to know and of course he would want to, but Herbert . . .'

'He must have asked if I'd won.'

'He's not completely conscious so if I'd told him he might not have understood. But the doctors are optimistic. You'll be able to tell him yourself in a few days.'

Mara walked across to Jamie's car. I put my soul into winning that race, she thought, and they won't even tell him I've done it. She looked at Jamie sitting in the Riley.

I put my heart on the line and what good has it done me? Suddenly she felt very tired.

They did not speak for the next half-hour. But the silence was no longer cold, it was warm and intimate and needed no words. In spite of Mara's hurt, she understood: Jamie had pushed her back for both their sakes. And I would have done it, she thought. I would never have gone back to Alexander if Jamie had asked me to stay.

As they reached the outskirts of London they drew nearer to each other. Each dreaded the parting. Each knew the other dreaded it. But much as they loved each other, they knew they could not help each other. To help was to prolong – to tempt. Coming over Putney Bridge they began to talk, their words bouncing out staccato.

'I love the river.'

'Especially at night.'

'Must be lovely to have a house on the river.'

'I gather they're very expensive.'

'I imagine they are.'

'A bit damp in winter.'

'Still I'd love one.'

'So would I.'

It did not matter who said what. It was all meaningless.

Up the Kings Road they sank into bitter silence. Only another mile, Mara said to herself. Only another six minutes. Five minutes. Now she longed for the parting to be over, with all the hopelessness of a woman on the scaffold who kneels for the inevitable axe.

As they swung round Hyde Park Corner they passed a bus queue straggled along the side of St George's Hospital. Mara looked at the grey, tired, waiting faces. 'There we are,' she said through gritted teeth. 'That's me.'

'It doesn't have to be.' He pulled the car sharply to the side of the road but kept the engine running. 'You don't

547

have to go back.' He turned to her but didn't touch her. 'But if you stay with me I want you to understand I'm not interested in an illicit affair with you. I don't want stolen moments with someone else's wife. I want you to be my woman, my lover and my friend, so don't begin unless you intend to see it through. You and I aren't half-measure people. We want all or nothing, and I want all or nothing of you.'

It seemed to Mara that the traffic stood still and that the winking tail lights of the cars diving into Park Lane were suddenly suspended, frozen in that moment. The park on her left, with its fuzzy darkness beneath the trees and its fuzzy greyness above them, was a background to a picture, and nothing, except for Jamie and herself, was living or real. She was sitting beside him, her hands clasped in her lap, and still he did not touch her. She was glad of that. If he had taken her in his arms she would have wanted him so much she would not have been able to think. She sat there, aware of him beside her yet totally isolated in her thoughts. What would it be like going back to Alexander, living with Alexander, making love with Alexander, knowing all the time that she could have been with Jamie? It had been difficult enough before. Now it would be impossible. 'Take me with you,' she said softly.

As they drew away from the kerb Mara looked back. The grey-faced people were still waiting in the bus queue.

Chapter 31

Jamie's house was in one of those lovely irregular squares which cling to the side of Hampstead Hill: the sort of square where elderly once-famous painters sit on benches on summer evenings surrounded by their grandchildren, and where the houses, each slightly different from its neighbours, look like the backdrop to a pantomime. Tall red-brick houses with extraordinary turrets added by previous owners enamoured with the castles of Bavaria look down their grey-slate noses at smaller houses whose architects had preferred the regency period. Jamie lived in one of these.

'I'll give you a guided tour,' he said, opening the navy-blue front door and steering Mara through a narrow hallway into a drawing room which was really two rooms with an arch in the middle. 'Oh, I see Mrs Badger's been at it again.'

'Mrs who?'

'Badger. Isn't it wonderful? That really is her name. She comes and "does" for me, as she calls it, but she will pile all the books on top of each other in the corner and I like them in piles according to what they're about.'

Mara laughed. The room was full of books: on shelves, in piles, on tables. 'I can see her point,' she said. She examined the room. It was friendly and lived in, and the leather chesterfield sofa and the two armchairs looked as though they were well sat in – and enjoyed being sat in.

So this was where he relaxed after a hard day.

Jamie took her by the arm and led her across the drawing room to a small back study, also full of books.

So this was where he worked.

And then he took her back through the hall to the dining room – six chairs around a highly polished mahogany table; Mrs Badger's pride and joy.

So this was where he ate.

'Like it?' Jamie stroked her hair.

'Yes. Yes, I do.'

He took her hand and led her back into the hall and up the stairs, past a bathroom and two bedrooms on the first floor, then on up again, saying, 'Now you'll see why I couldn't resist this house.' He hesitated. They knew so little about each other's tastes. 'At least I hope you will.'

Mara walked into the attic, then turned slowly to look at it. Someone had knocked down the walls of what had once been three small rooms and turned it into a huge space which stretched right up to the rafters and at each side to huge sloping windows, one looking up the hill towards the village, the other looking down towards the heath. And the feeling of space was accentuated by the unbroken whiteness of it: white walls, white rafters, even shiny white floorboards. The only colour was the deep dark red, the colour of port, of the curtains and the bedspread and the Persian rugs, which wove the red with greens and blues. It was masculine but still intimate, bright but not stark, a world of its own high above the city lights. In a funny way it reminded Mara of her attic bedroom in Koblenz, except that this was the cave of a much less cluttered Aladdin. 'Yes, I do see,' she said.

So this was where he slept – and made love.

Suddenly Mara felt horribly nervous. She walked over to the window and looked up towards the village. Supposing he found he didn't like her any more. Supposing she wasn't as he remembered. Supposing . . . it didn't work. She tried not to think of Alexander.

Jamie came up behind her and put an arm around her shoulders. 'Don't think about it,' he said. 'We love each other and we want to be together. Just remember that.'

Mara smiled. 'You're right. Of course you're right, but . . .'

He turned her to face him and pulled her close until he held her tightly against him. 'There are no "buts" about it. All this mental dissecting *after* you've made a decision' – he kissed her forehead – 'is totally retrogressive. You . . . we . . . have decided what we want. Now we have to go for it. Of course there'll be obstacles, there always are, but so long as we keep our eyes on the winning-post, we'll get there.'

He made it sound so simple. Mara wished his indomitability was as easily communicable as the warmth from his arms.

'Of course what I should have done' – he ran his thumb along the groove of her collar-bone – 'is to have dragged you straight up here and given you no time to think. Never mind about the drawing room and the dining room. Straight to the bedroom.'

Mara snuggled up against him. 'What, and ripped my clothes off?'

'Sure.' He began to undo the buttons down the back of her dress. 'And thrown you naked and sobbing on the bed.'

'But . . .' She pushed down his arms and slipped off his jacket.

'But what?' He kissed the corner of her mouth.

'You would have to get undressed as well.'

'That is true.' He undid the last button of her dress, which sank to the floor in a silky whisper.

Mara kicked away the dress and turned her attention to his tie and shirt. 'I might have run away by that time.'

He unbuckled his trousers. 'I'd have tied you down.'

'You mean you would have raped me?' Her lips clung softly to his.

He undid her brassiere. 'Definitely.'

'Just once?' He was now completely naked but she still wore her cream silk cami-knickers.

'Oh, no.'

'How often?' She ran her fingers up the backs of his thighs and felt the hardness of his leg muscles.

His hands came up under her cami-knickers and squeezed each buttock as he pulled her to him. 'At least twice.'

'Only twice?' Her knickers fell to the floor.

He pushed her up against the wall. 'Three times if you were lucky.'

'Really.' She touched him. 'No more than that.'

'It would depend if . . .' He touched her.

'If what?' She reached up to him.

'If you were . . .'

'Yes.' It was more a sigh than a word.

'A good girl.' He lifted her on to him and took her there against the wall beside the window, where the lights from the village made patterns on their bodies.

They made love again, gently, sleepily, in the big bed. Then they fell asleep. And in the morning when Mara woke she found the room bright and rosy from the sun which glowed against the deep red curtains. Tentatively she peered over Jamie's sleeping head at the clock on his bedside table. It was six. She lay back and watched the room and the one ray of sunlight which burst through a crack in the curtains by the window where she had looked up at the village – by the window where they had made love. The ray of sunlight was so bright and white that particles of dust danced along its beam, trapped into it, or so it seemed.

'What are you doing?' muttered Jamie, rolling over towards her.

'Nothing.' A pause. 'Looking.' Another pause. 'Being happy.' She kissed his ear. He kept his eyes shut. She kissed his neck. He mumbled. She ran her tongue down his chest. He snaked his fingers through her tawny mane. She pushed down the bedclothes. He sighed. She buried her face in the soft pit of his stomach. He wrapped his legs around her.

'What's the matter?' he asked when he finally pulled her up to him. Mara was picking at the gap between her front teeth. 'Teeth falling out?'

'No, I've got something.' She pushed her tongue up against the backs of her teeth.

He peered at her teeth and smiled, then picked from between them a short, dark curly hair. 'One of mine, I think.'

Mara blushed and curled up next to him, and fell asleep.

She woke this time with Jamie shaking her. 'Want some coffee?'

'Umm.'

He nudged her. 'So do I.'

'Umm.'

He nudged her again. 'The kitchen's downstairs.'

She hid a smile in the pillow. 'Milk and one sugar for me.'

He pushed her towards the edge of the bed. 'It's all down there and as a special treat you may borrow my dressing-gown.'

She tried to wriggle back, away from the edge of the

bed, but he wouldn't let her. 'I'll smoke a cigarette if you make me get up.'

'You can't. I threw them away.'

'Beast!'

'I'll pull your hairs out one by one – all of them – if you don't make the coffee.'

She rolled over on her stomach. 'No you won't. No. Go away, you . . . No. No.' She was laughing and scrabbling at the bedclothes. Never had love been so much fun – not even with Jamie. Before, she had been too in awe of him and too afraid of losing him. She would have shot out of bed, made the coffee, and brought it humbly to him. But not now. Not now that she had the confidence of knowing he loved her, the confidence which allowed her to be herself and which brought out all the spontaneity and fun in her; qualities she hardly knew she possessed.

Jamie grabbed her round the waist and tried to turn her over. 'All my other women make me coffee,' he growled in her ear.

'Well, things are going to be different now I'm . . .' She ended in a shriek as he began to tickle her. Then, suddenly, she stopped giggling and squealing; she had remembered her father-in-law. 'I think I ought to telephone,' she said uncertainly.

Jamie released her. 'Yes, of course. It's in the study.'

Mara started to dress. 'It's just that I'd like to know how my father . . . how he is.' Was the Old Man still her father-in-law now that she had left his son?

Jamie was propped against the pillows watching her. 'You realize they'll wonder where you've been.'

'Yes.' She did not look at him. The finality of what she had done, of her night with Jamie, came over her, and though she did not regret one minute of it, she dreaded

554

the explanations and the inevitable hurt she was to do to Alexander.

Jamie asked, 'What will you say?'

'I don't know.' She tried to keep her voice light and cheerful.

'You'll have to see him, you know. You must tell him to his face.'

'Yes.' Twisting her arms over her shoulders to button her dress, Mara went downstairs. It's all right for you, she thought, you don't have to face him.

Five minutes later Mara was back.

Jamie smiled at her. 'Well?'

'He's dead.'

'No?'

'Yes.' Mara walked over to the window, pulled back the curtains and looked up at the village. 'I have to go back. I promised Lady Henrietta I would.'

'For ever?' His voice was flat and noncommittal.

'No, of course not.' In the square just below the house an old man was walking his dog, a dog like Prince. 'Just for a little while. Until Alexander's all right.'

'How long?'

'I don't know.' She turned back to face the room, trying to take in every detail of it so that she would be able to recall it in the days ahead. 'But what else can I do? What else?' She longed for Jamie to reassure her, although she knew that nothing he could say would be enough.

Chapter 32

Samuel Rushton was buried in the churchyard at Gaunt, some ten yards from his old friend Sir Henry Gaunt. 'The Old Man of British Motoring' was how one national newspaper described him. 'The Sons who succeed him' ran the caption under a photograph of Herbert and Alexander. Mara was referred to as 'The young and lovely Mrs Rushton whose win at Brooklands on the day of her father-in-law's untimely death was heralded as the re-emergence of Rushton-Gaunt in the world of motor-racing.'

As they came out of the church Lady Henrietta drew Mara to one side. 'I told him you won, dear,' she said. 'I insisted, and I doubt if Herbert will ever speak to me again. Not that I mind.' She patted Mara's arm and Mara braced herself for the inevitable question, 'Where were you the night he died?' but Lady Henrietta said nothing, she moved on to talk to the Taylors, leaving Mara surprised and relieved.

When Mara had left Jamie she had taken a taxi to Lady Henrietta's, expecting to face an angry barrage of questions, not only from Alexander but from her hostess. However, Alexander was still at the hospital and Lady Henrietta had gone out, so Mara went up to the bedroom prepared for her, and by the time she came down again they had all returned and no one said anything, they were much too preoccupied with the arrangements for the Old Man's funeral. And because Herbert was there, Mara hadn't liked to ask if her father-in-law had been told she'd won. She had sat silently as they talked, thinking of Jamie.

On the morning after the funeral Mara stayed in bed till lunchtime. She lay beneath the bedclothes, eyes closed, thinking about the Old Man. She pictured him as she'd first seen him hugging Alexander, tears on his granity cheeks: as he had been after the Gemelli had crashed, unhappy but never broken: then as he had been at Brooklands, a lion in his natural element: and finally, sitting in his wheelchair in the corridor of the Hand and Spear, the last time she'd seen him, when he'd said, 'If I can't have you as my son I'm glad to have you for my daughter-in-law.' He had died whilst she had been with Jamie, perhaps as they'd made love in the early hours of the morning, as they'd whispered, 'I love you'. She remembered what he had said about liking her just so long as she made his son happy; and wondered whether it was mere coincidence that he wasn't here to stop liking her. To leave Alexander was going to be hard, to have left and never seen the Old Man again would have been worse. Of course she wasn't going to see him again anyhow. It seemed so strange. And what also seemed strange was that he and Jamie and Elenora were the most important people in her life and yet the Old Man and Jamie had never met.

She thought of Jamie, his image formed against her closed eyelids. Jamie. She strained the imagination of her ears to hear his voice. Jamie. How she longed to be with him. To touch. To see. To feel. To laugh with him. Jamie.

She thought of Alexander. It seemed so cruel of her to exclude him from the important people. But I didn't exclude him, she thought, he simply doesn't travel with us. She could hear him coughing in the next room. He was unwell again, his lungs were slowly burning away. Was it another coincidence that her lover specialized in the very complaint from which her husband suffered?

After lunch Mara wrote to Jamie. She did not dare telephone him, though she longed to hear his voice, because the line went through the village exchange and the telephone operator, a sister of Mrs Wright, the receptionist at Rushton-Gaunt, was notorious for listening in. It took her an hour to think of what to write; she had to do it right the first time – she could not risk someone finding half-written attempts in the wastepaper basket. Dear Jamie. My dear Jamie. Darling Jamie. No, definitely not darling. In the end she settled for:

Jamie,
I love you and miss you and long to see you. I'll try to come to London next week – Tuesday if possible.
    love
    Mara

To avoid suspicion Mara wrote a number of other letters, then opted to ride into Gaunt herself to post them, telling Jenkins that Mahogany needed the exercise. As she set off she thought, no half-written love letters, no telephone calls, posting the letters myself, all the sordid rules of the illicit affair.

She returned the long way, via Elenora's cottage. But it was locked and there was no sign of Elenora. Probably for the best, Mara told herself to ease her disappointment, I wouldn't have been able to stop myself from telling her everything, and it's better not, not just yet. She rode on up the field and cut into the woods, joining the very path where some ten months earlier she had talked herself out of leaving Alexander. It had been autumn then and the ground had been wet and the leaves golden, now it was

558

mid summer and the recent dry spell had left its mark on the grass and the earth. Looking down at the parched grass, Mara suddenly wished it could have been spring. But that's silly, she told herself. Silly and superstitious.

As she headed down the field towards the Dower House, someone called to her. She looked around to find Damon standing halfway up the field. 'I thought I might find you here,' he said. 'They told me you'd gone to post some letters.'

'Yes.' Mara slid down off her horse. 'I much prefer the path through the woods to the road, even though it's longer.' She hoped he hadn't noticed her blush when he mentioned the letters. 'This is a nice surprise. I thought you were going back to school today.'

'I was, but Mother wanted me to stay another day because I won't be back till the middle of August. I'm going to stay with a friend in Monte Carlo.' His eyes filled with thoughtful amusement, and Mara wondered uneasily what he was going to do in Monte Carlo.

She fell into step with him. 'What about Atalanta? I saw her briefly at the funeral, that was all.'

'Oh, she's gone back to school but she said to thank you for suggesting she came to the race, she didn't thank you herself at the funeral because Father was there.' He smiled ruefully. 'What a family we are!'

Mara said, 'Alexander told me she's going to Paris in the autumn.'

'Yes, she's going to be "finished". Art galleries and *la-plume-de-ma-tante*! But I'm so glad you two get on now. I suppose you didn't before because you're both so alike. Survivors. She and I are much closer too, now. We were always close but it took her a few years to see the light where Father is concerned.'

'And what about you, Damon, are you a survivor?'

559

He smiled vaguely. 'Oh, I'm a victim – and a victimizer.'

Two days later Mara received a letter from Jamie.

Mara,
Can hardly wait for Tuesday. Am lecturing in the morning but will be home by 4.00 P.M.
    Love you
    Jamie

She knew she should burn the letter – destroying the evidence was another rule – but she didn't. She kept it: her first letter from Jamie. And she knew she ought to tell him to be careful what he wrote, but she couldn't bear to. That would be to acknowledge that the sordid rules applied to them and that they were no different from any other two people who play illicit games.

She put the letter in the iron box with the letters from her father and from Hans, where it stood out white and crisp against their yellowed paper and faded writing. Jamie's locket had slipped down into the corner of the box. She fished it out and twisted the chain between her fingers, remembering how she had thought a heart meant love. And it does, she told herself. It's just taken a bit longer, that's all, and she kissed the locket before putting it back in the box.

On the Monday afternoon, the day before Mara was due to go to London, the solicitor, Mr Lewis, gave a formal reading of Samuel Rushton's will. The family gathered in the drawing room at the Park: Herbert and Sophia on the sofa: Mara and Alexander in armchairs: Mr Lewis standing with his back to the fireplace, facing them, the will in his right hand. The executors, he informed them, were Herbert, Alexander and himself. 'Mr Rushton was very anxious to keep matters in the family but he felt it would be a good idea to have an outsider to . . . er . . . arbitrate if need be.' He glanced apprehensively at Herbert.

The list of minor bequests was dealt with quickly. Everyone listened, except for Mara who was thinking about Jamie. Eventually there was a pause and she thought, well that's that, and prepared to stand up.

But there was more to come. Mr Lewis adjusted his spectacles and said ominously, 'That is the end of the minor bequests.'

Herbert exclaimed, 'Thank God for that. There's going to be nothing left. Three thousand pounds to Mortimer! I always said the Old Man had lost his marbles.'

They all wriggled uncomfortably and Mr Lewis gave Herbert a pained look. 'I will . . . er . . . read on.' He fumbled with the papers, and his fumblings and his hesitant speech irritated them, but they said nothing; not even Herbert. '"The residue of my estate,"' Mr Lewis raised his voice on a wave of self-importance, taking pleasure in his mild way in their impatience, and satisfaction in the knowledge that he already knew what they longed to hear, '"The residue of my estate, comprising Rushton-Gaunt Motors, Rushton Park and its environs including the Dower House, and the farmhouse known as Les Vieux Orangers at Barjon in the region of Provence, France, and . . ."'

Herbert interrupted him. 'The what?'

'The farmhouse known as . . . er . . . I believe it means the Old Orange Trees . . .'

'All right, all right. I'm not asking you to read the whole thing again, I just want to know what the hell this is all about.'

'I think what my brother is trying to say' – Alexander

was ultra polite to make up for Herbert's rudeness – 'is that we had no idea our father owned property abroad.'

'It was Mr Rushton's private property.' Mr Lewis permitted himself a small smile as he emphasized the word 'private'. 'I believe he used to stay there quite often before the war.'

Alexander had that look of puzzlement which can only be satisfied by hearing a rational explanation. He said, 'Yes, he used to go to France but he didn't stay in one place . . . I mean, he used to travel round. That's why we couldn't contact him.'

Herbert laughed. 'The old devil! All the time he had some French tart hidden away in a love-nest.'

Alexander frowned. 'Herbert! Please!'

Mara stifled a giggle.

Sophia looked worried.

'Well, is it worth anything?' demanded Herbert.

Mr Lewis ignored Herbert and looked straight at Alexander. 'I believe it's not very large, just a farmhouse with two fields. A peasant farmer and his wife look after it in exchange for use of the fields.' He read on from the will, '"And that Pierre Gramont or his descendants continue to have full use of the two olive groves in exchange for looking after the property and that should the property be sold these olive groves are to be gifted to Pierre Gramont or to his descendants."'

Herbert said, 'I mean is it worth anything? Money?'

'I shouldn't think so, not much.'

'Then for goodness' sake let's go on.'

Mr Lewis adjusted his spectacles yet again. 'Very well. Where was I? Yes. "And all my remaining worldly possessions shall be held in trust for my sons Herbert and Alexander and upon their deaths for their sons, on the understanding that Rushton-Gaunt Motors should continue to be administered in the manner in which I have administered it and that all female relations, including widows of deceased Rushton males, be furnished with the means to live in the style to which they are accustomed during their marriage. This arrangement does not apply in the event of a divorce.'

Herbert gave a bitter laugh. 'So much for all my years of hard work.'

Alexander was looking extremely nervous. 'So Herbert and I are to run the business together?'

'Yes, that is correct.'

Mara felt overwhelmingly relieved that soon she would be out of it. Of course she felt sorry for Alexander, but now she had Jamie she could view it all dispassionately; she could stand back and see that Alexander was not only a victim but that in a perverse way he wanted to be a victim: it was his role and he had chosen it to assuage his guilt for having, through order of birth, benefited. He could not see that his own great quality of honesty was inherent, and that Herbert was inherently dishonest. Instead, he saw his honesty as being akin to an expensive suit; something which Herbert also would have acquired had there been money around in his childhood. So the more gross and unpleasant Herbert became, the more Alexander felt guilty. But he did not take off his suit of honesty and it didn't occur to him that he couldn't do so because it was a part of him, or that his father, whose childhood had been on a par with Herbert's, had had that same honesty. He merely played the victim.

Mr Lewis was droning on, '"My son Herbert, being the elder, shall retain the right to live at Rushton Park, until his death whereas my son Alexander being the younger shall retain the right to live at the Dower House until his death. Upon the death of Herbert, the right to

563

live at the Park passes to the eldest living Rushton male and the right to live at the Dower House to the second eldest male and so on and so on, regardless of whose father is the elder."'

Herbert said, 'What's he trying to do? Make us marry early and breed like rabbits?'

Sophia said, 'Supposing Damon doesn't want to go into Rushton-Gaunt?'

'He'll have to,' replied Herbert.

'But if he doesn't want to.' She was looking at the solicitor. 'Our son isn't very business-minded, Mr Lewis.'

'He may resign in favour of a brother.'

'We have only one son.'

'Then in the . . . er . . . unfortunate circumstances that Mr and Mrs Alexander Rushton do not have a son . . .'

Herbert laughed maliciously. 'They're not likely to have any.'

Mr Lewis felt very uncomfortable, but carried on. 'There is a codicil. It applies to Mrs Mara Rushton.'

Hearing her name, Mara sat up. 'Yes.'

'"In the event of there being no adult Rushton male, on the deaths of my sons my daughter-in-law, Mara Rushton, shall administer to the business known as Rushton-Gaunt or put in charge of it whomsoever she considers worthy and fit. This arrangement ceases should she be divorced from my son Alexander."'

They all turned to look at Mara, who had understood only the last sentence, 'This arrangement ceases should she be divorced from my son Alexander.'

After a moment Alexander said in an appalled voice, 'You mean Mara would run the business on her own?'

'Yes.'

'A woman!'

'Yes.'

564

'Good God!'

Herbert looked at his brother, then at Mara, and started to laugh. 'Don't worry, it won't come to that. Damon's not dead yet. Bad luck, Mara. Damon's going to get the lot, and God help Rushton-Gaunt when he does – if there's anything left by that time.'

Chapter 33

The will filled everyone's minds, except Mara's: Jamie was in hers and there was no room for anything else. By the time she reached London she had forgotten all about the strange codicil. Jamie was all that mattered. Jamie in his little house, waiting for her, wanting her, loving her and making love to her, with a tenderness and an urgency made all the more poignant by the minutes ticking past.

But on the third day Jamie brought it all back to her. They were lying in bed, revelling in the soft aftermath of their love-making, when he asked, 'Why haven't you had any children?'

Mara told him about the bargain Alexander had extracted from her and about her visit to the doctor, ending with, 'I pretended it was me, but now . . . oh yes, I still haven't told you' – she explained about the will – 'so he's sure to want to try again. I wish you'd seen their faces when the solicitor read out the bit about me running Rushton-Gaunt. They were appalled.'

'But that ceases if you and Alexander are divorced?'

'Yes, and I went scarlet when he said "divorce". They all turned to look at me. I had this horrid feeling that the Old Man knew – that all of them knew.'

'So now's he's desperate for a son?'

'He hasn't said so but I know he'll bring up the subject once he's better.'

'And?'

Mara rolled over on top of him and brought her face close to his. 'You don't really think I'm going to . . . ?'

He linked his arms across his bare back. 'Of course not, but won't he wonder?'

She looked at his dark hair which stood out in unruly tufts and appeared as the dark lines of an engraving where it touched the white pillow. 'I may have to tell him,' she said. 'I hope not. Not yet. But I don't think he'll . . . try for some time. We never did very much. The last time was – several months ago.'

'So the quicker you leave him the better.'

She kissed his eyelids. 'Don't worry! He's no danger when he's not well.'

'I meant for us.' He tightened his hold on her. 'All this secrecy is not my style.'

'But it's better than nothing,' she said quickly.

Jamie did not answer.

'Isn't it? Isn't it?' she insisted.

'I suppose so. But in the meantime I'd better go on being careful, we don't want to start our family early.'

Back at the Dower House, Mara found Alexander in bed and Atalanta on a chair beside him, wearing a tennis dress. They looked up as she came in and Alexander smiled. 'Hello,' said Mara, walking over to the bed and kissing him on the cheek. 'Aren't you well? I thought you were better.'

'I was until yesterday, but now you're back . . .'

'Yes.' She turned to Atalanta. 'Been playing tennis?'

'I've been to Gaunt Hall.' She pulled a face. 'The Robinsons had a tennis party. I wouldn't have gone but Father insisted, he said it was unneighbourly not to, but who needs people like them? Ugh!'

Mara laughed. 'I've only met them a couple of times and they must have been at the Hall for at least six years.'

'That's because nobody invites them.' Atalanta stood up. 'Can I ask Jenkins to give me some orange juice?'

'I'll come down with you.' It was a good excuse not to be left alone with Alexander.

Once they were alone Atalanta said, 'I suppose you're not going up to the works in the next few days?'

'Why?'

'I wanted to come with you, I haven't seen Pete for weeks and I'm going to France next month. Then I won't see him for ages. We thought we'd see a lot of each other now, while I'm here, but not a bit of it. Father will hardly let me out of his sight.' She touched Mara's arm. 'Will you take me . . . please?'

Mara hesitated. She hadn't been up to the works since the day before the Old Man's funeral, because to go there meant to see Herbert, but she looked into Atalanta's anxious eyes and said, 'Very well, let's go now. But how will you manage to speak to him?'

'Oh, I'll find a way.'

They drove straight up there and walked round the back to the workshops. It was all much easier than Mara had imagined. There was no sign of Herbert, but Smithy, Terry and Jackson were in one of the testing-bays. They greeted her like a long-lost friend. 'I'm sorry I haven't been up before,' said Mara, feeling guilty, 'but . . .'

'We understand, miss. Things ain't what they were.' They crowded round her and lowered their voices. 'Do you think we'll be racing next season, miss?'

Mara shrugged. How could she tell them that she wouldn't be there next season? She was suddenly aware that Atalanta had rejoined the group although she hadn't been aware of her departure. 'I think we'd better go,' she said. 'I just wanted to come up and see you all.'

They grinned at her understandingly, as if they were all children under the same cruel teacher.

Mara and Atalanta found Herbert waiting beside the car. 'What are you two doing up here?' he demanded.

Mara answered him coldly. 'I came up to see Smithy and the rest of the team, and Atalanta came with me.'

He took a step towards her, reminding her yet again of Herr Steiger. 'There isn't a team any longer.' A triumphant smile flickered across his coarse features. 'We've pulled out of racing so, Mara, there's no reason for you to come up here again.'

'I shall come up when I want to,' she snapped. 'You're not the only director of Rushton-Gaunt.'

'Not Rushton-Gaunt any more, my dear sister-in-law, but Rushton Motors.' He laughed when he saw her look of surprise. 'Obviously Alexander hasn't told you.'

Without saying another word Mara got into the car and, after dropping Atalanta at the Park, she went home to Alexander. 'Herbert says that you've changed Rushton-Gaunt to Rushton Motors,' she said angrily. 'Why?'

'Because . . . er . . . Herbert . . . we feel that Gaunt is no longer . . .'

'So you've let him drop poor Sir Henry.' She looked at him in disgust, then turned and walked out of the room. Later she told herself, 'Don't be silly! It's not your problem any more.' Nevertheless, she couldn't help but care.

Two weeks later Mara was back in London, ostensibly to buy clothes and visit friends. In reality she did none of these things, she merely lived for Jamie. Snatched lunches with Jamie. The odd half-hour between the clinic and a lecture. Hours sitting on hard chairs at the back of lecture halls listening to Jamie talk, not understanding a word, happy just to be there. Then there were those few but glorious hours in the attic bedroom – the stolen moments before she took a taxi back to Mayfair and Lady Henrietta.

One afternoon in late September Mara didn't go straight to the Dower House when she reached Gaunt, but to the cottage, with the glow of Jamie's love-making still on her cheeks and in her eyes, and the early-evening mist sparkling in her hair. She wasn't even sure that Elenora would be there because she'd been in Italy since the middle of June, and Mara had neither seen her nor heard from her since the night when Jamie had been at the cottage. But the cottage had a lived-in air and as soon as Mara knocked Elenora opened the door. She took one look at Mara and said, 'You're in love.'

Mara blushed. 'Is it . . . ?'

'Obvious? Yes.'

'Oh dear.'

Elenora closed the door on the damp evening and led Mara through into the studio. 'I've been back two days,' she said, waving her hand towards the crates of books and canvases, 'but I just can't get round to unpacking. I was going to telephone you – you know I have a telephone now – but then, well, I thought you'd come when you wanted to. I left for Italy in a hurry.' She raised her chin as though overcoming some sadness. 'Sit down! Have a cigarette! I'll make some coffee.'

'I'm trying to give up,' Mara said, longing to smoke.

'It's Jamie, isn't it?'

Mara sat at the rough wooden table. 'Yes.' She picked at the uneven grains, running her fingernail along the soft grooves. 'How long have you known?'

'Oh, I had my suspicions. He told Sarah that he'd been

570

very fond of you, and then when he asked me to get you to come here . . . But I'd have known the minute I saw you together, you move as one person. I can certainly see what you see in him. He reminds me a little of . . . of your father-in-law.'

Mara said eagerly, 'You saw that too.'

'Yes. It's their attitude to life and the way they go straight to the point.' She paused. 'Are you going to leave Alexander?'

'I want to but he's ill again and I feel it's, well, a little too soon after his father died.'

Elenora had her back to Mara. 'Yes.'

'So I don't know what to do. You see, I was going to leave the day the Old Man died. Oh, I must tell you, I went up to the works and Herbert not only ordered me off but told me it's no longer Rushton-Gaunt but Rushton Motors. I was furious. I tried to have it out with Alexander but . . . Poor Sir Henry!'

Elenora sat down opposite Mara and lit a cigarette. 'Don't expect me to give up smoking just because you do.'

Mara smiled. 'I don't.' There was a deep but quiet sorrow in the shadows under Elenora's eyes, which was new and, she presumed, due to some unhappiness in Italy. 'Is anything wrong?'

'No, no, I was just thinking about you. Divorce is bad enough without adding to it. There's a terrible sense of failure – and guilt. You will feel guilty, you know, however healthy Alexander is when you leave.'

'Did you leave . . . for someone?'

'No. But I met someone very soon afterwards.'

'But you didn't marry him?'

'No. We had five wonderful years together.'

'And you never saw him again?'

571

'Oh yes. We went on seeing each other but by then we knew that it would come to nothing. You see, we were better off as we were . . . as lovers . . . as friends.'

Mara was terribly curious. 'Do you still see him?'

Elenora looked beyond Mara to the vivid paintings on the walls. 'Can't you guess who it was?'

Mara hesitated.

'Yes.' Elenora smiled as she watched the dancing colours on the walls. 'It was your father-in-law.'

'But how did . . . ?'

'How did I meet him? In London. He came to buy some paintings from a gallery belonging to a friend of mine – not Paul's gallery and not my sort of painting – good solid stuff, like Constable and Turner, and we began . . . talking.' She turned to Mara and smiled, and the strong lines of her face softened and the sheen of her green eyes grew brighter.

Mara said, 'And no one ever realized. But surely the people round here suspected?'

'I didn't live here then. He came to me in London, or we went to Barjon.'

'To the farmhouse?'

'Les Vieux Orangers. The Old Orange Trees.'

Mara could not help laughing. 'So it was you.' She told Elenora what had happened when the will was read, adding tentatively, 'I'm surprised he didn't leave it to you.'

'I didn't want it.' Elenora pushed back a strand of grey-streaked hair. 'Or anything. Not after . . . you see, it was a chapter of my life, in our lives, private and beautiful. I did not want it spoiled by sordid gossip.'

'But he never sold the farmhouse.'

'No. And he never went back either, not after the summer before the war. A whole month we stayed that summer. I would paint. He would walk. He used to go right up into the hills to a flat black rock.' She pointed at the lump of rock on the shelf, the one Mara had often touched and puzzled over. 'He loved it up there. He used to say there was something mystical about the place. I think I felt it too.' She paused. 'No, I could never go back to the farmhouse.'

'So you came here.'

'Here and London. He wanted me to meet his children but I wouldn't. They were nothing to do with us. But he was so anxious for me to see where he came from, in the end I came when they were away. We drove past this cottage one evening and I fell in love with it. It was the only thing I wanted, and he gave it to me. That was when we knew we would not marry but we could not bear to lose each other. He used to come here, night after night, through the woods, just like you do. Our woods, we called them.' She lit another cigarette and watched the smoke rise. 'He was a wonderful man, Mara, and I loved him deeply.'

Mara put her elbows on the table and rested her chin on her hands. 'Did he want to marry you?'

'Yes.'

'Was he very upset when you wouldn't?'

'Yes, but he understood.' Elenora laughed as a thought occurred to her. 'I would have been your stepmother-in-law.'

'Did you ever regret your decision?'

'For us, yes. For being the châtelaine of Rushton Park, never. It would have killed what we had.'

Mara and Elenora had so much to talk about they didn't notice the time pass. Their relationship had changed over the years, or perhaps not so much changed as developed. They had started as experienced older woman and curious girl. Then whilst Elenora had remained on course, Mara had deviated; to bright young thing who didn't want to think; to bright young thing for whom the world was suddenly not so bright; to what she was now: a woman who had learned that life was an uncertain game – a woman not unlike Elenora.

'I'll show you something,' Elenora said when Mara eventually rose to leave. 'Here, in the hall. You see those two blue paintings on the stairs, the ones I call my fake Picassos? Well, I'll tell you a secret. They're genuine. So's the Gauguin in my bedroom. So's the Chagall in the kitchen. So's the Constable.'

Mara said, 'I've never seen a Constable here.'

Elenora pulled a face. 'I should hope not. Not in my house. It's in the cellar. Can't bear that sort of thing. He only bought it for me because he was convinced the Picassos were rubbish.' She laughed at the memory of his words and opened the front door on to the cold wet night.

'But there's one thing I don't understand,' said Mara. 'Why wouldn't you come and see him at the Dower House?'

'For the same reason. Doers and watchers.'

Mara laughed. Doers and watchers! What a long time ago that was. She hesitated, curious but not wanting to pry. 'So you never saw him at the . . . end?'

'I did, but not often. Smithy used to bring him here occasionally. The last time was the day after you and Jamie were here.'

'Did you tell him?'

'No, it didn't seem fair. On him or on either of you.'

Mara thought of her parallel lines. They had almost crossed but not quite. 'You know what is really extraordinary,' she said, 'the only time I've been to France, apart from my weekend in Deauville with Alexander, was the summer before the war when I went to Paris with my parents. How funny to think that you and he were in France too.'

'But we are each other's destinies – Samuel and I, you and Jamie.'

Mara touched her arm. 'I just wish that we four . . .'

Elenora's green eyes glittered. 'Yes.' She sighed, then seemed to pull herself out of her regrets. 'You know what I found most amusing about you and Jamie?'

'What?'

'That no sooner had Sarah told me Jamie had been fond of you than you suddenly appeared on my doorstep' – she gave Mara a friendly nudge – 'pretending to be concerned for poor old Percy.'

'And you let me believe that he and Sarah . . .'

Elenora laughed. 'It wasn't a complete lie, Sarah does like him. But it served you right. You had a cheek coming here after all that time and only because you wanted to pump me for information.'

'I didn't. I would have come anyway. You old cow!'

Elenora cackled with laughter. 'You went green with jealousy.'

'I was spitting.' Mara could laugh about it now. 'Absolutely spitting.'

They embraced tenderly under the dripping ivy. 'Two old cows,' they said to each other, laughing.

October and November passed in a flurry of golden leaves and shortening days, but Mara did not notice. She lived only for her visits to Jamie. She counted the days, then the hours, then each half-hour until she went. And on her return she counted again: this time yesterday: this time two days ago: this time last week. A never-ending cycle of extremes – extreme happiness – extreme despair.

Sometimes they talked about Koblenz. 'What happened to everyone?' she asked. 'Do you still see them?'

'Well, Sayers went back to his farm. I stay with him and his family whenever I'm in that part of the Mid West. I see Durrant too. The other doctor, the one with fair hair. He has a practice in up-state New York. When we go to America we'll have to go and visit them. They've often talked about you,' he chuckled, 'but I've always done my best to change the subject.'

'And Rook? How did he manage without his legs?'

'He didn't have to for long. He was killed in a car crash.'

'Oh, no!'

'The driver was drunk.'

'I thought you weren't meant to drink in America.'

'You're not. But every American worth his salt carries a hip-flask and every town has its speakeasies. Liquor has become the forbidden fruit.'

One day when Mara arrived at the house in Hampstead, Jamie opened the door and said, 'I have a present for you. Close your eyes and no peeping. Close them, Mara!' He went behind her and put his hands over her eyes, saying, 'I don't trust you,' and walked her into the drawing room. 'Now look!' he took his hands away.

'Where? What?'

'On the floor.'

There was a large trunk on the floor. She knelt down beside it and lifted the lid. Inside were rows of tightly packed books. For a moment she stared blankly at them, then with a small cry she picked up one. 'My father's books! Where did you . . . ?'

He knelt down beside her. 'When I heard you wanted everything sold, I decided to buy them. I suppose I hoped . . .'

Mara opened the book and stared down at the print. Tears blurred the words. She lifted the book and buried her face in the thick parchment paper. Gently Jamie pulled her towards him and took the book from her hands. 'You're turning it into papier-mâché, Stork,' he said.

Each time they met Jamie would ask the same question. 'When are you going to leave him?'

'I don't know,' she would answer, and she would remember Elenora's words – 'Divorce is bad enough without adding to it' – and say, 'I can't leave him when he's ill.'

At first Jamie would hug her and say he understood, but gradually the strain of their affair began to tell. One day as she was about to leave he turned on her angrily. 'You can't leave him because he's ill. You can't leave him because his father's died. All that I accept. But now it's not just because he's ill but because he's arguing with his brother. Well I for one, Mara, can't go on for ever as we are. You have to do something – see his doctor – find out how ill he is. But I'm not going on and on. I told you that at the beginning.'

Mara was stunned. Having found each other it had never occurred to her they might part. 'Jamie.' Tears welled in her eyes. 'Don't. Please don't say that. I couldn't bear it if we . . .' She could not even say it. 'Oh, please.' She threw her arms around him. 'I know how you feel, I feel it too, but I'd rather see you this way than not at all.' And she clung tightly to him, terrified in case he said he would rather not see her at all than this way.

From that day a knot of panic grew in Mara. She tried to quash it, but it was there. She became frantic with worry in case Jamie left her, wild with frustration at Alexander in case he caused it. She could hardly bear to go into his room and see him lying there, so ill, so threatening. Panic made her careless. Panic made her stay late with Jamie, made her visits more frequent, made it all more obvious. And panic made her nervous and tense and irritable. Just as she had done in Koblenz she began to resent Jamie's work; to resent the clinic; to resent his lectures; to resent his growing reputation – anything which kept him from her during those precious days she spent in London.

Things were brewing to a head but she could not stop them or stop herself from saying what she said. One afternoon she arrived at the house to find Jamie hard at work. 'I must finish this lecture,' he told her, giving her a cup of coffee and an apologetic grin. 'It's terribly important. All about a new idea on treatment. Won't be more than ten minutes.' He went into his study and sat down at his desk.

Half an hour later Mara was still sitting by the fire and Jamie was still writing. Another half-hour, he still wrote, she still sat; only now she was furious. She went over to Jamie and put her hands on his shoulders. 'I must go in an hour.'

He patted her hand. 'Not much longer. Can't work with you standing behind me. Go and sit down by the fire.'

'I've been sitting for over an hour already, Jamie.'

'Yes, I know, but this is very important.'

Mara snapped, 'And I'm not?' She knew she was wrong but she was almost crying from disappointment.

He swivelled round on his chair. 'Don't be silly, Mara!'

'I'm not being silly. I've come all the way down to London, longing to see you, and then you're busy. I only have today. I told you so in my letter. But you don't care. Oh no, work comes first.' She turned away from him, so angry she could have walked out then and there and never seen him again.

Jamie was equally annoyed. 'So you feel ignored, do you? You feel I don't care because I didn't open the door and drag you upstairs and ram myself into you. Is that all we're about, Mara? Is that' – he grabbed her by the back of her thigh – 'what you want?'

'No, of course not.'

'Don't lie to me, Mara.'

'I'm not. And if you think you can keep me – let go of my leg – hanging around and then just . . .' She tried to kick him away.

But Jamie stood up quickly, pinned her arms behind her back and forced her forward until she was trapped between him and the edge of the desk, which caught her just below the hips. 'If you think you can go storming off like a spoiled child, you've got another think coming,' he said. And he flipped her skirt up over her head and forced her face down on to his paper-strewn desk.

Back at the Dower House, Mara went over that afternoon until she convinced herself that Jamie hadn't really wanted her but simply taken her in frustration, and her sense of panic grew. It made her say stupid things and do stupid things, without realizing they were stupid until after she had said or done them – until Jamie told her they were stupid. As in Koblenz, she began to lose her individuality, only this time she was not a limpet clinging to Jamie, she was a limpet to their situation. It was as if she were on a see-saw, rocking violently between her desire to leave Alexander, however ill he might be, and her fear of leaving him when he was ill – and the subsequent deleterious effect her guilt would have on her relationship with Jamie. And all the time it seemed that the see-saw was on a slippery slope, sliding further and further down as she rocked more and more violently. Sometimes she longed for Alexander to die, and was appalled at doing so, but could not stop herself, or else she longed for him to recover and to fall in love with someone else; both easy solutions for her. At the Dower House she spent hours lying on her bed, Jamie's locket clutched in one hand, his only letter to her clutched in the other, whilst the muffled sound of Alexander's endless coughing beat in time to her own irrepressible voice of panic. 'Don't leave me! Don't leave me! Don't leave me!' Alexander to her. She to Jamie.

And panic made Mara grasp at minor details and blow them up out of all proportion, or fail to see the importance of others, and pass them off lightly. One such occasion was a conversation she had with Lady Henrietta, who said to her one morning when Mara was staying with her yet again, 'I've never asked you where you were the night your father-in-law died, and at the time I was too busy to think about it. In any case, it's none of my business. But I must put my foot down at your conducting a flagrant affair from my house. I'm fond of your husband, though he has his shortcomings, and I believe in family ties. Now I've nothing against an affair handled with discretion and you're most welcome to stay with me, but not if you're going to stay out half the night. One must keep up appearances in front of the servants.'

By the time Mara met Jamie for lunch that day, she had mulled over Lady Henrietta's words so many times that she had expunged her initial reaction – despair that her love should be despatched so glibly – and ended up by regaling him with an amusing account of it.

Jamie listened in silence, his face growing darker as she talked, and although Mara knew she should stop, for some reason she couldn't; if anything her manner became more flippant. When she had finished he said, 'So you think it's funny.'

They were lunching in a small Italian restaurant near Holborn, one of those with salami and cheese in the window which from the outside could be just another sandwich bar, but inside are small and warm and intimate, and run by excited Neapolitans and their motherly, moustached wives. Mara looked across at the cheeses in the window. 'I didn't think it funny at first,' she replied miserably. 'I felt . . . dirty.'

'Then why the hell do you pretend otherwise? A discreet affair! If I'd thought that's all you wanted . . .'

'But it isn't.'

'Are you sure?'

'Of course I am.'

He seized her wrist and his voice rose so that the people at the other tables turned to watch. 'I believe in family ties too,' he said. 'I want us to be a family. A proper family. Not a money-grabbing empire like the Rushtons. I want us to be together. I want children by you, with you.'

Nervously Mara ran her tongue across her dry lips.

'Don't you want children?' he asked her.

'Well, I . . .' She had never really wanted a child before, but as she sat looking at him, thinking about him as a father, picturing herself lying in a hospital bed holding his newborn baby, and looking down at that baby and knowing it was a part of him, and of her, of both of them, she felt a sudden and intense longing to have his child. 'A boy or girl?' she asked.

He lifted her hand to his mouth and nibbled at its soft palm. 'Either. Both. Two of each.' His eye caught his watch. 'Oh, my God, it's after two. I must go.'

They parted on the pavement outside the restaurant with the office workers hurrying past them. He went one way: to the clinic. She went the other: to her car and the Dower House, and another two weeks of waiting until she saw him again. Fourteen days before she could be sure of him and sure that he had forgotten his anger, that it had not come back to him later when he was alone and made him decide he could wait no longer – and that he preferred not to see her at all than to see her like this.

Driving northwards out of London, Mara put herself in Jamie's shoes. How would I feel if he had a wife? If he'd promised to leave her and then weeks passed and he didn't? If he delayed . . . made excuses . . . said she was ill . . . said her sister was bullying her? She braked sharply to avoid a child and a black car following nearly went into the back of hers. Would I stand for it? Of course I wouldn't.

She stopped at a village, went to the post office, bought some writing paper and envelopes, and wrote a short note:

Jamie,
You're right – this isn't what we wanted. We're killing each other and it's up to me to heal the wounds. I'm going to see Alexander's doctor as soon as I'm back. At least then I'll know I'm not leaving a dying man.
    Be patient with me.
    I love you,
        Mara

When Mara came out of the post office the same black car which had nearly hit her was parked on the other side of the road. Its bonnet was up and its driver head-down in the engine. You ought to buy a Rushton-Gaunt, Mara told him silently, stepping into her own sleek and reliable model.

She drove on, her mind on Jamie, her eyes seeing Jamie – and not the black car which came steathily along behind her.

Mara telephoned Doctor Phillips. 'I would like to talk to you about my husband.'

He answered her in a professionally soothing voice. 'Of course, Mrs Rushton. Shall we say four o'clock tomorrow? No, I'll come to you.'

Mara couldn't bear to leave without saying goodbye to the works and everyone there, although of course she couldn't actually say goodbye. But at least when they heard she'd left, they would remember that she'd come up to see them beforehand, that she hadn't just gone as if they meant nothing to her. She also wanted to get out of the house. Knowing what she was going to do to Alexander, she couldn't have borne it if he'd called her to him and told her how much he loved her. I don't care what Herbert says if he sees me, she thought as she started her car, I don't give a damn. They – Smithy, Terry, Jackson, Pete, Mrs Wright – are much more important than he is.

Nevertheless she was relieved to find that Herbert wasn't at the works. It meant she was free to talk and joke with everyone, and it was obvious that they felt freer without him there. 'Is it true we've pulled out of racing?' she was asked again and again.

What could she say but, 'I'm afraid it's not up to me.'

'Of course. Of course.' They too felt the ripples of

insecurity emanating from the raised voices of her husband and her brother-in-law, and they understood her uncertainty. Or thought they did.

The last thing Mara did before leaving was to go into reception and look at her cup, sitting among all the cups won by her father-in-law. I'd take you with me, she told it silently, but you belong here.

It was nearly four o'clock by the time Mara drove away from the works, and the sky was thick and grey. As she went over the track, trying not to look at its neglected surface, it began to snow, huge wet flakes dropping down on her windscreen and forcing her to slow down.

When she finally arrived home at ten minutes before four, Jenkins greeted her with the words, 'Mr Herbert and Doctor Phillips are in the drawing room, madam.'

'Mr Herbert!'

'Yes, madam. Didn't you see his car in the drive?'

'No. It was snowing so hard.'

'Shall I bring in the tea?'

'Yes.' Why had Herbert come and how was she ever going to get rid of him and ask the doctor what she wanted to know?

Both men were wearing dark suits and standing with their backs to the fire, so that their legs were flickering with orange from the flames and their bodies were black and stark against the white marble mantelpiece. Their heads were tipped very slightly towards each other and they were conversing in undertones with all outward signs of gravity, as a couple of undertakers in the house of the bereaved might do when they wish to appear solemn but are really wondering who will win the two-fifteen.

Herbert spoke first. 'Ah, Mara, there you are.'

Mara gave him a barely civil nod, and said to the doctor, 'I'm sorry I'm late. I was caught in the snow.'

Doctor Phillips smiled. 'Only ten minutes, Mrs Rushton. Oh, good' – he saw Jenkins and the tea tray had followed Mara – 'some tea.'

Irritated at having to perform her hostess duties with the teapot at such a time Mara sat down and poured out the tea.

Doctor Phillips said, 'I asked your brother-in-law here because I thought you might need support. You obviously want to know about your husband and, I must say, I normally try to hide the truth from nervous young wives, but Mr Rushton and I both feel you're a courageous young thing and you can take it.'

Mara sat back in her chair and clasped her hands in her lap. To all intents and purposes she looked calm and reasonable, but then neither of the two men could feel her thudding heart or see how her stomach churned. She looked straight at Doctor Phillips. 'Yes?'

The doctor took a deep breath. 'Well, without going into too many medical details, Mrs Rushton, the damage done to your husband's lungs during the mustard gas attack has not responded to treatment and I'm afraid to say never will.'

'You're saying he's not going to get better?'

'Yes. The brutal fact is our English climate could hardly be worse for him.'

Mara looked at the fire, half hidden by their trouser legs. 'How long?' she asked, but she was thinking, how long before Jamie and I can be together?

For the first time Herbert joined in. He had been bouncing from foot to foot as a ballet dancer might do when longing for the moment when he can leap on to centre stage. 'Doctor Phillips says he won't last six months if he stays here, but if he were to move to a warmer, drier climate, well, who knows.' He looked to the doctor for support. 'Isn't that so?'

The doctor nodded. 'Can't promise anything but there's no doubt about it. He'd be better off in, say, Switzerland. People make miraculous recoveries there. But in all honesty I doubt if he'll live more than a couple of years wherever he goes.'

Herbert laid his arm along the mantelpiece and tapped his fat fingers on its white surface. 'Yes,' he said, a malicious gleam coming into his eyes as they settled on Mara. 'Yes. Switzerland . . . or . . .' He did not finish his sentence.

Mara sat perfectly still. She was aware of the doctor saying goodbye to her, of him telling Herbert that brandy was good for shock, and of him leaving. Then of Herbert calling for brandy, of the clink of glass against glass as he poured some, of him lifting the glass to his mouth, of him not offering her any – not that she wanted it. But they were things beyond the perimeter of her thoughts: things which did not matter. What mattered was that Alexander was dying and she did not want him to die. She knew that now she was facing the reality of his death. She knew too that she was fond of him and always would be, and she wanted him to get well and live: to meet another woman and be happy with another woman, so she could be happy with Jamie. So they could all be happy. Alexander deserved happiness as much as she did. More than she did. Because he was good – where she wasn't, though she tried to be. But now he was dying and in his lingering illness lay her dilemma: to leave and carry the guilt of having left a dying man: to stay and risk losing Jamie.

Herbert had taken up his place by the fire again. 'So you see, Mara, the Old Man's love-nest is a godsend.'

Mara looked up at him, not bothering to hide her dislike. 'What do you mean?'

'That Provence is warm and dry.'

Jamie was in England. She couldn't go to Provence. She said disparagingly, 'Warm and dry it may be, but you're not suggesting Alexander should live in some ramshackle farmhouse, are you?'

Herbert smirked and the liquor glistened on his lips. 'It isn't ramshackle. I sent one of Lewis' clerks out to check it. Apparently it's small but most attractive.' He laughed. 'An ideal place for an invalid and his devoted wife.'

Mara stood up. 'So you've been planning this all along.'

'Not planning' – he helped himself to more brandy – 'merely hoping. And why shouldn't I hope? I didn't go to a fancy school, I worked my guts out from the age of fourteen, I still work my guts out. Why should I have to have a sick man's signature on every single document? Why should I have to explain everything to him in order to get that signature? Oh, I'm happy for him to have a reasonable allowance, but the business should be mine. Mine!'

'And the sooner he's out of the way the better?'

'Yes.'

Mara took a step towards him. 'You don't care about Rushton-Gaunt.'

'Rushton Motors now, Mara.'

She ignored his interruption. 'You don't care about anything except money. You don't even care if Alexander lives or dies.'

Herbert slammed down his glass. 'Don't talk to me about caring! All you care about is your fancy doctor.'

Mara froze.

'Yes,' he went on, laughing cruelly, 'I know all about it. I had you followed – remember the black car? Going

587

up to London every two weeks. Coming back all pink and glowing. Did you think I didn't realize?'

Mara longed to hit him, but she stopped herself. She didn't want to bring herself down to his level. Without a word she turned and walked towards the door.

But Herbert hadn't finished. He was enjoying himself. He grabbed her arm and pulled her back. 'Too proud to talk to me are you?' he sneered down into her face. 'Looked at me as though I'm dirt for years, you have, but you're nothing but a two-timing little minx. My poor brother! I warned him about you. I told him what you were like, right at the beginning.'

Mara yanked her arm free. 'What I do is none of your business.'

'Then you don't mind if I tell Alexander?'

Mara took a few steps backwards. She was trembling with rage. 'Tell him what you like. I was going to tell him myself anyway.'

Herbert stared at her with surprise. 'You were going to leave him! Leave all this!' He waved his hand to encompass the room, the house, and its contents. 'I don't believe it.'

'No, I'm sure you don't.' Mara's confidence was returning. She told herself that Herbert was no more than an unpleasant and vulgar man, whose unpleasantness and vulgarity stemmed from his own sense of inferiority. 'You and I have different values,' she said coldly. 'You couldn't possibly understand.'

'Values?'

'Yes.'

'Values that let you leave a dying man?'

'That's entirely between myself and Alexander.' Mara was trying desperately not to let Herbert see how his words, 'leave a dying man', had affected her.

Herbert laughed. 'You're a tough nut, Mara, and I admire you. Don't like you. Never have. But I admire your nerve, though you're wrong in this. It's not just between you two. You see' – he helped himself to more brandy – 'to be blunt, if you leave my brother there'll be nobody to take him abroad – or take him anywhere – and so long as he's here, he won't let go. I know Alexander. It might only be six months, but I'm sick of it. Sick of it!'

'There's no question of my leaving England,' said Mara firmly. 'But as to whether I leave Alexander, that's for me to decide.'

'So you can't do without the worthy doctor, eh?' Herbert licked his lips and grinned. 'Can't do without your fortnightly poke? Tell me, Mara, what does he do to you? And what do you do to him, eh?'

Eyes blazing, she raised her arm and lashed out at him. 'Shut up! Shut up, you pig!'

Still grinning, Herbert parried her blow, smashing into her forearm with the side of his hand, so hard that she cried out with pain. 'Hit me, you little bitch, and I'll hit you back,' he snarled. 'My God, if you were my wife I'd teach you a lesson. And I'd enjoy it.' He moved towards her. 'I'd ram myself into you so hard you wouldn't be able to walk. I'd make you do all those things you do with your American doctor. I'd . . .' He was panting with excitement, and in his wanting her Mara regained her advantage. At the hunt ball she'd suspected it, then dismissed the idea as being ridiculous, but now she was sure he wanted her, almost as much as he disliked her.

'I wouldn't let you touch me if you were the last man alive,' she said, disdainfully eyeing his pot belly. Then she turned and walked towards the door.

But Herbert wasn't beaten yet. Her look of disdain made him want to strangle her, the idea of her sneaking off to give her lover what he himself wanted, had always wanted, but till now had never admitted to wanting, brought forth all his cunning. 'If you won't take Alexander to Provence, I'll tell him about your lover and I'll tell him that as a gentleman he's honour-bound to throw you out. And he will.'

Mara stopped just before the door. She looked back at Herbert and laughed, and was about to say she wouldn't need throwing out, she'd be gone anyway, when he cut in. 'If you leave Alexander, don't think that'll be the end of it. I'll make damned sure every newspaper in the country hears of it. "Eminent American doctor persuades German wife to abandon dying English war hero." I'll even give them the photographs. Oh, yes, I've got plenty. The lovers kissing in the street. The lovers in their Hampstead nest. It's amazing what a camera can do if you forget to draw the curtains. And I'll name your doctor. Doctor Jamie Turner. Just think what that'll do to his career. No decent woman will dare go near him. And he'll never get away from it. People will always remember. He'll be ruined. You'll have ruined him. How he'll hate you! Not at first, of course. Not whilst you're young and attractive and can bounce around a bed, giving it to him as he wants it. But later. When you're old and he doesn't want your body any more. When the passion's gone but he's still paying for it, slaving his guts out in some small provincial hospital, his clever ideas wasted on farm labourers' tonsils. And he'll look at you. My God, how he'll hate you!'

Mara tried not to listen, but she was incapable of shutting out his words because in his coarse way he was articulating all her deepest fears. When he had finished speaking, she said, 'What about Alexander, don't you think it'll ruin him too?'

Herbert shrugged. 'Alexander's dying and, as you so rightly said, I don't care what happens to him.'

Mara went straight out of the house, not even bothering to take a coat, and drove through the snow to Elenora's. Only there, sitting at the table, a cup of coffee in front of her, did she give way to tears. Hot angry tears mixed with words of rage and despair. 'What am I going to do? How can I leave Alexander when he's dying? How can I drag Jamie's name through the papers? Herbert's right. He'll hate me. I know he will. But what can I do? I can't bear to lose him. Not again. I love him. I've always loved him. I'll never love anyone else as I love him.'

Elenora handed her a lit cigarette. 'Take it! This isn't the moment for giving up.'

Mara wiped her face on the back of her hand and took the cigarette. But her hand was wet and it made the cigarette damp so that the paper split and the tobacco burst out, which added to her despair.

Elenora lit another and gave it to her, saying, 'No one else can decide for you. Only you know what's right. You have to follow your instinctive gut-feeling.'

'I know, I know.' Mara jumped up and walked round the studio, smoking fiercely and kicking at the floor. 'I know it would be wrong for me to leave Alexander but I also know I can't face life without Jamie. I can't go back to what I was, to living with Alexander, not now I know Jamie loves me. This is my second chance. I'll never get another one.'

'If Jamie loves you he'll wait for you.'

'It might be years.'

'They'll pass more easily for you if you go to the farmhouse. Staying here would be terrible. You'd be tempted.'

Mara stubbed out the cigarette in the sink. It hissed

591

angrily as it touched the wet porcelain. 'I don't care if I'm involved in a scandal,' she said, 'I'd give up everything for Jamie.'

'But Jamie would care. Not about his name but his work. Herbert's right. It would ruin him, at least as far as this country's concerned. The English are very conventional. Politicians and doctors have to lead exemplary lives. Very few get away with it. Lloyd George was an exception – and not just because he was a Welshman.'

Mara picked up the lump of black rock. She toyed with it in her hand, as she had so often done and as Jamie had done. She could almost feel his fingers touching her. What would he say if she told him about Herbert? He would say . . . She would be asking him to choose between his work and herself. Which would he choose? He loved her, she believed he did, but she wasn't everything in his life as he was everything in hers, she never could be. A leg or an arm, that's what she was, something he would miss for the rest of his days but would gradually become used to not having. She stared down at the lump of rock and she saw Jamie sitting at her father's desk in Koblenz organizing the hospital, then sitting on her bed in the attic telling her about Rook, then bending over the injured child in the clinic, then standing on a platform expounding his theories with all the enthusiasm of one who longs to save life and thinks he may have found a way of doing so. And she knew her answer. If she were to tell him there was a choice, and he chose her, she would live in fear of his regret; and he *would* regret, because her fear would destroy them. If on the other hand he chose his work, the one thing he could not live without, she knew she would feel bitter resentment towards him and no amount of rationalizing would soften the blow. Whichever choice Jamie made would ruin them

– would kill their love – would be the first page of the final chapter. The End. So for Jamie there had to be no choice. Mara put the rock back in its place on the shelf, and made the first totally unselfish decision of her life.

Chapter 34

Provence, 1928

Beautiful, peaceful Barjon was Mara's exile, but it was no more able to hold her than the beauty and peace of Elba had been able to hold Napoleon, who had longed as she did for the familiar fray. No sooner had she and Alexander unpacked than she said, 'Let's go down to Cannes.'

He looked round at the old farmhouse with its flagstones and mellow walls. 'We could go next week.'

'No, let's go now. I can't bear it here, it's so quiet.' She went upstairs to change, calling over her shoulder, 'I'm taking a suitcase so we can spend the night.'

Mara was already in the driving seat by the time Alexander came out carrying a small case. They drove down through the narrow streets of Barjon, ignoring the curious stares of the villagers, out of the old stone gateway, and on down the narrow bumpy road until they hit the coast, the wildness of the High Var behind them, the glittering moneyed world of Cannes ahead.

'What shall we do?' Alexander asked, looking doubtfully at the unEnglishness of the place: the jewellery of the women on the promenade sparkling in the wintry sun, the gesticulating waiters in a nearby bar, the smell of French cooking, the whiteness of the houses.

'Let's go there,' said Mara, pointing to the bar. It was the smartest.

'Very well.'

They sat down at a table near the front. All around them groups of people talked and laughed, but they knew no one. 'We'll try somewhere else next time,' said Mara.

'Yes.' He stared miserably at the sea.

Mara sighed. So this is my lot, she thought. 'I want to have a look at the shops later,' she told him, 'French clothes are so wonderful.' A girl walked along the promenade, her layered skirt slightly longer at the back than at the front. 'Hems seem to be dropping and I must buy some new things. We can meet up later.'

'Oh no, I'll come with you,' he said hurriedly.

They stayed in a hotel and spoke to no one, hardly even to each other, and the next day they drove dejectedly back to Barjon.

The following week she again insisted that they went to Cannes. This time they tried a different bar, just as full of people they didn't know. But what did I expect? she asked herself, watching Alexander trying not to cough.

'Perhaps we should try Nice next time,' she said, simply for the sake of saying something.

'Yes, if you like.'

'But what would you like?'

Before he had time to answer Mara felt a hand on her arm and she turned to find herself looking up at a girl with a dark geometric haircut, vaguely familiar although Mara couldn't place her. 'You're Mara Rushton, aren't you?' the girl said with a heavy French accent.

Mara nodded.

'You do not remember me, I see. I am Zizi, a friend of Yves Lejeune, we all . . . er . . .' she looked doubtfully at Alexander.

Now Mara remembered her and she cut across the girl, 'Yes, of course. I don't think you met my husband, Alexander.'

They all shook hands and, after asking what they were doing there and exclaiming in horror when Mara said they lived in Barjon, Zizi whisked them over to her table. Mara went eagerly. Alexander shambled along behind.

'This is Mara Rushton,' cried Zizi, pushing Mara towards a table where four people sat drinking crème de menthe. 'She's a famous English racing-driver, a friend of Yves Lejeune.' They looked suitably impressed. 'And this is her husband . . . er . . . Alexander.' Zizi introduced them to an elderly and over-made-up Hungarian countess, an oily young man in two-tone shoes – what in England were called 'co-respondent's shoes', a third-rate English film star who played damsels who enjoy their distress, and Ross, an American matinée idol clutching at the remnants of his youth.

The countess seized on Alexander and began telling him about her first husband, 'An Englishman, so sweet but so boring.'

Zizi turned to Mara. 'Did you know Yves was married last month?'

Mara shook her head. 'But I hardly know him so it's not surprising.'

Zizi's sharp little face twitched with amusement. 'I went to the wedding. She's American. All legs and dollars.' She laughed at her own joke, then asked, 'Will you be racing again next year?'

'No, Alexander's not well enough for us to live in England for the time being.'

'So you said. But why did you choose Barjon, it's so primitive?'

Mara pulled a face. 'You're telling me! We have a house there, that's why.'

'Don't worry.' Zizi patted her hand. 'You have us now.'

The matinée idol left and immediately they began to pull him to pieces. 'Poor Ross,' said Zizi,'he keeps saying he's resting his voice.'

The countess laughed. 'What voice?'

'The one he had before he ruined it with too much whisky.'

'Nothing's a secret here,' said the film star with a giggle. Her over-bright curls glittered as she turned her back on the countess who was prattling to Alexander. 'We even know how much you-know-who spent on you-know-who last week.' She winked at Zizi and they both tittered. Mara laughed too. At least it was better than Alexander's monosyllables.

After that first meeting Mara and Alexander spent at least two nights a week in Cannes. Mara would have been glad to stay there all the time. In all honesty she didn't particularly like the people they met, they'd got in with the fast, hard-drinking set, and she knew that Alexander would have much preferred to know the elderly English who sat drinking tea on the terraces of their hotels, like spectators at a cricket match. But for Mara, Zizi and Ross and their crowd were much more amusing, even if they were bitchy about each other, and probably about her too once her back was turned. At least they stopped her from brooding over Jamie. She hadn't heard a word from him since that snowy night when, on returning from the cottage, she had written to tell him that Alexander was dying, that she felt she could not leave him, and that they were going to live in France. Of course she had hoped – expected – to hear from him in the month before their departure, but nothing. No letter. No telephone call. And since she'd been in France, no message came through Elenora, although Mara knew that he'd twice been to the cottage. 'He did not mention you so I didn't,' Elenora had written to her. Over and over again Mara asked herself if she had been wrong. Should she have told him everything and let him choose? Should she have spelt out Herbert's intentions and said, 'Now, choose between us. Your work or me!' But each time she thought, no, I was right to spare him.

On one of their visits Ross took them to a party. As they drew up outside an enormous white villa from which music and light poured out on to a terraced garden, Alexander said, 'Do you really think it's all right for us to come, Ross?'

Ross laughed. 'Why ever not?'

'We haven't been invited.'

'She won't mind. That's what she's come for.'

'What do you mean?'

'That having been the devoted wife of an ironmongery millionaire – he's now gone off with a starlet – she's come here to spend her massive alimony. She wants to meet people.'

Alexander looked uncertainly at the villa. 'But we don't know her.'

Ross laughed again. 'Nor do I,' and he swept them in to the false brightness supplied by nuts and bolts.

After an hour Alexander told Mara, 'I'm going back to the hotel, I can't stand it. Will you come with me?'

Mara was about to say, 'No, I'm enjoying it,' but she wasn't. There was something horribly pathetic about their aged doll-like hostess twittering in a corner as hordes of unknown dissolutes swilled down her champagne and munched their way through her caviar. It was obvious that she felt, with so many titled persons in her house, she had 'arrived'. She was too new to the Riviera to know that few of the titled could afford to eat caviar in their own homes, though that wouldn't stop them from pulling her to pieces tomorrow, if they weren't already doing so. 'I'll come with you,' said Mara, and she looked over at Ross who was wavering towards a tray of drinks. He wouldn't even remember they'd been there.

After that party Alexander flatly refused to go to Cannes again, but that didn't stop Mara. Every two or three weeks she would drive down to Cannes, to be bored, to drink, to smoke, to sit around and gossip. Long inane cocktails overlooking the sea with people she despised but couldn't do without.

Then one afternoon in early spring – for of course it would happen in the spring – Mara was sitting with Ross and the countess and Zizi at their usual table in the usual bar and Ross was talking about France. 'Cannes, Nice, Paris and Deauville, they're the only places worth living in. And I know what I'm talking about, after all, I know the country like the back of my hand. And I know the French too.' He smiled at Zizi.

'No you don't,' she replied, 'you only know waiters and countesses, Ross.'

'Okay, but I do know the country.'

Mara thought of the villages she passed through on her way down to Cannes, villages where the young men had all been killed in the Great War and the old men scratched out a living amongst the olive trees, where the women gossiped as they did their washing in open troughs in the village square, where peasants slept beside their donkeys in the midday sun: villages like Barjon. 'Do you know the High Var?' she asked him.

'Where?'

'Behind there.' She pointed to the hills above the coast.

'Good God no! Why should I want to?'

Mara stood up. 'I must go, I have to get back.'

'Where to?'

She looked at him, at the countess, at Zizi, seeing them for exactly what they were: vain and pathetic. 'To the High Var,' she answered with a smile, and she turned and made her way across the bar towards the exit.

Mara set off up the coast road until she came to the turning for Barjon. There she began the long climb up into the High Var, away from Cannes and the sea, and immediately she felt as though a weight had been lifted from her shoulders. Her suitcase bounced on the back seat, Alexander's newspapers slid around beside it, the car grumbled over the bumpy road, and she began to hum. Just short of the village she stopped the car and lit a cigarette, and sat there smoking and looking over to the terracotta roofs and the mellow stone walls, caught by the evening sun where they tumbled over the crest of the hill and into the olive groves below. And Mara realized that she loved this place and that if she had to be without Jamie she would rather be without him in Barjon than anywhere else.

That was two years ago. Since then she had avoided Zizi and Ross and the Riviera crowd, only going to Cannes once a month, to draw money from the bank, to buy little luxuries, and to collect letters from Damon and Atalanta written secretly to her at the *poste restante*. She had told them not to write to her at Barjon because Alexander would be hurt if she didn't let him read their letters, and Atalanta's were full of Pete, just as Damon's were full of how much he hated his father. In Cannes Mara also collected *The Times*, which Alexander could not live without – a whole month's back copies at a time, printed words from a world she no longer needed.

She was on her way back from Cannes now. Thank heavens that's over for a month, she thought as the red roofs of Barjon came into view. No more hat, no more

600

gloves, no more trying to make myself look smart for four whole weeks. What bliss! She remembered the vast sums of money she'd once spent on clothes, and laughed out loud.

Children waved as Mara drove slowly through the twelfth-century gateway and up along narrow streets to the village square. Old Madame Gramont, known to everyone as Maman, the wife of old Pierre Gramont who looked after the farmhouse in Samuel Rushton's day, came waddling out of the butcher's shop. She called to Mara, asking after her journey as though Mara had visited another planet for the day – which Cannes was to Maman, who had never been there. 'Monsieur Alexander's a little better today,' she told Mara, patting her shoulder and beaming down into the car. 'He sat out in the sun this afternoon. But I told him not to stay out too long. The sun may be shining but the air's cold. And I've baked some bread, soft just as he likes it. And I did the chicken as you said, Madame Mara.'

Mara nodded. Maman came every morning to cook and clean with the help of Jeanne, her niece, and every day the farmhouse shone like a new pin and delicious smells wafted from the kitchen. She stretched over into the back seat and grabbed three small packets. 'I bought you a little something,' she told the old peasant woman. 'Some tobacco for old Pierre. A bar of soap for Jeanne. And for you, Maman, your favourite. Chocolates.'

'Chocolates!' Maman took them from Mara carefully as if they were made of egg-shell china. 'Oh, Madame Mara, you shouldn't!' Looking at Maman's face Mara was reminded, not for the first time, of Smithy. They had the same cheery roundness and bright eyes, the same laughter-lines and wrinkles, the same look of a happy robin in a garden full of worms.

601

Leaving Maman in the square, Mara drove on slowly, weaving her way up through the maze of narrow streets and alleys, stopping every so often for donkeys to shift their hind legs or for children to retrieve their balls. Patience. Peace. The dying sun slid off the red roofs and the old men shuffled towards the café. Barjon.

Immediately above the village Mara turned left down an even rougher road, no more than a track, passed between two gnarled orange trees, Les Vieux Orangers, and into the cobbled courtyard around which the two-storey farmhouse was built. As she stopped Bobo, the donkey, poked his head out of his stable on one side of her and Alexander opened the front door on the other.

He called out, 'Mara, is that you?'

'Yes.'

'Good journey?'

'Yes.' She collected up the newspapers and the parcels of shopping and walked towards the doorway where he stood, silhouetted against the warm light.

He kissed her on the cheek and took the newspapers. 'Get everything done?'

'Yes, except for my hair. I wanted to have it cut but there wasn't time.'

He touched her hair which had once been a razor-sharp bob and now was an unruly mane about her shoulders. 'I don't know why you want to cut it. I like it long.'

Mara smiled vaguely. 'Long hair and cloche hats don't go.'

'Don't they?' He stood aside to let her pass, adding in a flat voice, 'There's a letter for you.'

'Oh.' She looked quickly at the hall table. Never could she stop herself from hoping. 'Oh, yes.' She tossed her hat on to a chair to hide her disappointment. 'It's from

Elenora.' How silly she was to hope. What could be better than a letter from Elenora? She would read it over and over again, smiling as she pictured its writer in her cottage. They had seen each other only once since Mara had left England and that had been last summer. Elenora had been in Paris for an exhibition of her work and she had come down to Cannes by train for one night. Mara had gone in to meet her. How quickly that day and night had passed. How much they had talked. How much there had not been time to say.

'I recognized her writing,' said Alexander. 'I hope she's well.' He still disapproved. 'I had a letter too, from Herbert. They're all well and they . . . er . . . send their love.'

Mara knew he was lying. Secretly she had read Herbert's letters to Alexander, which arrived with regularity once every six weeks. They were full of how well the business was doing and how many titled suitors Atalanta had, but never once had there been a mention of herself. Nor was Damon dealt with except in passing. But Herbert can't beat us, thought Mara. There had been a letter from Damon and one from Atalanta at the *poste restante*. Damon was now at Oxford 'but I steer clear of the Park', he had written. Atalanta's letter had been full of Pete Smithy. 'I pretend to Father that I'm having a very social time and go out with lots of men,' she wrote, 'but I can't wait till I'm twenty-one when Pete and I can be married.'

Mara crossed the uneven flagstones of the hall and went through into the drawing room. It was a beautiful low-ceilinged room with huge bay windows looking down into the valley; a room that was light and cheerful by day and warm and cosy by night, when the shadows of the flames from the fire danced, as they did now, on the reddish walls and on the leather backs of the books which lined one side of the room.

'Maman lit the fire,' Alexander told her, padding along behind like a faithful dog – like Prince.

Mara stoked the fire. 'Did Maman lay the table?'

'I think so.'

'Good.' She went through into the small dining room – Maman had laid the table – and beyond it into the big farmhouse kitchen with its red provençal floor tiles and endless copper pans swinging above a long black kitchen range.

Alexander lowered himself into a comfortable chair beside the stove. It took him time to sit down. His movements were slow and he had put on weight. 'Old Pierre came and shut up the chickens.'

Mara smiled and nodded. The chickens were the bane of her life. She loathed the sound of them and the sight of their scaly legs, but Maman insisted she kept chickens: a good wife always kept chickens. Once Mara had protested, 'I'm sure Madame Elenora wouldn't have kept chickens,' and the old woman had pursed her lips and replied, 'Madame Elenora was not a proper wife. She wouldn't marry poor Monsieur.' She had given Mara a questioning look, 'Monsieur Alexander does not know about his father and Madame Elenora?' and when Mara shook her head, Maman simply said, 'Then I'll make sure no one tells him.'

'And I fed Bobo,' said Alexander. 'The ungrateful beast nearly bit me.'

Mara nodded. 'Thank you for all you've done.'

At last Alexander could wag his tail. Even if Mara went out only for an hour or two, upon her return he listed all that had happened and all he had done, waiting for her thanks and approval before he could relax.

Mara tasted the chicken casserole and added some seasoning. Alexander sat watching her. After a while he said, 'You look very smart in that suit. Much smarter somehow than you used to look in London when you were always buying clothes.'

'Spendthrift was I?'

'A bit.'

She took off her jacket. It was hot in the kitchen. 'It's just the comparison which makes me look smart to you.'

Alexander looked puzzled.

'I mean you're used to seeing me in homespun skirts and cardigans knitted by Maman.' His slowness no longer made her impatient.

He nodded. 'Or baggy trousers when you ride Bobo. You know Maman disapproves of women in trousers.'

'I know she does.' Mara chopped up a tomato. 'Don't worry, she tells me just what she thinks. Mind you' – she looked at his old trousers and comfortable tweed jacket – 'you're hardly a fashion plate yourself.'

'No. And to think we used to dress for dinner every night.' He looked away from her, his face falling into lines of sadness, and Mara knew how deeply he missed the past. 'I keep saying this to you, darling,' he said a little later, 'but we could easily afford to have living-in servants.' .

Mara shook her head. 'No thanks, I prefer it this way. Maman and Jeanne do everything and, anyway, where would we put living-in servants? There's your room, my room, the spare room, and the bedroom that's full of my clothes.' She laughed. 'The ones I never wear any more. Oh no, the house is far too small, even if we hadn't had the little room made into a second bathroom. You know the whole village thinks we're mad. Two bathrooms!'

'We could always have some more rooms built on,' he persisted. 'It wouldn't be too difficult.'

'And have workmen tramping all over the garden just when it's beginning to look so pretty? No, thank you.'

'I was only thinking of you.'

'Well, I'm happy as I am.' She went through into the dining room and lit the paraffin lamps, electricity being unknown in Barjon. Regularly, every month, Alexander brought up the same subject: servants. Although Mara was sure he was fairly contented, it was as though he felt he, an Englishman, ought not to be content without the trappings of his position. She came back and stood in the doorway. 'Do you miss England a lot?' she asked him gently.

Alexander didn't meet her eyes. 'Yes, I suppose I do. I've felt better here than I had for years before we came, that is until this last month when I seem to cough a lot at night. But I'm too English to live outside England and not miss it, I'm too English to adapt as you do, I'll never understand people here or the way they think.'

'Do you want to go back?' she asked. They had never talked about that.

'No, no. I couldn't bear to be so ill again. I couldn't bear to face Herbert day after day, arguing . . . oh, no.'

'And you're not suggesting we go and live in Cannes?'

He looked at her in horror. The decadence of the Riviera had appalled him. 'Good God, no! I always thought the men were the most frightful bounders and the women . . . I couldn't bear the way their thick lipstick cracked into the lines of their upper lips. Every time one of them kissed me – foreigners always kiss each other – I used to shudder.'

Mara howled with laughter. It wasn't often Alexander made her laugh, and now he looked at her with pleased surprise, as if he'd bought her some trifling present only to find it was exactly what she'd always wanted. 'I know, I know,' she spluttered, clutching the doorpost. 'You should have seen your face. Eyes closed. Teeth gritted.'

He tapped his legs with his big flat fingers. 'Did it show? How dreadful! I tried to pretend I enjoyed it. Oh no, I couldn't bear to have to do that all day long.'

Mara wiped the tears of laughter from her eyes. 'Well, that's a relief.'

'If I have to live anywhere outside England,' he said, suddenly very serious and looking straight at her, 'I want to live here with you. It's just that . . . this isn't what you expected when we married. A sick husband. A lonely farmhouse. No maid. I know you didn't want to bring Rachel, but . . .'

'Poor Rachel! What on earth would she do here? She's perfectly happy with the Taylors.'

'You should have had another maid,' he persisted, 'or at least some proper servants.'

Mara put the plates to warm. 'Servants! Meals on time. Dressing for dinner. Strangers in the house. They may do everything for you but you pay a price for having them.'

'What do you mean? Their wages?'

'No, not that. I mean you lose your freedom.' She explained it to him exactly as she might have explained it to a child. 'You may be their employer and they may be at your beck and call but you lose your freedom just as much as they lose theirs.'

'I see.' He didn't really.

Mara went through to the drawing room. Alexander shambled after her. 'I don't want you to be bored, that's all,' he said. 'You used to love balls and hunting and people, and here you have none of these things. You don't even have a horse. Perhaps we should have brought Nutcracker with us.'

'What, and leave poor old Mahogany behind?'

'We could have brought them both.'

'They'd have broken their legs within a week in these hills. No, they're much better off with Alison.'

'Oh, I'd forgotten.' He produced a letter from his jacket pocket. 'Alison's going to marry some Army chap.'

'Oh, good.' They'd never had much in common but Mara was pleased for Alison.

He nodded. 'I'll ask Sophia to buy a wedding present on our behalf.' He paused and looked round the room. 'You don't even have electricity.'

Mara knelt down to stoke the fire. Whenever he listed all the things she was missing, he never mentioned Brooklands and racing. The only time they had spoken of Brooklands was a year or so earlier when they had read of Henry Segrave's death. 'They all get killed sooner or later,' he'd said pointedly, and Mara had replied, 'Not all, your father didn't,' but she'd thought, Parry Thomas and now Henry Segrave. And they'd come back to her: Parry Thomas with his Fair Isle sweater, his blue and white car *Babs* and his dog Togo; Henry Segrave with his aristocratic good looks. For a while she'd felt sharp nostalgia for those winter days at Brooklands.

'I have other things,' she told him, prodding a log with the poker, 'I have the sun and the mountains. I can ride Bobo right up into the hills where a horse would fall and break its legs. I have Maman and the villagers, who accept me for what I am, dressed as I please. And I have this house which I love.'

'And you've got me to put up with.' He stroked the top of her head where the light of the fire shone warmly on her tawny hair, picking out the red and turning it into a coppery halo.

'Yes.' She reached behind her, patted his calf and stood up.

He stepped back to let her pass. 'So you don't miss . . . anything?' He needed constant reassurance. His unsureness of her now they lived in a foreign land, surrounded by people whose language she had picked up quickly because she had a good ear for languages, but he spoke badly because he had an Englishman's fear of making mistakes, was far greater than when they had lived in England. He was so totally dependent on her.

But Mara was halfway across the room when he spoke, and she kept on walking just as though she had not heard his question.

The next couple of months were perhaps the most peaceful Mara had ever known. She existed on a plateau of contentment: no anguished gullies: no frenetic peaks: no actor and director – there was no audience to play to: no bus queue – there was nothing to wait for.

In the two years since she had come to Barjon she had passed through all the stages of withdrawal: misery; disbelief; bitterness; rage; resignation; and finally arrived at this plateau, where she was aware of beauty, of trees and flowers and wind and sun. Day after day she would ride Bobo up through the yellow broom which covered the hills like a golden fleece, until she reached the flat black rock, the one her father-in-law had loved, from where she could look down on the village and the plain beyond, and beyond that, on a clear day, to the glitter of the distant sea. There, on the black rock, Mara would sit and smoke – she couldn't smoke in the house because it made Alexander cough – and listen to the cries of birds and the bleating of the sheep and the occasional shout from the fields far below. She had found the black rock by chance, following a stony path which twisted in and out of stunted trees and other jagged rocks until suddenly she had found herself standing on it and looking down on the valley. There was no question it was not *the* rock; none of the others was flat or black.

Sometimes when Mara was up at the black rock and the wind was blowing up off the sea and into her face she would remember the Deutsches Eck and the running rivers. Other times it would remind her of the windswept works track and the distant glitter of the sea would be the windows of the office building sparkling in the sun. But most of all when she was up there it was the Old Man who came to her, because this had been his place. The scuffling of some tiny animal through the grass would cause her to turn, half expecting to see him striding across the hills towards her, his white mane blowing in the wind, his granity face caught by the sun, for of course he would now be beyond his wheelchair.

On the days when the weather was bad or the mist lay so low over the village that Alexander begged her not to ride in case she got lost, Mara would wander into the village and visit Maman's aged mother, finding peace in the stone kitchen of the old peasant's cottage where the numerous grandchildren climbed all over her, wanting to know why she was tall and fair when everyone else they saw was short and dark.

Then, at the end of April, Mara's dreamlike existence ended. Alexander woke one night coughing blood. She drove him down through the dawn to the hospital in Cannes. He was kept there for three weeks, having endless, useless treatments. Mara stayed in a hotel nearby, and every day, when she visited Alexander and smelt that smell of hospitals, she was reminded of Jamie. He came back to her in waves of longing as she sat beside Alexander's bed or as she walked down the wide bright hospital corridors, and he did not leave her when she went out into the street or when she walked alone beside the sea. She missed him as she had not missed him since her first months in France, and she longed to go back to Barjon where there was nothing to remind her of him.

In the end the doctors told Mara, 'There's nothing we can do for your husband, madame. We can give you some pills to ease the pain, but . . .' They shrugged helplessly and said that war did not end with the last bullet. So Mara took Alexander back to Barjon, wrapped in a blanket and still coughing blood.

But before they left Cannes she picked up his month's supply of newspapers, and a few days later, when she was talking to Maman in the kitchen, she heard him calling to her. Thinking something frightful must have happened, Mara ran upstairs two at a time, only to find Alexander sitting up in bed, excitedly gasping for breath. 'Look! Look!' He waved a page of newspaper at her. 'Look! Read it!'

'What?' She took the page.

'There! There! Read it! Do you think if I wrote to him . . .'

'Who?' She searched down the page until her eyes fell on a heading, 'New Treatment of Lung Diseases'. Below it was a short paragraph and out of the general blur of the words one name leaped up at her: Doctor Jamie Turner. Her hands began to tremble, shaking the page so she could not read it, her mouth went dry and her face felt alternately hot and cold.

'Well?' said Alexander. 'What do you think?'

'I . . . I'm just reading it.' She forced herself to read:

'The eminent American lung specialist, Doctor Jamie Turner, recently returned from a lecture tour in his native land, has been expounding his revolutionary and highly successful treatment of damaged lung tissue.' There was more but Mara could not read on.

'Mara, we must write to him,' Alexander was saying. 'Perhaps he can help me. Oh, I know he won't come here . . . too busy . . . but he might recommend . . . if I wrote. I always wish I'd seen him when we were in England. I wouldn't have minded meeting him socially as well.' He coughed. 'Always liked the chap. Perhaps you should write for me, Mara.'

She put down the page. 'Well, I . . .' She needed time to think.

'Why not, darling? Surely he would . . .' He began to cough, coughing and coughing until streaks of blood dribbled down his chin. 'Surely he would try – for you.'

'But he wouldn't have time to come here.'

'I know, but . . .'

'And he can't treat you without seeing you. He might prescribe something that killed you.'

Alexander closed his eyes and sank back into his pillows. 'I'm going to die anyway,' he said very quietly, 'so he won't kill me. But he might be able to give me something to take away the pain. He might give me another year. Even just another six months. Can you imagine what it's like, lying here, knowing you're . . . ?'

A tear escaped from his closed eyelid and rolled down his waxen cheek, and suddenly she realized he had never told her he was afraid to die and she had been so wrapped up in herself that she had never given a thought to what it must be like to live beneath the executioner's axe. 'I'll write to him tonight,' she promised, kissing his damp forehead.

It was an impossible letter for Mara to have to write. She thought back to the morning when they had left the Dower House for ever and how she had hoped, even at that last moment, that he would save her. And the temptation: temptation to write just once more: temptation to telephone him. But he hadn't come and she hadn't contacted him. So she'd left England not knowing, as she still didn't know, if he were angry or sad or just, with his silence, respecting the wishes he imagined were hers.

Now, alone in the drawing room, with her knees tucked under the flap of the desk, she dipped her pen in the ink, addressed an envelope to Jamie at the clinic, and sat and wondered what to write. In the end, afraid to sound as though she presumed he still cared for her, she stuck to the facts and wrote:

Dear Jamie,
Alexander read in *The Times* about your new treatment and he has asked me to write to you. At present he is . . .

She then went on to describe his symptoms and the pills the doctor in Cannes had prescribed. To end was the most difficult. Would he be pleased to hear from her? Or angry? Finally, because she did not know the answer, she merely signed herself 'Mara'. No 'Love'. No 'Best wishes'. Just 'Mara'.

Five nerve-racking, nail-biting weeks later Mara received a reply.

Dear Mara,
I am extremely sorry to hear Alexander's condition has deteriorated in spite of your move to a place of high altitude and warm dry climate. As I am sure you will appreciate, it is impossible for me to prescribe a course of treatment without examining a

patient. I therefore recommend you continue as directed by your own doctor.

Jamie

No 'Love'. No 'Best wishes'. Just 'Jamie'. And the address on the top of the paper was that of the clinic; he hadn't even allowed her the intimacy of knowing if he still lived at the house in Hampstead. So when she re-read his letter, as she did over and over again, taking it out of the iron box, studying it, then refolding it and putting it back with those faded other letters, she could no longer picture him there with certainty.

Alexander's disappointment at the news that Jamie could not help him was devastating. It was as if he were a drowning man who had seen the lifeboat approach, then suddenly veer away. He grew steadily weaker. He no longer tried to get up. He lay in bed, his face glistening with cold sweat and his breath rasping throughout the house. And every hour or so he would ring the little silver bell to summon Mara; for a drink; for another pillow; to shut the window; to open the window; or merely just to see her and know she was there. He was a dying man and he knew it, but he faced his shrinking future with such calm courage that Mara, who could no longer leave the house and who was thin and tired from running up and down the stairs, begrudged him nothing.

One very hot Sunday towards the end of June, Alexander was particularly bad. He couldn't sleep, he couldn't eat, he couldn't breathe without coughing. All day Mara sat with him in the stuffy bedroom, mopping his brow, straightening his bed, trying to persuade him to drink, holding his hand, until she almost fainted from heat and exhaustion. Finally, in the late afternoon he fell asleep and she was free to creep away. Not daring to have a bath in case the rattling of the water-pipes woke him, she went down to the pantry, stripped off all her clothes – thankful for once that Maman was not around – pulled out a large enamel basin and stepped into it. Jugful and jugful of cold water she sluiced over herself: face, breasts, stomach, legs and arms tingling. Then, without bothering to dry, she wrapped a length of bright blue cotton around herself and padded barefoot across the courtyard to the wicker chairs and table which lived in the shade of the orange trees.

Settling down into one of the chairs, she stretched out her legs so that they caught the last rays of the dipping sun, tipped back her head into the shade so it didn't, and closed her eyes. The length of cotton clung to her damp body, her hair hung in wet tangles down her back, the dust stuck to her wet feet in streaks of pale powder against her suntanned skin. But what did it matter? No one ever came to the farmhouse on a Sunday.

With half an ear Mara listened for Alexander's bell, with the other she absorbed the familiar country noises: the odd shout from the fields, the gentle clucking of the hens, the tuneless braying of a donkey. In the distance she could hear a car groaning as it climbed the steep hills. She listened vaguely. It drew nearer. Reached the village. Stopped. She yawned. Relatives from another village paying a Sunday visit. She yawned again. The car had started up. She pictured it weaving its way through the narrow streets of Barjon. Visiting the baker? No. The butcher? No. She heard the engine rev as it dragged the car out of the village and she glanced up the drive, wondering who it was and where they were going. Then the engine died down and she closed her eyes again. But almost immediately it started up and when she looked up the drive she could see it had turned down towards the farmhouse. With irritation she watched it approach, idly recognizing it as a Bentley. Lost tourists. It had happened before. Pink-faced English or Americans, stumbling over their school-learned French.

The car had stopped some twenty yards away. A girl with a high-pitched voice was saying, 'My dear, isn't it quaint.'

Another replied, 'Yes, but fancy *living* here.'

Mara kept her eyes half closed. She did not move. Let them come. Let them stumble over their French. She felt a certain sadistic pleasure as she anticipated how their faces would sink into idiocy when she replied in perfect English – her compensation for the disturbance.

A man's voice was talking but Mara could not catch his words. Then the first girl giggled and said, 'We'll stay here, thank you. We're absolutely terrified of chickens aren't we, Amelia?'

Through the fuzz of her eyelashes Mara saw the car door open and a man step out, partly obscured by the orange trees. She wondered how long it would take him to see her. Would he call loudly, 'Is anyone at home?' Or would he wander round, then jump guiltily as though he were a thief when he saw her sitting there? Mara watched him walk across the courtyard. Then she froze in her chair and her hands gripped each wicker arm so tightly that her knuckles stood out white against her tanned skin. How could she not have recognized him? The lithe loping strides. The stubborn jut of his chin. The dark hair with the lock which always fell forward. Jamie.

He stared across the cobblestoned courtyard, level with her now, heading for the front door. But something, perhaps it was the vivid blue of her cotton shift or perhaps it was the mere animal instinct of knowing when one is watched, made him turn and see her. He swung round towards her and stopped about two yards away. 'Mara!' He paused and looked hard at her, his eyes moving down from her unmade-up face to the tangled ends of her damp hair sticking to her bare suntanned shoulders, to the blue cotton wrapped tightly round her hips, and on down to her long bare legs and her bare and dusty feet. 'Good God, I'd never have recognized you!' He started to smile, then thought better of it.

Mara shrugged helplessly. She could think of nothing to say.

Still unable to believe his eyes, Jamie said, 'I was on my way down to Monte Carlo with some friends when I noticed on the map we were passing near you, so I thought I'd come and have a look at your husband.'

'Oh,' she murmured weakly. She had forgotten all about Alexander and the letter and had been wishing she had brushed her hair and that her toenails were not quite so ingrained with dirt.

But Jamie interpreted her monosyllabic reply to mean something else. He asked, 'He is still alive, isn't he?'

'Oh, yes.' She wanted to shake her head to see if she was dreaming.

'Good. Shall I . . .' He glanced back at the car and the waiting girls. 'Shall I have a look at him?'

'Yes.' Mara stood up slowly. 'What about them?' She nodded towards the car.

'Okay if they come inside? It's been pretty hot driving down.'

'Yes, of course.'

Mara waited whilst he fetched the girls and watched with hidden satisfaction as they teetered nervously past the chickens, their high heels catching in the cobbles and their damp and creased silk dresses clinging to their pale-stockinged legs. Jamie introduced them. Amelia and

Clementine. Sisters. Amelia was pretty and petite: Clementine was less pretty and overweight. They both had brown curly hair cut fashionably short. They shook hands with Mara, their long well-manicured fingers incongruously white against her own dark paw. Then they looked at each other and giggled, and Mara knew they were thinking her odd and 'gone native', and it made her angry because they, in their London clothes and their face-powder caked by the heat and their own sweat, looked far more ridiculous than she did.

Mara showed them all into the drawing room, where the girls threw off their hats and collapsed into armchairs with gasps of relief and Jamie walked to the window and looked out. 'I'll make some tea in a minute,' she said, and went up to Alexander to tell him Jamie was there.

After Mara had taken Jamie to Alexander she went downstairs again; but to the kitchen, not the drawing room. She needed to be alone, to recover, to think. But she was too stunned to think clearly so she concentrated on what she was doing: on boiling the kettle, on laying the tea tray, on finding some biscuits. When all that was left to do was to wait for the kettle to boil, she still didn't go back into the drawing room. Instead, she leaned against the whitewashed wall beside the stove, the wall cool against her hot back, the red floor tiles cool beneath the hot dry soles of her feet.

It was there, still leaning against the wall, that Jamie found her. He looked at her, then at the tea tray, then at the otherwise deserted kitchen. 'Don't you have any servants?' he asked.

'I have two women who come in the mornings, but not on Sundays.'

'Oh.' He was surprised but made no further comment on it, nor on how she came to be padding around barefoot

618

wrapped only in a sarong. He picked up a biscuit and said, 'I've examined your husband and I reckon he would benefit by having a different course of treatment. The pills he's taking at the moment merely dull the pain. Unfortunately the lung tissue is too badly damaged for him to live very long. I must warn you of that. But he could survive for a year or two, maybe longer.'

Mara nodded. 'I understand. Thank you.'

He looked at her and for a moment she thought he was going to say something about the two of them. There was a sort of shall-I-or-shan't-I hesitancy in the way he stood, half turned away from her, with his arms hanging by his sides and his fingers twitching. And there was that same hesitancy in his eyes. A light which was not just the sheen of their brilliant blueness. Then it was gone. 'The kettle's boiling,' he said, retreating behind a barrier which was not just formal but vaguely hostile. 'What I'll do . . .'

'Yes.' She picked up the kettle and poured the boiling water into the silver teapot, one of the luxuries they had brought with them from the Dower House.

Jamie watched her, his eyes on her bare arms whose brownness was turned to gold by the sun-bleached down on them. 'What I'll do,' he repeated, 'is to have a prescription made up. It'll probably take three or four days. Then I'll . . . umm . . .'

'Yes.' She turned to face him. Was he coming back? Was he going to ask her to collect it . . . from him? Or would he merely leave it at some chemist for her to collect, or send it up by taxi? She waited, rigid with anticipation, setting her face so that no disappointment would show if she was not to see him again.

'I'll bring it up and explain the dosage to you.'

'Thank you.' She lowered her eyes and bit the sides of her mouth to stop herself from smiling. Then she picked up the tea tray, rejecting his offer to take it for her, and carried it out of the kitchen, walking right round him so as not to touch him even with her elbow. But by that very avoidance she touched him as surely as if she had laid her hands on his body.

Mara spent practically all of the following day wondering what to wear for Jamie's return. She kept telling herself she was being stupid – such things no longer mattered between two people who knew each other as well as they did. What was more, he had already seen her at her scruffiest. And more than that, he no longer cared. But that did not stop her from trying on all the dresses, which had once made her look fashionable and sophisticated but were ridiculously out of place on a wild-haired girl in a lonely farmhouse. In the end it was all for nothing. Jamie came back a day early and found her brushing Bobo in the yard and still padding barefoot through the dust. Only this time her hair was dry and she was wearing an old white shirt of Alexander's which stopped some way short of her knees.

'Don't the people in the village disapprove?' he asked, putting down his black leather doctor's bag and looking at her legs.

Mara went on brushing Bobo; she needed something for her hands to do. 'No one comes here once Maman leaves.'

'Maman! I think I passed her just above the village. An old peasant woman. She stopped me and gabbled at me, but I didn't understand a word except she knew I was a doctor.'

'Yes. That would have been her.'

'Well' – the barrier was still there – 'how's Alexander?'

'The same.' She went on brushing. 'He coughs a lot at night.'

'Can he sleep?'

'Not much. He's either too hot or too cold and when he does fall asleep he wakes himself up by coughing.'

He watched her in silence and Mara was intensely aware of him doing so. After a few minutes he asked, 'And you? Do you get any sleep?'

She stopped brushing. 'Not a lot.'

'And not a lot to eat either.' He was sympathetic but still totally professional.

'It's hardly worth cooking for one.' She carried on brushing.

'I thought so. You were never fat but now you're like a rake.'

Mara pulled a face. 'Thanks.' She remembered how he had once told her she looked old and wondered what he thought of her now.

Jamie was hesitating again. He was standing some yards from Mara, watching her as she brushed the dust from Bobo's tubby body. There was a slight wind blowing up the valley and it caught his hair, ruffling it. It seemed to Mara that he was torn between allowing it to blow him into the house, and on, and away, as the rational part of him wanted to do, or taking a firm stand against the wind, and talking to her. She wished she could do something to make him see that they should talk, but as always when she felt things that mattered to her were beginning to go wrong she became awkward. Added to that, there was Jamie's character. He was decisive and he disliked indecision in himself or in anyone else. And he disliked anything which caused indecision. So in a perverse way he was blaming Mara for his hesitancy, and she knew it, and it made her all the more awkward and ineloquent.

'Do you intend to stay here?' he asked abruptly.

'Yes.'

'Even when Alexander dies?'

'Yes. Where else would I go?' She raised her hand but not her eyes, afraid that if he saw the underlying question in them he would back off.

'England?'

'No.'

'You might have to.'

'Why?'

'If there's another war.'

'There won't be.' No one Mara had ever met, except for Jamie, talked of war as though it happened with predictable regularity. Of course there'd been wars in the past, lots of them, but everyone knew that after the appalling loss of life in the Great War there'd never be another; everyone, that was, except for Jamie.

'Well, we'll see,' he said. 'But I hope not, for your sake. This place suits you. I always said you were a chameleon.'

'Oh?' She wondered to whom he had spoken of her and why.

'Yes,' he went on, but there was nothing intimate in the way he spoke – he might have been discussing a piece of furniture. 'Yes, you're just like a chameleon. In London, you were smart and glamorous. Here, except for your colouring, you could be a half-dressed peasant. You should be an instructor on a survival course. Why, even your character changes to suit your surroundings.'

Mara was surprised. 'I don't think it has.' She talked to herself so much she was sure she would have noticed.

For a brief moment it seemed that the barrier between

them was about to disappear, but Jamie picked up his bag and his abruptness returned. 'I'll go now,' he said, and he marched off into the house.

Whilst Jamie was with Alexander, Mara washed her face, brushed her hair, dabbed some scent behind her ear, decided against changing her clothes because it would look too obvious, and made some tea. She was sitting demurely in one of the wicker chairs under the orange trees when he came back. 'Some lemon tea?' she offered.

'Thanks.' He sat down.

'How is he?' she asked, not looking at him but infinitely aware of his long body sprawled in the wicker chair.

'I've given him an injection to make him sleep. Ah, thanks.' He took a cup of tea. 'Good. I like it with lemon. Now, when he wakes up I want you to give him as much milk as he'll take. And this.' He opened his leather bag and produced three bottles of medicine. 'Two spoonfuls at night and one in the morning. And here's another prescription. I've put "repeat as required".' He handed her a piece of paper. 'If he goes more than twenty-four hours without sleeping, give him an injection. Do you know how?'

'No.'

He produced a syringe. 'Like this. But make sure you get all the air out.' He held up the syringe. 'See! Like that.' A drop of liquid fell into the dust. 'Okay?'

'I hope so.'

'Try!' He passed the syringe to Mara and for a second their hands touched, but he drew his away rapidly, almost as if he'd been hurt.

With an effort Mara controlled the trembling in her own hands and pressed the end of the syringe until water fell again. 'Like that?'

'Fine.' He took it from her. 'Now, to give the injection.

First, disinfect the area. Buttocks. Top of the leg. But don't hit a vein and don't go jabbing it into the same place every time. Second, you grab hold of the area.' He reached up and pulled an orange from the tree above. 'Like this.' He squeezed the orange until its rough hide grew taut and shiny. 'Third, you jab the needle in.' He jabbed the needle into the orange. 'Fourth, you press the end and, as you see, the liquid goes down. Then you pull it out, swab the area, and that's it. You try!'

Mara tried twice before he said, 'That'll do. You can practise later. I'll leave you plenty of syringes. And I'll leave you a couple of bottles of disinfectant.'

She nodded. 'Thank you.'

'And finally,' he continued, 'when the end comes and the pain grows bad, give him these.' He gave her a bottle of pills. 'One a day to begin with, then increase the dosage as he needs them. But not more than four a day or you may kill him.'

Mara looked at the small white pills. 'What are they?'

'Morphine.'

'But I thought morphine was . . .'

'Addictive?'

'Yes.'

'Will that matter if he's dying?'

'No.'

She stared at her dusty feet and twiddled her toes in the soft hot dust. 'Will you come again?'

'No. We're leaving the day after tomorrow.'

We? Who was 'we'? Jamie and Amelia? Jamie and Clementine? Or Jamie and some other girl? A girl to whom he might perhaps say that evening, 'I tried to be as quick as possible but Mara kept me talking.' In an act of sickening despair, Mara ground the rough heel of one foot into the soft arch of the other. 'Are you going back to London?'

'No. Rome. A medical conference. Then to America for another conference.' A pause, as if he were weighing up whether to tell her something. A slight relaxing of his hands as he made his decision. 'I shall stay over there for a bit . . . see what I can do to help. The situation's desperate since the Wall Street crash, nearly one man in three is out of work, the shanty towns are appalling, no one can afford medical help and, my God, they need it! Durrant and I are going to work in a free clinic, as ordinary doctors. Even old Sayers is going to come and give a hand.'

'How are . . . other things going with you?'

'Very well. My book's been published and it sold very well considering there aren't too many lung specialists around.'

'I didn't know you'd written one.'

'I started it after . . . after you'd left.' He fiddled with his watch. 'And what about you, do you miss motor-racing?'

'Occasionally, but it seems like another world. I miss the team, my father-in-law, the mechanics, and I miss the . . . atmosphere of the works and of Brooklands, but as to the actual racing, I can't believe I ever did it.'

'What do you do all day here?'

'I go to Cannes once a month . . .'

'Only once a month?'

'Yes. We used to go a lot at first, but' – she looked up at the sunbaked hills and the stunted trees which clung to their steep sides, and to the shadows of those stunted trees which were creeping, like molten lava, across the dry earth – 'I prefer being here.' Suddenly she couldn't think of anything to say to him because what she wanted to say she couldn't. And because she couldn't say what she wanted to, she wanted him to go. Now. Immediately. Not to prolong the inevitable. To leave her to her orange trees and the sinking sun and the hot dust under her feet. She stood up without looking at him. 'I must feed the donkey.'

He answered, 'And I must go. They're expecting me for dinner.'

'Who?' She hadn't meant to ask but had said it before she could stop herself.

'Amelia, Clementine and a couple of other friends.'

Mara said nothing. She walked across the courtyard to the barn. Amelia, Clementine. Stupid giggling bitches. She went to the back of the barn and began raking up a bundle of hay, viciously whacking at the earthen floor with her rake.

'Couldn't you have told me to my face?' said Jamie from behind her.

Mara swung around to find him lounging in the doorway of the barn. She hadn't heard him approach and couldn't think of anything to say.

'I said, couldn't you have told me to my face?'

She swallowed hard. 'It seemed easier by letter.'

'For you, yes. But what about me? Can you imagine how I felt getting that letter?'

She looked down at the rake in her hand and the hay at her feet. 'I'm sorry . . . I'm sorry.'

'Sorry!' He moved forward menacingly, blocking out the sunlight and casting the barn into gloom. 'Is that all you have to say? Sorry! After all we'd promised each other, Mara, you couldn't even face me. Just a letter. Just, "Dear Jamie, the doctor says Alexander will die within six months unless he is moved to a warm dry climate. My father-in-law owned a house in the South of

France and it is suggested that he go and live there. Obviously he cannot go alone and in the circumstances I realize it is my duty to stay with him. Love. Mara."' Jamie repeated her letter word for word, making the words Mara had written and rewritten that snowy night nearly four years ago seem far more callous than she had meant them to be.

'I couldn't come,' she said miserably. 'I was afraid.'

'Afraid I'd make you leave him? Make you abandon a dying man?'

'No. That I'd never have the courage to go through with it.'

Jamie moved nearer. 'But it didn't stop you writing and asking me to help him,' he said bitterly. 'Out of the blue. After all this time. But no kind inquiry as to how I am. Oh no, just selfish little Mara wanting help. You remember what I said to you at the cottage, about you only coming running when you've nothing else in your life? Well I should have said you only come running when you want something.'

His unfairness stung her, bringing tears to her eyes. Everything she ever did where Jamie was concerned was wrong. She had longed to put in some personal message, longed to know how he was, but had been frightened in case he thought her presumptuous. 'I didn't want to write, but he begged and begged me. He was dying. How could I refuse him?' She tossed the rake away from her. 'And don't think you're the only one who's been hurt. Don't you think I've wondered how you are? Thought about you endlessly? Do you think I wanted to . . . to . . .' A tear ran down her dusty cheek. Angrily she brushed it away.

'Then why the hell did you write that letter? Why the hell did you just cut me off?'

'Because I had to.' She glared up at him through her tears and the tangled edge of her unruly hair. 'I had to. And I did it for you.'

Jamie's eyes narrowed to blue slits between his dark lashes. 'Did it for me?'

'Yes. I saved you from ruin. My brother-in-law knew all about us. He'd had me followed. He said if I left Alexander he'd see your name was dragged through the mud. He said you'd never be able to work in England again. That you'd probably be struck off. So, don't you dare tell me I'm selfish! I sacrificed my happiness to save your career.'

'Then why' – he grabbed her by the shoulder and forced her to him – 'didn't you tell me the truth?'

'Why do you think?' Her face was just below his, looking up at him through the half light. Her breasts were tight against his chest, her thighs against his thighs. 'I knew you hated all that secrecy. All those stolen hours. If I'd told you about Herbert you'd have been disgusted. With him. With us. With everything.'

'But at least the decision would have been ours. Ours together. Not you deciding and me forced to accept without knowing why. That's what I can't forgive you for – what I'll never forgive you for.'

'But can't you see why I did it?' she cried in desperation. 'If I told you, you'd have had to choose – your career or me – you'd have hated me if you'd given up your work and I'd have hated you if you hadn't. I did it for you, Jamie.' She hammered on his chest with her clenched fists, as if somehow she could beat her words into him. 'For you. For me. For us. Can't you see that? You must see that.'

He looked down into her face and not for the first time, since he had found her sitting under the orange

628

trees on the previous Sunday, did he find her more attractive than he had ever found her when she had been smart and glamorous and Londonized. It didn't matter to him that she was dusty and scruffy and her hair looked as though she never brushed it. Nor did it matter that her face, dried by the sun and the wind, showed little lines about her eyes. She had never been pretty and she wasn't pretty now. But she had that same look about her which had appealed to him when he had first seen her in Koblenz, shouting down the stairs at Alexander, and when he had seen her at Brooklands after she had won her race. That same tough vibrant courage. And mixed with it was the vulnerability he had seen in her face in the attic room in Koblenz. It was those two things, her courage and her vulnerability, which he loved so much and which made her beautiful.

'You do see, Jamie, don't you?'

He remembered how he'd hated her. 'The only thing I can see is that I should never have come here.'

'But you're not sorry?'

He remembered how he'd felt when he read her letter. 'I shouldn't have come.'

'Was it only to see Alexander?'

He remembered the bitterness. 'Stop it, Mara!'

'Jamie, don't be angry.' She moved against him and slowly slid her arms up his shoulders and around his neck. She wanted him so desperately she didn't care about anything except having him. The years of trying to forget him welled up inside her, released by the anger she had felt just now. She stood on tiptoe and brushed his mouth with hers, her legs trembling against his, her nipples hard against the cotton of Alexander's shirt.

Jamie tried to push her away. 'Stop it, Mara! You know . . .'

629

'Know what? Know that I still love you. That I've always loved you.' She ran her hand up the inside of his thigh.

'Stop it!' Jamie tried to sound convincing. Once, at his most bitter, he had wanted revenge. But revenge depended on him not caring. Now he felt a traitor to himself; to the himself who had suffered. 'It's wrong,' he said. 'Alexander's . . .'

'Is it wrong?' She nibbled at the corner of his mouth and her hand moved higher and higher. 'Perhaps it is. But I'm fed up with trying to be right. And you want to, I know you do. I can feel you do.' She began to unbuckle his belt.

'Of course I bloody well want you. Of course I . . .' He pushed her backwards into a pile of hay, throwing himself down with her, kissing her savagely and pulling roughly at her shirt. 'But I don't want to want you.' He shoved her shirt up above her waist. 'I don't want to think about you.' He tugged at his trousers. 'I don't want anything to do with you.' He did not wait to undress her but took her as she was, with her shirt pushed up, hammering into her as though he truly hated her and everything to do with her, grinding her into the prickly hay, not caring if she enjoyed it, hoping she didn't, more violent still when he realized she did. Then, as soon as he was satisfied, which was really no satisfaction but more of an angry surrender, he stood up and began to dress.

Bruised and sore Mara watched him from the pile of hay. He as good as raped me, she thought, and I still liked it. I still love him. But she did not feel exhilarated, she felt sad and flat.

'Don't you think you'd better tidy yourself?' he said curtly.

She stood up, smoothed down her shirt, and pulled the hay out of her hair. 'Are you going already?'

Jamie didn't look at her. 'You could hardly expect me to stay.'

She justified her question. 'You weren't anyway.'

'Exactly.'

'Will you write to me – let me know how you are?' she hated herself for asking.

'No.'

'Supposing something goes wrong with Alexander's treatment. Can I contact you?' She hated him for making her ask.

'No. And it won't go wrong if you follow my instructions. I've written it all down for you. You'll find that in the linen bag.' He walked to the doorway. Mara followed, unable to believe in his indifference. He turned and said, 'Look, Mara, I know I was wrong to come here but you can't blame me for what happened.'

'I don't.'

'Good. Because I can honestly say that when I came here I may have wanted to see you but I had no intention' – he looked bitterly at her – 'of rolling in the hay with my patient's wife.'

'So you blame me. It takes two, you know.'

'Of course it does. It was my fault too. I've spent ten years wanting you or kidding myself I don't want you, and old habits are hard to break. But I don't want this sort of thing and I don't want to want it. Stolen moments. Illicit meetings. I hated it before but I loved you then.'

'And you don't love me now.'

'I don't know. I don't want to think about it. But I do know you're incapable of really trusting, and I can never forgive you for not having trusted me. For having just left – for the hurt.'

Mara took a step towards him. 'Jamie, please! Doesn't it mean anything to you that I still love you?'

He looked from Mara to the farmhouse, then back at Mara. 'Do you? Perhaps you do. Perhaps I love you too.' He gave an awkward laugh, that same laugh with which he had once rejected her, and walked briskly away to his car.

Mara shouted after him, 'Do you think you'd be happier with someone else – some stupid boring little girl?'

'Maybe I would.' He got into the car. 'Maybe that's what I need.'

'You'd hate it.' She stamped her foot. 'You'd be bored.'

'I have my work. At least they wouldn't interfere with that.'

'But I don't interfere. That's what all this is about.' She was standing by the car door, looking down at his dark head, clenching and unclenching her fists in spasms of rage and injustice.

Jamie glanced up at her, then looked away again. 'We destroy each other, Mara. I disrupt your marriage and you disrupt my life. I really did believe it could work, but I was wrong.' His voice was sad and resigned, and that gave Mara the courage to put her hand on his shoulder.

'You can't stop loving someone just like that,' she said gently. 'Do you think you can drive away and forget me?'

He knew he was weakening. She was standing so close he could feel her breath on his cheek. He longed to reach out and touch her, to lead her back into the barn, to take her in his arms and make love to her. Not with brutality as he had before, but with love. To tell her that he loved her, that she was right when she said he couldn't forget. It would be so easy for him to stay the night, and to come back for other nights with the excuse of treating Alexander. There could be nights when he went to sleep with her in his arms and mornings when he woke up with her beside him.

But suddenly it all came back to him in waves: how he had hated her: how he had promised himself he would never again let her, or any other woman, come close enough to hurt him: and how, at his most bitter, he had promised himself revenge. He pushed her hand away. 'Forget it, Mara.'

She was stunned by his change of mood. 'Forget what?'

'Everything.'

'I can't. Not even today.'

'Today!' Mara had once, long ago, in Koblenz, been determined to repel Jamie so that he would never tempt her again. He now had to do the same. He had to wound her in the cruellest way possible. 'Today was just sex,' he said, turning on the engine and revving it loudly. 'I promised myself if I ever got the chance I'd . . .'

'But Jamie, you just said you didn't want . . .' She felt as though he were whipping her round in a circle of despair and confusion from which every exit was blocked.

'Said what? That I didn't want to? Don't you believe it. Why, I promised myself when I got your letter, if I ever got the chance I'd screw you, yes, screw you. I'd screw you just once.' The car moved forward as he released the clutch. 'And then I'd leave you just as you left me.'

Chapter 35

There were three results of Jamie's visit.

The first was that no sooner had he disappeared up the drive than Mara sank into the most appalling abyss of depression, from where, had it not been for the discreet sympathy of Maman and the dependence of Alexander, she would probably have committed suicide. She seriously considered doing so. Over and over again she opened the bottle of white pills and tipped them into the palm of her hand, rolling them round and round as she thought of how Jamie had said, 'Don't give him more than four a day or you may kill him.' There were ninety in the bottle. But at the last moment something inexplicable always stopped her from taking them, though her depression went on and on, or so it seemed. At night she would cry herself to sleep and in the morning wake with her face stiff from dried tears, and lie there for a minute, stunned by her own awakeness. Then back it would all come, rolling over her in waves: Jamie didn't want her: it was over: the final chapter: The End: hours of crying later, Mara would force herself to dress and struggle through yet another day. Sometimes she would go out to the barn and sit in the hay, engulfed in the smell of dry grass and her memories. When she had left Jamie in Koblenz to marry Alexander she had been desperate. How much more desperate was she now, twelve years later. Before, she had thought she would always love him. Now, she knew it.

And to make matters worse Mara was thirty on the first of August and she suffered from the horrible realization that comes to most people on their thirtieth birthday – that time was not on her side. She went up to the black rock and stood on the edge of it, willing herself to take the final step. But again something stopped her. Perhaps she wouldn't die. Perhaps she would be maimed. She might lie for hours on the jagged rocks below, waiting for someone to find her. And even if she were killed outright, what would happen to Alexander? How would he take the news of her death? It was this, partly, which stopped her. If she could consider the effect of her death, then she was seeing beyond it, and that meant she was still involved in the future.

The second result was that Alexander's health improved so much through Jamie's treatment that within a month – to Mara's horror – he began muttering about being 'a proper husband' soon.

The third result of Jamie's visit was that Mara was pregnant. For several weeks she had had a strange feeling that she might be and it was no great surprise when the doctor in Cannes said, 'Congratulations, madame. Your first baby. Why, your husband will be delighted.' Perhaps that was another reason why she hadn't taken the pills or stepped from the rock.

They were three separate results, but they were connected. Knowing she was expecting Jamie's child gave Mara something to live for. Now she had a part of him, growing inside her, something he could never take away, something which would always be his and hers. By the time Mara had paid the doctor and left his surgery the sickness of despair, which had been with her every day of the last two months, had passed. In its place was a calm sadness. But when she reached Les Vieux Orangers and saw Alexander sitting under the orange trees waiting for her, she was faced with another problem, also connected. Alexander's recovery meant that she was not forced to confront him with a child which could not possibly be his, as long as she pretended to be less advanced than she was. So far she had rebuffed him gently. But could she bring herself to tell him she expected another man's child when she knew he longed for one? Could she face his unhappiness and the knowledge that, if his health deteriorated as a result of it, she had sacrificed his recovery on the altar of her personal distaste as being touched by a man other than Jamie? And, finally, did she have the courage to admit the truth? For Alexander's sake and for the sake of her own cowardice, Mara did what she had to.

A month later she told Alexander she was pregnant. Just as the doctor had predicted, he was delighted. Immediately he wrote to Herbert. Mara had not the heart to ruin his excitement by trying to stop him, although she could imagine the reception the news would have at the Park. They'll be down on their bended knees praying it's a girl, she thought ruefully. Serve them right if it's a boy. She thought of Jamie and wondered if it would look like him. Dark hair. Blue eyes. Oh no, not blue eyes! It would be all right at first, Maman said most babies had blue eyes. But later! She patted her stomach and begged it not to have bright blue eyes.

Of course Mara thought about telling Jamie – but pride stopped her. Pride and Alexander. If Jamie knew the truth he might want to see the child. He might demand his rights, not that he had any, but formalities had never stopped Jamie Turner doing what he wanted. No, let him rot in mediocrity with the boring little wife he hoped to find. Let him work his guts out and feel that work was all that mattered. Let him try to forget her. Then one day – perhaps – she would go and see him, and say, 'You have a child, Jamie, a son, a grown-up stranger whose childhood you missed out on.' But even as Mara planned her revenge, she pictured herself walking down a street, looking young and attractive, her child beside her, or perhaps even in her arms. They would bump into Jamie. He would look at her, then at the child. She would tell him the truth. He would say he loved her. No, he would say he loved her before she told him the child was his. But whichever way it was, the child would be very young, because she couldn't envisage all those years without seeing Jamie.

As the months passed and the baby inside her grew, so did Mara's contentment. Of course she was afraid. Afraid of the unknown pain to come. Afraid of something going wrong. There was no doctor for miles and, although she had provisionally booked herself into the hospital in Cannes, there was little hope of her reaching there when the time came. For one thing, her time would come two months before it was generally expected.

Winter was remarkably mild, at least up until the end of January. Then overnight it became bitterly cold, and not a brisk dry cold. It rained, and even when it wasn't raining the clouds lay like a cold wet blanket over the valley. Damp invaded everything, the house, the beds, clothes. Nothing, not even a blazing fire, could get rid of it. In fact the fires merely made condensation, which made more damp. It was the worst kind of weather for Alexander and his health suffered. Neither Jamie's medicine nor the injections, nervously given by Mara, could help him. For the first time he took the small white pills, not every day, just on those days when the pain in his lungs made him cry out as he breathed.

'I don't know what to do,' Mara confided to Maman one morning after she had been up most of the night, 'he gets worse and worse.' She slumped over the kitchen table. 'And I'm so tired, so very, very tired. Perhaps I'd better try to see that doctor in Cannes. It's not so wet today. They say the road was impassable yesterday, but I might get through if I start now.'

Maman shook her head. 'No, Madame Mara, you can't go. You can't drive the car over all those bumps.'

Mara looked down at her stomach. Compared to many expectant mothers she didn't think she showed that much. 'I'm sure I could. After all I'm only . . .'

'Five months!' Maman gave Mara a long hard look. 'Do you think I'm stupid as well as old? No, that baby comes in April, if not before. But don't worry' – she handed Mara a cup of hot milky coffee – 'everything'll be all right for you. I'll be here. I know what to do. I helped Jeanne's mother with Jeanne and her sister. My son trusted me with his wife.'

She knows, thought Mara. But how could she? She only saw Jamie once, that time she stopped him on the road. But Maman did know and Mara knew it, and she found it strangely comforting.

Alexander grew worse. He was now taking four pills a day. Mara didn't dare give him any more. To begin with, when she had increased the dosage, they'd had their effect; he dreamed wild dreams and talked as if his dreams were reality, but the pain went. Now it didn't. Nothing could make him sleep. Nothing could stop him coughing. Nothing could halt the relentless pace of dying.

At first he tried to fight it. He would say, 'I don't want to die, I want to be with you and the baby.' But one morning at the beginning of March, after a terrible night when he had coughed and coughed and Mara, exhausted, had fallen asleep on the floor beside his bed despite his coughing and the baby's kicking, he gave up. 'I can't go on,' he whispered as she bent to smooth his sheets, 'I just can't.' He closed his eyes. For a terrible moment Mara thought he had died. Panicking, she grabbed his wrist and felt for his pulse, weak with relief when she found it still beating. But she hadn't the strength to straighten up. Still holding on to Alexander's wrist, she lay down beside him and fell asleep.

Maman found them like that. She took one look at Mara's grey, drawn face and Alexander's grey sleeping one, and said, 'From now on Jeanne and I will stay here. No, don't tell me you can manage on your own. You can't. Go to bed, Madame Mara. Go on! Bed!'

As Mara stumbled out of the room, she muttered, 'You will wake me if . . .'

'Of course.'

Now the day went round in a different cycle – not in mornings, afternoons, evenings and nights, but in two-hourly turns of being with Alexander. And Mara became obsessed with being with him when he died, to the extent that Maman often had to drag her away, and even then she would try to stay awake for fear of not hearing if she were called. She was haunted by the thought he might open his eyes for the last time, look for her, and not find her. So much she had withheld from him: her love: her time: a child. Why had he put up with it? That's what she couldn't understand. Never had she thought so deeply of Alexander as she did during these days. What he'd felt? What he'd hoped for? How much he must have hidden his feelings while she'd been so obsessed with Jamie that she had hardly noticed his existence, except to lament it. She'd always thought of Alexander as being weak, but he wasn't, not all the time. Just with Herbert and herself. She knew why with Herbert: guilt. But why with herself? Why had he let her walk all over him?

The end came at dawn. Mara was taking over from Maman when Alexander said very clearly, 'Mara and the baby. Hold my hand, Mara. Sit on the bed. I want to talk to you, I don't have much longer, you know.'

Mara sat down beside him, with Maman muttering that she would send Jeanne for the priest. 'But he's not Roman Catholic, he's Protestant,' Mara whispered back.

'Don't worry,' muttered Maman, 'the Lord knows we don't have a Protestant priest. He won't mind.'

'What are you talking about?' Alexander asked, moving his fingers in Mara's hand.

'Nothing, nothing. I was just telling Maman I'd like some coffee.'

'I see. Now, listen carefully. This house will be yours. My will is with the bank in Cannes, they'll tell you all about it, and Herbert will . . . will' – his voice dropped to a hoarse whisper – 'provide for you. For you and the baby. And . . .'

Mara interrupted him, 'Don't talk, you'll tire yourself.'

He shook his head slowly. 'But I must. I want you to promise me something.'

'Yes. Anything. What?'

'To call the baby Oliver if it's a boy. Oliver like my brother who died. Remember I told you about Oliver?'

'Yes. Oliver. And if it's a girl I'll call her Olivia.'

'Yes. And you'll tell the family when it's . . .'

She hadn't intended to, but what could she say? 'Yes.'

'You . . . won't . . . forget.'

'No.'

He lay silent for some fifteen minutes. Mara knew he was alive only by the slight rasping of his breath. She sat there, holding his hand and thinking about her promises. Of course she had wanted to call the baby Jamie if it were a boy and of course she had had no intention of ever contacting Herbert.

Alexander spoke again. His voice was much weaker

and Mara had to bend her head to hear him. 'I want you to forgive me before I die,' he said.

'Forgive you!' It was she who should be asking for forgiveness.

'Yes. Your brother.'

'Hans.'

'I killed him. I shot him. In . . . in the back. I didn't want to but . . . orders . . . had to obey orders. Should have refused . . . always regretted it . . . shot him in the back . . . saw him fall . . . saw his hair catch the sun.'

'But, Alexander . . .'

'No, don't interrupt. Have to tell you. That's why I came to your house in Koblenz. Had to be sure . . . haunted me . . . shooting a man in the back.'

'But, Alexander . . .'

'No. Listen! I should have asked you when he died . . . should have that first day. But I liked you. So I thought – hoped – I was wrong. Then you told me. You told me he'd died that day. Christmas Day 1914. Remember. You were standing by the window . . . couldn't sleep . . . I tried to make it up to you . . . couldn't bear to tell you. Married to your brother's murderer!'

'But, Alexander!' Mara shook him, forgetting how ill he was. 'Listen to me! You didn't shoot Hans. You met him all right. He wrote and told me so. But you didn't kill him. Wait! I can prove it to you.' She hurried out of the room, coming back a minute later with Hans' faded letter in her hands. 'Look! Read it! Oh no, it's in German, I'll tell you. It says, "I met an Englishman today, a few years older than me, but no different. We all met Englishmen. They're just like us. I used to think they were animals – that's what we're meant to think – but they're not. Now when I see one die I think, he has a mother and a father and a sister just like me, and I

641

imagine them crying and hoping he died a quick death. But he didn't. No one does. No one will. Death comes screaming in the mud. It's pointless, mindless, stupid. A farce. I want no more of it. Next time they order me to fire, I shall refuse. They can shoot me but I can't go on shooting other people. Now I understand Papa. I am giving this letter to a friend of mine. If anything goes wrong, he will post it."'

'Then, how did he die?' asked Alexander.

'He was shot . . . as a deserter.'

'A deserter!' A mixture of relief and repugnance came into his eyes.

'Yes, but he didn't run away. The friend put his own letter in with Hans', just a few lines.' She unfolded a small piece of paper which had been tucked into the envelope, and translated, '"I would like you to know, Frau Vogel, that your son did not desert. On the evening of Christmas Day, an hour after he gave me this letter for you, we were ordered to fire on the English. Hans refused. They shot him where he stood, in the trench. He died quickly and bravely. He was my friend."' Mara looked at Alexander. 'The letter was unsigned. He was afraid, just as they were afraid others might follow Hans.'

Alexander whispered, 'You never . . .'

'Told you?' Mara stroked his hand. 'No, I didn't. I knew you despised my father, not because he was German but because he was a pacifist. What would you have said if I'd told you my brother was a deserter?'

Alexander closed his eyes and lay perfectly still for some time, and when he opened them again he said, looking at her with immense fondness and understanding, 'I'd . . . have . . . said' – a long pause – 'we don't . . . choose . . . our brothers.'

Chapter 36

The baby was born on the day after Alexander's funeral. It was a boy. And from the moment Mara was handed the scrawny, mewling bundle and she looked down at his red, puckered face, she felt an overwhelming desire to protect him from everything: from all the sadness in the world; from hunger; from loneliness; from all that she herself had suffered. Oliver. She held him in her arms. Oliver. Even for a newborn baby he was appallingly ugly – everyone said so, but not Mara and not, of course, to Mara. Because to her he was beautiful and she said so. 'He has blue eyes,' she told Maman, peering into his half-closed eyelids.

Maman nodded. 'All babies have blue eyes. They change later' – she gave Mara one of her hard looks – 'if they're going to change.'

It was over a month before Mara could drag herself away from Oliver for long enough to drive down to Cannes, and it was only the necessity of drawing some money and registering Oliver's birth that made her go. She took a long letter to Elenora and a short one to Herbert. Just enough information to comply with her promise to Alexander.

At the bank the manager ushered her into his office, was profuse with his sympathy, read the will to her, and explained, 'Your husband left you everything, madame. The farmhouse. Its contents. And the . . . er . . . monies in his account, which amount to' – he studied his ledger –

'just over eight thousand francs. Nothing to worry about there, madame. And on the first of June and on the first of December you receive . . . er . . . in English money . . . er . . . three thousand pounds. Absolutely nothing to worry about. Nothing.'

Mara withdrew two thousand francs, saying, 'I probably won't come again for some time.'

Again, the bank manager expressed his sympathy. 'But at least you have a son,' he said, beaming at her. 'I too have a son, I know what having a son means.'

Mara nearly laughed out loud. She couldn't help wondering how Elenora would have reacted to such blatant chauvinism. She must remember to tell her when next she wrote.

Having a baby changed Mara, and did not change her. She loved Oliver because he was her own, worrying when he cried, worrying too when he didn't, constantly running to his cot and sometimes even waking him up to make sure he was still alive. For Oliver she would have done anything. For him she was a tigress protecting her young. Emotions Mara had never suspected herself capable of poured out of her when she looked at him. But it was for him alone – not for babies in general. The endless talk with which Maman and Jeanne now bombarded her, about this baby's cough and that baby's new bonnet, was not for Mara, and much as she loved Maman and was fond of Jeanne she gradually began to long to be alone.

It was not that she hadn't accepted Alexander's death. She had had to. She had seen him die. Watched as the lines of pain smoothed away. Seen the peace come into his face. Looked for his pulse and found no flicker. But she needed time to grieve, because she did grieve for him far more than she had expected. She needed time to come through the void which he had left behind him and regroup her thoughts on the other side, to accept not just the theory of his death but also its reality, and she could not do this unless she was alone.

Strangely enough Maman understood. The only comment she made was, 'I'll come just in the mornings then. You can leave the baby here with me whilst you ride. But remember, if you ever need me, even in the middle of the night, all you have to do is come.'

After that, as soon as Maman arrived each morning Mara would go out. Sometimes she would go up to the little churchyard above the village, to Alexander's grave, to sit on the stone wall which surrounded the cemetery and wonder what it was like to be buried. Other times, if the weather was good, she would ride Bobo up into the hills, to the black rock. There she would sit and smoke, and remember how Alexander had disapproved of smoking and wonder if he could see her smoking now. And if it was damp and she had difficulty lighting her cigarette, she would half expect to find a semi-visible hand with big flat semi-visible fingers pinching out the flame.

Oddly, Mara thought seldom of Jamie and had no desire to see him. These were Alexander's months and she owed them to him and to him alone. The summer, the autumn, the winter. Long dark months rolling into each other. Long evenings of solitude in the house where they had lived together. Thinking about Alexander. Missing Alexander. Yes, she did miss him. She missed his kindness and the sense of security he had given her, she missed the steady plod of his footsteps and his slightly puzzled smile, and she regretted deeply that they'd never been close enough for him to confide in her about Hans. But Mara wasn't unhappy in her solitude: she came to know herself in a way that is only possible when one is alone.

At the beginning of March the bad weather cleared and it was fine enough for her to ride up to the black rock. She hadn't been able to go up there since before Christmas. Sitting, smoking, and watching the tiny dots of peasants tending their fields far below, she thought, in a hundred years' time there'll be no one left on earth who's here today. Not one of those little dots. Not one of all the people who rush round the streets of London – or Paris – or anywhere. Other people will live on Earth. Someone else will sit on this rock and look down at the fields and the plain and the sea, just as I do, just as the Old Man did before me, but they'll never know I used to sit here and that I used to love this place. She stroked the smooth black surface. Only you'll know.

Then she rode down into the valley which was bathed in sun and spring. The months of grieving were over.

A week later Mara received three letters.

The first was from Damon. Since Alexander's death he and Atalanta wrote direct to Barjon. Just a brief note. 'I shall be in Paris at Easter so I'll drive down to see you. I'll tell you everything then. Don't write to me at the Park whatever you do. In spite of what happened, I'm glad about the baby.' That last sentence was most puzzling . . .

The second letter was from Elenora. She hadn't written recently because she'd slipped a disc at Christmas and had been immobile, but she was better now. She had seen Damon and he'd said he was going to see Mara soon.

The third letter was from the bank manager asking her to call as soon as possible, which she did. Just as before he ushered her through the marble banking hall and into his office. Only this time there was none of the reassuring sympathy; he was embarrassed. 'This is most awkward, madame,' he said, looking down at his hands, 'most awkward indeed. You see, we didn't receive your usual three thousand pounds at Christmas. I didn't write to you because I didn't want to worry you. These things happen.' He gave her a stiff smile. 'Even banks aren't infallible. I presumed it was a slip-up at your brother-in-law's bank.'

Mara nodded and said nothing. She sat opposite him, on one side of his desk, knowing intuitively what was coming.

'But after we had written three times,' he went on, 'and having no reply, I asked our London branch to investigate. The result was this.' He produced a letter. 'I'm so sorry to distress you by having to show you this, madame.'

Mara took the letter, it was from Herbert. All it said was, 'I hereby notify you that I have instructed the bankers of Rushton Motors not to remit any further monies to Mara Rushton.'

It was as if the little rug of security, left to her by Alexander, had been pulled from under her feet. She sat staring at the words, feeling sick with anger and with fear. Koblenz rose up before her. Poverty. Loneliness. Starvation. But not just for herself – for Oliver as well. 'What can I do?' she asked eventually.

'I would advise you to apply to the executors of your father-in-law's will, madame. Your husband told me that he had left provision for the . . . er . . . widows of his sons, and of course now you have a son, well, there should be no problem.' He held out his hand for the letter and Mara passed it to him. 'Until now,' he went on, 'the six-thousand-pound allowance was paid from the Rushton Motors account on your brother-in-law's instructions, but since he has withdrawn these . . .'

Mara said, 'My brother-in-law is one of the executors.'

'Who are the others?'

'My husband was one and Mr Lewis, my father-in-law's solicitor, is the other.'

He smiled. 'Then you must write to this Mr Lewis. The law is on your side, madame, but in any case this Mr Lewis will make sure you get what you deserve.'

What I deserve, thought Mara. But I don't deserve anything. Oliver isn't a Rushton, he has no right to Rushton money, he's my responsibility and it's up to me to provide for him. 'How much money do I have left?' she asked.

'Er . . . about five hundred English pounds.'

It seemed a lot of money but Mara knew it wasn't. Not when she had Oliver and Maman and the car, and years and years of future. 'I must draw some today,' she said.

The bank manager nodded. 'Of course, madame. And don't worry, until this Mr Lewis has made a suitable provision for you, I would be happy to make you a small loan. You and your late husband have been among our most treasured customers.'

Mara stood up and held out her hand. 'You've been very kind, monsieur, and I appreciate your advice and your offer, but I have decided not to pursue the matter.'

'But, madame, you must. It's your right.'

'No.' She shook her head.

He was convinced that the death of her husband had so badly shaken her that she felt unable to communicate with those outside her family. 'Perhaps you would write to your brother-in-law,' he suggested kindly. 'I believe his wife died in December and . . .'

'Did she? I'd no idea.' Was that the explanation to Damon's odd sentence?

'Yes. Perhaps he was so upset, madame, that he . . .'

'I doubt it.' She shocked the bank manager. 'You don't know my brother-in-law.'

It was five years since Mara had seen Damon and the days leading up to his arrival should have been full of excitement, but instead they were blackened by worry. What was she going to do? How was she going to live? By the time Damon arrived she was a nervous wreck and her initial sight of him, elegant, very, very pale, and infinitely more beautiful, did nothing to calm her. What could she possibly have in common with him? When he took her in his arms and kissed her on the cheek, she, with her unruly hair and her face which never now completely lost its suntan, felt like a brown toby jug in the arms of an exquisite porcelain figure.

But it was all still there – the words half spoken but understood. She realized that as soon as they talked. 'I'm sorry about your mother,' she said, leading him through into the drawing room.

'Don't be!' He looked round at the reddish walls and the leather-backed books. 'She led a dog's life.'

'What did she . . . die of?'

'She was pregnant.' He slumped down into an armchair. 'Forty-three years old and half a dozen miscarriages and still he made her try for another child.'

'Was it because of Oliver?'

'Yes. When Father got Alexander's letter he kept saying it would be a girl, but when you wrote and said you'd had a son, he went wild. Screaming and yelling about you having a lover.' He didn't give her the questioning look most people would have, that wasn't Damon's way. Secrecy was in his nature and he respected it in others. He said, 'The first thing I knew about Mother was when Atalanta telephoned to say Mother was pregnant

649

and very ill. Apparently Father hadn't wanted me to know about the baby, hardly anyone knew, and anyhow I hadn't been to the Park for months. I spend most of my time in London or Oxford. I've finished university, but I still have a house there because I like the place. Of course I went straight to the Park after Atalanta's call. Mother died two days later.'

'But . . .'

'But what? Why did he do it? Because he wanted another son. Remember the will. Oh, don't look surprised, everyone knows what it said. Yes, he wanted another son, because' – he gave a derisory laugh – 'I'm not exactly the sort of son a Rushton should have.'

To Mara's surprise Damon not only liked Les Vieux Orangers but he was extraordinarily good with Oliver. From being afraid he would be bored and that the villagers would not take to him, she was almost jealous to find everyone adored him. Oliver chuckled contentedly on his lap, Maman made him special cakes and biscuits, and even Bobo allowed himself to be ridden by Damon. And Damon seemed as surprised as Mara to find himself so popular – he wasn't used to popularity except with his own set. But the simple people of Barjon loved him for his beauty and his gentleness, and either did not see or ignored the darker side of his character. They also loved him because they loved Mara and they were pleased to see her happy, and relieved to think her relatives had not, after all, abandoned her. Families stuck together in Barjon.

Of Les Vieux Orangers Damon said, 'I love this place. I couldn't live here as you do, because it's too isolated. But when I'm old I'd like to live somewhere like this. I'd like to die here and be buried in these hills.'

Of the black rock he said, 'There's something mystical

about it. And I know what you mean about the people all being gone and someone else sitting here. I used to feel that about the woods, those ones which run from the Dower House to Elenora's cottage.'

Of his father stopping Mara's allowance, at first he only said, 'The bastard!' But on his last evening he brought up the subject again, asking her if she intended to do anything. 'I think you should,' he said, 'after all the Old Man specified that widows must be provided for.'

Mara shook her head. If Damon had guessed about Oliver, she would have admitted it and explained why she did not want Rushton money, but he hadn't, and why should he, he'd never met Jamie. And Mara preferred it this way. Oliver was her secret.

'Why not?' he asked. 'If you wrote to Lewis I know he'd make sure you had it. I'm sure he thinks, probably because Father's told him so, that you're still receiving Alexander's allowance. If he knew . . .'

They were in the kitchen and Mara was cooking supper while Damon lounged in the old armchair where Alexander had always sat. 'You're not to tell him,' she said sharply.

'But . . .'

'Damon!'

'If you don't want me to, of course I won't.'

'I don't want you to.' She chopped the meat into small cubes. 'Stew all right for you? I'm afraid the butcher didn't have anything else.'

'Yes, fine.' He lit a cigarette. 'So what are you going to do?'

'Find a job, I suppose. I'll have to eventually, though heaven knows what.'

He groaned. 'It's all so stupid! Rushton-Gaunt . . . I refuse to say Rushton Motors . . . haven't been near

Brooklands since you won the Hatton-Gaunt Cup. Smithy says you're the only decent driver they've ever had apart from the Old Man, everyone except Father is longing to get back into racing, and here you are, about to get some crummy job.'

Mara smiled. 'How are Smithy and the rest of them?'

'Battling on. When I go back I'll tell them I've seen you, I don't care what Father says, and anyway none of them will tell him.' He paused. 'Do you ever miss it?'

'I miss them.'

He lit another cigarette. 'If you're serious about this job business, then I think you should try Paris. After all, you're not going to find anything around here, but I'm sure you would there. Paris is *the* place now. It's full of English and Americans. Musicians. Painters. Writers. People like Scott Fitzgerald.'

Mara thought of Charles and Cynthia. *The Beautiful and the Damned*. How long ago that all seemed!

Damon carried on with enthusiasm. 'Some of them hang around Montmartre – you remember Montmartre? Toulouse-Lautrec, can-can and all that. But St Germain is the place, at least I think so. Really, I'm sure you could find a job. There's an American woman who runs a bookshop called Shakespeare and Company, and there's a café called Aux Deux Magots where everyone goes. You'd love it. It's exciting – bizarre – streets full of people all night long. You'd have no problem with all your languages.'

Mara laughed. 'Where? In the café or on the streets?'

'Don't laugh. It's only an idea. I'm just trying to help you.'

She stopped smiling. 'Yes. Thanks. I'll think about it. The trouble is, I have this house and the thought of . . . but you're right, I must do something. It's just that' –

visions of earnest intellectuals came into her mind – 'I know I'm silly, but clever talented people always make me feel so inadequate.'

Damon was surprised. '*You* lack confidence? *You* who used to slither around in those clothes not even Atalanta would dare wear?'

Mara picked up a potato and began to peel it. 'That's different.'

'And what about your motor-racing?'

'Racing's different too. It doesn't require . . . brains.'

'But it takes courage.'

'I suppose it does.' She looked round the farmhouse kitchen and it seemed incredible that she had ever had the confidence to move in the bright world Damon referred to – or, in fact, ever had the courage to do anything at all.

That night Mara was too preoccupied to sleep. Eventually she went downstairs to make herself a cup of tea. Coming back up the stairs, some fifteen minutes later, she noticed a rather sickly smell outside Damon's bedroom door. She stopped. Sniffed. Listened. At the bottom of the door, which didn't fit well into its frame, there was a small strip of pale light. 'Damon!' she called. No answer. 'Damon!' she called and tapped. Still no answer. She was about to open the door when she hesitated, wild thoughts running through her mind. Would he? Here, in her village? Here, in her house? Surely not!

Very quietly Mara opened the door. Damon was lying on his bed, fully clothed. He was spreadeagled on his back with arms outstretched and eyes shut, and in one hand he held a pipe. It was still lit. 'Damon!' Mara approached the bed. The sickly smell was almost overpowering. 'Damon!' She touched his shoulder.

Damon opened his eyes and looked up at her, trying

hard to focus on her face. 'Hello, Mara,' he said dreamily, slowly lifting the pipe to his mouth and sucking it. 'What are you doing here?'

'I saw the light and I thought . . .'

'That I had some village boy in here?'

'No, of course not.'

He sucked at his pipe again. 'Don't lie to me, Mara! You never do. You and Elenora.' His voice tailed off and he smiled again.

Mara said, 'Very well then. Yes, I did wonder.'

'Of course you did. But you needn't have worried, I wouldn't corrupt your village boys, I'd never do anything to hurt you, I'm too fond of you, Mara. Of you and Elenora and' – he waved the pipe at her – 'Mother Opium.'

Neither Mara nor Damon referred to her nocturnal visit next morning. They kissed each other goodbye and promised to write. But after he'd gone Mara went up to his bedroom and sat on the bed. All that remained was a faint sickly smell.

That year, 1931, Mara would think of later as her ostrich year. Bury your head, and the world won't see you. Bury yourself, and your problems will go away. Except of course they wouldn't. And Mara knew it. But for the time being she was incapable of taking the big step, because it would mean leaving Oliver with Maman until she could provide him with a home, and she couldn't bear the thought of being without him. It would be leaving a part of herself behind, the most important and most fragile part. Something might happen to him. He might become ill – fall – break a leg – get lost – and she would be far away. Often when she was sitting on the floor, playing with him, she looked at his cheeky little face and thought, not long now, and she turned her head away so he couldn't see her tears. Another thing which upset her was that she would miss whole stages of his growing up, other people would see them but she, his mother, wouldn't.

And what if he forgets me? Supposing I come back to collect him and he doesn't know me, he'll refuse to go with me. Oh, if only there was another way. But there wasn't. To provide a home for Oliver she had to have money and for that money she needed a job, and she wasn't so naïve as to imagine it would all happen overnight. However much Damon had enthused over Paris and been convinced she'd have no problem in finding work, Mara was sure that once she went it would be several months before she was in a position to have Oliver there. For one thing, if she was working she would have to arrange for someone to look after him and it would take time for her to find a person she trusted enough for that.

In the end two things happened to pull Mara's head out of the sand, and they both happened in March of the following year.

First of all, Maman announced she wasn't going to take any more money from Mara. 'No, Madame Mara,' she said firmly when Mara tried to pay her. 'No. Do you think I'm stupid as well as old? Meat once a week. No new clothes. The car needs mending. No visits to Cannes. No, I'm not stupid but, if you'll forgive an old woman, I'm beginning to think you are. It's no good sitting here watching your money trickle away, you must do something to make it trickle in as well as out, and, as you know, there's nothing for you to do here in Barjon. So, now listen to me, Madame Mara. Old Pierre and I have already decided we will take the boy when you go.'

The second thing was one of those bizarre coincidences which force one along the path of life. An English couple, driving through Barjon, knocked down and killed a donkey. Without a word of French between them, they faced a barrage of angry villagers. Mara was called down from the farmhouse to help. Luckily she managed to sort things out. There were smiles and apologies and the unfortunate donkey was paid for. The English couple, who before Mara's arrival had half expected to be lynched, thanked her profusely and gave her their copy of *The Times*, saying, 'Living up here you must be desperate for news.'

How wrong they were! Mara couldn't have cared less about the outside world. However, she glanced through the paper. And there, on the Court Circular page, tucked amongst the other forthcoming marriages, she found: 'Doctor James Turner to Miss Sarah Bucklethwaite.'

So Sarah, with her attraction inexplicable to women, had won.

In a funny way the news was a back-handed relief. Subconsciously Mara had clung to Les Vieux Orangers because she'd hoped Jamie might come back one day. Now she knew he wouldn't. He was going to marry Sarah. As with Alexander's death, Mara saw the facts: clear, bold, unmistakable. Of course it took her a while to accept. Tears of desperation. Letters written late at night telling Jamie about Oliver, torn up next morning when pride returned, letters written to Elenora telling her about Oliver in the hope that she'd pass the information to Jamie, again torn up, because if Jamie wanted her then he must want her for herself and not just because she was the mother of his son. Also Mara knew that whatever way she contacted him, directly or indirectly, once he saw her poverty-stricken state, he would say, 'You only come running when you want something.'

Chapter 37

Paris, 1933

It wasn't as easy to find work as Damon had thought. Not at all. There were plenty of Americans living out their artistic experiences in St Germain and there were plenty of cafés and bookshops and art galleries, but there were also plenty of other people as desperate for work as Mara. Evening after evening, her feet aching, she would stumble back to her little room in the small scruffy hotel just off the Boulevard St Germain. There she would lie on her bed listening to the rattle of the shutters as the shops closed at the end of a working day – a working day for others, not for herself. Then later she would hear laughter and music – jazz, always jazz – from the brightly lit cafés. Never had Mara felt so lonely as she did that early summer in Paris, her loneliness compounded by her longing for Oliver and, when she allowed herself to think about him, for Jamie.

Once, when she was trailing disconsolately back to her hotel, a white Hispano-Suiza roared past her, its flying stork emblem catching the evening sun. Mara stood and watched until it disappeared. She thought of Colonel Mackintosh and wondered how he was. How long ago it seemed since she'd stood in the Paddock and said, 'I'll race, and this time I'll win.'

Was that really me? she asked herself, as she climbed the stairs to her little room. Where on earth did I find the courage? She opened the door and kicked off her shoes.

And the Old Man, he believed in me – she lay down on the narrow bed – so I must have had something – she closed her eyes – I wonder where it went. She fell asleep.

But Mara had to keep going. Over and over again she plucked up the courage to go into a café or a gallery or a shop and ask the proprietor, 'Do you have any work? Do you need any help?' The reply was always the same, 'No, mademoiselle, we don't need anyone. We've too many already.'

One evening, hungry and dispirited, Mara went into a small café and ordered a bowl of soup. Hardly had it arrived before two young men of about twenty-five – they looked like students – sat down at her table without asking if she minded, and launched into a discussion as to whether or not the riot in the Place de la Concorde in early February had been for or against Communism.

Mara listened vaguely. In Barjon she'd heard nothing about this riot, but since coming to Paris she'd heard of it constantly – as a reason why there was no work – as a reason why there'd be no work for anyone soon. As she listened to the argument, she studied the two young men discreetly. One was fair and of medium height; in fact, very ordinary except that he had a nice smile. He was obviously far less intense than the other, who was tall and thin and very dark, with a rather beaky face and sallow skin and a nervous jerky way of talking, as though his boundless energy could find no outlet in his skinny body. But in spite of all that, there was something rather appealing about him. He reminded Mara of a featherless baby blackbird pounding up and down inside its nest.

The fair one left. The dark one stayed. 'And what do you think, mademoiselle?' he demanded. 'Don't you think I'm right? I mean, it's perfectly obvious. The working men of Paris have risen, they've had enough.'

He banged his fist on the table and the cutlery jumped. 'Enough! Enough of Stavisky and his kind.'

Mara sat and said nothing. She was torn between her embarrassment at the attention her companion was attracting and her pleasure at having someone to talk to. But the trouble was, she had no idea what he was talking about and no idea who Stavisky was. 'I don't know,' she said rather lamely when she began to fear her silence would drive him away. 'I don't know much about it.'

'Can't you read?' That was just the sort of thing Jamie would have said.

'Yes, of course I can.'

'But don't you read a newspaper? Everyone knows about Stavisky the swindler, and all those politicians who kept quiet because they'd had a finger in his filthy business.' He suddenly stopped talking and studied Mara. 'You're not French, are you? I can tell by your accent.'

'No. I'm half English and half German.'

'So am I.' He jerked upright. 'Well, not quite. But half German. My father was German. My mother was French. Father dead. Mother dead.'

Mara said, 'German father. English mother. Father dead. Mother dead.'

'Orphans.' He held out his hand and Mara shook it. 'This calls for an orphans' celebration.' Without waiting to see if Mara agreed, he wriggled round in his chair and called for a bottle of wine.

I hope he's going to pay for it, she thought. He'd better. She was down to her last four hundred francs.

'So?' He smiled at her and his dark eyes became warm and genuinely friendly.

'So what?'

'What are you doing here?'

'I'm looking for a job.'

'What can you do?'

'Not a lot.' The wine was cheap and rough, but it had its effect. Mara felt almost drunk. A wild thought came to her: if she couldn't find a job perhaps she should find herself a man to keep her. But immediately she was furious with herself for thinking such a thing.

'What have you been doing till now?' he asked.

Briefly Mara told him about Alexander and Oliver and Les Vieux Orangers. It was remarkably easy to talk to a stranger, particularly after a few glasses of wine. She even told him about Herbert stopping the allowance, but she didn't tell quite how wealthy the Rushtons were or where their money came from. To have said, 'The Rushtons of Rushton-Gaunt, I used to race at Brooklands, I beat Yves Lejeune, you've probably heard of him,' would have sounded ridiculous coming from someone for whom a bowl of soup was a whole meal.

'Don't tell me what it's like,' he said when she finished her story. 'When my father died two years ago I discovered he'd lost most of his money gambling. There was barely enough to pay for my studies – law – so I now have to work to keep myself. I'm three years behind as it is, for my age. I was ill as a child and Mother died when I was ten. I know just what it's like. Of course, the state should pay. Pay me. Pay you. That's what happens in Russia. But what can you and I do? Start another revolution?' He helped himself to one of Mara's precious cigarettes. 'No, of course we can't. Too busy working, which reminds me' – he leaned across the table, twisted Mara's arm, and looked at her watch – 'time for me to get going.'

'What do you do?' she asked, wishing he didn't have to go.

'I play the piano in a café called La Renaissance. It's

near the Deux Magots. You must know Aux Deux Magots.'

Mara remembered that was the café Damon had talked about. She nodded.

To her relief he paid for the wine and to her surprise he paid for her soup as well, saying, as Mara tried to repay him, 'Forget it! It's only money.'

Outside on the pavement he shook her hand. 'Well, goodbye. And good luck. I'll probably see you around.' He turned and walked away.

Mara turned quickly in the other direction, her acute loneliness accentuated by his brief company. I wish I was the sort of person who made friends very quickly, she thought. Friends with people who are . . . different. I had lots of friends in England – well, acquaintances – and I could have had a lot more if I'd wanted to. But I suppose we were all doing the same thing, so we were bound to make friends. Cynthia. Charles. Jeremy. Mind you, I wouldn't want them here. They wouldn't understand. Elenora would. Damon would, I think. Atalanta, perhaps. She wandered slowly up the street.

Suddenly a hand landed on her shoulder. It was him again. 'Hey, let's meet tomorrow. Same time. Same place.'

Eagerly, Mara turned to face him. 'Oh yes. Do let's.'

'See you then . . . umm . . .'

'Mara. Mara Rushton.'

'Leon. Leon Rosenthal. A good Jewish name.' A hesitant pause whilst he looked at Mara as though expecting her to make some comment. But when she didn't, her father had had a number of Jewish friends though it occurred to her now that the Rushtons hadn't, he gave her a beaky smile and bounded off. This time Mara watched him go, laughing to herself as he wove through the traffic taking no notice when taxi drivers hooted furiously at him.

Having a friend made all the difference. Mara still couldn't find work, she still spent all day looking, her money still dwindled – but at least she had someone to talk to: someone who commiserated and encouraged. Leon was an odd sort of friend, though. Casual. Frank. His language poured forth in a stream of obscure intellectual hypotheses and the very worst kind of French expletive. And it was all said at the top of his voice and with a great deal of arm-waving. What Mara found most odd about him was that he never showed the remotest interest in either herself or any other woman. He was a friend, yet she was sure if one day she failed to meet him he would soon be talking equally as enthusiastically to someone else.

About two weeks after they had first met, Leon arrived at the café waving his arms and shouting with excitement. 'I have some good news for you,' he cried, grabbing one of Mara's cigarettes and slumping down in the chair opposite her. 'Good news. Guess! Guess!'

She laughed at him. 'You've found me a millionaire.'

'You're not after that, are you?' He looked disgusted.

'No, of course not. Come on! Tell me! I was only joking.'

He relaxed, as much as he was ever capable of relaxing. 'I'll tell you in Russian. That'll teach you.'

'I might speak Russian. For all you know I might be . . . what's her name . . . Anastasia.'

Leon loved it when Mara played along with him. He leaned forward and whispered, 'Then I'll tell you in French so as not to blow your cover. First' – he stabbed the air with his finger, reminding Mara again of Jamie –

'the old tart in the café where I work has finally got the boot and they need another one.'

'Another tart! I thought you just said . . .'

'Fool!' He grabbed another cigarette. 'A waitress. A cashier, when they get to know you and when old Madame Papin the proprietor's wife is away, something for which we all pray because she's a bitch of the first order. Of course they have Chantal, the other waitress, but she's an incorrigible baggage who's only interested in sex, so she's no good as a cashier. She'd give all the money away to the first man she wanted. Ah, yes, the money. Five nights a week, eight till two, like me. Eight francs a night plus tips. More than three English pounds a week. Pretty good, eh?'

Mara tried to look enthusiastic. Three pounds! She used to think nothing of squandering that on a hat she might wear only once.

But Leon was so pleased he didn't notice anything was wrong. 'Come on, let's drink to your future,' he said, and called for another bottle of wine.

'When do I start?' she asked.

'Next week. But remember, I told them you'd worked as a waitress before, so for God's sake don't say you haven't. And,' – he gave her green cotton dress a doubtful appraisal – ' it might be an idea to wear something a bit . . . brighter. You could be very attractive if you tried.' Totally unaware of the effect his words had had on Mara – they'd made her feel old and careworn – Leon went on brightly, 'And the second piece of good news is this.' He filled her glass. 'You remember I told you I shared an attic with Jacques, the friend who was with me when we first met?'

'Yes. Vaguely.'

'Vaguely! You should listen intently, Mara. You should . . .'

She cut him short. 'Get on with it.'

'Well, Jacques' father's died so he has to go home and live with his mother. So you can have the other room. Only fifteen francs a week.'

'What! Live with you?'

Leon laughed at her astonishment. 'Live with me! Live with me! Mara, get rid of those bourgeois notions. Aren't there men living in your obscene little hotel, sleeping under the same roof as you?'

'Of course there are,' she answered crossly. First he had made her feel old and careworn, now he was making her feel stupid and narrow-minded.

'Then what's the difference between that and sleeping under the same roof as me, a friend?'

'None.' She said it though she was unconvinced. Leon's was a curious world.

'Exactly.' He helped himself to yet another of her cigarettes. 'You'll have your room. I'll have mine. We share the kitchen and the sitting room and, of course, the bathroom, but there's no hot water, I'm afraid. And I also have the garret as my study.'

'And you smoke my cigarettes.'

He laughed but wasn't at all embarrassed. 'I'll buy some more when you run out,' he said calmly, 'then you can smoke mine.' A pause. 'Oh yes, another thing. You can bring your son to live with us.' His face lit up and Mara instantly forgave him for hurting her feelings. 'Madame Leblanc, the porter's wife, adores children. She'd look after him and she wouldn't charge much, if anything.'

Mara smiled. 'Could I bring Oliver? I can't afford to yet, but . . . you wouldn't mind?'

'Why should I?' He divided the last of the wine between them. 'Let's drink to us! If we have sex we have it and if we don't we don't. I shouldn't think we will, but who cares if we do.' He raised his glass.

And Mara, determined not to be thought a prude, raised hers and said, 'Exactly.'

Rather naturally Mara couldn't help wondering what she'd let herself in for: living – sharing – with a man she hardly knew: working in a café. It was a miracle she didn't catch the next train back to Barjon. However, a lot of her fears disappeared when she saw Leon's attic.

He had once had a passion for Mexico and all things Mexican. Mexico had gone, to be replaced by Russia, but the Mexican things remained in the small bright attic. Its white-painted walls were covered with posters of bullfights, its plain wooden floorboards littered with Mexican rugs and gaudy cushions, and its bedrooms had no furniture, just mattresses on the floor, covered with red and green woven rugs. After the drabness of her hotel bedroom Mara was enchanted. She particularly liked the odd shape of the sitting room, whose white rafters were exposed up to the apex of the house, and she knew why she liked it. It reminded her of Jamie's bedroom.

The only room Mara didn't care for, but it wasn't hers anyway, was the garret. It was a small boxroom, reached by climbing six rickety stairs, with just a desk and a chair – and a huge brooding picture of Stalin. 'We could have it in the sitting room if you like,' Leon suggested, beaming up at the grim face.

'No,' Mara replied hurriedly. 'I think it looks much nicer where it is.'

Mara liked the views from the attic too: from her bedroom across the jumbled rooftops of St Germain:

from the kitchen and the sitting room down into the narrow street, where the porter's wife gossiped endlessly on the pavement and the butcher kept up a running battle with his neighbour, the greengrocer. And she liked living with Leon. He was amiable in his neurosis and hopelessly untidy, but meticulously clean. Twice a day he filled the bath with cold water and climbed in, singing tunelessly as he soaped his skeletal body.

Pretty quickly Mara realized that Leon wasn't what would be called a diligent student. His intentions were good. Every morning at eleven he would have a final cup of coffee and say, 'Now, no more talk till six o'clock,' but within an hour or two one of his friends would tap on the door and down he would come. Leon didn't have many friends, he put far too much energy into those he had to have any left for more, but the ones he did have, perhaps eight or ten, he was devoted to and saw frequently. He called. They called. Any time of the day or night. Singly. In pairs. Sometimes not in the same pairs. Sometimes all of them together. Like Leon they were intensely interested in politics, and they accepted Mara's arrival with friendly incuriosity, being far too bound up in the problems of the world to wonder about the sudden appearance of an individual.

The café was another matter. The dream of old Monsieur Papin, the rotund and garrulous proprietor, was to tempt the Americans away from the Deux Magots, which he regarded as his successful but unworthy rival. Several times a day he would waddle off to see how they were doing, then hurry back as fast as he could, brimming with ideas to make the terrace of La Renaissance as attractive as that of Aux Deux Magots. Other ideas too he copied, from them and from other cafés. Leon, a jazz pianist, had been one. Mara, an English-speaking waitress, was another.

But hardly had Mara been introduced to him on her first evening than he looked at her cotton dress, not the green one but a yellow one marginally brighter, and said, 'No, no, mademoiselle. Too old-fashioned. I want you to look like that.' He pointed at a woman in an exotic bright red garment, the sort of thing Elenora might have worn, adding, 'Tomorrow you wear something like that.'

Mara nodded miserably. Having settled her hotel bill and paid Leon a month's rent she had only eighty francs to her name, and she couldn't possibly go and spend it on clothes.

'Good! Good!' Monsieur Papin patted her arm with his huge hand. 'Now, to work, Mademoiselle Mara. To work.'

And to work it certainly was! Mara simply couldn't imagine why he wanted more customers: the place was packed all evening. And all evening, with just one twenty-minute break, she took orders, served orders, took money, gave change, running backwards and forwards from the kitchen to the terrace, until her feet were sore and her head was splitting. Every time she paused, just for a moment to catch her breath, old Madame Papin would come down the stairs from their flat above and cry, 'Mademoiselle! Customers! Quick!'

Finally, at two o'clock Mara was free to limp home with her eight francs and her miserly tips clutched in her hand.

'How did it go?' asked Leon, skipping irritatingly along beside her.

'I'm exhausted.'

'Didn't Chantal help you?'

Mara stumbled over a pile of rubbish left on the pavement outside a restaurant. 'She wasn't there.'

'Probably met a new man.' Leon chased an alleycat halfway across the road. His energy was unbelievable. 'What did you think of my music?' His expression showed clearly that she should have complimented him already.

'Oh, very good. Very good. I've always liked the piano.' She'd been so busy she'd hardly heard it. Now she remembered what Monsieur Papin had said about her clothes and wanted to tell Leon, to ask his advice, but she was so tired she couldn't speak.

Instead, she told him next morning. 'What can I do?' she asked. 'What do I have that's suitable?'

Leon was sitting on his bed, reading a book. 'Nothing,' he replied, and went on reading.

'Well, suggest something.'

'What?' He didn't look up.

Mara grabbed the book from him. 'Help me. Don't just sit there! I'm going to lose my job and I can't afford to buy anything new. Come on, Leon! Do something!'

'I warned you,' he said, standing up slowly.

'Well, you should have told me more definitely.'

He laughed. 'Women!'

Mara clenched her fists and moved towards him. 'Women!'

'All right. All right.' He raised his hands in mock terror. 'Don't panic! I might have something.' He dug around amongst a pile of cushions and blankets. 'I had a friend staying who'd lived in India and she left some stuff behind. Here!' He produced a battered suitcase and opened it. 'What about that?' He held up a pair of baggy purple silk trousers. 'Just the thing for a sultan's favourite. And here! A white silk tunic to go over them.'

'Won't she mind?' asked Mara, picking up a purple and gold scarf.

'Why should she?' He rummaged through the case and produced a gold coin necklace. 'They're only possessions.'

When Mara came back into Leon's room, some ten minutes later, he clapped his hands with glee. 'Marvellous. Wonderful! Turn round!'

'Like this?' She spun round on the soles of her bare feet, the purple and gold scarf tied around her waist swirling after her and the gold coin necklace, pressed down on her hair as though she were a Red Indian princess, tinkling on her forehead.

'Yes.' He waved his arms. 'Oh, Alibaba, grant me the secret of eternal youth!'

'No, my son,' Mara did a little dance, 'not until you tidy up your room and do last night's washing-up.'

'You know,' said Leon, retrieving his book and flopping down on the bed, 'Jacques said you were stunning but I could never see it till now.'

Mara skipped over and pecked him on the cheek. 'Thanks. I'll let you off the washing-up. And I might even cook you your favourite lunch – spaghetti bolognese prepared by my own fair and lovely hands.'

'I have a much better idea.' He grabbed her by the arm. 'Bed.'

It was the beginning of a wonderful friendship. They were brother and sister, friend and friend, lover and lover. No ties. No commitments. No automatic sharing of a bed. They loved but were not in love, yet neither looked for love elsewhere: Mara because only other sex was on offer and only love would have tempted her: Leon because he was not a sensual person, he was an aesthete and an intellectual and he found as much satisfaction in a good discussion as he did in a woman's body. But he was all that Mara wanted at that time. She found their love-making reasonably satisfying and, above all, he made her laugh. Sometimes at the most intense moment he would mutter into her ear, 'Rushton-Russia-Rushton-Russia.'

Day after day in the bright little attic they teased, commiserated, talked and argued, just like a couple of puppies scrapping in a basket. 'You're an uneducated Philistine,' he would say. 'Ah, when you've grown up and seen the world as I have,' she would reply. 'You've no social conscience,' he would say. 'If you weren't so untidy I might have time for one,' she would reply, throwing armfuls of his dirty washing all over him.

Now Mara loved Paris as much as she had hated it during those first lonely weeks. She loved the mellow bridges over the Seine and the wide sweep of the Champs Élysées and the shadowed arches of Notre Dame, but most of all she loved the chattering streets of St Germain: her home. Only two things were missing. Oliver. She thought of him constantly and wrote endlessly to Maman, receiving in return short stilted replies from the priest because Maman couldn't write. Jamie. She tried not to think about him, to wonder, to hope, but every now and then something or someone would remind her of him, and she would stop what she was doing or saying and disappear into the secret garden of her thoughts.

Almost without being aware of it Mara had become a personality in St Germain. 'Mara from the Café La Renaissance.' 'Mara, you must know Mara. Dresses like a Cossack . . . always in baggy trousers . . . rather exotic. Yes, that's the one. Good-looking girl. Lives with Leon, the pianist.'

Gradually American and English writers and painters,

some successful, some not, began dropping into the café to see Mara. None of this was lost on old Papin. Quickly he employed another waitress as well as the sleepy-eyed and unreliable Chantal, leaving Mara free to drift between the tables, stopping to chat with one or to ask at another, 'A little more wine? Another beer? How's the book coming on? The play? The picture? No, I haven't been to the ballet this year. You designed the costumes? But how wonderful. Why, yes, we'd love to go. Leon adores all music and I love the dancing.'

It all came out so easily – the talk – the chat – and yet, six months earlier Mara had been living in solitude, convinced she'd never have the confidence to do anything. It's extraordinary, she thought from time to time, how one can do things if one has to. And I enjoy it. A waitress in a café. What would Mortimer say!

And what on earth would any of her London friends have said if they could have seen Mara gossiping with Chantal, the red-haired, sleepy-eyed waitress who was, as Leon had rightly described, an incorrigible baggage who wanted nothing more than to tumble through a series of comfortable beds. 'I find all men attractive,' she would tell Mara, yawning, 'that's my problem.' Once when old Madame Papin berated Chantal for walking down the street with her buttons undone and her bosoms showing, Chantal complained to Mara, 'It's not as if no one's seen them before. They were only saying hello to friends.'

'And trying to find new ones,' Mara quipped.

'Why not? At least I'm not like Yvette.' Yvette was the waitress hired to help Mara. 'Reading novelettes and waiting for Mr Right to come along. And what a wait! Thirty-nine though she says she's only thirty-four. They'll need a pick-axe when she finally . . . What are you laughing about, Mara?'

* * *

In early November Mara received a telegram from Elenora: 'Arriving Paris November eighth stop will call on you following morning stop returning London that afternoon.'

Two days later Elenora came bursting into the attic. 'How good it is to see you.' She hugged Mara to her. They drew back and looked at each other and laughed, and hugged again. 'I'm only here for a day but I just had to come. Oh, it's been so long! And I'm afraid I have to be at a gallery in half an hour, and then I must go to another one, so I'll have to take you with me if we're to see anything of each other. You will come, won't you?'

'Of course I will.' Mara tried to hide her disappointment, she'd hoped they would at least have the morning to themselves.

Elenora looked up as the garret door opened. 'Ah, you must be Leon,' she said.

Leon came down the stairs holding out his hand and smiling. 'Yes, I am. But why are you staying such a short time? Mara's been longing to see you!' He put an arm round Mara's shoulders. 'Haven't you?'

Mara saw that Elenora had taken in his gesture and she wished he hadn't touched her, but to shrug off his arm would have been churlish.

Elenora pushed back a strand of hair, now more grey than black. 'I wish I could stay longer but I have another exhibition opening in London tomorrow,' she laughed. 'Suddenly everyone wants my paintings. My small following has grown into a flock and to satisfy them I have to fly Imperial Airways, Paris and back in forty-eight hours. Oh, for the peace of a ferryboat!' She sat down carefully on one of the Mexican cushions and looking around her, said, 'Isn't it lovely up here!'

'How's your back?' asked Mara, sitting down opposite.

'Much better. Mind you, after juddering around in that beastly aeroplane . . .'

'I've never flown, what's it like?'

'Peculiar.'

'Frightening?'

'For me, but you'd enjoy it.'

'I used to think I would but after the Gemelli . . .'

Leon was puzzled. 'Why did you say that to Mara?' he asked Elenora.

'Because anyone who enjoys the thrill of motor-racing stands a good chance of enjoying the terror of flying. Or rather, people who hate one probably hate the other. I'm in the "hate" category.'

Mara looked from Leon to Elenora. 'I haven't told him about Brooklands or Rushton-Gaunt,' she said.

'Well I'm sorry if I let the cat out of the bag.' She turned to Leon. 'Madam, here, used to be one of Britain's very few lady racing-drivers. She even beat your Yves Lejeune.'

Leon was looking at Mara in the way people do when they discover someone they think they know well did something extraordinary in their past. He couldn't have been more surprised if Elenora had told him that Mara was Queen Nefertiti reincarnated. 'Even I've heard of Rushton-Gaunt,' he said after a few minutes, 'but I never connected Mara Rushton with them and you've never once said anything about racing. My God, you beat Yves Lejeune.'

After a quick cup of coffee Elenora and Mara left the attic and went to the first gallery. There Mara waited while Elenora talked. Then they set off again, hurrying through the cold streets, their conversation continually broken as other pedestrians pushed between them. Several times Mara was on the point of asking Elenora about

Jamie but there was no time to steer their talk in his direction and, to her frustration, Elenora didn't so much as mention his name.

Elenora said, 'I'm sorry not to have seen Oliver. How much longer are you going to leave him at Barjon?'

Mara answered, 'I hope to bring him to Paris after Christmas, I'm saving hard and I've already arranged with the porter's wife to look after him. I can't wait, I knew I'd miss him but I'd no idea how much.'

They said goodbye outside the second gallery and Mara walked back to St Germain. It had been so frustrating not to be able to talk that she almost wished Elenora hadn't come. There'd been so many things she'd wanted to ask, about Damon, about Atalanta, Rushton-Gaunt and everyone, but she hadn't wanted to talk of them in front of Leon.

When she returned to the attic Leon said, 'So tell me about Rushton-Gaunt and your racing.'

Mara shrugged. 'There's nothing to tell.'

'Do you miss it?'

'I miss the people – some of them.'

'Why didn't you tell me about it?'

'It's another chapter.'

By December Mara had saved enough money to take a two-week holiday. 'I want to fetch my son from Provence,' she told old Papin late one evening as they were clearing up.

'Your son, I had no idea . . .'

'Yes, he's nearly two. I left him with a family when I came to Paris but now I want him with me.'

'Of course, of course.' He patted Mara's hand as she gave him the evening's takings. He was fond of Mara. He'd put her pay up to ten francs a day and she was worth every centime of it. 'But who will look after him?' he asked cautiously.

'Madame Leblanc, the porter's wife. It's been arranged.'

'And your husband?' Madame Papin appeared in the kitchen doorway, lips pursed in disapproval.

Nosy old cow, thought Mara, forcing herself to smile. 'My husband died a month before my son was born, madame. That's why I came to Paris to look for work.'

Old Papin nodded sympathetically, but his wife gave Mara a look of disbelief and disappeared into the kitchen, muttering darkly about girls who gave way to lust. Embarrassed, the old proprietor clinked the coins on the counter and said loudly, 'I remember the first day you came here, mademoiselle . . . I mean, madame. Such a terrible dress. So old-fashioned. But I told myself, that girl has style. And I was right. I was right.'

Mara watched him begin to count the notes. 'Thank you, monsieur.'

'Oh, yes.' He smoothed one note flat. 'Only here nine months and you look more at home in St Germain than any of them. You're a true bohemian, mademoiselle . . . madame. Ah, you'll have to forgive an old man, I'll never remember. But you know what you remind me of?'

Mara smiled and shook her head. She was tired. It had been a very busy evening.

'That lizard. The one which they say changes its colour to suit its surroundings.'

'A chameleon,' she said very softly, staring at the deserted café. But it was not the empty tables or Leon carefully closing the piano that she was seeing.

Chapter 38

It seemed to Mara as though she had never been away from Barjon. Everything was exactly as it had been: Maman, old Pierre: the red roofs: the old men shuffling across the square to the café. Only Oliver was different. Bigger. Walking. Almost talking. But still blue-eyed. When Mara arrived he was chasing a cat round Maman's kitchen and at first he took no notice of her.

'I don't think he remembers me,' she told Maman dejectedly.

Maman reassured her, 'He'll be all right in a minute. He's talked about nothing else but your coming. Mummy come, Mummy come, all day.' She looked at the wide sleeves of Mara's purple woollen jacket. 'Perhaps it's because you look different, Madame Mara.'

'Do I? I suppose that's living in Paris.' Mara glanced round Maman's primitive earthen-floor kitchen. 'I hope Oliver's going to like it there.' She sat on a rough wooden stool and watched him stretch out his chubby hand towards the cat. She thought of Paris in August: the heat, the dust, the deadness of the afternoons when everyone who could afford to go away had gone and the city was taken over by tourists. 'Perhaps he could come back here in the summer for a month or so.'

Maman's face brightened. 'Whenever you like. We love him. There! You see!' Oliver had crept up behind Mara and he was fingering the hem of her jacket.

Mara picked up her son and hugged him, pressing her

face into his dark hair and wondering how she could have borne to be parted from him for so long.

Nothing else had changed. Les Vieux Orangers was just as it had been. Mara walked through the rooms. They were cold but everything was in its place. She lit a fire in the drawing room and watched the flames dance on the reddish walls and on the leather backs of the books. She went out across the courtyard to the barn. It was damp but it still smelt of hay, although none was there – she'd given Bobo and the chickens to the Gramonts in exchange for looking after Oliver. With Oliver toddling beside her, she went up to the cemetery and sat on the wall by Alexander's grave. The warm tranquillity of summer had given way to the cold tranquillity of winter.

On Mara's last day she borrowed Bobo from old Pierre and rode up to the black rock and looked down on the fields and the plain and the distant sea. It was all just as it had been, and she still loved it, but she'd moved on because she'd had to.

Returning by train to Paris, Mara and Oliver shared a compartment with a German couple. Mara didn't let on that she understood German. Their conversation didn't interest her – it was all about Adolf Hitler.

Chapter 39

September 1938

More than four years after that journey, when Mara had sat and listened to the German couple talk about Adolf Hitler, she and Oliver returned to Paris, again by train, after a month in Barjon. But to Mara it was suddenly a different Paris. She sensed the uneasiness in the streets. The unrest. She noticed the refugees. Many of them were Jews. She saw mothers kiss their soldier sons goodbye. From every newspaper, broadcast and conversation words like Hitler, Mussolini, Sudetenland, Anschluss jumped out at her. Of course Mara had heard them all before – and the endless rumbling of war, of mobilization, of the Maginot Line. But she'd heard it all so often and for so long she'd become anaesthetized, as the young do when they hear the old going on and on, year after year, about the country going to the dogs – but it never happens: Rover seems quite happy in his basket.

Yet all the signs had been there had she wanted to read them.

A year earlier Leon had chucked in his recently acquired position as a junior partner with a highly respectable firm of lawyers and gone rushing off to join the International Brigade and fight in the Spanish Civil War, only to return three months later: he was too flat-footed for the long marches. But Mara had not seen this as a real war. She'd merely tried not to laugh about Leon's flat feet. After all, a civil war in Spain meant Spaniards fighting Spaniards even if German bombs were dropped from German planes and Mussolini had sent fifty thousand Italians to Franco's aid.

Nor had Leon's fateful pilgrimage to Russia the previous Easter opened her eyes to what was happening in Europe. Russia was a long way away. And hadn't she always said his impassioned Communism was too idealistic? However, she was very sympathetic towards his broken dream. With twenty other young French Communists he had set off singing. And they all came back singing – except for Leon. He slunk into the attic, pale and thin and miserable. 'Don't laugh, please,' he begged Mara. 'I couldn't bear it. Russia was my Mecca.'

'Was?'

'Yes.' He looked as though he were about to cry. 'I wish I'd never gone. I've killed my dream.'

'Was it that bad?'

'Oh no. At first I thought it was wonderful. They treated us magnificently. Then one afternoon I went for a walk on my own, we weren't meant to but I couldn't see why not. I hadn't gone very far before a man came up to me. He was a Jew. He spoke to me in Yiddish. I understood most of it because my grandmother spoke Yiddish.'

'What did he say?'

'He said, "Tell the world about the purges and pogroms. Tell the world Stalin is a monster." Then he was gone. Just like that. One moment he was there. The next he was running off up an alleyway.'

'What did you do?'

'I went back to our hotel, luckily I hadn't been missed, and I didn't tell anyone about it, not until we returned to Paris and I told our leader. He was furious with me. I tried to explain why I'd kept quiet but he wouldn't listen.

He kept saying the man was obviously deranged and that I should have told our Russian hosts immediately. He said I was a . . . disgrace to our group. But I was right not to say anything. I know I was. The man came to me as a Jew to a Jew, and I would have been wrong to betray him.'

Mara stroked his dark head. 'Yes, you were right.' And she thought of the unknown Russian Jew who had perhaps risked his life to speak to Leon.

But still Mara did not bother about the tumbrils of war rolling towards Eastern Europe.

Now she did. And she was frightened. Her capacity for putting problems aside until she was in the mood for dealing with them, to do her ostrich act as she had done in Barjon, meant that when she did pull her head out of the sand the gravity of those problems hit her extra hard because she had not benefited from the process of gradual acclimatization. Just as the sudden shock of knowing Jamie was to be married had tipped Mara out of her cocoon and made her leave Barjon, so the realization that war was not a vague possibility but an all too real probability changed Paris from a city which Mara loved to a place where she and her son might be trapped by an enemy. She became frantic if Oliver, now six and a half, went further than the street door. Once when Leon was meant to be looking after him Mara, coming home from the market, found Oliver playing with some children three streets away. Horrified, she dragged him back to the attic where Leon, completely oblivious, was talking to two Jewish refugees.

'Can't you even look after him for an hour?' she screamed at Leon. 'Can't I trust you to do that?'

The refugees shuffled to their feet and Leon muttered, 'I'm sorry.'

'Sorry's no good. Supposing he's killed. Supposing . . .' Mara went into her room, taking Oliver with her, and slammed the door.

Later they made it up. Not physically, that side of their relationship had petered out, but with words.

Mara said, 'I'm sorry.'

'I'm sorry too.'

'It's only because I'm frightened.'

'I'm frightened too. Those men told me what is happening to the Jews in Germany.'

'I saw all the soldiers in the street and I thought . . .'

'They've mobilized the reserves.'

'Will you be called up?'

'Not unless war breaks out – then everyone will be. But I've been thinking that perhaps . . . perhaps I should leave Paris. Perhaps we should all leave Paris.'

'Where would you go?'

'Palestine. It's the only home for a Jew.'

'But I thought the British . . .'

'Yes, they're there. But we belong to Palestine . . . to Israel. And you could come with me. You and Oliver. I wouldn't want to go without you. After all' – he touched Mara's hand – 'I almost think of him as my son. I wish he was.'

Mara smiled and said nothing.

Suddenly there wasn't going to be a war any more. It was 'peace in our time'. Neville Chamberlain left Munich to tell the British and President Daladier left Munich to be greeted by cheering crowds as he drove through the streets of Paris. Mara and Leon hugged each other. They hugged Oliver. And Mara tore up the instructions she'd copied down on how to extinguish an incendiary bomb.

Then Damon turned up unexpectedly, and Mara thought, if people can still travel things must be all right.

However, Damon's visit was not a success. He had been to the attic a number of times but previously he'd come alone. This time he brought a friend, a fair-haired cherub-faced boy named Frederick who held out his soft hand to Mara with all the enthusiasm of a bishop offering his ring to the kiss of a dirty peasant.

'Frederick's at Oxford,' said Damon, by way of explanation. 'And he's furious with me.'

'That's not true.' Frederick's disdainful glance drifted over the Mexican rugs and the bright cushions. 'It's just that we're expected at my grandmother's château near Tours and . . .'

Damon cut him short. 'Seeing Mara's much more important.'

'I'll make some coffee,' Mara said hurriedly. 'Or would you prefer something else?'

Damon smiled at her. 'No, coffee's fine.' As Mara went into the kitchen she heard him add in undertones to Frederick, 'If you don't shut up you'll be sorry.'

When she came back with the coffee she sensed an uneasy truce. Frederick was standing by the window with his back to her. Damon was lolling on a cushion on the floor. 'Where's Oliver?' he asked.

'At school.'

'Near here?'

'Yes. About five minutes' walk.' Although Mara knew it would be no problem to fetch Oliver for an hour she didn't suggest it. Neither did Damon. He sensed she did not want her son to meet Frederick. All he said was,

'Have you decided what you're going to do about his later schooling?'

'Not yet. It depends on what I can afford.'

Damon kicked at the floor. 'I still think you should write to Lewis.'

Mara shook her head. 'No.' She poured out the coffee and handed a cup to Frederick, who took it with distaste. Nasty little weasel, she thought, looking at his silky moustache.

'And Lady Henrietta thinks you should too,' Damon went on. 'She was appalled when I told her what Father had done. She sends her love, by the way.'

'How is she?'

'The same. The Dowager Queen Bee of Society. But I like her, in small doses. Oh, and Elenora sends her love too. You know she's hurt her back again? That's why she hasn't been over to see you for so long. It keeps happening.'

Mara nodded. 'I haven't seen her for nearly five years. The last time was during my first winter in Paris, when Oliver was still in Barjon.'

Damon lit a cigarette. 'Do you realize, she must be in her late fifties? I never think of her as being that old . . . as being much older than I am.'

Mara smiled fondly. 'Nor do I. And how's Atalanta? I haven't heard from her for a couple of months.'

'She has . . . problems.' He glanced at Frederick but said no more.

Mara sensed Damon didn't want Frederick to know his sister loved someone who was little more than a mechanic, and she wondered if it were to protect Atalanta or to protect himself from Frederick's ridicule – or a bit of both. 'How about everyone at the works?' she asked.

'They're all still hoping you're going to come back and

put Rushton-Gaunt back on the racing map. I saw Smithy last month and told him I hoped to see you soon and he said to tell you . . . what was it . . . er . . . oh yes, he hoped you haven't forgotten your cornering.' Mara laughed. 'I hadn't the heart to tell him you didn't even have a car, I think they all imagine you're driving round in some flash French model.'

Damon and Frederick stayed for over an hour and, much as Mara loved Damon, she was glad when he said they must go. The presence of Frederick had made all their conversation awkward. Whilst they were saying goodbye and Damon was again trying to persuade Mara to fight Herbert, Leon came pounding up the stairs.

'I forgot my wallet,' he said, rushing into his room and out again. 'Must run. Oh, hello Damon. Nice to see you again. Hello.' He nodded at Frederick as he hurried out of the door.

'What was all that about?' Frederick asked in a petulant voice. 'Who was that man? Why couldn't he speak English? Not everyone speaks French like dear Damon and . . . er . . . you.' He looked at Mara as though speaking French were a club from which he was unfairly excluded.

Mara did not answer him. She kissed Damon on the cheek and told him to give her love to everyone.

But as they were going downstairs, that odious petulant voice came wafting up to her. 'Good God, Damon, you never told me she was shacking up with a Jew.'

At the beginning of March Elenora finally came to Paris. Stiffer. Greyer. But still the same Elenora; the same angular face which softened so easily with compassion, the same hard stare which was not really hard, the same outrageous clothes, the same straggly hair. She was just a little older, that was all. So was Mara. She was going to be thirty-eight in August. The idea was horrific, even though everyone said she looked no more than thirty-two or thirty-three, and Leon said she didn't look a day over fifty – which was Leon's kind of compliment. But they weren't flattering her, she had the bone structure – wide cheekbones and a firm jaw – which at eighteen had made her look older than she was but at twenty-eight had made her look her age. Since then she had aged very little.

And Elenora told her so. 'What's more,' she said, eyeing Mara's long, lithe body, 'you're one of those lucky people who never get fat.'

Mara laughed. 'Don't you believe it. I'd be as fat as a pig if I didn't have to run up and down these stairs all day. I used to be able to eat anything I liked but now . . .'

'Now she sits and watches me eat,' said Leon, 'and you should see the way she drools over my food. She says, "Just give me a mouthful," and before I know where I am she's eaten the lot.'

They all laughed.

Of Mara's friends, Elenora was Leon's favourite. From the moment he had first met her, on her previous visit, he had liked her and he couldn't have enough of her company. This meant the two women were never without him and Mara had no chance to speak of Jamie. Not that she wanted to bring up his name, simply that she wanted Elenora to have the opportunity of doing so.

On Elenora's last evening Mara put her foot down. 'I want to talk to Elenora about the past,' she explained gently to Leon. 'Would you mind if we had dinner alone?'

'Won't you have to work?' he asked dejectedly. After his brief foray into Spain, Leon had never gone back to practising law. He preferred to play the piano in the evenings at La Renaissance and to have his days free for helping refugees.

'I've asked Papin for the night off.'

'I see.' But he didn't. He felt excluded.

Mara and Elenora chose one of those small warmly-lit restaurants which cling to the steep cobbled streets of Montmartre. The sort of place that has well-tended plants outside and red and white check tablecloths and rush-seated chairs inside. But where the food is excellent, and the house wine comes from the proprietor's second cousin's daughter-in-law's neighbour's vineyard.

It was wonderful for Mara to be alone with Elenora. The older woman was her mentor as well as her friend. To Elenora she could confide her innermost fears about Damon. 'You know he smokes opium,' she said. 'I caught him doing so at Les Vieux Orangers.'

'Yes, I know he does.'

'Is he an . . . addict?'

'I'm not sure. Sometimes, when he's been with me for several days and I know he hasn't smoked, I think he can't be. Other times I think he must be. I bumped into him once in London when his supplier had let him down and he was in a terrible state.' Elenora picked up the menu. 'Come on! Let's order! Snails for me.'

'And for me.'

'And let's have mushrooms in garlic too. Then I'll have . . . umm . . . steak au poivre, and lots and lots of potatoes.'

Mara broke off a piece of bread and covered it with lashings of butter. 'Yes.' She took a bite. 'Let's make pigs of ourselves.' The crust of the bread had stuck between her front teeth and she pulled it out, then she ate it. 'I shall have veal Provençale in honour of Barjon, not that many people there can afford to eat veal, and chocolate gâteau.' She smiled to herself. 'A double portion.'

'Getting back to Damon' – Elenora dipped some bread into the garlic sauce – 'I gather he came to see you with . . .'

'The dreaded Frederick. Yes. I do wish he could find someone . . . nice. What's it matter if he prefers a boy, so long as it's someone nice? Nice is a dreadful word, but you know what I mean.'

'Yes, I do. In many ways it would be better if he didn't live in England because, of course, it's illegal.'

'Do you think he's . . . discreet?'

'I doubt it. He's too beautiful, that's the trouble,' Elenora said slowly. 'Everyone wants him. Everywhere he goes temptation offers itself.' She moved back as the waiter brought her steak, saying, 'Let's have another bottle of wine!'

'So tell me the gossip,' said Mara, hoping Elenora would mention Jamie or if not at least Sarah.

'I'll start with the little people first. Alison Taylor-that-was is now the very contented wife of a brigadier. Both her children are avid members of the Pony Club.' She drank some wine. 'Paul . . . you remember . . . who owned the gallery has become extremely conservative, he even turned up at the cottage wearing a bowler.' They laughed. 'But I am fond of him.'

'And Zak?'

'Zak went off to Spain to fight with the International Brigade, wrote a lot of poetry, brought it all back, and to the amazement of everyone it was published. It's really quite good.'

Mara ate a potato with her fingers. 'What about Atalanta? Damon told me she was having problems but the "dreaded Fred" was there so he didn't tell me what they were, although I can imagine.'

'Pete!'

'They haven't split up?'

'Oh, no.'

'Then why don't they get married?'

'Because there's no way Herbert would accept Pete as a son-in-law and old Smithy's so devoted to Samuel's memory he'd made Pete promise not to tarnish the name of Rushton by eloping with Atalanta and causing a scandal.' She paused. 'You see, Smithy's the old school, Samuel was his boss and he finds it hard to accept that his son should marry into the ruling family, so to speak. He came to see me about it a couple of years ago and I tried to explain that Samuel would have been delighted, but he didn't really believe me. Or not so much he didn't believe me, he simply doesn't think it's right.' She picked up her knife and fork. 'I see a lot of Atalanta, she comes to the cottage just like you used to.'

Mara thought, it's twelve years since I caught them in the woods, and she said, 'Atalanta is nearly twenty-eight, it could go on like this for ever. Herbert must suspect.'

'You know what the Rushtons are like. Herbert suspects but pretends he knows nothing. Of course, being such a social climber himself he doesn't think she actually wants to marry Pete. And as for Atalanta, well, she'd rather have Pete this way than no way at all, so she's prepared to compromise and wait till Herbert's dead or whatever.'

'Is Herbert dying?'

'Not dying, but rumour has it that he's not himself, as they say. Only rumour, of course. I gather he's been spending a great deal of money, Rushton-Gaunt money, and things aren't going too well with the business. Apparently he sometimes orders the same thing five times. Five wirelesses – all identical – arrived at the Park one day.'

Mara was appalled. 'I'd no idea it was that bad. Surely someone can stop him, he might bankrupt Rushton-Gaunt. You don't think he's doing it on purpose?'

'I don't know, but he's as mad as a hatter.'

'And to think he once tried to make out the Old Man was mad! What's going to happen?'

'Hopefully he'll be locked up. The trouble is there's nobody to put him away. They're all terrified of him and I don't blame them. He has the most frightful temper.'

The waiter took their plates and brought Mara a mountain of chocolate gâteau. 'What about Doctor . . .'

'Phillips? He's so old and gaga himself now he wouldn't know a maniac if he saw one. Atalanta tried to talk to him but she got nowhere. Probably terrified he'd be locked up too. No, I'm afraid to say that unless Herbert murders someone, nothing's going to happen till he bankrupts the company. The only saving grace is that he hasn't got rid of the Smithys. They run the whole show now. Without them, Rushton-Gaunt would fall apart tomorrow. At least Herbert's sufficiently sane to see that.' She paused. 'Atalanta told me in confidence, but I know she won't mind you knowing, that she and Pete went to see Colonel Mackintosh . . .'

'He taught me to race.'

'Yes. Well, they thought that he might be able to help, being a great friend of Samuel's.'

'And?'

'They'd hoped he could come in as an adviser to temper Herbert's wilder excesses, but he said there was nothing he could do unless Herbert asks him to.'

'What about Lewis?'

'He's not a director of Rushton-Gaunt, and he's much too frightened of Herbert to interfere.'

Mara lit a cigarette.

Elenora said, 'Smoking again?'

'Why not?' She smiled ruefully. 'You know, Damon never mentioned any of this.'

'He's hardly ever there. I get my information from Atalanta and local gossip. Oh, and another thing, I believe Herbert sometimes talks about Sophia as though she were alive. Guilt, I suppose. Now, let's have some brandy.'

'And coffee.'

Elenora pushed back her straggly hair and studied Mara's face. 'You haven't told me anything about yourself yet. What are you going to do?'

'Do?'

'Yes. There'll be a war on pretty soon, whatever anyone says, and France won't be a good place to be caught in.'

Mara stirred her coffee. 'Things seem to have calmed down. Last September I was very worried but . . . well . . . perhaps Hitler's satisfied.'

'I doubt it. Why should he be?'

'That's what Leon says.'

'You're not staying because of Leon?'

'No.'

'So you're not in love with him? Last time I was here it was pretty obvious there was . . . something between you.'

'There was. There still is. Friendship. Apart from you, he's the closest friend I have – I've ever had. We were lovers but we're not any more, and not for any particular reason, it just petered out. But that hasn't made any difference to our friendship.'

690

Elenora was silent for a few minutes. Then she said, 'I wanted to be sure you weren't in love with him.'

Mara put her cigarette on the edge of the ashtray. She was suddenly very aware of the rush seat digging into the backs of her thighs and the wooden slats of the chair cutting into her vertebrae.

Elenora said very quietly, 'He didn't marry Sarah.'

Mara swallowed hard and looked at the check table-cloth. 'Why?'

'He felt he didn't love her enough, not as he knew he was capable of loving.'

It seemed to Mara that the small restaurant closed in around them until only she and Elenora were there: the other diners cut off behind a nebulous barrier, their conversation reduced to an incoherent burble. 'When did it happen?'

'About six months after I last saw you.'

'But that's years ago. Why . . .'

'Why didn't I tell you? Because you never mentioned him in your letters and every time I wrote and asked you if you were happy, you said you were. Remembering how contented you and Leon seemed together, I thought perhaps you had finally got over Jamie.'

Mara nodded. 'I've been very happy in Paris and very happy with Leon. But it's not . . . the same. It never has been.' She hesitated. 'How did he break it off?'

'They were meant to be getting married that Christmas – the Christmas after I saw you – but Jamie had doubts. They came to have lunch one day and it was obvious to me that he was unsure. Then he went to America for a month without her, and when he came back he told her.'

'Was she very upset?'

'At the time. She adored Jamie, but it could never have worked because she was too much in awe of him.

691

She's met someone else now, someone much more suitable, who isn't attractive and dynamic but he makes her feel secure and special. He's done wonders for her! I hope they'll marry, that's what Sarah wants more than anything despite her avid feminism.'

'I never liked her,' said Mara, 'and she didn't like me, but I'm sorry she was hurt.' A pause whilst she fiddled with her packet of cigarettes. 'What about Jamie . . . now?'

Elenora's green eyes twinkled. 'Oh, he's doing very well. I saw him a couple of weeks ago. He pops in whenever he's in the neighbourhood.'

'That's not what I meant.'

Elenora laughed. 'I know. You want to know if he has someone else.'

'Well, has he?'

'The answer to that is, I don't know. However, instinct tells me he has a lot of girlfriends but no one . . . special. At least no one special who lasts.'

'Does he . . . does he ever mention me?'

'He did once, about four years ago. He told me he'd loved you very much but that it was all over.' From across the table Elenora examined Mara's guarded face. 'Does he know about Oliver?'

'No. No one does. Was it his . . .'

'Eyes? Yes. That and the way you've never tried to claim any Rushton money for him. Which I agree with. I take my hat off to your honesty, Mara.'

'Did Jamie tell you he came to Les Vieux Orangers?'

'Yes, but he didn't tell me . . . everything. I just suspected something must have happened by the way he was so emphatic about it all being over. Then when I saw Oliver for the first time last week, well . . . Don't you think you should tell Jamie?'

'No. No. He said he wanted to forget me because I disrupted his life. He even said what . . . what happened between us at the farmhouse was his revenge. That he'd planned it.'

'And you believed him?'

'Yes and no. I believed that he believed he wanted to forget me, but I didn't really believe it had been his revenge. But when Alexander died, and he didn't contact me, then I did believe.'

'Why didn't you contact him?'

'Because he always says I only come running when I want something . . . when I'm down, and if he'd seen me, eking out my money at Barjon or working as a waitress in Paris, he'd have convinced himself he was right. Anyhow, he could easily have written to me.'

'Perhaps he was waiting for you to do so.'

Mara asked quickly, 'Why, has he said so?'

'No.'

'Then why should I make the first move? I'd just be inviting him to trample on me. And why should Jamie know about Oliver? Why should he see him? Because, of course, he would want to.' Mara's grey eyes glittered with angry tears.

'You still love him?'

'Yes. Yes, unfortunately. I've always loved him.' Mara bit her lip and frowned to hide her tears. 'But if he didn't want me for myself, I don't want him to want me just because I'm the mother of his son.'

'He might find out about Oliver.'

'How? He doesn't know where I am.'

'If you come back to England.'

'I won't.'

Elenora lit a cigarette. 'You may have to.'

On the following day Germany invaded Czechoslovakia.

Chapter 40

Mara and Leon had almost made up their minds to leave Paris, although they couldn't agree on where to go – Leon wanted to go to Palestine but Mara didn't – when, one night in early June she woke up to hear someone hammering on the street door. Lying in bed, listening, Mara heard Monsieur Leblanc, the porter, moving to answer the hammering, heard voices, heard footsteps, then someone tapped on the attic door. For one wild moment she thought it might be Jamie. Jamie come for her at last. But it wasn't Jamie. It was Damon. He came stumbling into the attic, white-faced and bedraggled. 'I . . . I had to come.' He collapsed on to a cushion. 'Don't send me away, please. I'm sorry if . . .' He buried his face in his hands and his shoulders shook with muffled sobs.

'What's happening, Mummy?' Oliver appeared in the doorway of Mara's bedroom – he slept on a mattress at the bottom of hers. 'Why's Damon crying, Mummy? Why's . . .'

'It's all right.' Mara stroked her son's dark mop of hair. 'Damon's hurt his head, that's all. He'll be better in the morning.'

'Where's Leon?' Oliver rubbed his sleepy eyes.

'He's at work. He'll be back soon. Now, come along.' She ushered Oliver back to his mattress and wrapped him in his blankets. He was asleep again by the time she kissed him.

Firmly closing the bedroom door behind her, Mara said, 'What's happened, Damon?'

'I . . . I . . .'

Before Damon had time to finish his halting sentence, Leon returned. 'What's . . .' He looked down at Damon, then at Mara, and he mouthed, 'I'll bring him some brandy.'

Later, when Damon had calmed down and Leon had tactfully withdrawn to his own bedroom, Damon told Mara, 'I was caught with Frederick.'

'Oh.' She tried not to look or sound shocked. 'Oh. Who . . . er . . .'

'Father. At the Park.'

'Oh, God!' She grabbed a cigarette and poured herself some brandy.

'That's just what he said. Oh, God! That and a lot else.'

Mara felt a brief flash of sympathy for Herbert. 'I can imagine.'

'And that wasn't all. He found my pipe. We'd been smoking. Poor Father, he thought it was hashish. That was bad enough, if he'd known the truth . . .'

'What did he . . . do?'

'He gave me a hundred pounds and told me to get out of the country within twenty-four hours and never come back. He kept the pipe and said if he ever heard I was in England he'd go straight to the police and tell them everything.'

'That won't do much good, not unless he goes immediately.'

Damon shrugged. 'He's not stupid. He knows once the police started watching me they'd catch me sooner or later . . . at something. You see, he also knows – I'd no idea he did till this happened – that I've been in trouble

695

before. Not for drugs. For the other. I was caught . . . I won't tell you the details. But I got off.' A pause. 'I bribed the witness.' He looked up at Mara with pleading eyes. 'I had to. You must see that.'

She sighed wearily, from despair. 'What are you going to do now?'

'I hoped I could stay here for a bit, just until I sort myself out. I promise . . . I promise I won't be any trouble. I'm going to stop smoking opium, I know I can, I sometimes don't touch it for several days. And I swear to you, Mara, there won't be any . . .' He raised an eyebrow and smiled tentatively. Even with his white face and dirty hair and his eyes red from crying, Damon was beautiful: in fact, almost more beautiful because he was so utterly appealing.

'Of course you can stay. Just one thing, please don't upset Leon. It's not a very good time to be a Jew.'

Damon closed his eyes. 'I'm sorry about what Frederick said. I know you heard.'

'Yes, I did.' Mara walked over to the window and looked down on the street. Dawn was approaching. But there were no glistening rays of sun. Not yet. Just the grey light which precedes them and which has no shadows. It made the street look like an over-exposed still-life photograph of closed shop-fronts and rubbish piled on the pavements and alleycats having their breakfast from someone's dinner of the previous night. Mara thought of Jamie, and had an extraordinary feeling that he was thinking of her. Don't be a fool, she told herself. Don't start building up all that again. She turned to look at Damon. He was fast asleep, and some horrible voice deep inside her whispered that he was going to bring great unhappiness to the bright little attic.

* * *

But Mara's fears were being proved wrong: Damon was angelic. He played with Oliver, he helped Mara, he listened patiently whilst Leon extolled the virtues of Palestine, something which Mara wasn't good at, and he charmed all who met him, even old Madame Papin. Often he would give a hand at La Renaissance if they were busy. He was so kind to Yvette, still waiting for Mr Right, that she abandoned her romantic novelettes and fell in love with him, and he was so complimentary to Chantal, now the astonishingly faithful wife of a butcher, that she told Mara she almost wished she wasn't married. And he kept his promise to Mara. There were no boys. There was no opium either, although she suspected he sometimes smoked hashish with a friend of Leon's, a Negro jazz singer called Don.

And Damon entered into their discussions about leaving Paris too. The where – when – how – they should go. 'We must stay together,' he would say, looking from Mara to Leon, 'after all, we're a family.'

'Yes, we are,' Leon would reply. 'We could all go to Palestine.' He would smile hopefully at Mara. 'Why not? You'd like it there, I know you would.'

Each time Mara thought, they're right, we are a family, I'm being selfish not to say I'll go, I've no real reason. But something held her back, and it wasn't just that she couldn't see herself living in a country so different.

All through June and July they talked about going, possibly to Palestine, but they didn't leave. Like most people, they were lulled into a false sense of security by the Munich agreement, by "peace in our time", and by the warm summer days. Of course Austria had been annexed, but it was German-speaking. And Sudetenland had been invaded, or ceded, but the inhabitants were of German origin. Then there was poor old Czechoslovakia, but it was a long way away. From time to time Mara wondered what had happened to her home in Koblenz, and when she saw pictures of jack-booted Nazis in the newspaper, she imagined them tramping through her father's rose garden, kicking at the rose bushes which he had nurtured and she had nearly ruined. And what of Koblenz? Did a new generation of boys like her brother Hans march through the narrow streets? Did people sit on the Deutsches Eck and read *Mein Kampf*?

Of the three of them Leon was the most anxious to get away. Not only was he a Jew but he also held French nationality. If war was declared he would be called up – the reserves, which had been mobilized the previous year then partially demobilized after Munich, were, it was being said, about to be mobilized again. 'And you won't be in a very good position,' Leon told Mara, desperate for her to make up her mind to go to Palestine. 'I know you became British by marriage, but your father was German. If France goes to war with Germany, you might find yourself . . . under suspicion.'

That was what made Mara face up to things. If something happened to her, what would become of Oliver? 'I'll decide by the end of August,' she told Leon and Damon. 'I promise.'

But ten days before Mara was due to give her answer – she had almost decided to give in and go to Palestine for the sake of their little unit – Damon disappeared. They were all sitting over the breakfast table when Monsieur Leblanc brought up a letter for Damon from England. He opened it, read it, let out a howl of despair and walked straight out, dropping the letter as he went.

'Shall I go after him?' asked Leon.

Mara shrugged helplessly. 'Perhaps I'd better see what's

gone wrong.' She retrieved the letter. It was from Atalanta.

Dear Damon,
Before I tell you what's happened here, I want to assure you that I don't blame you for anything. Whatever you did at the Park – Father wouldn't tell me but I've a good idea – this isn't your fault. It would probably have happened anyhow, sooner or later.

As you know, Pete and I have loved each other for years, and the only reason why we haven't married is because of Smithy, who made Pete promise not to do anything to tarnish the name of Rushton! Of course it's been difficult for us, but we've managed. Elenora's been a brick about lending us her cottage. And of course we intended to marry as soon as Father died.

Father's suspected for some time, I know he has, though he's never said so. He couldn't believe it was serious. He's kept Pete and Smithy at Rushton Motors – even Father realized he couldn't do without them – let's face it, they run the business. (That's another thing. I gather it's not going well. Mostly Father's fault.)

Anyhow, after you'd gone Father went wild. He kept screaming about you – and then he turned on me. He said I was a tramp and that Pete was only after my money (and presumably my body if I'm a tramp!) Well, you know what a temper I have! I told him the only reason we hadn't married was because of Smithy and that we would as soon as he (Father) was dead – and that we couldn't wait. I thought he was going to kill me! If it hadn't been for poor old Mortimer he would have. Then I fled to Elenora's, but in the meantime Father had gone to the works and sacked Pete and Smithy. You can imagine how bad I feel about it. What would Grandpa say! The worst was that Father put the word around that he'd sacked them for dishonesty – that they were the reason why Rushton Motors was doing badly. So, of course, neither of them could find another job in the area. Smithy's too old anyhow (over seventy). Why people took Father's word is something I'll never understand, after all everyone round here knows what he's like. But luckily Pete found a job (not such a good one but all right) in Manchester, and as soon as he'd found us somewhere to live I went up there and married him (on 3 August) with Elenora and a friend of hers called Zak as our witnesses, and now I have a job selling fur coats. And sometimes, if I'm lucky, I model them for customers. Can't say I enjoy it but I had to do something. Pete doesn't earn much and needless to say Father cut off my allowance. But if Mara can work as a waitress . . . Oh, how the mighty are fallen! Send my love to her.

Well, I must stop. I have to wake up at seven to get to work on time. Once again, Damon, *don't* blame yourself. Perhaps it's all for the best.

Lots and lots of love
Atalanta (Smithy!)

PS. I suppose you know the government's trying to get all the British to come home.

'What does it say?' Leon asked. Mara told him. 'Well,' he said, 'he does blame himself, doesn't he? That's why he ran out. But I'm sure he'll come back. He'll be back by the time you've taken Oliver to school and done the shopping.'

Mara nodded. She did so want to believe him.

Damon didn't come back. Not that day. Or the next. Or the next. Mara and Leon sat in the attic waiting for him, listening both for his footsteps on the stairs and to the wireless. The news was bad. Peace negotiations between France, Britain and Russia had broken down. Then, the unbelievable, the great bear of Russia and the eagle of the Third Reich walked hand in hand.

'I hope he's all right,' said Leon.

'Yes, so do I.' They were both thinking about the unknown Jew.

By the end of August Mara was frantic. Damon had been missing for ten days. The news was growing worse. The streets were full of troops and refugees. She knew she should leave, but she couldn't go without Damon. She was all that stood between him and total self-destruction.

'Have you thought about where you're going?' Leon asked her. 'I know it's difficult, what with Damon missing, but it is the last day of the month.'

Mara shook her head. 'I can't go without him. I can't just leave and . . . I just can't.'

'How long will you wait?'

'I don't know. Till he comes back, I expect.'

'What about Oliver?'

'If things get worse I'll take him down to Barjon. He'd be all right there with Maman.'

Leon lay down on his bed and stared at the ceiling. 'You've never taken me to Barjon. Is that because it's a part of your old life?'

'Yes.'

He smiled. 'It doesn't matter. I guessed that was the reason.'

Mara looked at his familiar, beaky face. They knew each other so well and yet there were vast areas of her past which she had never discussed with him. 'I hope you're not staying just for me.'

'You know I am. For you and Oliver . . . and for Damon. Poor old Damon, I don't envy him. The trouble is though, I'm going to have to go soon but I can't bear to leave you here on your own. I have a horrible feeling if I do, I'll never see you again.' He rolled over to face Mara, who was leaning against the doorpost. 'But if war breaks out and I'm still here, they'll want me in the Army – till they find out about my flat feet. Tell me one thing, Mara, if Damon hadn't disappeared, would you be coming with me to Palestine?'

She sighed. 'I don't know. Probably. I'd almost made up my mind to say yes.'

'But there's something stopping you, isn't there? And it's not just the thought of a new country.'

701

'Yes, I suppose there is.'

He frowned and thought for a few minutes. 'Were you in love with your husband?'

Mara glanced quickly behind her, but Oliver wasn't listening. He was engrossed in his efforts to write his name. 'No,' she replied, 'I wasn't in love with him. But I was very fond of him.'

Leon nodded. 'I never knew he was so . . . rich until I heard Elenora talking about him. Rushton-Gaunt. The Rushton Empire. I've known you for six years and,' he yawned, 'I thought I knew you well. But I don't. Have you ever been in love?'

'Yes.'

'With whom?'

'Someone I met when I was eighteen – and later met again in London. I was going to leave Alexander for him but in the end I didn't.'

'Are you sorry you didn't?'

'I don't know. No, I'm glad I didn't leave Alexander because it would have been cruel. He was so ill. But I am sorry that . . .' She shrugged her shoulders.

'Does Elenora know him?'

'Yes.'

'So that's why you wanted to talk to her alone?'

Mara saw that he felt betrayed by her, because they had been so close and yet he had known nothing of this essential factor in her life. She saw too that he felt she had manoeuvred him out of the way on Elenora's last evening so that she could talk about her secret, and still keep it from him. But if she lied to him, and denied it, she would only hurt him more. 'Yes, I did want to talk about him,' she said. 'At least, I did and I didn't. You see, the last time I saw him he told me he wanted to forget about me, and then I read that he was going to marry someone else.'

'Did he get married?'

'No.'

'So you're still hoping . . .'

Mara smiled ruefully. 'I suppose I am.'

On 1 September Leon woke up Mara with the news that Germany had invaded Poland. 'It's started,' he cried. 'It's begun!'

Mara shot out of bed. 'I must take Oliver to Barjon.' She began pulling on her clothes and shouting at her son to get up and get dressed.

'But you'll never get through,' protested Leon, 'the trains are full of troops. Everything's in chaos.'

Mara packed a small bag. 'Of course I will. It may take a bit longer, but I'll be back within a day.'

Oliver stumbled over the mattress. 'Mummy, where are we going?'

'To Maman.'

'And where is Leon going?'

'He's staying here to wait for Damon.' She looked at Leon. 'You will wait, won't you? I'll be back by tomorrow morning at the latest. Please, Leon! I know it's a lot to ask you, but if he comes back and finds us all gone I may never see him again.'

Leon gave her a sad smile. 'I'll wait till tomorrow evening. But I must go out for an hour, I have to buy my ticket. You see, there's a ship leaving Marseilles for Palestine on the fourth. I decided yesterday, after what you told me, that I must go even if you won't come. I have to make my own life.' He turned away and there were tears in his eyes.

Mara put her arms round him. 'Go and buy your

703

ticket,' she said, 'and when you do, find out if there are any spare berths. Don't book us one but if Damon comes back, you never know, we might all end up by going.' She kissed him on the cheek, and it seemed impossible to her that within a few days they might be separated, that she wouldn't hear him droning on about Palestine, as he'd once droned on about Russia, that she wouldn't be nagging him about his untidiness, that she wouldn't see him jump up and down with enthusiasm or wave his arms when he was excited: that she wouldn't see him at all.

The journey was appalling. People rushed one way: to the country. Troops rushed the other: to the front. Where the train usually took five hours, it now took ten. Stopping. Starting. Going backwards. Drawing inside sidings to let troop-trains pass. Mara had a seat as far as Lyons. Then she changed trains, and had to stand with Oliver clutching her legs. When she reached Cannes it was late evening and she'd missed the bus to Barjon. In desperation she persuaded a taxi driver to take her up to the village and bring her back again, without Oliver. At Barjon there was no time to do more than gabble at Maman that she might be back in a few days, and ask her to make sure Oliver stayed nearby. Then she sank into a taxi, thanked God for Maman, and went back to Cannes to begin all over again: the crowded trains: the pushing: the shouting: the people in flight.

It was seven o'clock on the following evening when Mara dragged herself thankfully up the stairs to the attic. Leon was waiting for her. 'I've cooked spaghetti bolognaise,' he said. 'Sit down. You look dead.' He said it, but he didn't actually look at her.

'I am.' She collapsed on to a cushion. 'Damon's not back?'

'No.' He went into the kitchen. 'Wine?' He came out and gave her a glass.

Mara smiled. 'Get your ticket?'

'Oh. Oh, yes.' He went into his room, came out, went into the kitchen, came out.

Mara watched him. 'What's the matter? Is something wrong?'

He fiddled with his glass of wine. 'Nothing. Nothing.'

'Don't be silly.' She lay back on the cushions. 'Come on. Tell me! Has something happened to Damon?'

'No.'

'Well?'

He gave her an anguished look. 'He came today.'

'Who?'

'The man you were talking about.'

Mara sat up sharply. 'Jamie?'

'He didn't say his name.'

'Then how do you know it was him?'

'Elenora gave him your address. And I knew. I just knew. He's Oliver's father, isn't he? They look so alike.'

Mara nodded. 'Yes.' A pause. 'Well . . . where is he?'

Leon went to the window and looked out. 'I . . . I told him you didn't live here any more.'

'You what?'

Leon turned to face her. 'I'm sorry, Mara, I know I was wrong, I knew it as soon as . . .'

'Don't you realize what you've done? I love that man. My God! And you told him I . . . But why? Why?'

'Because I knew if he found you, you'd never come to Palestine with me – you and Oliver.'

'Where did he go?'

'Mara, please don't be cross with me. I'm sorry. I just wanted us all to be together and . . .'

She grabbed his arm, digging her fingernails into him.

705

'Shut up! Shut up! Tell me where he went. I don't care about anything else. I don't care how sorry you are. Just tell me where he went.'

'I don't know. He just went. I'm sorry, Mara.' Leon wrapped his long thin arms around her and clung to her, longing for her to say it didn't matter.

But Mara couldn't. It did matter. She pushed him away and went into the kitchen, where the bolognaise sauce was bubbling merrily in its pan, turned off the gas and stood watching the bubbles subside. She couldn't bear to look at Leon. She was so angry, she knew that if he apologized again she'd hit him.

Leon watched her sheepishly from the doorway. 'If I find Damon for you, will you forgive me?' he asked quietly.

'You won't be able to find him.'

'I might. He's probably hanging around Pigalle.'

'You can't go up there. Not at night!'

'Why not?'

'Are you mad? You might get beaten up. You know what happened when that gang of fascists caught a Jew in the metro. They threw him under the next train.'

Leon didn't answer immediately, but finally he said, 'I'd rather that than have you hate me.'

And he turned and walked straight out of the attic.

Chapter 41

Within an hour of Leon leaving, Mara's anger cooled and she began to feel guilty. Poor Leon, he'd only gone one step further than what she'd felt the previous morning – that she couldn't imagine life without him. Her guilt increased. Why should he look for Damon? Guilt and worry. She'd driven him out into the night city where fascists threw Jews into the paths of oncoming trains. If something happened to Leon it would be her fault. Supposing she never saw him again? After all their years of friendship they would have parted with him thinking she hated him. Parted on angry words. Parted without saying goodbye.

For hours Mara watched and waited by the open window. A clock struck nine – then ten – then eleven – but she couldn't drag herself away: she sat with her arms resting on the wooden sill and her chin on her hands. Exhausted from her journey and drained by worry, she kept drifting off into the troubled dreams of semi-sleep, where Leon was running for his life, where Damon was Hitler dressed up as a woman, where she, herself, was chasing Jamie through the streets of Pigalle. Then footsteps in the street would wake her and she would jerk back to reality, still trembling from her dreams, and think: He's here. He's safe. Or if there were two lots of footsteps: They're here. They're safe. But always the footsteps went on and away.

She tried to keep herself awake by thinking about Jamie and wondering under which roof, of the hundreds she could see, he was sleeping, or calculating the likelihood of him coming back. Had he believed Leon? There was no reason why he shouldn't. But even if he didn't come back, the way was now open for Mara to contact Jamie and she knew she would. Which made it all the worse that she hadn't stopped Leon from going.

To pass the time she compared Jamie and Leon. They both made her laugh. They were both aroused by causes. They both expected dedication in others. Only here they differed. Leon expected dedication to *his* cause, Jamie didn't mind so long as everyone had *a* cause. And she had learned something from each of them: from Leon, to be friends with a man: from Jamie, that love doesn't mean submission and, perhaps most important of all, to establish her own morality and to decide what was right and wrong for herself. The trouble was, he didn't always agree with her decisions.

Nevertheless, Mara knew she could never feel about Leon as she did about Jamie because Leon, for all his thirty-one years, was a boy whereas Jamie was a man. Jamie would never depend on her. She could never depend on Leon. Jamie led. Leon followed. He would follow her because she was stronger than him, just as Jamie was stronger than her. And Mara needed that. She knew she did even though she hated to admit it.

It was half-past twelve when she suddenly noticed, or thought she did, two shadows moving slowly along the street towards her, some two or three hundred yards away. She leaned forward and peered at them. Now it was only one shadow and it had stopped. Then it was two shadows: one stayed on the pavement whilst the other began to cross the road, only to be pulled back by the one on the pavement. They began to move again, very, very slowly, and although they were too far away for

Mara to recognize she was absolutely sure it was Leon and Damon – Damon wandering in a daze and Leon coaxing him along. 'Oh, Leon, what a saint you are! Of course I'll come to Palestine. We'll all go. What does it matter if I love Jamie, if I spend my life loving him, what you've done tonight deserves whatever I can give you.'

She jumped up and hurriedly began to tidy the sitting room. The attic was like a pigsty. The kitchen sink was full of unwashed plates. How stupid of her to have sat at the window worrying when she should have been making everything nice for their return. She was rushing round tidying up, when she heard a car drive past and raucous voices shouting. She ran to the window. A large black car was weaving drunkenly up the narrow street towards the intersection. Leon, standing directly under the street light, was trying to pull Damon out of the path of the oncoming car. For a dreadful moment she thought it was going to hit Damon, but with a screech of brakes it stopped short. The front passenger door opened and a man climbed out. Weak with relief, Mara gripped the window-sill. Now Leon and this helpful stranger would bring Damon home.

Then suddenly all the car doors flew open and five men came piling out, yelling, 'Death to the Jews! Death to the Jews!' Fists held high, they converged on Leon, jostling each other for a better place.

Frozen with horror Mara saw Leon release Damon as he turned to face his attackers, and although she was too far away to see his expression she knew it would be one of surprise but at the same time not of surprise; this was what he had always half expected. She saw the fists come down on him and heard him shout. Then she realized she was screaming, 'No! No! No!' And mingled with her screams and the shouts from Leon and the yelling of the

709

drunken men, was an eerie hyena-like laughter from Damon, who stood in the middle of the road watching what he thought was some weird sadistic dream.

That laughter snapped Mara out of her trance. She yanked open the door and thundered down the stairs, pushing aside poor old Monsieur Leblanc, who was standing in the hallway. 'No! No!', he hissed, grabbing at her shirt. 'Don't go! Let the police deal with it. My wife is telephoning them.'

Mara pulled away from him. 'It's Leon. They've got Leon. I must . . .' She darted out and up the street, running as fast as her legs would carry her, spurred on by a taxi which had drawn up as she had left the house and was now following her, and which, in her panic, she thought contained more drunken men. Level with her, the taxi door flew open and a man jumped from the moving vehicle.

'Mara!' He grabbed her by the shoulder. 'Stork!'

In her subconscious she knew who he was but the momentum of her flight and her terror over-ruled all else. She kicked out at him, screaming, 'It's Leon. It's Leon!' and broke away, only to be pulled back again. This time a fist came up and caught her on the side of her jaw; not hard enough to knock her out but hard enough to send her staggering against a doorway where she sank slowly to the ground. The man who had hit her ran on. Mara could see his legs. She tried to stand up and follow but she couldn't. Her head was spinning round and round and her limbs had lost their coordination. All she could do was to sit in the doorway and watch the scene enact itself.

The six drunken men had heard Mara screaming and now they saw a man running towards them, some fifty yards away. They hesitated. Another victim. But then the shrill blast of a police whistle and the roar of a fast-moving van echoed along the street. With one accord the aggressors leaped into their car. But as they drove off the whole moving picture slowed right down: the man running was now shouting and waving his arms: the car, drawing away, rose at one side. First the front wheel. Then the back wheel. It seemed to take hours to do so, just as if it were determined to flatten whatever lay in its path.

Then everything speeded up. The car roared away. The running man reached Leon. The police van flashed past Mara. It stopped at the intersection. Three policemen jumped out. They ran to the victim and the man kneeling beside him. Windows all around were thrown open. People leaned out. They shouted, 'What is it? What has happened?' The taxi driver touched Mara's arm, and said, 'He hasn't paid his fare.' She ignored him. Her head was still spinning and she felt sick. Grabbing hold of the doorpost she pulled herself upright. The policemen were lifting the body into the back of the van. The man who had hit her was arguing. He glanced up the street towards her, then followed the body into the van. Mara took a few unsteady steps in their direction. She was about to cry, 'Wait! Don't leave me!' when some distance beyond the van Damon rose up behind a parked car and began to run up the street as fast as he could go, just as a hare rises up from the grass on hearing the hounds, and runs.

The police shouted, 'Stop! Stop or we'll shoot.' A hand with a gun came out of the van window and took aim.

Another voice shouted, in English, 'Don't shoot! It wasn't him.'

But the hare kept running – and what good is English in the night streets of Paris?

The bullet hit Damon in the thigh and he faltered but

711

he kept on running. Now the police van was chasing him. Surely a gunshot man couldn't escape. But Damon didn't even know he was wounded. It was all part of his weird sadistic dream.

The roar of the van died to silence. The taxi driver drove off muttering about foreigners who didn't pay. One by one the windows closed. Mara was alone in the deserted street. She walked unsteadily to the place where Leon had lain. There was a pool of blood on the cobbles. It was smeared by the tread of a tyre. She stood looking down at it, stunned, unable to believe what she had seen. But it had happened. The blood was there. She bent down and laid her hand in it: it was warm. Then she stood up and walked slowly back to the house, past the frightened face of Madame Leblanc who whispered, 'I called the police', and up the stairs to the attic where she and Leon had lived for the last six years, where he would never again come bounding in with his arms waving, where he would never again drive her mad with his untidiness or bore her with Russia or Palestine. Or make her laugh.

For the rest of the night Mara wandered up and down the sitting room. She was exhausted and her face ached, but somehow by her not going to sleep Leon remained in the present. If she went to bed and slept, when she woke up it would be tomorrow and Leon's death would be yesterday – in the past. She saw the blankness of grey dawn, followed by the early-morning sun, and when she heard the noises of the street, the shutters and the voices and the cars, Mara felt she had cheated yesterday of Leon.

She went into his room and lay down on his mattress. On the floor beside it was a brown leather wallet. Inside was Leon's passport. She looked at his photograph and smiled at his beaky face, and turned on the wireless because Leon had loved the wireless. There was an interview with an official from the War Office, then music; soulful music of the kind which Leon had listened to, with his face bewitched by its beauty. She looked in the leather wallet for his ticket, for the berth which would go to Palestine without him. She took it out and studied it. And then, for the first time since his death, tears welled in her eyes. There wasn't just one ticket – there were four: Leon Rosenthal: Damon Rushton: Mara Rushton: Oliver Rushton. Covering her face with her hands, Mara leaned back against the pillows and cried. She cried for Leon, for all of them, but mostly for Leon and his shattered dream.

Suddenly the music broke off and a solemn voice announced that the Republic of France and Great Britain were now at war with Germany.

It was no consolation to Mara that Leon would not have got away.

Chapter 42

Mara knew someone was trying to wake her. She could feel her arm being shaken and could hear her name. 'Mara! Mara!' But she didn't want to wake up, not yet, not ever. But the hand went on shaking her and the voice kept on and on, 'Mara! Mara!' until she had to open her eyes.

Jamie was kneeling on the floor beside the mattress. Mara couldn't think what he was doing there, although she wasn't surprised to see him. For a moment she lay and looked at him blankly through eyes still filled with sleep, unable to comprehend what had happened or why her head ached and her jaw felt stiff. Then, she remembered. And she stretched out her hand and touched the four crumpled tickets. 'They killed Leon.'

'I know they did. I was there.'

'Were you?' She bit her lower lip.

'Yes. I hit you. Do you remember me hitting you?'

'Yes.' She closed her eyes and wished he would go away.

But Jamie shook her. 'Mara, open your eyes. Let me have a look at them. I want to see if you're concussed.' He lifted her eyelids and peered at her eyeballs.

'Where did they take him?' she asked.

'To the police station. I would have come back before but they made me go with them.' He did not tell her that he had pretended to have no idea who Leon was. It

714

wasn't in his character to tell a lie, but he didn't regret this one. The unfortunate young man was dead; nothing could bring him back. To have given the police Mara's address would have involved her in hours at the police station: would have meant she couldn't leave Paris.

'I saw the car,' she said tonelessly, screwing up her eyes in an effort to block out the image of those lifting wheels.

Jamie answered her in his doctor's voice. 'He was unconscious. He didn't feel anything.'

'What will they do with him?'

'There'll be a post mortem.' He studied her carefully. Of course he had expected to find her bruised and upset but she was in a far worse state than that. She was in deep shock and her face was deathly pale, except for the bruise on her jaw, the black shadows under her eyes and the blood on her cheek. The blood puzzled him. He was sure he hadn't hit her that hard. He hadn't wanted to hit her at all but he had had to. If she had reached Leon's aggressors they might have turned on her.

Mara lifted one of the tickets to her face and pressed it against her cheek. 'I killed him, you know. He wouldn't have gone if I hadn't been cross with him.'

Jamie frowned. This unemotional self-accusation was a bad sign. Should he try to shock her back to reality or would that make her worse? On any other day or in any other place he would have left her until she was stronger – but today he couldn't. 'How did you get that blood on your cheek?'

Mara opened her eyes. 'Blood!' She touched her cheek. 'Blood!' She sat up straight. 'It's Leon's blood. I . . . I . . .' She was back in the street, bending down, with her hand flat on the wet cobbles. 'I . . . I . . .' Suddenly she knew she was going to be sick. Pushing Jamie aside she

715

staggered to her feet and went crashing towards the bathroom.

Mara began to think she would never stop being sick. She was leaning over the lavatory, holding her hair off her face with one hand and steadying herself against the wall with the other. She didn't hear the door open behind her or hear Jamie come in, she knew only that someone took her firmly by the shoulders and that a cool hand clamped itself on her forehead and held back her hair for her.

Eventually Jamie sat her down on the edge of the bath. With one arm still around her, he ran some water into the basin, picked up a sponge and gently washed her face. Then he washed her hands. 'A lot of people do what you did,' he said, soaping her fingers. 'It's like going to visit the body of a dead friend or relative. A way of accepting that they really have gone.' He handed her a glass of water. 'Now, swill your mouth out.' She did.

'I thought I'd done something . . .' She was beginning to tremble.

'Sacrilegious? Obscene? Think about it this way, if you had been killed would you mind if Leon touched your blood?'

'No.'

'Well, then?' He smoothed her hair down on either side of her face. 'I think you'd better go to bed.'

Mara nodded. 'I'm sorry I was sick. I often am when I get . . . upset.'

He smiled. 'Don't be a mug! Have you forgotten I'm a doctor?' He dragged her to her feet, as though she were a rag doll, and half carried her to bed. But this time he took her to her own room, settling her down on the mattress and wrapping the blanket round her.

Mara felt incredibly tired but a little better. 'You haven't told me what happened to Damon.'

'He got away.'

'He was hit.'

'Yes.'

'He'll come back here. I'll have to wait for him.'

Jamie smiled but didn't answer. How could he tell her that in four hours' time he was going to have to wake her up? How could he tell her that they had to leave Paris, that they had God knows how many hours of travel ahead of them? He walked to the door. 'Get some sleep. Call if you need me. I'll be here.'

'Yes.' Mara rolled over and faced the far wall, and by the way her shoulders were shaking Jamie knew she was crying.

For a moment he stood and watched her, frowning. He had had mixed emotions about seeing her again. Of course he'd never forgotten her and often he had regretted what he had said to her. When Alexander had died he'd nearly written to her – well, he had written, hundreds of letters, but he hadn't posted them. Two days ago, when Elenora told him about his son, he'd driven straight to Dover and taken the night ferry to Calais, determined to bring the boy back at all costs and cursing Mara for staying in Paris at such a dangerous time, even if she were only staying because of Damon. And he had kidded himself that it was only his son he wanted. Perhaps if he had found Mara smart and glamorous, as she had been when he had first met her in London, it would have been true. But finding her like this, dreadful though she looked, was another matter. There was in her, and perhaps more than ever, what he had always loved about her: courage and vulnerability.

* * *

It seemed like only a few minutes later when Mara was being woken up again. 'I've made you some coffee,' said Jamie. 'Come on!' He lifted up her head and held the cup to her lips. She still looked pretty awful but there was a little colour in her cheeks.

Obediently Mara drank the coffee. Then she ate a piece of buttered toast. 'What time is it?'

'Three o'clock.'

'Has Damon come back?'

'No.' He was longing to ask her where his son was but he sensed she would tell him in her own time. Just as he sensed that much as he longed to take her in his arms and reassure her, she would freeze away from any physical contact. Whilst she had been sleeping he'd cleared up the flat, though not touched Leon's room except to look at his passport and the four tickets scattered over the mattress. Elenora had told him only that Mara and Leon were friends; the sight of those four tickets had told another story, or so he thought. So had the photographs in the leather wallet. Mara had missed them. They were happy family pictures: Mara sitting in a café with a small boy on her lap: Leon giving that same boy a piggy-back ride: Mara and Leon walking with the boy between them: Mara, Leon, the boy, and a very beautiful young man whom he presumed must be Damon. Studying the pictures of his son, for he knew it must be his son, he had felt terribly jealous. And not just because of the relationship between Leon and his son but also because of the obvious affection between Leon and Mara.

Mara had closed her eyes again and was drifting off into sleep. Jamie shook her. 'Mara, you have to get up. We must leave Paris. War's broken out.'

'I know. I heard it on the wireless. You can leave but I can't, not till Damon comes back.'

'I'm not leaving you here.'

'I'll wait for a couple of days.'

'Then where will you go?'

Mara looked at the clothes hanging behind a curtain in the corner of her room. She could see one of Oliver's jumpers. Thank God she'd taken him to Barjon, at least he was safe there. She glanced at Jamie. Did he know about Oliver? For the first time she wondered what he had been doing in the street late at night. She asked him.

'I was sure you lived here even though Leon said you didn't. I was coming back. I thought the best time to catch you, if you were here, was in the middle of the night.'

'I see. Well, I'm very grateful but you must go now. I'll be all right.' She would wait for a week, then she would go to Barjon.

Jamie said very firmly, 'I'm not going without you even if I have to drag you to Calais.'

'But I can't go to Calais.'

'Because of your son?'

'Yes.'

'Don't you think you'd better tell me about him?'

She looked at him. Until now she'd been too ill to notice that his hair was greying around the temples and that the lock which always fell down over his forehead had the odd white hair amongst the dark. His face was just the same, except for a few more lines around his eyes, and he still had the same smile, half-apologetic, half-mischievous. Oliver had that smile too. And he had Jamie's blue eyes. And he had a mop of dark hair, though perhaps not quite so dark as Jamie's. 'I suppose Elenora told you,' she said.

'Yes, she did. She was worried about you . . .'

'And you're worried about him. Well, he's safe. He's in Barjon.'

Jamie looked at the bruise on Mara's face, the bruise he had given her. He hadn't saved her from the men just because she was the mother of his son. He had done it because he'd been frightened for her and because he'd wanted to protect her; because he loved her. 'I'm worried for you too,' he said softly.

Mara met his eyes. 'Thank you.' She was immensely grateful Jamie did not try to touch her. The attic was a part of her life with Leon and she owed it to Leon not to betray him in the rooms where together they had loved and laughed.

She had been right about the difference between Jamie and Leon. In her bruised and exhausted state she could never have coped with organizing their departure. Jamie took charge of everything. He pushed her into the bathroom and told her to wash: it might be the last time for days. He found her a small suitcase and told her to pack what she needed. He went out and bought some food and made a picnic: there might be no food on the train. He reminded Mara to write a note to Damon saying she'd gone to Barjon and he gave her some money to leave with the note. He fetched Madame Leblanc and, with Mara translating, paid her a month's rent.

'What about all this?' he asked Mara, pointing at the Mexican rugs and cushions.

'I'll tell Don, a friend of Leon's, he can have them. I must go to the café where I worked and tell them I'm leaving. Don lives opposite it.'

'And the rest of Leon's things? Does he have any relatives?'

'No.' Together they sorted through Leon's belongings. Jamie was calm and matter of fact, for which Mara was grateful. 'I'll just keep these,' she said, picking up the leather wallet, the tickets, a handful of photographs, and Leon's wireless.

Of her own clothes Mara took very little. She needed most of the space in the suitcase for the wireless and Oliver's clothes. The iron box, with all those faded letters and Jamie's locket, she had left at Barjon: they seemed to belong there. 'I'm ready,' she said, coming out of her room wearing a pair of black cotton trousers and a man's collarless cotton shirt, dyed bright yellow.

'You look like a Chinese peasant,' said Jamie, smiling.

Tentatively Mara smiled back. 'We may have to sit on the floor of the train.'

In the hall Madame Leblanc hugged Mara tearfully and begged her to look after herself and the little boy. Outside in the street they met Don who had just heard about Leon. He too hugged Mara tearfully, promising to take great care of Leon's possessions. 'I may go home to Trinidad,' he said, 'but if I ever come to England, I'll let you know. Give me your address.'

'I don't have one,' replied Mara. 'I'll have to send it to you when I do.'

Jamie, who had been standing back, watching Mara enfolded in the big Negro's embrace, said, 'You could give him mine. It's still the same – Hampstead.' She nodded and Jamie quickly wrote out his address and gave it to Don.

It seemed to Jamie that everyone they saw in the street hugged Mara and commiserated with her over Leon's death, then begged her to come back and see them. He was very surprised at the affection all these very ordinary people felt for her and at her obvious affection for them. And the more people came to her and spoke of Leon with tears in their eyes, the more convinced he became that although not legally married Mara and Leon had been a couple, and that she was now a grieving widow.

At La Renaissance old Papin clasped Mara to his corpulent body. Don had only just told him about Leon and he was distraught. 'It won't be the same without you two,' he sobbed. 'But you're right to go to the country. You shouldn't be here, you and Oliver.' He gave Jamie a suspicious look. 'Who is this?'

Jamie understood enough French to know that Mara had passed him off as a cousin of her late husband.

Then there was Yvette to be hugged and given Jamie's address. And Chantal to be visited in her husband's shop, also to be given Jamie's address.

'I don't want to hurry you but . . .' Jamie said as they left the butcher's shop.

Mara nodded. 'I'm ready now.'

While Jamie flagged down a taxi she stood looking sadly up the street to the café where old Papin was rearranging the tables on the terrace, and beyond that, almost too far to see but so indelibly imprinted on Mara's memory, to the street door where Madame Leblanc stood gossiping. To where Leon had dashed in and out, arms waving with the excitement of some new cause.

Chapter 43

The journey to Barjon was even worse than the last. They were advised to go via Dijon, but when they arrived there was neither the connecting train nor was there anywhere to sit, except on the platform which was hot and dirty and crowded. Every so often a train would be announced and everyone would scramble to their feet, pushing and shoving, only to groan and sit down again when yet another delay was announced.

After the third occasion Jamie asked, 'What is it this time?'

'Troop-train.' Mara was trying to make herself comfortable on the concrete platform but there was only room for her to sit with her legs bunched up under her chin. 'He said ours would be here at ten. What's the time now?'

'Eight. Let's have something to eat.' He handed her a cheese roll. 'And maybe we should sit back to back and lean against each other. Something makes me think we're here for the night.'

He was to be proved wrong. The train did come at ten. However, it only took them as far as Mâcon, just short of Lyons, before it shuddered to a halt and reversed into a siding. They spent the rest of the night being shunted backwards and forwards, which meant that Mara and Jamie, who were squashed at one end of the corridor with only room for one to stand and one to sit, had little sleep. The one standing leaned against the window, the one sitting sat hunched up amongst cigarette ends and sandwich wrappings. They took it in turns, Mara insisted, and every time the train jerked to the right, the one standing overbalanced on to the other. Eventually they both stood, side by side, looking out of the dirty window. There were several other trains in sidings, all packed with people. They could see the dim glow of the lights and they could hear muffled voices, and when the dawn came they could see the carriage silhouetted, black against the grey sky. It reminded Mara of her brother playing with his train set and her father saying, 'The thing to do, Hans, is to keep them all moving.' They needed her father now. The only trains moving were the troop-trains rushing northwards.

'Will you have to fight?' Mara asked Jamie.

'No, I expect they'll want me as a doctor.'

'If America comes into the war?'

'No. I'll offer my services before that. After all, England's as much my home as America, now.' He looked at Mara's yellow shirt, now streaked with dust, and wondered why he always found her most appealing when she was looking dirty. 'I've been thinking about Damon,' he said. 'Elenora told me of his problem. You know, it might be possible to cure him . . . if he wants to be cured.'

'Do you think so?' A flicker of hope came into Mara's eyes and she turned to face him. 'I'm sure he's not an addict, well, not completely addicted. He didn't touch it at all during his first ten weeks with us, I made him promise he wouldn't, and I can't help feeling he might have kept it up if it hadn't been for . . .' She explained about Atalanta's letter, adding, 'I loathed her until she was fifteen, she loathed me too, but now I'm very fond of her. I just hope she won't blame herself if . . .' Mara couldn't bring herself to say it.

Jamie nodded. He'd heard the whole story from Elenora; about Herbert; about the way he had cut off Mara's allowance; about Atalanta; about her marriage; and not least about how Mara had come to Elenora on that snowy evening when Herbert had revealed he knew about Mara's lover. And hearing it from Elenora had made Jamie see that although he had had every right to be hurt by that letter Mara had sent him she had had her reasons for doing so. It had been Elenora who had said to him, 'You can't have it both ways, Jamie. You want a woman who thinks for herself, so it's no good being angry because her thoughts don't coincide with yours.'

Jamie returned to the subject of Damon. 'How do you know he didn't smoke opium in Paris? Addicts become very cunning.'

'Oh, I'm sure he didn't. He used to smoke a bit of hashish with Don, but that's all. And he didn't do it very often. I've smoked it myself and it didn't do me any harm.'

Jamie was surprised. 'Have you?'

'Why, haven't you?'

'As a matter of fact, I have. As a doctor I wanted to assess its effect. But I wouldn't recommend . . .' He stopped and frowned. If Mara had been any old person he would have said, 'I wouldn't recommend experimenting with drugs,' but she wasn't any old person. She was someone whom he had told to make up her own mind about things, and she had.

'I only tried it once,' she went on. 'Out of curiosity. Leon and I decided to try it last year.'

Jamie said nothing. Leon this – Leon that – always Leon.

* * *

It was late afternoon when they reached Aix. Mara had been chatting to an old peasant about her life in Barjon, a village he had never visited but which he understood because he too lived in a village in that area. As the train drew into Aix he held out his hand to Mara, saying, 'Goodbye madame, and good luck. It has been a pleasure for me to talk to you. I have never spoken to a foreigner before.'

Jamie said, 'He seemed a nice old guy.'

'Yes.' Mara told him what the old man had said.

She had hardly finished explaining before there was a knock on the window by her elbow. The old man had come back. 'The train goes no further tonight,' he shouted up. 'If you like, you and your husband can come with me. My village is only twelve kilometres from Barjon. You would have to go over the mountains but there's a path. My son knows the way. I can't offer you a bed for tonight but you're welcome to eat with us and sleep in our barn.' He looked up at her expectantly, his weather-beaten grizzly face smiling as he waited for her answer.

'What do you think?' Mara asked Jamie after she had translated.

He looked round at the packed train, at the bored, hungry children sprawled across the laps of their bored, hungry parents. 'Anything's better than this. I say we go.'

'So do I.' She smiled at him, and just for a moment it seemed as though nothing separated them.

It was pitch dark when they arrived at the peasant's cottage, where his beaming wife ushered them inside to meet their son and his wife and their three children, all of whom were fascinated by the strangers. Over a generous meal, they plied Mara and Jamie with questions about who they were and where they were going, and Mara

726

answered as best she could, without disclosing that she and Jamie weren't married; that would have embarrassed them.

The old man had been visiting relatives in Avignon. It appeared that he went every September and he shrugged off his wife's suggestion that he had been unwise to go. 'War doesn't frighten me,' he said, urging Mara to give Jamie some more rabbit casserole. 'I fought in the last one, old though I was, and I survived. What does your husband think of the war, madame?'

Mara translated.

'Your husband is American,' said the son. 'Will America come into the war?'

Again Mara translated. The old man lit a pipe. The son asked questions.

Mara was nearly dropping with exhaustion by the time the old man showed them to the barn. 'I'm afraid you'll have to sleep on the hay,' he apologized, 'and I have only one spare blanket. Well, goodnight, madame, goodnight, monsieur. Sleep well!' He went back to the house, leaving them in the dark.

Tossing the blanket on to the hay, Mara walked over to the little window. She thought about Leon. Nearly twenty-four hours had passed since she had run screaming up the street, since she had seen the black car lift itself on to him, then over him. Twenty-four hours. Yesterday. The past. And now she was standing in a barn with Jamie, and once again they were enveloped in the smell of hay. She smiled.

Jamie was standing by the doorway watching her. He knew she was thinking about Leon. Her smile, he was convinced, was for some past intimate memory; the way she had gone straight to the window, he was convinced, was to keep a distance between them. And he was angry.

Did she really think he would imagine – just because they used to be lovers – that he would automatically expect to make love to her tonight because circumstances forced them to share a barn and a blanket? 'I need some air,' he said coldly, and he went outside.

Mara thought, so he still holds that letter against me. What a fool I am to hope he could forget it. She took off her trousers but kept on her shirt, wrapped herself in one end of the blanket, and settled down in the hay, closing her eyes firmly.

A few minutes later Jamie came back. He did the same, only he kept his trousers on. Both pretending to be asleep, they lay beside each other in the hay, each remembering another hay-filled barn, each acutely aware of the other. It was some time before either of them fell asleep, and it was Jamie who did so first. Mara knew he was asleep because she recognized of old his deep-sleep breathing.

In the morning, after a breakfast of bread and black coffee, the man's son walked with them until they reached the bottom of a steep hill. 'That's it.' He pointed to a stony path, little more than a sheep track, which zigzagged up through the rocks and the stunted trees. 'Keep straight on till you reach the second hill, then take the right fork. It will bring you to the hills above Barjon. You'll recognize the village, won't you, madame?'

Mara nodded and smiled, and thanked him on behalf of both of them.

'Just one thing' – he touched her arm – 'if you see some men up there take no notice. They won't harm you.'

Mara was surprised by his remark. It had never occurred to her that anyone round here would hurt her.

The young man realized some explanation was called

for. 'We who know the mountains well may be called upon to defend them,' he said, and he turned and hurried back towards his home.

Struggling up the hillside, Mara and Jamie talked about the young man's explanation. 'Surely he doesn't think France is going to be overrun,' she said, grabbing at a bush to pull herself along.

'He obviously does.' Jamie, who was a few yards ahead of Mara, looked back to see how she was coping. 'Here!' He stretched out his hand.

'Thanks.' She took hold of it. But as soon as she was level with him she released it. 'What could a bunch of peasant farmers do against German tanks?'

'What tank could come up here? No, they'd be much more likely to arrange escape routes.'

She thought of Leon. 'For Jews?'

He knew she was thinking of Leon. 'Jews and others. Escaping prisoners of war. Airmen forced to parachute out of their damaged planes. When any country is invaded there are always pockets of resistance fighters.'

By mid afternoon they had done about eight of the twelve kilometres, and they were exhausted. 'I must sit down,' Mara groaned. 'My legs are killing me.'

Jamie gave her an encouraging smile. 'Okay. But let's find some shade. I can see some trees at the bottom of this hill. Come on! Only another three hundred yards.' He wanted to take her hand but she gave him no indication she would welcome it.

Mara thought, he's only interested in seeing Oliver. We might as well be strangers. She lost her footing and slithered down in a flurry of loose stones, but she stood up quickly before he was forced to help her.

Not only was there shade at the bottom of the hill, there was also a fast-running stream which at one point, just below where they stood, cascaded over a rock into a wide clear pool.

'Water!' Mara knelt down and scooped it up into her mouth. 'Water!' She splashed it over her face and neck. 'And a pool.' She scrambled down to it. 'I'm going to have a swim.' She waded across the pool to a large flat rock on the other side, casually stripped off all her clothes and plunged naked into the water.

Purposely looking in the other direction Jamie sat down in the shade. She seems to think I'm a eunuch, he thought angrily.

Eventually Mara came and sat down near him and attacked the bread and cheese which the old man's wife had given them. She had washed her clothes as well as herself, and the black trousers hung on a bush to dry, while the yellow shirt clung to her, damp and semi-transparent.

Jamie jumped up. 'I think I'll have a dip too.'

Mara closed her eyes. 'Wake me when it's time to go.' But she didn't go to sleep. Instead she watched Jamie's naked body through the fuzz of her eyelashes. His muscles rippled in the sunlight. Drops of water sparkled on his back and chest. He floated on his back. He swam on his front, his dark head bobbing up and down. Then he lay down on the rock, where she had lain. And except for his height and the paleness of his skin, which would have been remedied had he spent more time in the sun, he looked from the distance of some thirty yards like any other man in the area. No one seeing him would have believed he was an eminent doctor. He was as perfectly at home in these hills as he had been in his dinner-jacket at Jeremy and Cynthia's ball, and in his shirt sleeves in the cottage, and Mara was just as irritated. And he calls me a chameleon, she thought, wondering how he would take to Oliver and how Oliver would take to him. Half of her desperately wanted them to get on, half of her didn't. For if Jamie didn't want her then she didn't want him feeling at ease in her territory – or with her son.

By the time Jamie came back from the pool Mara really had gone to sleep. She lay sprawled on the grass with her head in the shade and her long bare legs in the sun. He stood looking down at her, amazed at her power of recovery. Apart from the black and yellow bruise on her jaw she looked remarkably well. The sun had caught her face and her arms, as it was now catching her legs, and had turned them lightly golden. Her hair which had been drab and dirty was soft and sun-streaked. There was something utterly defenceless about the way she lay, on her back with her head tipped to one side. But at the same time there was something very challenging about her long lithe limbs and her slightly parted lips.

'Wake up, Mara!' he said abruptly, turning away from her. 'Come on! It's time to go.'

This time Mara walked ahead. Jamie followed, trying to concentrate on the path and not on Mara's legs or the bottom of the yellow shirt which moved up as she stretched up. Again he was angry with her. The casual manner in which she carried her black trousers over her shoulder was an insult.

At one point, about an hour after they had set off, Mara suddenly stopped dead. 'Did you hear that?'

'Just someone shooting birds, I expect.'

'Yes. Probably.' She trudged on.

In the late afternoon they reached the brow of a hill and there, some three kilometres below them, Mara saw the red roofs of Barjon. 'Look!' she cried. 'There it is. And I know this place. 'We're at the black rock. Come on!' She turned to Jamie, her face bright with pleasure.

'I'll show you. There's a special place here, a flat black rock, where I always used to come. So did my father-in-law.' She scurried off down a path, pushed through the bushes, and came out on the rock. Jamie followed.

'Isn't it wonderful?' She sat down. 'This is my favourite place. I used to sit up here for hours after Alexander died. Damon liked it too.' She told him about their conversation concerning all the people who would be gone in a hundred years.

Jamie smiled. He was surprised. He'd never thought of Mara as a person who questioned.

After a few minutes she said, 'Do you remember that lump of black rock at Elenora's, the one on the shelf?'

'Yes, yes, I do.'

'That came from here. My father-in-law and Elenora were . . .'

'She told me.'

They sat in silence for some time, again acutely aware of each other. Mara kept thinking, It's up to Jamie to make the first move. If a . . . screw is all he's after, then I'd rather have nothing. And Jamie kept thinking, I'm not going to begin anything till I know it's for keeps.

In a very stilted voice he asked, 'Why didn't you marry Leon?'

'Marriage didn't come into our relationship.'

'But you were lovers?'

'Yes.'

'And you were intending to go to Palestine with him?'

'No.'

Jamie frowned. 'Mara, there's no need to . . .'

'I suppose you saw the tickets?'

'Yes. I'm sorry if I was prying.'

Mara lay back against the rock. 'It doesn't matter. No, I wasn't intending to go, not when he bought the tickets.

732

I didn't know he'd bought them for all of us until after . . . But he did want us all to go. A sort of dream . . .' She sighed. 'If he'd come back with Damon I would have gone. I decided that while I was waiting for them. It was the least I could do.'

Jamie looked down at the fields far below and at the plain beyond and at the glistening sea beyond that. There was indeed something magical about the beauty of this place. 'Why do you say that?' he asked.

'Because the only reason he went looking for Damon was because I was cross with him.' She looked up at Jamie. He was sitting with his knees bunched up and his chin resting on them.

'Why were you cross with him?'

Mara was surprised by his question. Wasn't it perfectly obvious to him? He knew the way she felt. 'Why do you think?' she asked.

He stared out at the sea. 'I've no idea.'

'Because he told you I didn't live there any more.'

'Really?' He looked down at her where she lay on the rock beside him. 'So you weren't in love with him?'

Mara shook her head. 'If I'd been in love with Leon there would have been no question of not wanting to go with him' – she raised an eyebrow – 'would there?'

Jamie started to laugh.

'What's so funny?'

'You. Me. Us.' He flopped down on to his elbows and smiled at her, his beautiful half-mischievous, half-apologetic smile. 'For the past thirty-six hours I've thought that you . . . well . . . were in love with him.' Suddenly Jamie was no longer jealous of the young man lying in the street, who unbeknown to Mara had been still alive despite his appalling injuries when Jamie reached him, but had died a minute later.

Stretching out her hand Mara touched Jamie's face. 'No, there was nothing like that between us. He was a friend. A wonderful friend.'

Jamie seized her hand and kissed its soft grubby palm. 'What mugs we are! All through that dreadful train journey I was longing to hold you but I kept thinking, no, she's not yours to hold.'

Mara smiled. 'Did you really want to? How funny. I wanted you to too, but . . .'

'But what?' He held on to her hand.

'I thought perhaps you were still angry about . . . the letter, and that you were only interested in seeing Oliver.'

He looked at her with the same acceptance of what they were to each other as he had done in the cottage when he'd taken her hand in his. 'I tried to kid myself it was only Oliver,' he said, 'just as I've been trying to kid myself for years that I didn't want to see you again.'

Mara laughed. 'So have I.' She wanted to ask him about Sarah but sensed he would tell her in his own time.

He rolled over so that his body was half on top of hers and he kissed the bruise on her cheek. 'Why didn't you contact me after Alexander died?' he asked, looking down into her face.

'After what you said to me!' She tried to sit up but he grabbed her wrists and held her arms down beside her head, hooking his leg over her and pressing her down on to the rock. 'Why didn't you contact me?' she demanded.

'It's no use being angry,' he said, a hint of amusement in his voice, 'you can't get away from me, we're going to sort this out once and for all. I didn't write to you because I reckoned you'd contact me if you wanted to see me . . . you always had in the past.'

They were fighting again but Mara couldn't stop herself from telling him the truth. 'I didn't write to you because I

734

knew you'd say I only came running when I wanted something.'

'I probably would have.'

'Exactly!'

'But only because you won't give an inch.'

'What about you!'

He thought for a moment, still holding her down. 'But I'll admit something.'

'What?'

'Or perhaps I won't considering what a little hell-cat you are.'

Mara glanced at him. A moment ago she had wanted to make love to him, now she wanted to strangle him.

'I'll admit' – he buried his face in her neck, – 'that I wrote hundreds of letters to you but I ripped them all up next day.'

'Did you? So did I.' She laughed as he released her arms and hugged her to him.

'Next time one of us has to admit to something first, it's your turn,' he murmured, nibbling at her ear.

Mara chuckled, and said in a prim and teasing voice, 'I've nothing to admit to.'

He pushed his nose against hers and shook both of their heads slowly from side to side, saying, 'There's sure to be something. Don't tell me that's our last fight.'

They looked into each other's eyes and laughed, and Mara said, 'I kept hoping Elenora would mention you in her letters.'

'And I' – he slipped his hand inside her shirt and caressed the softness of her shoulders – 'kept hoping she would say something about you. And, damn me, she never said a word. Not till the day . . . when was it? I've lost track of time. Three days ago, I think. Anyhow, the day we heard Poland had been invaded. Then she rang me up and said she had to see me urgently.'

'And she told you about . . . Oliver?'

He kissed her. 'Yes. She said you'd probably be cross, but she felt she had to tell me.'

'Well, I'm not cross.' She ran her hands up and down his arms. 'Not at all cross.' And she shivered, but not with cold. With desire for him. With wanting him.

'What fools we are,' he murmured, unbuttoning her shirt and kissing the valley between her breasts, 'but it's still your turn first next time.'

'Really!' The word came out in a little gasp. Of pleasure. Of desire. Of the exquisite agony of wanting him and knowing that he wanted her. Of knowing that he would take her, there on the rock, which was hard beneath her as he was hard above her. And of knowing that however much she wanted him, and she did want him in every nerve of her body, he would meet that want and satisfy it. And she would want more. And more. And he would meet her always. Because that which existed between them was love in all its forms, uninhibited by boundaries or limitations . . .

They lay on the rock, warmed by the late afternoon sun, whispering and laughing and caressing. Saying how much they loved each other. Promising they'd never again be separated. Never again have misunderstandings. Never have suspicions. Never be angry. Never hurt each other.

'But I enjoy fighting with you,' he said, 'because I enjoy making it up again.'

'The trouble is we take such a long time to do so.'

'Yes.' He kissed the end of her nose. 'We'll have to have a rule. All fights must be settled by bedtime.'

'By bedtime or at bedtime?'

'In bedtime.'

He lay back and closed his eyes, then suddenly he touched her arm. 'Ssssh!'

'What?'

'I heard something – or someone.'

'Where?'

'Behind us.'

'A sheep?'

'Maybe. But we'd better get dressed.'

They dragged on their clothes as fast as they could and set off towards Barjon. To begin with the path ran along the side of the hill and was quite wide and not very steep, and they walked hand in hand or with their arms around each other, but as it began its descent into the valley it grew narrower and little rocks skidded underfoot and went bouncing down ahead of them. 'I think I'd better go ahead,' said Jamie, releasing Mara, 'then I can catch you if you fall.'

'Shouldn't I go ahead?' she suggested. 'I know the path better than you do.'

She was standing just above him and he turned to face her. 'We're not fighting already, are we?' He raised a quizzical eyebrow.

She made as if to kick him, but didn't kick him, and they carried on. But after a couple of yards Jamie stopped dead. 'You know about Sarah?' he said, looking round at her.

'Yes.'

'It's one of those things I'll always feel bad about. I suppose everyone has something like that in their life – a memory which leaves a nasty taste.'

Mara looked down at the olive groves on the hillside below. 'Were you fond of her?'

'Yes, but not in the right way.'

'Were you . . . ?'

'Lovers? No. I must have been crazy to even think of marrying someone for whom I didn't have . . . that sort of feeling, but I wanted the antithesis of you. I'd spent six months in America working in a shanty town, where I'd met dedicated girls, like Sarah, and I suppose I felt that if I married Sarah I'd lead a simple, dedicated life. But I was wrong – and I hurt her.' He turned and carried on, slowly, and Mara followed feeling deflated. What he had done to Sarah had come between them and she felt as though he were blaming her. She thought of Oliver and told herself she didn't care what Jamie thought or felt and merely wished he would hurry up so she could see her child.

But Jamie stopped again, just as suddenly as he'd done before, and turned, smiling and holding out his hand to her. 'There was always you, lurking in the background,' he said. 'Damn you! You and I are meant for each other.' He pulled her down closer. 'You're my kindred spirit.' He paused and added teasingly, 'What a dreadful thought!'

Mara laughed. 'I'll remember that kind remark.'

'It's true. Sarah was my Alexander – she was too good.'

'Aren't I good?'

He blew her hair back from her face. 'No, you're unspeakable.'

'As unspeakable as my coffee when you put salt in it?'

'Worse.' He touched the bruise on her cheek. 'That was good American coffee, you are as unspeakable as English coffee with salt in it.'

'I wonder why I have to fall in love with the least gallant man on this earth.'

'You mean I've never given you any flowers.' He bent and picked a blade of grass. 'Here, have a substitute.'

Mara tucked the blade of grass behind her ear. A few yards later she put up her hand. 'It's gone, I've lost it.'

738

Jamie pretended to be offended. 'How could you be so careless with my present!'

She ran back up the path, laughing. 'Here it is.'

'Are you sure it's the right blade?'

'Of course I am.' She came back to him, plaiting the blade into her hair, and he hugged her to him, rubbing his dusty face against hers. For a moment they stood there, fused into one on the rocky path with the parched hill rising behind them and the sun setting red into the western sky. Then they drew apart but still holding hands went on down the path, slithering into each other because now it was not wide enough for two people but they did not want to separate.

As they neared the village Mara drew away from him saying, 'Look, Jamie, the villagers . . .'

He gave her a quick peck on the cheek. 'It's okay. I understand.'

At the end of the drive leading down to Les Vieux Orangers they met old Pierre riding Bobo. Mara ran up to greet the old man and to ask after Oliver.

'He's fine, Madame Mara. A bundle of mischief but we love him. And we'll miss him. I suppose you'll be going back to England now?' He looked from Mara to Jamie.

'I expect so.' She introduced Jamie as the doctor who had treated Alexander and she hugged Bobo. 'You haven't seen my nephew, have you?' she asked old Pierre. 'You remember him? He came here once.'

The old man shook his head. 'I remember him well but I haven't seen him.' He paused and then asked her slowly, 'If we want to use the farmhouse whilst you're away, Madame Mara . . .'

'You and Maman? Of course you can.'

Old Pierre looked at Mara, then at Jamie, then up at

the hills which glowed red in the setting sun. 'I meant
. . . well . . . one never knows with this war on.'

'You mean . . .' Mara thought of the young man who
had said to her, 'We who know the mountains well may
be called upon to defend them,' and she said, 'You may
use it for whatever you like.'

The old man nodded. 'I'll go and fetch the boy and
some food for you.'

The farmhouse was warm and stuffy. Mara threw open
the windows and gazed down on the valley. Any minute
now Jamie was going to see his son. What would he think
. . . feel . . . about Oliver? What would Oliver think . . .
feel . . . about Jamie?

It was as if Jamie could read her thoughts. 'Are you
going to tell him the truth?' he asked.

'Perhaps eventually,' Mara frowned, 'but not at the
moment. Not until . . .' she was cut short by the sound of
running feet.

'Mummy!' Oliver burst in and dashed across the drawing room to Mara. 'Mummy, you're back.' He flung his
arms round her knees.

'Yes, of course I'm back.' She hugged him, and over
the top of his tousled head she saw Jamie watching them.
'I always come back, don't I?'

Oliver laughed and hugged her. 'Old Pierre says you
have a strange man with you. Is it Leon?' He spun round
and shouted, 'Leon! Leon! Where are you?' He noticed
Jamie. 'But that's not Leon, Mummy.'

'No, Oliver, this is Jamie. He's an old friend of mine.'

Jamie swallowed hard. In his profession he was used to
children, but he wasn't used to meeting his own. 'Hello,
Oliver,' he said, holding out his hand, 'I'm afraid you'll
have to speak to me in English.'

740

Oliver shook the big hand offered to him. 'That's all right. Mummy and I always speak English when we're alone. We only speak French for Leon's sake because he's not very good at English. Mummy, where is Leon? And where's Damon?'

'He's . . .' she began, but she was interrupted by old Pierre and Maman, bearing bread and wine and cold chicken. There were more hugs and kisses, but eventually the old couple left.

'I only made up two beds,' Maman told Mara as she climbed up on to Bobo. She gave Jamie a doubtful look.

'I'll make up another one,' Mara assured her. 'There are plenty of blankets.' She went back into the house where Jamie was doing his best to talk to Oliver. 'He may take a bit of getting used to you,' she mouthed over her son's head.

Jamie nodded. But the problem wasn't that, it was that Oliver had expected Leon. He tried to accept it as logical and told himself he was being stupid to be angry with Mara, who was just trying to be kind, or with Oliver, who wanted another man. After all Oliver had no idea that he, Jamie, was his father and had he passed Oliver in the street ten minutes earlier, he would not have known he was passing his son. Or would he have known? He was too confused by his feelings for Oliver to know the answer. But what he did know was that this unknown little boy with his mop of dark hair and blue eyes and his impish grin inspired in himself a mixture of emotions which he had never experienced before.

Mara went through into the kitchen to prepare supper. Oliver followed. 'Mummy, what's happened to Leon?'

She sat him on the kitchen table. 'Leon's dead, Oliver.'

'Why?'

She thought quickly. 'He was knocked down by a car.'

'Did it hurt?'

'No.'

'So he's not coming back?'

'No, Oliver, he's not.'

He climbed down off the table and went into the drawing room and Mara heard him say to Jamie, 'If you're a doctor, will you show me how you cut off a leg?' She didn't know whether to be relieved or appalled.

Later, when Oliver had gone to bed and Mara and Jamie were eating their supper, Mara said, 'He seemed to take it well. Almost too well.'

'Children are often like that. They accept things, so long as they're told the truth.' He smiled and laid his hand on Mara's arm. 'He's an engaging little scamp.'

She had been longing to know what Jamie thought of Oliver. 'Yes, he is. I suppose he's a bit . . . of a little terror, but he's good when he knows he must be.'

'I hope he'll take to me.' Jamie kissed her on the ear. 'I have a horrid feeling if he does it'll be thanks to my gory description of amputating a leg.'

Mara leaned against him. 'Oh, Oliver loves that sort of thing. He's quite used to hearing gory details. After all he's lived in the streets of St Germain. Everyone says what they think there. I wouldn't be surprised if he knows the facts of life already.'

Jamie laughed. 'Well, that'll save me from having to tell him.' He paused and took a deep breath. 'I think we ought to leave here tomorrow.'

'Tomorrow!' Mara drew away from him. 'I can't leave tomorrow, I've got to wait for Damon.'

'But we've no guarantee he'll come here. We must leave or we'll get trapped. There are boats from Marseille for Southampton but we're not the only ones trying to get back to England. You are coming back, aren't you?'

'Yes. Yes, I suppose so.' She stood up and walked over to the stove. 'I don't want to abandon this place, because I love it. If I didn't have Oliver and . . .'

'Thanks very much. After this afternoon I'd hoped . . .'

Mara picked up a fork and waved it at him. 'You didn't let me finish what I was saying.'

Jamie laughed. 'Sorry . . . madame.'

'That's better. If I didn't have Oliver and . . . if I didn't have you, I would stay here, war or no war. Obviously now,' she smiled at him, 'I'll come to England. Only I can't leave without Damon. I'm all he has. You must see that, Jamie, and you mustn't try to make me go. We have each other. Damon – only has me. If you can't wait for me, I'll follow you when I can. Don't you trust me? I thought we were going to trust each other from now on.'

Jamie went to her and put his hands on her shoulders. 'Of course I trust you.' He kissed her forehead. 'It's just that if we're separated now, it may be weeks before we're together again.'

'Then wait for Damon with me.'

'It's not just you and me. What about Oliver?'

Mara stepped back. 'He's perfectly safe here. He's been safe here for seven and a half years.'

'Yes, but . . .'

'What? Are you trying to suggest I don't have Oliver's welfare at heart?'

'No, but . . .'

'Yes, you are.' Mara walked past Jamie and out of the kitchen.

'I'm not.' He grabbed her arm.

She wrenched it away. 'Then what are you suggesting? That I let you take him?'

'Why not? If you're so keen to stay . . .'

'Why should I let you take him? You've only just met him.'

'He's my son.'

Mara marched across the hall to the bottom of the stairs. 'He wouldn't go with you.' She knew she was being cruel but Jamie's suggestion that she was being irresponsible where Oliver was concerned had hurt her deeply.

Jamie raised his voice. 'That's a foul thing to say. Is it my fault I didn't know about him?'

'Sssh! You'll wake him.' She started up the stairs.

'For God's sake, Mara . . .'

Mara leaned over the banisters and glared down at Jamie. 'I've looked after Oliver all his life so don't you suggest I don't know how.'

Jamie said nothing. Then suddenly he started to laugh. 'You know something? The first time I met you, you were leaning over the banisters at Koblenz giving Alexander a hard time. Now you're leaning over these ones giving me a hard time.'

Mara came down the stairs and put her arms around him. 'I'm sorry I was so cruel. It's just that . . .'

Jamie tipped her face up to him and kissed her gently on the lips. 'You're right. Not about staying. About Oliver. You have looked after him all these years and you've done a pretty good job of it. It's only that I want to share that job with you. Understand?'

Mara hugged him to her. 'Yes.' She nuzzled his chest. 'We mustn't fight.'

'We mustn't fight over Oliver.'

'No.'

He smoothed her hair back from her face. 'You know what Elenora says is the matter with us? She says I want

744

you to think for yourself but I don't like it when you don't think as I want you to.'

'That's not what's the matter with us,' said Mara, laughing, 'that's what's the matter with you.'

Before Jamie had time to answer her, there was a sharp knock on the front door. They looked at each other in surprise. 'Do you think it's the old man?' he whispered.

'Not at this time of night.'

'Stay there!' He walked to the door and opened it.

A man in rough country clothes was standing on the doorstep. He was small, wiry and in his mid to late thirties, with the weather-beaten complexion of a hill farmer. He muttered something to Jamie who shook his head and looked at Mara.

'What is it?' she asked the man. 'You'll have to tell me. Monsieur speaks very little French.'

The man glanced quickly round the hall. 'May I come in?' His voice was quiet and gentle.

'Yes. Of course. Is something wrong?'

In answer, the man handed her a scruffy piece of paper on which was written Damon Rushton, followed by her name and the address of the farmhouse. The writing was poor and looked as though each letter had been dictated separately to someone unaccustomed to spelling. 'Is this you, madame?'

'Yes. What's happened?' She pointed at Damon's name. 'He's my nephew. Do you know where he is?' She was desperate to know but she didn't want to frighten the man.

'He's dead, madame. I came to tell you. He died this afternoon. He had been wounded. We found him up there,' he pointed to the hills, 'lying in the sun.'

'How did you find him? What was he doing? Come into the kitchen and have some wine.'

The man shook his head. 'No, thank you, madame. I must go. I just came to tell you. We . . . I . . . found him lying in the grass. He had walked for miles. He was delirious most of the time. We . . . I . . . tried to help him but there was nothing we could do. The nearest doctor is a long way away and we couldn't have carried him that far. I'm sorry, madame . . . monsieur. Very sorry.'

Mara asked, 'Where did you bury him?'

The man looked embarrassed. 'Up by the black rock.' Then he turned and walked out of the door, and in the light from the hall they saw him pick up his rifle which had been left propped against the house. Then he was gone, into the night.

Mara said, 'They shot him, didn't they?'

'I imagine they had to.'

'Yes.' She shook her head slowly. 'But it's kinder to kill a wounded animal and he was a very wounded animal.' Without looking at Jamie she walked up the stairs and into her bedroom and closed the door.

Left alone, Jamie wandered through the drawing room. He wished Mara would let him comfort her, that he could go upstairs and take her in his arms and tell her that he loved her and that he would always be there to protect her. In Koblenz she would have welcomed him. But since then she had learned to cope with her sorrows in her own way, by herself. In her withdrawal, he saw more than anything else that she'd grown up along her own path, a path which ran parallel to his and joined his in many places, but not in all. He had wanted her to be independent, and now she was. He lay down on the sofa and after some time he fell asleep.

When he woke up it was morning and he was covered by a blanket. In the kitchen he could hear Mara saying,

'Oliver, a man came last night to tell us that Damon has died. He's gone to join Leon.'

There was a long silence, than a frightened little voice said, 'Mummy, you're not going to die too, are you?'

Burying his head in the blanket, Jamie listened to Mara comforting their son.

There was now no reason for Mara not to leave Barjon. She collected up a few things: the odd item of clothing, some clothes for Oliver, the iron box with its faded letters and Jamie's locket.

At eleven Jamie said, 'I think we should go. The bus leaves in half an hour. Are you all right?'

She smiled wearily. 'Yes. Yes, I'm fine. It's all a bit of a shock.'

He put an arm round her and kissed her forehead. 'We'll come back here for lovely long holidays when the war is over.'

'Yes.' She leaned against him. 'Let's hope it doesn't change.'

At the top of the drive she looked back at Les Vieux Orangers. It was basking in the morning sunlight. What would happen to it before she saw it again? She wished she could have picked it up and taken it with her.

In the village endless people hugged her and wished her good luck. They were genuinely sorry to see her go, and they were all very fond of Oliver. Jamie received a few curious looks but Mara explained him away as the doctor who had treated Alexander: doctors were well respected.

The last person to say goodbye to was Maman. 'You'll come back, Madame Mara?'

'Of course I will.'

'All of you?' Maman twinkled through her tears.

'Maybe.'

'Tell me something,' Maman whispered in Mara's ear, 'was it the doctor who gave you that bruise? I'd never have taken him for a violent man. Passionate, yes, but not a wife-beater.'

Mara was saved from having to reply by the postman. He ran up, waving a letter. 'Ah, Madame Mara, thank heavens I caught you. This arrived a week ago, I was about to give it to the bus driver to take back to Cannes, but I can give it to you, it is addressed to Damon' – he pronounced it like Maman – 'Rushton.'

Mara thanked him and took the letter, kissed Maman again, and turned to walk the three hundred yards down the hill to where the bus stopped. The villagers watched her from the gateway, calling to her, wishing her luck, and waving each time she looked back. Jamie was ahead of her carrying the suitcases. Oliver darted backwards and forwards between them. They were the only people taking the bus to Cannes that morning and as Mara reached the point where it stopped, turned, and went back the way it came, she could see the cloud of dust moving slowly up the side of the valley which heralded its lumbering approach.

'It's for Damon,' Mara told Jamie. 'I suppose I'd better open it.' It was from old Mr Lewis, the Rushtons' solicitor, and had been sent to Damon in care of Mara's bank in Cannes. It was dated 23 August and it said:

Dear Damon,
I regret to have to inform you that your father has had to be confined to a mental institution. As you are aware, a number of us have felt for some time that this was the only solution and when Doctor Phillips retired last month, his successor, Doctor Hale, came to see me and said that it was quite unsafe for your father to continue at the Park.

You will also be aware that under the terms of your grandfather's will you are now in sole charge of Rushton Motors, formerly known as Rushton-Gaunt Motors, there being no other Rushton male above the age of twenty-one. Should you for some reason wish to relinquish this charge, the only person to whom you may do so is Mrs Mara Rushton.

I must advise you that the business has not been doing at all well recently and it would require very careful management to save it from bankruptcy. Much as I am loath to suggest you sell your grandfather's beloved Rushton-Gaunt, I do feel that with your lack of experience in this field it might be the best solution. Were I a younger man I should offer to help put the company back on its feet, but I too am old and about to retire. A number of prospective purchasers have already made tentative inquiries so an early decision would be advisable. Of course if you decide not to sell, your presence here is imperative. In any case, with the current unsettled climate, it might be advisable.

I am writing to you care of Mrs Rushton's bank in the hope that this letter reaches you. I am sure that Atalanta has your address but as you must know, she is no longer here.

Mara handed the letter to Jamie. 'Damon's dead, so it passes to you,' he said, after reading it. 'What are you going to do?' Somehow the letter had brought a coolness between them.

'I don't know.'

'Presumably you'll sell and take the money.'

'I'll think about it.' Mara watched the bus draw nearer. She thought of that other bus queue in London, when she had made up her mind to leave Alexander, when she had gone with Jamie. Then the Rushtons had come between them. Now the Rushtons were between them again. She looked at him but he was purposely not looking at her, giving her no indication of how he wanted her to choose. The bus drew nearer. The wind caught her hair. She could have been back at the Deutsches Eck. Or on the track. Or at Brooklands. She thought of the Old

749

Man and what Rushton-Gaunt had meant to him, and of Leon and what Palestine had meant to him, and of Jamie and what he meant to her. Jamie was her dream. Palestine had been Leon's dream. Rushton-Gaunt had been the Old Man's dream – and she couldn't sell a dream. As Mara watched the bus approach, she realized sadly that if Jamie couldn't accept it then there was no hope for them however much they loved each other, for she would resent him if she gave up Rushton-Gaunt just as much as he would have resented her had she caused the downfall of his career.

The bus was almost on top of them. Mara couldn't bear the uncertainty any longer. 'I've made up my mind,' she shouted at him above the roar of the engine. 'I'm not going to sell. I'll get Pete Smithy and . . . Colonel Mackintosh to help me run it, but I'm not selling. Oh, no, Rushton-Gaunt are going to get back into racing. We're going to be' – she laughed as the big wheels of the bus sent up a cloud of dust – 'up there with the big 'uns!'

At first Mara thought Jamie hadn't heard. He lifted Oliver up into the bus and climbed up after him. Then he turned and looked down at her. 'Thank God for that!' he said. 'I thought for a moment you were going to flog it and take the money.' He held out his hand to her, and he smiled that beautiful half-mischievous, half-apologetic smile. 'Come on, Stork, it's a long way to the Finishing Post.'

Mara took his hand and went up the steps. They sat on the long seat at the back, Oliver on one side of Mara, Jamie on the other, and as the bus turned to go back down the hill she looked up, at the gateway where Maman stood tentatively waving, at the red roofs of the houses, and at the hills beyond. She thought of Alexander buried in the little cemetery, of Leon lying in some Parisian mortuary, and of Damon in his unmarked grave near the black rock. Each in his way had tried to subject her to his own needs, but Jamie hadn't. He'd stood beside her at the bus stop but not tried to influence her decision. He'd left her to make up her own mind, and she had, and she'd chosen right – for him and for her.

And it came to Mara that life is a race and you never know if you're winning.